DAYS OF TICHO

DAYS OF TICHO

Empire, Mandate, Medicine, and Art in the Holy Land

DAVID M. REIFLER

gefen
publishing house
JERUSALEM ◆ NEW YORK   Est. 1981

Cover Design: Leah Ben Avraham/Noonim Graphics
Typesetting: Irit Nachum
Cover image of Dr. Avraham (Albert) Ticho
1950 ink on paper, 18 x 25 cm
Anna Ticho, Israeli, born Moravia, 1894–1980
Israel Museum, Jerusalem, Bequest of Anna Ticho

ISBN: 978-965-229-665-8

1 3 5 7 9 8 6 4 2

Gefen Publishing House Ltd.
6 Hatzvi Street
Jerusalem 94386, Israel
972-2-538-0247
orders@gefenpublishing.com

Gefen Books
11 Edison Place
Springfield, NJ 07081
516-593-1234
orders@gefenpublishing.com

www.gefenpublishing.com

Printed in Israel

Send for our free catalog

Library of Congress Cataloging-in-Publication Data

Reifler, David M., 1952- author.
Days of Ticho : empire, mandate, medicine, and art in the Holy Land / David M. Reifler.
    pages cm
Includes bibliographical references and index.
ISBN 978-965-229-665-8
1. Tikho, Avraham Albert, 1883-1960.   2. Ophthalmologists—Palestine—Biography.
3. Public health—Palestine—History—20th century.   4. Jews—Czech Republic—
Boskovice—Biography.   5. Ticho family. I. Title.
RE36.T55R45 2014
617.7092—dc23
                                2014031144

TO KAREN

CONTENTS

Plates follow page 74

PREFACE

As befits the best of clichés, this book is about "the life and times" of Dr. Avraham Albert Ticho.* A Moravian, Viennese-trained ophthalmologist, Dr. Ticho immigrated to Ottoman-ruled Jerusalem in 1912 at the age of twenty-eight and married his cousin, the artist Anna Ticho, later that year. Their story is told here in detail until the founding of the State of Israel. It is presented with a wide supporting cast of characters and with a variety of historical perspectives: of medicine, art, civilian institutions, governments, and war; the struggles and growth of the Yishuv, the Jewish community in Palestine; and the conflicts that arose between Jews and their Arab neighbors.

This work grew out of a paper presented to the Cogan Ophthalmic History Society in Charleston, South Carolina, in March 2008. A good start in the direction of a broader project, it already included a plethora of notes and many valuable contacts with museum curators, archivists, and members of the Ticho family. By a happy coincidence, my first visit to the Ticho House in July 2007 occurred around the time of a Ticho family reunion hosted by Charles and Yocheved Ticho, in honor of their birthdays and the publication and book-signing of a rich family history as told by Charles. By means of an introduction from Charles's cousin, ophthalmologist Dr. Karl Ticho and his wife, Dr. Sayah Ticho of Chicago, my attendance at this gathering was very cordially welcomed. Here I also first met Miri Debbi (Kritzler), who had earlier written a

---

*   The name Ticho (טיכו) is pronounced "tē'-kho" with an accent on the first syllable and the "ch" in the name pronounced as in German. (See "Hebrew-to-English Transliteration and Pronunciation" below.)

history of the extended Ticho family, and the Ticho House Museum Curator, Timna Seligman, who introduced me to the Israel Museum's archival holdings and to her predecessor, Irit Salmon, the author of a fine book about the Ticho House.

Subsequent research led me to the stacks, microfilms, and dusty folders of libraries, archives, and museums, in New York, Vienna, Tel Aviv, and Jerusalem. My grateful acknowledgments to professionals and assistants who helped me along the way are mentioned separately elsewhere. With the help those individuals, Dr. Ticho began to emerge as a bridge to a bygone era, a gateway into the history of ophthalmology, the history of Jerusalem, and the history of great world events. The title of this book, *Days of Ticho* (in Hebrew ימי טיכו, *Yemei Ticho*), is a play on words of a modern Hebrew expression that both evokes the pre-state era and references Dr. Ticho. For example, the expression might be used for an early-twentieth-century antique or an item of clothing that is out of date or old fashioned.

What could be added to the well-known story of Dr. Ticho's life and the story of Ticho House? The essential facts about these subjects seemed to be well known and conveyed to thousands of the annual visitors to the Ticho House from far and wide. But deeper investigation of the facts revealed several intertwined narratives: a love-story of first-cousins; the story of the pioneering eye doctor and his wife, the artist; and a social circle of Yekke intellectuals and a path that differed from mainstream Zionism.

Dr. Ticho was in the prime of his life at the time of the outbreak of World War I (which occurred exactly one hundred years ago this week). He was a participant in that war, which brought about a dramatically new geo-political and social order throughout Palestine and the Middle East. This new order came with heightened nationalist aspirations, but it also sowed the seeds of future wars and local, unresolved conflicts. As I write this preface, rockets continue to be fired by Arab militants into Israel while the Israel Defense Forces have responded with Operation Protective Edge. Meanwhile, the almost century-old map of Syria and Iraq may soon need to be redrawn again.

One nagging question that I tried to explore was related to a well-known episode in Dr. Ticho's life – a near-fatal stabbing by an Arab would-be assassin in November 1929. Considering Ticho's supposedly non-Zionist, apolitical sentiments, why was he the victim of this attack? As described in the book, the answer to this question will never be resolved, but the events of that year hold several clues. Perhaps Ticho was targeted simply because he was a physician, though it was more likely connected to specific actions that he took immediately following murderous riots in Hebron in August 1929. These riots were a part of widespread disturbances throughout Palestine in August 1929 (Hebrew date 5689, also known as *Tarpat* according to the vocalization of the Hebrew letters representing the number 689). The so-called *Me'ora'ot Tarpat*, the violent events of 5689, represented an important turning point in Jewish-Arab relations that all but sealed the ultimate fate of the British Mandate for Palestine and left problems that remain the focus of world attention today.

Over the years, there have been many attacks in Jerusalem by stabbing, many with apparent political motivations, and many of them that have gone unsolved. Sixty years after the stabbing of Dr. Ticho, the British newspaper the *Guardian* carried the following: "It is not known who knifed him as he was taking his regular route from his home to [work]." The article continued, "[He] was a wholly peaceable figure and, whatever his private reactions, he did not involve himself in political matters." The article was not about the unsolved Ticho stabbing case but about a new case that occurred on June 22, 1989, in the midst of the First Intifada. The sixty-four-year-old victim, Prof. Menahem Stern, tragically did not survive.* Prof. Stern was a recipient of the Israel Prize for Jewish history and one of the world's leading authorities on the period of the Second Temple. Ironically, he had written about rebellious Jewish zealots known as the Sicarii or "dagger-men."

While ancient events may not provide much guidance for grappling with contemporary issues, the days of the British conquest of Palestine and the Mandate are much closer to us in time. This book about Dr.

---

*   "Israeli Professor Stabbed to Death," *Guardian*, June 23, 1989; "Obituary, Mena-hem Stern," *Guardian*, June 29, 1989.

Ticho and his times touches upon many issues that we currently face in the Middle East.

Less violent medical-social issues that directly involved Dr. Ticho also continue to play out in modern-day Israel, such as the matter of private practice for physicians belonging to health care systems such as the Hadassah Medical Organization and Kupat Ḥolim, whose origins date to the early years of the British Mandate. Preceding British rule, Ticho was involved in supervising the very first Hadassah nurses in the "War against Trachoma" and contributed to the first modern medical book written in modern Hebrew; just as the Mandate was formally established, Ticho published some of the first academic papers produced by the Rothschild-Hadassah Hospital in Jerusalem. Later, the influx of refugee physicians and scientists from Central Europe further set the stage for the great medical and scientific achievements that remarkably come from such a relatively small country.

We return finally to Mrs. Anna Ticho, who appears somewhat in the background throughout much of this book. Mrs. Ticho's career comes more to the foreground in the final chapters, which detail several of her art exhibitions and her participation in the founding of the New Bezalel School of Arts. Her fame and her career further blossomed after Dr. Ticho's passing in 1960, and she was awarded the Israel Prize in 1980, shortly before her death. Dr. and Mrs. Ticho's activities, including their bequests to the Israel Museum, exemplify the Zionist enterprise at its finest. As Irit Salmon wrote, the Ticho House in Jerusalem, which was dedicated in May 1984 as a downtown annex to that museum, is "a living and fitting tribute to the Tichos." Hopefully this book contributes to their legacy while furthering an understanding of their times and ours.

DMR
July 29, 2014 / Menaḥem Av 2, 5774

ACKNOWLEDGMENTS

I am grateful to many individuals for encouraging me to write this book and guiding me on a path to its completion. I begin with my sister, Debra McElroy, who learned about Dr. and Mrs. Ticho from her visits to the Ticho House not long after it had opened to the public.

Once I began my research, I was kindly encouraged by several members of the extended Ticho family: Miri Debbi (Kritzler), Tel Aviv; Dr. Karl Ticho, Chicago; Dr. Uri Ticho, Emeritus Professor of Ophthalmology, Hadassah Hospital and Hebrew University Medical School, Ein Kerem, Jerusalem; and Esther (Daisy) Ticho; and, especially, Charles Ticho of Hackensack, New Jersey, who welcomed me at a family gathering, shared a chapter of his book then in press, and who most recently shared several photographs from his family album.

I also received encouragement from Dr. Nissim Levy, Emeritus Professor of Medicine, Technion, Haifa, and his wife, Yael Levy, who graciously hosted me in their home and shared their research material even before it appeared in their excellent biographical dictionary that is frequently cited in my notes.

Dr. Levy guided me toward the goal of a commercially published work in English. This goal has been realized through Gefen Publishing House and five individuals in particular: Ilan Greenfield, publisher; Lynn Douek, project manager; Kezia Raffel Pride and Ita Olesker, editors; and Fern Seckbach, indexer.

I am thankful for the help of many archivists, curators, librarians, and colleagues who helped me gather research materials and photographs: Timna Seligman, Curator, Ticho House, Israel Museum–Jerusalem; Susan Woodland, Director, Hadassah Archives, New York City; Boni

Joi Koelliker, Photo/Reference Archivist, American Jewish Historical Society, New York City; Rochelle Rubinstein, Deputy Director–Archival Matters, and Anat Banin, Photo Collections, Central Zionist Archives; Rachel Laufer, Imaging Licensing Manager, Israel Museum, Jerusalem; Michael Lenarz, Deputy Director, Jewish Museum, Frankfurt am Main; Eduard Feuereis, Jewish Museum, Prague; Ms. Michaela Laichmann of the Wiener Stadt- und Landesarchiv, Vienna; Mr. Joachim Tepperberg, Archivist, Haus- Hof- und Staatsarchiv, Vienna; Mr. Rudolf Habermann, Director, Südbahmuseum, Mürzzuschlag, Austria; MMag. Martin Georg Enne, Vienna University and Archive Services; Dr. Ruth Koblizek, Photo-archivist, Department and Collection of the History of Medicine, University of Vienna Medical School, Vienna; UniMag. Martina Gamper, MA, Research Assistant, Medical University of Vienna; and Mr. Tomáš Rataj, Archivist, Charles University, Prague; Dagmar Hamalová, Director of the Boskovice Museum; Kathy Bloch and Camille Shotwell Brown of the Spertus Institute of Judaic Studies, Chicago, Illinois; Stephen J. Greenberg, MSLS, PhD and Cynthia Burke, MILS, National Library of Medicine, Bethesda, Maryland; and Lois Huisman, AMLS; Sandra Kommit, RN, BA, MILS, Brian Simmons, AMLS, Mary Fuller, David Trowbridge of Spectrum Health Hospital, Grand Rapids, Michigan; Dr. Jacob Pe'er, Professor and Chairman, Department of Ophthalmology, Hadassah Hebrew University Medical Center, Jerusalem; and Dr. John Linberg, Former Professor and Chairman, Department of Ophthalmology, West Virginia University.

I am indebted to several personal guides in foreign cities who led me to repositories of materials and historic sites: Prof. Yehoshua Ben-Arieh, Emeritus Professor, Hebrew University, Jerusalem; Mr. Itzik Shwicki, Jerusalem Organizer, Council for the Preservation of Historic Sites; Irene Pollak-Rein, Director for German-speaking Countries of the Jerusalem Foundation; Gilla Treibich, friend and certified tour-guide, Jerusalem; Prof. Avi Ohry, Professor and Chair, Section of Rehabilitation Medicine, Reuth Medical Center and Sackler Faculty of Medicine, Tel Aviv; and, especially, Mr. Dima Schaminer, Graduate Student in Jewish Studies, University of Vienna who served as my guide, translator, and research assistant in Vienna.

Assistance with translations from German, Spanish, or Hebrew was kindly provided by several individuals: Hubertus Hug, Hamburg Germany; Uta Vilmont, RN, Spectrum Health Hospital, Grand Rapids; Dr. Don Blanchard, Portland, Oregon; Charlotte Stiller, Kalamazoo, Michigan, Eve Rider, Grand Rapids; Siglinde Stecher, Grandville, Michigan; Sari Cohen, Grand Rapids; Talia Atias, Grand Rapids; and Meira Glick, Hebrew Instructor, Hebrew University and Fuchsberg Center, Jerusalem.

At various stages, I solicited comments about early manuscript drafts from two knowledgeable friends: Mitch Kachun, PhD, Associate Professor of History, Western Michigan University, Kalamazoo, Michigan; and Rabbi David J. B. Krishef, Congregation Ahavas Israel, Grand Rapids. As I neared the completion of a first draft, I often discussed my progress on the project with my friend Willem Mineur, a graphic designer who ultimately helped me create a map of Jerusalem with landmarks at the time of Dr. Ticho's arrival there in 1912.

From beginning to end, I found encouragement from my wife, Karen. Her support and life-saving interventions made the completion of this work possible.

HEBREW-TO-ENGLISH
TRANSLITERATION AND PRONUNCIATION

The system of Hebrew-to-English transliteration ("Latinization") used in this book is as follows: Both א ('alef) and ע ('ayin) are denoted by an apostrophe before the vowel; both of the letters כ (kaf) and ק (kuf) as k; both ט (tet) and ת (tav) as t; both the undotted ב (vet) and ו (vav) as v; both the letters ש and ס are s; the silent, final-letter ה (hei) generally appears as h only in commonly used words such as mitzvah and aliyah; the letter ח (ḥet) as ḥ; and the letter כ (khaf without *dagesh*) as kh. The letter צ is transliterated as ts (but as tz in commonly used words such as 'aretz, 'eretz, and mitzvah, or the initial German "z"). Keeping the common English/German rendering of the organization and hospital, Lemaan Zion (למען ציון) is spelled without an apostrophe in the first word and with a capital Z at the beginning of the second word.

Transliteration of vowels is as follows: kamatz and pataḥ are transliterated as *a* (pronounced as ah in "father"); ḥolam and kamatz katan as *o* (pronounced as o in "bold"); kubutz and shuruk as *oo* (pronounced as oo as in "food"); ḥirik as *i* (pronounced as ē in seek); tseirei is as *ei* (pronounced as ā in range); segol and a sounded or non-sounded shva are transliterated as *e* (pronounced as eh or ə as in ebb).

A hyphen is placed after transliterated Hebrew prefixes with meanings such as "and," "in," "from," and "to," and an English pattern of capitalization for proper nouns is retained. For example, the phrase meaning "next year in Jerusalem" (לשנה הבאה בירושלים) is transliterated as "*le-shana ha-ba'a bi-Yerushalayim,*" with hyphens after prefixes and capitalization of the initial letter (and retention of the letter e) in the name of the Holy City.

Introduction

מילים, מילים, מילים, מילים...

Words, words, words, words...

From *Eliezer Ben-Yehudah*, a popular Israeli song, lyrics by Yaron London

In June 1912, the Viennese-trained ophthalmologist Dr. Avraham Albert Ticho left the port of Trieste aboard an Austrian steamer bound for Jaffa. Ticho's final destination was the Lemaan Zion Eye Hospital located just outside the Old City walls in Jerusalem. On a Friday afternoon the following week, Ticho arrived by train on the rocky and barren southern outskirts of the city, which was then a remote outpost of the Ottoman Empire. He was met at the train station by Mordecai Adelman, the hospital's local administrator. Dr. Ticho got settled in the hospital's residence quarters and then prepared for his first Sabbath in the Holy City.

On Sunday, Adelman took the twenty-eight-year-old doctor around town for interviews with local leaders. One such meeting was with journalist and lexicographer Eliezer Ben-Yehudah, publisher of the Hebrew newspaper *Ha-Or*. Adelman and Ben-Yehudah were old and close friends from their pre-immigration days in Paris.[1] Arriving separately in 1881, they had each immigrated to Jerusalem at the threshold of the so-called First Aliyah, the first wave of Jewish immigration to Palestine that encompassed the years 1881–1903.

Following his interview with Ticho, Ben-Yehudah wrote:

> This [past] Friday, the eye doctor of the Lemaan Zion Eye Hospital,
> Dr. Avraham Ticho, came to our city. Foreign newspapers have
> reported with praise of Dr. Ticho, who was an "assistent" to Prof.
> Bergmeister in Vienna, one of the most famous in the profession
> of eye diseases. Dr. Avraham Ticho has not come to our city for
> a few months like other doctors who have preceded him, rather
> with the serious intention to live here for at least a few years
> and perhaps – to settle permanently among us. He does not yet
> speak Hebrew, but he understands Hebrew, and he also promises
> to soon speak more in our language.[2]

Written in Hebrew, these words reflected Ben-Yehudah's life-mission, and
they were aimed, in part, at drawing Ticho into the cultural and language
wars of the day. The German language of Theodor Herzl's Zionist writings
and the proceedings of numerous Zionist congresses were gradually giving
way to the "Hebraic renaissance." At the Tenth Zionist Congress in Basel
in 1911, an entire session of the congress was conducted in Hebrew for the
first time.[3] By the time of Ticho's immigration, Zionist leaders had finally
come to value Hebrew as "an instrument of nationalism."[4] Symbolically,
the main entrance of the Lemaan Zion Eye Hospital was engraved with
the words "Eye Clinic" both in German (*Augenklinik*) and in Hebrew
(*Mirpa'at ha-'Einayim*).

The polyglot Ticho eventually learned to speak Hebrew very well. In
1913, he joined the recently founded Association of Hebrew-Speaking
Physicians in Jerusalem (Agudat Rof'im Medabrei 'Ivrit) that, together
with its sister-organization in Jaffa, eventually evolved into the present-
day Israel Medical Association (Ha-Histadrut ha-Refui'it be-[Eretz]
Yisrael). In 1921, he joined the Jerusalem Lodge of B'nai B'rith that
for many years had conducted its business in Hebrew, the first modern
organization to do so.

However, Ticho continued to prefer German and never adopted Hebrew
as his primary, personal language. He might be considered the prototypical
Yekke, a cultural elitist who remained socially and linguistically aloof,
socializing in groups of other German-speaking Jews of German and
Central European origin.[5] Ticho preferred to speak German at home, where

he read "Yekke" newspapers or later the English-language *Palestine Post*.[6] Neither Ben-Yehudah nor Ticho himself could have predicted that the word *"ticho"* would someday appear as an entry in dictionaries of Hebrew slang and that the Ticho name would become a part of the Israeli expression, *"mi-yemei Ticho"* (literally, "from the days of Ticho"). The expression is identified especially with the days of the British Mandate but can be taken to mean something that is old-fashioned or out-of-date.

Ben-Yehudah's article also made reference to other ophthalmologists who had practiced for a time in Jerusalem. Ben-Yehudah and Adelman had witnessed several eye doctors who had come and gone since their own arrivals in Palestine.[7] Among them was the first Jewish ophthalmologist in Palestine, Dr. Moses Erlanger of Lucerne, Switzerland, Ticho's predecessor at the Lemaan Zion Eye Hospital (1908–1910). Ben-Yehudah accurately assessed Ticho's prospects for permanent settlement in Jerusalem. After losing to Ben-Yehudah's own son in the courtship of the beautiful Leah Abushadid, Erlanger had returned to Lucerne to seek marriage and a private practice.[8] Dr. Ticho, however, was followed to Jerusalem just four months later by his fiancée who already had his last name, his first cousin, Anna Ticho. The eighteen-year-old Anna was accompanied by her mother Bertha.

When Albert and Anna were married in Jerusalem in November 1912, Ben-Yehudah's hopeful predictions about the Tichos' permanent settlement seemed to be coming true. Albert, Anna, and Bertha Ticho were thus part of a wave of immigration of about thirty-five thousand Jews who made their way to Palestine during the Second Aliyah, the second wave of Jewish immigration to Palestine whose dates are usually given as 1904–1914. Beginning with the last years of Ottoman control of Palestine, Ticho's career was marked by many historic events and groundbreaking personal achievements, including his training and supervision of the first Hadassah nurses in Palestine, Rose Kaplan and Rachel Landy, the cohosting of the first medical conference of Jewish physicians in Palestine, and his contributions to its proceedings that constituted the first modern medical book published in Hebrew.

After serving in the Austrian Army during World War I, Ticho returned to Jerusalem. In the days of the British Mandate he succeeded American ophthalmologist Dr. Joseph Krimsky as Head of Ophthalmology of the American Zionist Medical Unit (AZMU) and Head of the Department of Ophthalmology at the Rothschild-Hadassah Hospital. During this time Ticho also taught in the Hadassah Nurses' Training School and, representing the medical faculty, addressed its first graduating class in December 1921. He also published some of the first articles in the medical literature originating from Hadassah Hospital. As the AZMU made its transition from a wartime medical relief organization to a permanent medical organization, Dr. Ticho left the newly named Hadassah Medical Organization (HMO) to devote himself to his private practice.

Dr. Ticho performed over forty thousand major operations during his career. The majority of his patients were Arabs who came from all over the Middle East. Ticho generally disavowed any interest in politics, but he spoke out forcefully against the 1929 Arab riots in Hebron, where he was an eyewitness to the aftermath of the massacres. Soon afterwards, Dr. Ticho was himself stabbed in the back by an Arab would-be assassin. This personal attack seems to have been the main reason Albert Ticho closed his clinic in Musrara to practice exclusively out of his clinic and hospital just off the street that is now known as Reḥov Ha-Rav Kook, the site that is now known as Beit Ticho (Ticho House).

Over many years, with Anna Ticho as the consummate hostess, the Tichos' home above the hospital served as a cultural salon for the elite of Jerusalem. The Tichos' many important acquaintances – and particularly their circle of friends, many of them Yekkim like themselves – add considerable interest to the story of their lives. Woven into this story is the backdrop of social and political changes that transformed Jerusalem from a remote outpost of the Ottoman Empire to the capital of the State of Israel.

Dr. Avraham Albert Ticho died at his home on October 15, 1960, at the age of seventy-seven, after a long and successful career. He had taken his first forays into the pages of Jerusalem folklore and history on that historic day of June 28, 1912, at the age of twenty-eight. Before more fully describing Ticho's early career in Palestine and its significance, this narrative will first examine his family's roots and his formative years in Central Europe. The story, therefore, will begin in the small town of Boskovice, Moravia.

CHAPTER 1

1883–1887

BEGINNINGS

זה ספר תולדות אדם...

This is the record of a man...

Genesis 5:1

O n the Sabbath day that Avraham Albert Ticho was born, synagogues throughout the world began anew the annual cycle of Torah-readings with the portion of *Bereishit*, named after the first Hebrew word of the Bible (*bereishit* means "in the beginning"). The date was October 27, 1883 – Tishrei 26, 5644, on the Hebrew calendar. While praying for his wife's safety, Albert's observant father, Ignatz Ticho, heard this Torah-reading in the Loew-Baer Synagogue on Taplova Street within the Jewish ghetto, or *Judenstadt*, of Boskovice, Moravia.[1]

Ignatz's textile store (called A. J. Ticho) was closed for the Sabbath. He had purchased the two-story building a year or so before Albert's birth, and while the business occupied the first floor, Ignatz, his wife, Laura, and their family lived in the second story above the business. It was here that Laura Ticho gave birth to their new baby boy, who had been preceded by the eldest child, Sarah, ten years earlier, followed by four boys, Jacob, Josef, Max, and David. At the time of the ritual circumcision the following Saturday, the newborn baby was given the name Avraham in memory of his recently departed grandfather. While the name of Avraham was recorded officially in the town's civil records, family and friends would call him Albert.

After Albert, Ignatz and Laura Ticho had six more sons, Heinrich, Nathan, Sami, Paul (Baruch), Victor, and Alfred. The oldest sister, Sarah, was in her mid-twenties when the youngest of the Ticho children was born, a second daughter, Irma (appendix 1).

The name Avraham has a significance that goes deep to the roots of the Ticho family tree. Ashkenazi Jewish baby-naming customs – preceding even the invention of the Ticho surname – led to the repeated occurrence of the name Avraham in alternating generations. The earliest known ancestor of Albert Ticho was Avraham ben David (born c. 1660) who is known to have lived and died in Boskovice at a time when there were only about twenty-six Jewish households in the city, a time when the *hevra kadisha* (burial society) was first established.[2] His son, David ben Avraham (born c. 1685) in turn had a son who was named Avraham ben David (c. 1710–1789), but his son would obtain an additional name when, in 1730, he complied with the edict of Emperor Charles VI – the Familiants' Law or *Familiantengesetz* – that required him to take a surname. He chose (or was given) the surname Ticho.

According to family genealogists, it is likely that virtually every individual with the last name of Ticho can trace their ancestry back to the city of Boskovice and this particular individual.[3] Many theories about the origin of the Ticho name have been advanced. The name may have been derived from one of the cities of Central Europe having a similar sound, such as Tichov, a village in Shlesien, Poland, that was called Tichau in German.[4] In the Czech language, *tichy* means "the quiet one," whereas *ticho* has the meaning of "silence" or "quiet." However, the occurrence of Ticho as a surname is relatively uncommon. The first Avraham Ticho who took his surname at around twenty years of age died in 1789, and the next Avraham Ticho (1813–1882) was Dr. Avraham Albert Ticho's grandfather. The child born on October 27, 1883, was therefore part of at least the eighth generation born in Boskovice and the sixth generation to go by the last name of Ticho.[5]

While it is possible to trace the Ticho family's genealogy back to the seventeenth century, the beginning of Jewish life in Boskovice and elsewhere in Moravia can be traced back another six hundred years to the eleventh century.[6] An inscription on the oldest recognizable Jewish gravestone in the old Jewish cemetery of Boskovice probably dates to the year 1068.[7] The inscription read, "Adelins, the son of Samuel, died on the fifth day of Nissan 4829." This is around the time that Jews are known to have been present in Brno (Brünn), a larger city that lies thirty-two kilometers to the south and which, to this day, remains the regional capital of Moravia. Records from the Brno municipal high court refer to Jews of Boskovice in 1243.[8] The first evidence of a Jew living in Boskovice appears a full century later in 1343, while evidence of the first Jewish settlement dates to the first half of the sixteenth century.[9]

The expulsion of Jews from Brno and six other "royal" cities of Moravia in 1454 led Jews to settle in villages and towns under the protection of feudal lords on whose estates they performed various functions. Boskovice was one of these Moravian towns, which were all interconnected under a single chief rabbi and a semiautonomous rabbinic council. It is against this backdrop that Avraham ben David, the first known direct ancestor of Avraham Albert Ticho, was born in the year 1660. In his day, the spoken language of his Jewish community was a dialect of Yiddish (Judeo-German), but just over one hundred years later, the Jews of Moravia rather quickly abandoned Yiddish in favor of German. In 1782, Joseph II issued the Ordinance of Tolerance (*Toleranzpatent*) that forced Moravia's Jews to adopt German as the language of law, commerce, and education.[10]

The adoption of German by Moravian Jews eventually led to greater opportunities, but also some important restrictions. The Familiants' Law of 1727 placed a limit of 5,106 Jewish families in Moravia, allowing only the eldest male in a family to marry and raise a family. This "cap" assured the Czech nobility of keeping the services of the Jews and revenues from their taxation. The Familiants' Law remained in effect until after the failed revolutions of 1848, a period of about 122 years.[11] After 1848 a Jewish political community (Politische Gemeinde) was established in Boskovice, which became known for its municipal activities and in particular its fire brigade, founded in 1863. The lifting of Jewish settlement restrictions and the abolition of the Familiants'

Law allowed Albert Ticho's extended family to increase in numbers and also find avenues of economic advancement.

Post-revolution reforms began to percolate into the religious services of Boskovice's Temple (the "New" or "Major" Synagogue), reforms such as the introduction of a choir.[12] In spite of the religious reforms, Boskovice's *beit ha-midrash* (house of study) remained a bastion of Orthodox tradition and learning. For many years, the associated yeshiva (Jewish secondary religious school) was second in importance in Moravia only to the yeshiva in the city of Mikulov. The religious importance of the yeshiva and Boskovice itself further increased when Boskovice's Rabbi Avraham Placzek became the Chief Rabbi of Moravia (*Landesrabbiner*) in 1860. He thereupon moved the *Landesrabbinat* from Mikulov to Boskovice.[13]

While Ignatz Ticho respected Rabbi Placzek and his successor, Yehudah Eisler (who, like Ignatz, was a Boskovice native), he disagreed with some of the modern innovations at the Major Synagogue. Some, like Albert Ticho's father and grandfather, felt more comfortable at the Beit ha-Midrash which was now reestablished as a separate synagogue (the "Minor" Synagogue). The major benefactors of the Minor Synagogue were the Loew-Baer family, who owned a factory about five kilometers from Boskovice, and so this synagogue had been named after them.[14]

When Albert Ticho's grandfather Avraham Ticho married Rezi (Esther) Fuchs on October 1, 1838, the couple settled into Number 56 U Templu Street. The couple had at least five children: Marie (Miriam), Nettie, Ignatz, Bernard, and Phillip. The middle child, Ignatz Hirsch (whose Hebrew name was Yitzhak Zvi and who was Avraham Ticho's father) was born on March 27, 1846. Ignatz's youngest brother, Phillip (Pinchas) was born in 1855, and he was not only Albert Ticho's uncle but also the father of his wife, Anna Ticho.

The political reforms of the mid-nineteenth century, which resulted in greater autonomy of the Jewish community within the ghetto, led to greater business opportunities for Jews throughout Moravia, but also demands for military service. It was suspected that Albert Ticho's father, Ignatz, walked with a pronounced limp throughout his adult life as the result of a self-inflicted injury that enabled him to avoid military service during the Austro-Prussian War of 1866.[15] Young Ignatz made his living within the Jewish ghetto selling textiles to cloth merchants, traders, and tailors. The initials for the name of his store, A. J. Ticho, probably represented the Hebrew names of both his father (Avraham) and himself (Jitzhak, as rendered in German). On August 21, 1871, Ignatz Hirsch Ticho married eighteen-year-old Laura (Esther) Baer, the daughter of a rabbi from Holesov.

Ignatz and Laura Ticho raised their children in a traditional Jewish home. Their Jewish faith and their strong sense of Jewish identity and values coexisted with German as the spoken language in their home. Among their children, Sarah and Jacob (the two eldest) maintained the most traditional Jewish homes into their adult lives. The facts of birth order and the realities of the changing times brought further imposed Germanized education to the younger brothers.

In the beginning, the two-story building that housed the A. J. Ticho textile business and the family's residence opened out only into the Jewish ghetto, even though the opposite side of the building abutted the town square outside of the ghetto. A further easing of restrictions on the Jewish ownership of property outside the Jewish ghetto of Boskovice allowed Ignatz to remodel the building so that the storefront opened out into the central square of the city. This enabled him to reach his customers directly during the regular outdoor markets conducted on the square. There is no avoiding the symbolism and the importance of this architectural arrangement in Albert Ticho's life – the back of his home leading toward the Jewish ghetto, the front of the home now looking out upon a wider, secular world that was filled with opportunities in spite of the minority status of Jews in Moravia and in the Austrian Empire.[16]

To grasp these new-found opportunities, Ignatz Ticho sent each of his sons, beginning at about age eleven, to the German-language high school (Gymnasium) in Brno. This was a common practice among the emerging Jewish middle class in Moravia, where about three-quarters of all Jews spoke German as their mother tongue.[17] The oldest son, Jacob, was the first to return and join his father's textile business. Later, both David and Heinrich followed. Ignatz once joked with his sons that he would take the "smart ones" into his business and send the "less smart ones" to Vienna to study law and medicine.[18] This was true for Josef, Max, and Sami (law), and Albert (medicine), but in Vienna, youngest son Alfred switched from law to agronomy, and Victor became an expert jeweler.

The siblings of Albert Ticho who stayed in Moravia all made their living in the textile and clothing business. Just before the beginning of World War I, long before their father Ignatz Ticho's death in 1921, three of Albert Ticho's brothers, Jacob, David, and Heinrich, moved the A. J. Ticho business to Brno. Paul (he insisted on using this name now) and Nathan had also initially stayed in Boskovice with their families. Following World War I, they joined together and purchased a modern clothing factory in Boskovice, calling their business Bratří Ticho (Brüder Ticho or Ticho Brothers). Nathan moved to Brno, where he opened a factory outlet of Bratří Ticho. In the early 1930s Paul also moved his family to Brno, though he commuted weekly by train to and from Boskovice. Later, after their sister Irma's divorce in 1928, the two "Brüder Ticho" helped set her up to manage a *Schwester* ("sister") firm, Ticho and Spol (Associates), a sewing workshop for the production of women's coats.

All of the businesses run by the Tichos – in Boskovice, Brno, and Vienna – were confiscated by the Nazis during World War II. With Paul Ticho's arrest and incarceration at the Dachau concentration camp, the almost three-hundred-year history of the Ticho family's continuous presence in Boskovice came to a tragic end.

Today there are no Jews living in Boskovice. The larger of Boskovice's two synagogues has been restored as a museum, and a display about Dr. Albert Ticho is permanently exhibited there. The birthplace of Ignatz Ticho on U Templu Street was restored only recently through the efforts of his grandson, Charles, and there is a historical marker on the outside wall of the building. The Ticho family's Loew-Baer synagogue did not survive time and neglect and was torn down. Gone also is the building in which Albert Ticho was born, where Ignatz Ticho established the A. J. Ticho business, and where he raised his family.[19]

CHAPTER 2

1888–1901

BOSKOVICE AND BRNO

לפקח עינים עורות...מבית כלא ישבי חושך.

Opening eyes deprived of light...
from the dungeon those who sit in darkness.

Isaiah 42:7, from *Haftarah Bereishit* read by thirteen-year-old Albert Ticho

Though Albert Ticho's father could be strict and demanding, we are told that Albert's early childhood was decidedly pleasant. "Many children were always around the house and at meal time. Everyone would sit around the table quietly and politely as they had been taught, showing respect for their parents and siblings. On a school day, the daily routine would begin at sunrise when the children would wake up and quickly prepare to set off for school... selecting clothes from a pile in the center of the room. No one would complain about the appropriateness or size of the clothing...."[1]

There were many places for a young boy to play in the Jewish Quarter or in the woods and hills that surrounded the city. The grounds of Count Mensdorff-Pouilly's mansion abutted the ghetto to the south. Beyond these grounds and further up the hill, at an elevation of four hundred forty-eight meters, were the ruins of the Gothic-Renaissance Boskovice Castle that had been destroyed by General Lennart Thorstenson and his invading Swedish army in 1645. One may well imagine the games on

this hill that Albert and his friends would play, much as described by his
brother Alfred and as retold many years later.[2]

Phillip Munk, a contemporary of Alfred, Albert's youngest brother,
stated in a memoir:

> I have never again found an idyllic spot such as the town –
> Boskovice. It was not sunk into solitude in a forgotten corner
> of the world but was full of life and yet had its own unique
> hills, streams and forests which endowed it with a dream-like
> beauty.... Here we were in our youth in unbounded freedom.
> Here no cherry tree was too high, no stream too cold or too swift,
> no puddle too deep, no cave too mysterious, no crag too steep.
> With so much space and no boundaries, we would venture deep
> into the darkness of the woods. And yet, there was an irresistible
> magnet that always attracted us back to our little streets with
> their courtyards and passageways in the back where all of us
> congregated – the oldsters with their serious community politics
> and the youngsters with their romantic games.[3]

Among the "oldsters," Ignatz Ticho's successful textile business on
Boskovice's main square allowed him to provide a rather comfortable
middle-class home for his family in their second-floor residence.[4] There
were Jews of Boskovice who were wealthier than the Ticho family,
such as the Loew-Baers, who owned the nearby textile factory and the
family of Emil Ungar, who owned a profitable distillery business and a
fine home that the Jewish townsfolk called the "Kaiser-Haus."[5] Within
the broad category of the Jewish "middle class" of Boskovice, however,
there were many others whose standard of living was well below that
of the Ticho family.

As his family grew, Ignatz Ticho fortunately had the means to
enlarge his family's living quarters with small additions in the rear
of the building. The main rooms of the house were heated by tall tile
stoves on the coldest days of the year. In the evenings, gas candles or oil
lanterns were used to light the rooms. Most of the bedrooms had small
washstands with pitchers that were replaced daily. From the rear of the

building, a covered walkway led to the privy (toilet booth) that was located in the back of the yard. In the middle of the night, a trip to the privy could be avoided by the use of a small chamber pot kept beneath the bed.

With an improving financial situation, it was possible for the Tichos to employ a few servants to help with the daily chores of cooking meals, washing clothes, cleaning the glass chimneys of oil lanterns, and the additional winter chores of attending to the heating stoves. Of all the family's household servants, Albert and the other children were especially fond of their nursemaid, lovingly called Babicka (Grandmother), who remained with the family for nearly three decades.[6]

The model of combining a place of residence with a place for professional practice was recapitulated time and again in Albert Ticho's career as an ophthalmologist in Jerusalem. Here the hard-working couple, Dr. and Mrs. Albert Ticho, came to live a very elegant and cultured upper-middle-class life.

The roots of such success may be found in childhood opportunities and experiences. The attitudes of Ignatz and Laura Ticho toward education and their means for providing it were typical of middle-class attitudes in general and for Moravian Jewish middle-class attitudes in particular.[7] For young Albert Ticho and Jewish schoolchildren throughout the Austrian Empire, the pathway to middle-class professional life was first and foremost through education, and the language of this education was German. Beginning with the establishment of Jewish elementary schools (*Normalschulen*) in Moravia in 1782, Jewish children had been instructed in German rather than Yiddish, and these schools came under state supervision. The same ordinance contained broad Germanizing provisions that extended to secondary education and into adult life, including requirements for all business and communal affairs to be conducted in German.[8] Though granting basic human rights to the Jews lagged behind these educational reforms, full legal emancipation had finally been achieved with the creation of the Dual Monarchy of Austria-Hungary in 1867 (the Austro-Hungarian Compromise or *Ausgleich*). The Ticho children therefore benefited from a sound and progressive *Normalschule* that was run privately by the Jews of Boskovice and from opportunities extending even beyond the borders of Moravia. In Boskovice, only the wealthy families like the Ungars and Loew-Baers typically supplemented or replaced the *Normalschule* education by bringing private tutors into their homes.

In addition to a core curriculum of German and the technical sciences, the Jewish *Normalschule* of Boskovice also provided Jewish studies. Studies were amply supplemented in the home. Ignatz enjoyed engaging his children in a game of biblical quotations. He would "quote a portion of the Hebrew Bible and challenge the others to complete the sentence," rewarding the child with a smile or a pat on the head. The children would also ask their father to complete their quotations.[9]

Albert Ticho was still a student at the *Normalschule* when his oldest brother Jacob was called back early from his studies in Brno. The arrangement suited Jacob very well, and it was clear that his father, Ignatz, needed help with his growing textile business. Jacob had always been close to his father and would remain so through the business and through their religious practices.[10] Together they attended the Loew-Baer Synagogue for prayer and study in the Beit ha-Midrash. Jacob Ticho found great satisfaction in joining and eventually taking over the family business. His example stands in contrast to the non-business-oriented protagonist in a semi-autobiographical novella by Boskovice-native Hermann Ungar.[11] Meanwhile the second-oldest Ticho brother, Josef, was in his final year at the Brno Gymnasium, busily preparing for his "Matura" examinations. These examinations were a prerequisite to gain acceptance to the University of Vienna, where he hoped to pursue further studies and a career in law.[12] It is certain that Ignatz held out each of the two eldest brothers as examples for the younger ones, templates of acceptable paths to take into adulthood.

In the late summer of 1894, ten-year-old Albert Ticho entered the Brno Gymnasium, joining his older brothers Josef, Max, and David. This rigorous academic preparatory school was located in the heart of Brno, the regional capital of Moravia. Almost a century earlier, just six miles to the southeast, Napoleon had defeated a coalition of Russian and Austrian forces at the Battle of Austerlitz (1805). In the post-Napoleonic era, Brno became a center of industry within the Austrian

Empire, further developing close commercial ties to Vienna.

Direct train connections were established between the two cities as early as 1839. Throughout the rest of the nineteenth century, textile and metallurgical industries flourished in the city that was sometimes called the "Moravian Manchester." By the end of the century, Brno had emerged as a modern, if somewhat grimy industrial city, but one that embraced modern German culture. Its German Municipal Theater (Deutsches Stadttheater) combined culture and modern advancements as the first theater in the world to be entirely lit with Edison's electric lamps.

At the time Albert entered the Brno Gymnasium, German-speakers constituted about 70 percent of the inhabitants in the city and German cultural institutions predominated. Brno was one of six communities in Moravia where there were more than five hundred Jewish households, and its Gymnasium drew Jewish students from the surrounding smaller towns and the city itself. German-language (rather than Czech-language) secondary schools were chosen overwhelmingly by Moravian Jewish families. While Moravian Jews comprised approximately 2 percent of the country's inhabitants – about forty-five thousand out of a total population of 2.2 million – Jewish children accounted for about 15 percent of the students in Moravia's *Gymnasien* and *Normalschulen*.[13]

Each of the Ticho boys attended the German-language Gymnasium in Brno that stood on Eliščina Street, nowadays home to the Janáček Music Academy (the street is now called Komenského náměstí).[14] The Brno Gymnasium was designed by August Siccardsburg and Eduard van der Nüll in a grand, neo-Renaissance style and completed in 1862. Elegant sculpted columns of draped female figures (caryatids) flanked the main entryways. Like the *Normalschule*, the language of instruction was German, but unlike the Jewish-run *Normalschule*, the Jewish students were in the minority. The Josephine reforms of the late eighteenth century had provided for a system of secular Jewish schools at the primary level only. The Jewish communities of the monarchy were not expressly prohibited from establishing private middle and upper schools, but none chose to do so.[15]

In Brno, the Ticho boys apparently boarded with a woman who kept a kosher kitchen.[16] Her home and boarding house was probably near the home of their paternal uncle Phillip (their father Ignatz's youngest brother), who lived on the Zelný Trh, just a few blocks south of the Gymnasium. In the square was the 225-year-old landmark Parnassus Fountain with its sculptures of human figures, animals, and dragons. The fountain was once the source of water for a major part of the town of Brno. Here, in their open-air stalls, vendors sold fruits, vegetables, and fresh flowers.

Albert's Uncle Phillip made his living as a banker. He was much more assimilated into German culture than his brother Ignatz. Albert's cousins were raised without the rituals and ceremonies of their faith. Uncle Phillip was twice widowed with two children from each of his first two marriages: Robert and Eugen from his first marriage with Albert's Aunt Bertha (née Strakosh); and Ida and Fritz from his second marriage with Albert's Aunt Fannie (née Pollak). Phillip's third wife coincidentally had the same first name as his first wife. When Albert first came to Brno as a student in 1894, his Aunt Bertha (née Braun) was caring for her infant daughter, Else, and pregnant with her second child. On October 27, Bertha gave birth to a baby girl whom she and Phillip named Anna. Rudolph, the youngest of Phillip's seven children, was born in 1903.[17]

Unlike his brother Phillip, Ignatz Ticho felt strongly that each of his sons should have his education supplemented with religious studies, at least until the time of their bar mitzvah at age thirteen. Even so, the Hebrew teachers and Jewish religious leaders of Brno tended to be more secularized than those back in Boskovice. This is exemplified by Rabbi Baruch Placzek (a native of Boskovice), who had become the Rabbi of Brno and Chief Rabbi of Moravia after his father. The younger Rabbi Placzek was an enthusiastic ornithologist and naturalist, a friend of Gregor Mendel, and an admirer of Charles Darwin. His articles on songbirds and bird habitats and behaviors drew primarily on his observations in his garden below the Spielberg Castle (Hrad Špilberk) in Brno, a short walk from Mendel's garden at the Augustinian Monastery.

Albert Ticho's formative years in the Gymnasium were coincident with the emergence of modern Zionism as a political movement. Albert

came to Brno in 1894, the year that Captain Alfred Dreyfus was wrongly
convicted of treason by a French military court. Founded just one year
earlier, the Vienna-based Christian Social Party of Karl Lueger gained
traction from the events in France. From this point onward, Brno was
deeply connected with early organizing efforts of the Zionist movement.

While events in Paris were further unfolding, Jewish Vienna
University students who were spending their summer vacations in Brno
established two "holiday fraternities" (*Ferialverbindungen*). One of
these was the "proto-Zionist" organization, founded by Berthold Feiwel,
that was named Veritas.[18] The founding of the Brno Veritas in 1894 led to
the establishment of other Zionist organizations throughout Moravia.[19]
Within two to three years, Feiwel and others were helping Theodor
Herzl organize the First Zionist Congress. At the Basel Congress Herzl
decried anti-Semitism and declared: "Zionism has already brought
about something remarkable, heretofore regarded as impossible: a close
union between the ultramodern and the ultraconservative elements of
Jewry..... A union of this kind is possible only on a national basis."[20]
Although Albert Ticho was exposed to the rhetoric and the emotions that
lay behind it, he never embraced political Zionism with much passion.

With the exception of young Alfred, most of Albert's brothers
and sisters would turn out to be either warm to political Zionism or
completely opposed. They embraced their Jewish identities but also
the ideals of German aesthetics and humanism; for a long time they
continued to believe in a long, happy future in Central Europe. Pursuits
in business and the liberal professions required a liberal German
education, and they gave their full attention to these pursuits while
respecting the Jewish faith and traditions of their parents.

As the Ticho brothers, including Albert, rotated in succession
through the Gymnasium, they would spend the holidays back home
with their parents for several weekends during the school year. It was
possible for Albert and his brothers to take an afternoon train on the
Austrian Northern Railway (Österrich Nordbahn) to Skalice (Skalitz),
a town about five miles to the west of Boskovice, where a train station
was located at the crossing of the county road.[21] As the train pulled into
the station at Skalice on a clear day, the round tower of the Boskovice

Castle could be seen off to the east in the distance. The schoolchildren could reach Boskovice before sunset – the beginning of the Sabbath – either on foot or by one of two horse-drawn carriages that were operated by intensely competitive Jewish coachmen.[22] It was especially important and expected for them to return at the time of family celebrations.

In 1894, during Albert's first year away at school, such an event was the bar mitzvah of Albert's brother David – the celebration of David's thirteenth birthday and his reaching the age of personal religious obligations. A train ride and then a carriage ride over the undulating slopes of the Boskovice-Skalice Road brought the schoolboys home in time for the Sabbath family celebrations.

In November 1895, the Ticho boys at the Gymnasium – Max, David, Albert, and Heinrich – did not have to travel far for next major family celebration, the wedding of their twenty-two-year-old sister Sarah and thirty-year-old Dr. Isidor Reiniger. The groom was brought up in the strictly Orthodox Jewish home of his physician-father, Dr. Joseph Reiniger. The elder Dr. Reiniger was the head of the Jewish Community of Strážnice (Strassnitz), several kilometers to the south and east of Boskovice. As the provincial capital and largest city of Moravia, Brno was the logical place to bring together these two middle-class Jewish families to witness and celebrate the wedding. Albert's new brother-in-law would take up the practice of general medicine in his birthplace of Deutschkreuz, Austria, and later in Vienna where he and Sarah raised nine children.[23]

Isidor Reiniger practiced medicine in a dedicated and selfless manner without much concern for the financial security of his family. This stood in contrast to the example of an unscrupulous, local Boskovice physician with whom the Ticho family had their differences.[24] As a physician, Albert would later emulate his brother-in-law's selfless qualities in caring for the poor at reduced fees or even free of charge. On the other hand, Albert had a tremendously successful career and he was able to balance his generosity to the poor with fine compensation from patients of average and even great financial means.

The strictly religious Isidor made more than a passive effort to influence young Albert. He kept in touch with the boy after he and Sarah moved to Deutschkreuz. As Albert's own bar mitzvah approached, Isidor prepared a *drash* (homiletic speech) for Albert to memorize and recite. Finally, on a Saturday in early October 1896, the Ticho family celebrated Avraham Albert Ticho's bar mitzvah in Boskovice at the Loew-Baer synagogue. During the worship service, Albert was called for an aliyah (ascension) to the Torah by his Hebrew name, Avraham ben Yitzḥak. Here he recited blessings and read from the Torah and the book of Isaiah. A painting by Samuel Brunner, *Old Synagogue in Boskovice*, from about 1915 (thus painted some nineteen years later) shows this very moment in the Torah service, as the Torah (symbolically in the center of the painting) has been placed aside after its reading but not yet put away so that additional readings from the Prophets may be added.[25]

Albert Ticho's aliyah to the Torah certainly took place in this now gone but well-remembered place. The recitation of the speech that he received from his brother-in-law Isidor took place either here at this point in the worship service, or perhaps more likely after the service as the family continued to celebrate with a festive meal. The content of the speech was a commentary on the weekly portion of the scriptures that Albert had read that morning in the synagogue, probably the first chapters of the book of Genesis.[26] The writing of bar mitzvah speeches was a tradition that Isidor continued for each of Albert's younger brothers and also for many Ticho children of the next generation.[27]

In Vienna just eight months before Albert's bar mitzvah, Theodor Herzl had published a sixty-five page essay entitled *Der Judenstaat*.[28] Both Albert's father and his brother-in-law, Isidor, felt Herzl's ideas were too secular, and so political Zionism was not a part of Albert's formal Jewish education at the time. On the other hand, the period of Albert Ticho's studies in Brno was marked by growing anti-Semitism that presaged two events that particularly shocked Jewish communities in the Czech lands and beyond. The first event was anti-Jewish rioting in Prague in December 1897. Earlier that year, the Austrian Reichsrat passed a pair of ordinances demanding language proficiency in both Czech and German for all civil servants in Bohemia and Moravia. Mass demonstrations against Czech nationalists erupted in Vienna, forcing the Austrian premier and interior minister, Count Casimir Badini, to resign. In Prague and the Czech countryside, Czech nationalists struck back in what came to be known as the "December Storm." Attacks upon German stores and schools in Prague eventually expanded to Jewish synagogues and homes.[29]

After the Prague riots, anti-Semitic propaganda became a standard feature in the everyday life of Czech society, and violent anti-Jewish acts became more commonplace.[30] This atmosphere set the stage for a sensational trial that must have had a great impact upon Ticho. In September 1899, a twenty-three-year-old vagabond Jew, Leopold Hilsner, was placed on trial for the murder of a nineteen-year-old Czech seamstress, Anežka Hrůzová. The murder had taken place near the eastern Bohemian town of Polná on April 1, 1899. The proceedings were sensationalized by the press, who presumed that the victim's blood had been used in the preparation of Passover matzot. The opportunistic Czech politician Karel Baxa, who later became mayor of Prague, represented the family of the victim. During the trial, both the state's prosecuting attorney and Baxa made clear suggestions of "ritual murder."

Hilsner's conviction was appealed to the Supreme Court by Tomáš Masaryk, who would later become the first president of Czechoslovakia. Hilsner was retried with the accusation of an additional murder in October–November 1900 and sentenced to death for both murders, though the sentence was commuted by the emperor to life imprisonment in 1901. Thus the Hilsner Affair (or Polná Affair as it is also known) remained in the headlines as Albert Ticho graduated from the Brno Gymnasium and moved to Vienna.

By the time Albert Ticho graduated, Max had followed Josef to Vienna to study law as well. David had returned to Boskovice after additional college business studies in Brno to join the family business with his father and Jacob. Albert's younger brothers Heinrich, Nathan, and Sami were now enrolled in the Gymnasium with Sami now being the one to prepare for his bar mitzvah. Of course young Victor and Alfred were still in the *Normalschule* and living at home.

The family was proud to learn that Albert had been accepted to the University of Vienna. Like Josef and Max, the German education that they were providing for their children was leading another son closer to a career in the learned liberal professions. Albert Ticho would spend the next decade of his life immersed in studies and specialty training. He would encounter further opportunities but also adversities that would lead him yet further out into the world.

Chapter 3

1902–1905

Vienna

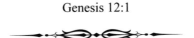

לֶךְ-לְךָ מֵאַרְצְךָ וּמִמּוֹלַדְתְּךָ וּמִבֵּית אָבִיךָ...

Go forth from your native land and from your father's house...

Genesis 12:1

It was the beginning of a new century when Albert Ticho graduated from the Brno Gymnasium and applied to the University of Vienna Medical School. On several occasions he visited his brothers, Josef and Max, who shared an apartment in Leopoldstadt (Second District). To the west, across the Danube Canal, there were far more elegant districts, with impressive palaces, theaters, and institutions, including the University of Vienna. On the east side of the canal in Leopoldstadt, there was a higher concentration of immigrants, and here Jews comprised over a third of the population. Because of the high concentration of Jewish inhabitants, the island formed by the canal and the Danube River was sometimes called Mazzesinsel (Matzah Island).[1]

Josef and Max's flat at Rembrandtstraße 19 was toward the northern end of Leopoldstadt in easy reach of the bridges and trams that they took to their classes. By the time Albert enrolled at the medical school in the early fall of 1902, Josef had already graduated from law school the previous May, and Max was on a course to graduate later that same year.[2]

By 1900, the glittering, multicultural city of Vienna had reached a population of about 1.7 million people, and it was growing. The outlying suburban districts had been annexed ten years earlier, adding another ten districts and creating a metropolis that had become the sixth most populous city in the world. At the turn of the century, the population of Vienna was increasing at a rate of about thirty-four thousand per year, with immigrants making up 65 percent of the increase. A high point at just over two million was reached in 1910.[3] Electrification of the inner districts had been substantially completed by the turn of the century and electrified tram lines marked Vienna as a city of the modern age.

The most important architectural feature of Vienna was the Ringstraße ("the Ring"), a two-and-a-half-mile-long boulevard that was completed in 1865. It followed the course of the torn-down medieval walls that had surrounded the Innere Stadt, the Inner City that was numbered as Vienna's First District. The elegant Ringstraße was lined with several monumental buildings that had been built in a variety of historical styles. At the northwest turn of the Ring, one of these buildings housed the halls and offices of the University of Vienna.

Completed in 1884, the university building had been designed by Heinrich von Ferstel in the Renaissance style as a symbol of rationalism and liberal culture.[4] On the ceiling of the university's main ceremonial hall, those assembled could look up at two Franz Matsch paintings, *Triumph of Light over Darkness* and *Theology*. In addition to a painting for the Faculty of Theology, commissions for three paintings representing the three other faculties had originally been given to another artist, the famous Gustav Klimt. However, these commissions had been rescinded in a storm of controversy, and the avant-garde paintings were not installed. Klimt instead had shown them publicly at "Secession" art exhibitions.[5]

Among the faculties at the University of Vienna, the medical school particularly was held in high esteem throughout the world. The school's illustrious professors practiced and taught their clinical arts at the Vienna General Hospital, the vast Allgemeines Krankenhaus, which had opened in 1784 and consequently predated the main building of the university by exactly one hundred years. The General Hospital was located just to the west and north of the main university within Alsergrund (Vienna's Ninth District). In 1900, Jews comprised between 11 and 20 percent of the residents of this district, among them Sigmund Freud, who lived and worked at Berggasse 19. Except for his last semester in medical school, Albert Ticho lived across the Danube Canal in Leopoldstadt. In the summer of 1907, however, Ticho found pleasant lodgings in an Alsergrund flat at Berggasse 39, not far from Freud's house, which is now a famous tourist destination.[6]

As Albert prepared to begin his medical studies, he rented a first-floor apartment at Krummbaumgasse 10 in Leopoldstadt, not far from his brothers' flat. He remained here throughout most of his first semester (October 1902–February 1903), but the following spring he moved to another modest flat nearby, just off the Danube Canal at Obere Donaustraße 85. Living here, he continued his studies and enrolled for the next semester (March–June 1903).[7] In order to commute from Leopoldstadt to his classes, Ticho would cross the bridge over the Danube Canal and follow the tram lines along the Schottenring, the northern side of the Ringstraße that stretched between the canal and the university.

Albert's first semesters concentrated on the basic sciences (appendix 2). The required curriculum for the first semester consisted of a weekly schedule that included anatomy lectures and demonstrations, chemistry lectures and laboratory, general biology, and experimental physics. Among these subjects, anatomy lectures and laboratories would continue into the next semester and beyond. The series of these anatomy courses was given by Prof. Emil Zuckerkandl, a Jewish academic who was well known in those days for a two-volume textbook on the pathologic anatomy of the nose and sinuses. Early in his career he had battled against the anti-Semitism of his German nationalist students, challenging each of them to a saber duel. Nowadays, his name is better remembered by the eponym describing bodies of cells adjacent to the abdominal aorta, the "organ of Zuckerkandl." In addition to the first-year lectures, Zuckerkandl also supervised the anatomy demonstrations and lab in Albert's second and third years (winter semesters of 1903–4 and 1904–5). Between Zuckerkandl's upper level anatomy lectures and demonstrations, the curriculum interposed summer semester physiology and histology (microscopic anatomy) courses given respectively by Profs. Siegmund von Exner and Victor von Ebner. Like their colleague Zuckerkandl, both of these professors are remembered for providing a variety of descriptions of anatomical structures that bear their respective names.[8]

In addition to Zuckerkandl, von Exner, and von Ebner, there were many other contemporary members of the medical faculty whose contributions found even greater worldwide acclaim just before and after the turn of the century. Among these were the three greatest works of Sigmund Freud – on dreams, the unconscious, hysteria, and sexuality – that solidified the organizing principles of psychoanalysis. Another was Karl Landsteiner's discovery of human blood types that opened up the possibilities of safe blood transfusions while yet further unveiling the complexities of the immune system.[9] Ticho would eventually take one of Landsteiner's courses, "Pathological Dissection Exercises," aimed at senior students who were preparing for their forthcoming examinations.

As early as his fourth semester in medical school (March–June 1904), even before his clinical rotations, Albert Ticho seems to have already developed an interest in ophthalmology with the obvious idea of forging a career in this specialty. Prof. von Ebner's general human histology course did not satisfy his interest in ocular histology. In addition to standard general histology, Albert took an additional elective under von Ebner entitled "Histology and Embryology of the Eyes."[10]

———◆———

Albert's demanding curriculum was balanced within his personal life by the proximity of an extended family in Leopoldstadt that began to multiply. While Albert was busy studying anatomy, physics, chemistry, and biology, and his brothers Josef and Max were just beginning their individual law careers, their sister Sarah (Ticho Reiniger) moved to Vienna in 1903 along with husband Isidor and their six children. Dr. Reiniger purchased two adjoining apartments in Leopoldstadt, close to the Danube Canal at Große Schiffgasse 5, space for both living quarters and medical offices. The three Ticho brothers each had a standing invitation from the religiously observant Reinigers to join them for Friday night dinner, where they would celebrate the Sabbath and where the bachelor uncles could dote on their several nieces and nephews.

In the fall of 1903, Albert moved into the Reinigers' apartment (or possibly a portion of Isidor's adjoining office flat). He lived with them for two years until he left for a one-year hiatus while he attended the Charles University in Prague (October 1905–June 1906), and he returned to live with them again for one more semester after his return to Vienna in the fall of 1906.[11]

Albert Ticho's extended family in Vienna also included his Uncle Phillip, Aunt Bertha, and their youngest children, including ten-year-old Anna. The family had moved from Brno to Vienna in 1904, and just as in Brno, their children could receive an excellent liberal German education in Vienna. Although comprising a minority of the population in the "liberal" districts (the aforementioned First, Second, and Ninth Districts), Jewish children were often in the majority in their *Gymnasien*. Anna's education, however, took a different track. Beginning at age twelve, Anna was provided with her first lessons in drawing, for it was common for the children of Vienna's bourgeoisie to be "raised with a heavy emphasis on the aesthetic side of life."[12] Three years later Anna was formally enrolled by her parents in an art school under the directorship of the painter Ernst Nowak.

Many in the Ticho family were happy with Phillip's relocation to Vienna. The move had disrupted a budding romance between first cousins – Albert's brother David and Anna's older half sister Ida (by Phillip's second wife Fannie).[13] The family probably did not envision that when Anna matured, Albert would follow a family pattern and likewise fall in love with his first cousin.

—◆—

The curriculum in Albert's third academic year continued to include laboratories – anatomy, histology, and pathology – but also his first introductions to clinical medicine. During the winter semester he took a course entitled "Physical Examination of the Ill," and in the summer semester of 1905, Albert attended the "Medical Clinic with

Praktikum" (hands-on clinical work) given by Prof. Dr. Leopold von Schrötter at the General Hospital early each morning. Prof. von Schrötter was both an internist and a laryngologist. He was the first chairman of laryngology at the University of Vienna and director of the world's first laryngological clinic at the Vienna General Hospital. (He is remembered for his elaboration of a syndrome of upper extremity swelling, Paget-Schrötter's syndrome).[14] His father, Moravian-born chemist Anton Schrötter von Kristelli, had long ago attained the chair of general chemistry in Vienna. It was through Prof. Anton von Schrötter that the family apparently received the title "Ritter von Kristelli" that would be passed down from father to son. Just a decade later, during World War I, Prof. Leopold von Schrötter's son, Hermann, would serve as the chief medical officer of an army reserve (or rear-guard) hospital in Jerusalem. Capt. Hermann von Schrötter would go on to serve as Albert's commanding officer when the Reserve Hospital relocated to Damascus (chapters 13 and 14).

While Albert enjoyed the medicine clinics of Prof. Schrötter, he was more inclined to the surgical disciplines, and the curriculum included an equal number of hours each day for the "Surgery Clinic with *Praktikum*" given by Prof. Dr. Julius Hochenegg, who had made many important contributions in the area of cancer surgery. On his way into the General Hospital, Ticho would pass by the statue of Hochenegg's mentor, Prof. Theodor Billroth, who arguably had been the greatest surgeon of his era in the latter half of the nineteenth century. Billroth's many triumphs epitomized new aggressive approaches to surgery that Hochenegg and others now employed.

In the spring of 1905, Albert was able to break away from his medical studies and travel by train to attend the Sunday afternoon wedding of his brother Jacob to Emma Krakauer. The wedding took place on April 2, 1905, in the city of Mikulov (Nikolsburg), Moravia. The newlyweds settled in Brno, moving into a large and comfortable apartment on the Legionarska Ulice (now called Trida Kapitana Jarose). The house was opposite the main square of Brno and not far from the park, and here their three children were born. A few years later, in 1908, David Ticho likewise moved to Brno after he married the twenty-two-year-old musician and singer Hilda Klauber of Vienna, and they also had three children.[15]

———◆———

In turn-of-the-century Vienna, three Ticho brothers set out to pursue careers in the liberal professions. They were following the well-trodden paths of Jews from Bohemia, Moravia, and other parts of the Austrian Empire. During the years 1901–1904, it is estimated that Jews comprised about 23 percent of the entire student body of the University of Vienna. Proportions of Jewish students varied between the different faculties, 15 percent in philosophy, 23 percent in law, but over 40 percent in the medical school. Overall, the proportion of Jewish students reached its peak of about 33 percent in the late 1880s. In 1885, over 60 percent of Vienna's medical students were Jewish. It was said that the decline over the next decades was the result of anti-Semitism within Vienna's student body.[16] Throughout Ticho's student days, the University was "a bastion of *Judenhetze*" (Jew-baiting). Inside the lecture halls chants of "*Juden heraus!*" ("Jews get out!") could be heard from gangs of Austro-German students, while outside of the lecture halls Jewish students were subjected to other intimidations and physical attacks.[17] About half of the members of the University of Vienna Medical School's teaching faculty were also of Jewish descent. Seeking academic advancement, several of Albert Ticho's instructors had renounced their Jewish faith and undergone conversion. It was relatively rare for a full professor to be Jewish by religion. Their chances were better to be an unpaid lecturer (*Privatdozent*) or a "titular" or associate professor (*ausserordentlicher Professor*).

The Ticho brothers' entry into the professions of law and medicine placed them on a path to become a part of the liberal educated class. In bourgeois Viennese society, being a lawyer (*Advokat*) meant being an intellectual. For intellectual Jewish doctors and other professionals, however assimilated they might be, the additional title of professor conferred status and a sense of personal "protection." Full and even associate professors of medicine and law were members of a small, select group. Sigmund Freud once described his promotion to a professorship as his "salvation."[18] Some of these aspects of Freud and

Vienna were described later by Albert Ticho's nephew Ernst, who had survived Dachau and the Buchenwald concentration camps and eventually studied medicine and psychiatry.[19] In *fin-de-siècle* (turn-of-the-century) Vienna, other notable Jewish physicians who made great contributions to Viennese cultural life included Arthur Schnitzler, an author and playwright who had given up medicine and endured harsh, often anti-Semitic criticism for the erotic content of his works.

Albert Ticho moved to Vienna, the Habsburg capital, at a defining moment in modern history. More than just a round number at the *fin-de-siècle*, it is said that Vienna at the beginning of the twentieth century was the birthplace of a major part of the modern culture and thought which forms the basis of our consciousness to this day. Whether in Berlin, Frankfurt, Prague, or Vienna, Jews of Central Europe, no longer confined to the ghetto, vigorously pursued higher education and embraced German culture, though there were many who felt alienated from the mainstream of that culture and its *haute bourgeoisie*.[20]

In contrast, the Zionist movement, led by Theodor Herzl, searched for a social normalcy for Jews beyond Europe's borders. Ticho was influenced by Herzl's writings such as his utopian novel *Altneuland* that was published in 1902, the year that Ticho began his medical studies at the University of Vienna. The following year, the controversies at the Sixth Zionist Congress in Basel, the so-called "Uganda" Congress, were of little concern to the young medical student. It is said that the "strain and wrangling" during that congress depleted Herzl's physical reserves and "hastened his untimely death." In June 1904, as Herzl's heart began to fail him, he went for a vacation in the Semmering Mountains, but his condition worsened and pneumonia settled in his left lung. His physician, Dr. Siegmund Werner, who also served as the editor of *Die Welt*, was the only person at Herzl's bedside when he died.[21]

Herzl's funeral procession in Vienna on July 7, 1904, began near his home in Währing, just about a mile from the Allgemeines Krankenhaus. Six thousand mourners followed Herzl's hearse in a chaotic one-mile procession to the cemetery in Döbling. Ticho did not join in the procession but he could not have escaped the extensive coverage of the event in Vienna's newspapers. Forty-five years later, Ticho would again be just over a mile away when Herzl was reinterred in Jerusalem on Mount Herzl, the highest part of the modern city.[22]

If Ticho did not espouse Herzl's political Zionism, he was certainly affected and inspired by it. In contrast, Adolf Hitler, who came to Vienna soon after Ticho's graduation from medical school, found inspiration from two anti-Semitic politicians who became his role models: Georg von Schönerer, who had organized the radical pan-German nationalists in 1882; and the more politically successful Karl Lueger, leader of the Christian Social Party, who was elected as Mayor of Vienna in 1895 and remained so throughout most of Ticho's years in Vienna.[23]

———◆———

Albert Ticho studied medicine in Vienna in an era of great freedom and assimilation for the Jews of the Habsburg capital. Ticho's ancestors in his native Moravia had been substantially "Germanized" following Joseph II's Edict of Tolerance (*Toleranzpatent*, 1782) and "naturalized" with full citizenship since the *Ausgleich* of 1867. In the course of over a century of reforms, much had changed for Jewish students but not quite everything. As Ticho pursued his studies, he could not avoid the great achievements and legacy of Jewish physicians who went before him, but he also could not help but be aware of their struggles.

The first Jew to gain a doctor's diploma in Vienna after the publication of the *Toleranzpatent* was Joseph Manes Österreicher, a Hungarian physician who worked in a health resort and gained the close attention of the emperor.[24] Including Jews having undergone conversion, the first Jew to graduate from the University of Vienna was likely Georg Joseph Beer, who graduated in 1786 with a doctor of medicine degree at the age of twenty-three. Beer's family had converted to Catholicism early in his life or perhaps even before his birth, but nonetheless Beer suffered from "poverty, worry, and persecution." In 1812, Beer was appointed as Professor of Ophthalmology at the University of Vienna, and through his many personal contributions and a lineage of many illustrious students, Beer's legacy continued into Albert Ticho's day and until today. He carries the fitting sobriquet "Founder of the Vienna School of Ophthalmology."[25]

The main entrance of Vienna's General Hospital was located in Alsergrund on Alser Straße, just a few blocks away from the main university building. Albert Ticho could look up at the sign over this entrance that had been placed there by Emperor Joseph II. In alliterative Latin it read, "*Solutio et solatio aegrorum*" – in almost equally alliterative English translation, "Cure and comfort the afflicted." Based on the model of the Parisian central hospital, Hôtel Dieu, Joseph II had decided to convert the existing ninety-year-old Great Poorhouse (Grossarmenhaus) into a vast general hospital. The institution with two thousand beds was opened on August 16, 1784. In Ticho's day, the windows to the famous Ophthalmology Clinic II where Carl Koller had worked under Prof. Carl Ferdinand von Arlt were located just above the Alser Straße entrance. Ticho could only look up as he passed by this famous clinic. Rotations in the general medical and surgical clinics of the hospital were needed before he could study in any of the specialized clinics.

Ticho was probably very familiar with stories surrounding one of the greatest advances in surgery that had taken place within Vienna's General Hospital – the introduction of cocaine as an anesthetic – a story that also contained elements of anti-Semitism. The discovery of the medical uses of cocaine was set in motion by Sigmund Freud, who in the summer of 1884 recruited the aspiring ophthalmologist Carl Koller to study the systemic effects of the drug. Koller reported his discovery in abstentia in Heidelberg, Germany, on September 15 and in person to the Vienna Royal Imperial Society of Physicians one month later.[26] The anti-Semitic aspect of the story emerged only the following year when a colleague-in-training called Koller a "Jewish pig" or "impudent Jew" in public at the General Hospital, and Koller reacted by hitting the man in the face. Though forbidden by this time, a duel with heavy sabers ensued and while Koller was unharmed, his opponent received two deep gashes. Koller quickly disappeared from Vienna, and after sojourns in Utrecht and London he immigrated to New York City in 1888, where he eventually became Chairman of Ophthalmology at Mount Sinai Hospital.[27]

During the years of Ticho's matriculation at the University of

Vienna, the Department of Ophthalmology was led by two professors who each directed the two ophthalmic clinics at the General Hospital – the aforementioned Prof. Ernst Fuchs, Director of Clinic II since 1885, and Prof. Isidor Schnabel, Director of Clinic I since 1895. Fuchs was the more preeminent of the two, often described as the greatest ophthalmologist of his time and whose carefully prepared lectures were considered masterpieces. His name is remembered by many eponyms in the medical lexicon and for a very famous textbook (*Lehrbuch der Augenheilkunde*) that appeared in multiple editions and translations.[28] The *Lehrbuch* contained a lucid and classic section on the infectious disease trachoma, and here Fuchs emphasized the prevention of the dissemination of the infectious disease and role of the physician as a role model in providing suitable guidance and instruction to his patients. Putting his principles into clinical practice, the University of Vienna established a special clinic for trachoma, an example of one of the first subspecialty clinics in the history of ophthalmology.[29] Hundreds of Fuchs's former assistants and students, including University of Vienna students such as Albert Ticho and foreign visiting postgraduate students, went out into the far corners of the world to implement these important public health principles.

Prof. Schnabel also carried a worldwide reputation. Before his appointment as full professor and the head of Clinic I, he had earlier served at other German universities in Austria, namely Innsbruck, then Graz, and then a penultimate appointment in Prague. The two professors, Schnabel and Fuchs, generally maintained a very congenial relationship, but there were inevitable areas of scientific controversy between them such as their views on the mechanisms of glaucoma and its anatomic effects upon the optic nerve.[30] Schnabel was an excellent teacher, "a master of the language and could present his thoughts in a perfect style; he always enthused his audience."[31] He made a great impression on his audiences and was loved and admired by his pupils. Ticho would have to wait until his senior year to attend Prof. Schnabel's courses and clinic. Meanwhile, for the intervening two semesters (October 1905 to June 1906), he went to study at the Charles University in Prague.

CHAPTER 4

1905–1911
PRAGUE AND BACK TO VIENNA

עת לבקש ועת לאבד...

A time for seeking and a time for losing...

Ecclesiastes 3:6

B y the spring of 1905, Albert Ticho had completed five semesters of basic science courses. This was the halfway point in his medical school curriculum, and from then on, his courses would be conducted in hospital clinics, operating theaters, as well as lecture rooms. That summer, Ticho had attended his first two daily clinics and *praktika*: "Medicine" with Prof. von Schrötter and "Surgery" with Prof. Hochenegg (chapter 3). With many other prerequisites to be taken, the most important upper level courses in ophthalmology would be deferred until his final year at the University of Vienna.

Medical students also had the option of attending other universities within the empire and applying earned credits toward their medical degrees. In Ticho's case, the Charles University in Prague was an especially attractive destination where he could use his knowledge of Czech out and about in the city. There was an excellent ophthalmology clinic in Prague under Prof. Wilhelm Czermak that would help prepare him for the additional ophthalmology courses back in Vienna. Ultimately, all of the special credits and achievements in ophthalmology would be

29

noted on Ticho's medical school diploma, but a good starting point on this track could definitely be found in Prague at the Charles University.

Prague, located along both banks of the north-flowing Vltava River (also called the Moldau in German), was then the capital of the imperial province and Kingdom of Bohemia. The river created a natural dividing line between the city's eight districts: five districts on the right bank and three districts on the left. The older districts on the right bank had been established within an eastward bend of the Vltava. Over a century earlier, Prague's Old Town (*Staré Město* or *Altstadt*) had been surrounded by ramparts and a moat on the remaining sides. The moat was filled in by the end of the eighteenth century, and a part of this line was marked by a broad street, the Na Příkopě (meaning "On the Moat") that corresponded to its German name, *Graben* (also meaning "Ditch"). As in the time of Ticho's sojourn in Prague, this upscale street continues to contain many of city's best shops and most popular cafés.[1]

Throughout his ten-month sojourn in Prague, Ticho lived in the northern part of the Old Town, renting two flats in succession at Dlouhá (Langegasse) 706 and then at Dlouhá 22. He therefore lived just a few blocks to the east of the heavily demolished Josefov District, the former Jewish ghetto that had been abolished in 1852. Josefov was tucked into the most northwest corner on the right bank and surrounded by the Old Town. Similarly, the Old Town was itself surrounded by the adjacent New Town (Nové Město or Neustadt) that extended another few miles beyond the Na Příkopě: eastward to the main train station (*Státní Nádraží Praha* or *Staatsbahnhof*) that first opened in 1855 at the eastern ramparts of the city, and southward about a mile to the university medical campus where Ticho would attend his lectures and clinics. Other areas of Prague were less visited by Ticho if at all, the more peripheral districts to the south and east and three districts on the opposite left bank that included the grounds of the imperial palace. It is unlikely that he visited suburbs such as Smichov on the left bank where many of Prague's Jews had migrated in the wake of urban renewal projects.

At the turn of the century, electric trams marked Prague as a modern city, but the system did not provide a direct route from Ticho's neighborhood in the northern section of the Old Town to his classes in the southern section of the New Town. On a nice day, he would have walked the mile or so to his classes at the medical faculty building and clinics at the Prague General Hospital (Allgemeines Krankenhaus). His route would likely have taken him through the Old Town Square with its many landmarks: the Rathaus of the Altstadt on the east and Tyn's Church (Teynkirche) and the attached Kinsky Palace to the west; then past the western façade of the university's venerable Carolinum with its beautiful halls that now only housed the law faculty. The smaller streets beyond the Carolinum would take pedestrians like Ticho past the German Theater, beyond the streets running to the Fruit Market (Ovocný trh) and onto the Graben with its many shops and cafés. Another half-mile walk southward through the New Town would bring Ticho to his destinations within the medical campus. Nearby were the offices and natural science laboratories of the Philosophical Faculty on Viničná ulice (Weinberggasse), where Albert Einstein would briefly work.[2]

In 1905, the population of Prague's eight districts was between about 216,000 and 225,000, but about 450,000 when Smichov and three other main suburbs were included in the calculation. Although the German population in Prague had severely declined throughout the latter half of the nineteenth century, the city was still divided along the lines of culture and language. Among the 450,000 or so residents of Prague there were approximately 415,000 Czechs, 25,000 Jews, and 10,000 "Germans," meaning non-Jewish German-speaking persons. About 56 percent of the Jews of Prague declared Czech as their everyday language, and so only 22,000 or about 5 percent of Prague's population declared German as their primary language. As Czechs outnumbered German-speakers by a wide margin, signage on the streets and for the electric tramlines was mainly written in the Czech language.[3] Two and a half years earlier in Vienna, Ticho had taken an elective language course in Czech that emphasized the Bohemian dialect. "*Syntax der böhmischen Sprache mit Übungen*," a three-hour-per-week course taught by Ferdinand Menčík, had included formal lectures and a language lab. This may have been an unusual course for a medical student to take, and perhaps Albert Ticho stood out in the small class. However, in taking this class, Ticho would be better prepared to acclimate to life in the Bohemian capital even though his affiliations were naturally toward the German-speaking minority.[4]

Just like German-speaking Jews of Moravia and Bohemia, the Czech-speaking Jews of Prague were inclined toward German for their higher education. In Albert Ticho's day, it was the traditional German institutions of Prague (and not its newer Czech institutions) that enjoyed international renown, and the education they provided could be applied in many other parts of Europe. In Prague, as in Vienna, Jews constituted a large percentage of the university student body though it was declining, from 31 percent of the German part of Charles University at the turn of the century to 20 percent by 1910. Even though more and more Jews in Bohemia were attending Czech-language secondary schools, the percentage of Jewish students in the Czech university remained flat at about 2 percent. Ticho's year-long studies in Prague mirrored overall trends among Bohemian Jewish students who opted for perceived quality, utility, and prestige over other considerations.[5]

Over the centuries, the scientific and medical faculties of the Charles University in Prague attracted professors and students from throughout the Czech lands and from many distant European countries. The university, founded by Charles IV in 1348 as the Corolo-Ferdinandea, was one of the oldest in Europe, and its traditional home, the Carolinum in the heart of the Old City, had been completed in 1383 exactly five hundred years before Albert Ticho's birth. Lectures in Latin were the norm during the sixteenth century in the days of the great Danish astronomer Tycho Brahe. In 1784, German officially replaced Latin as the language of instruction at the university, but there were still a few professors who continued teaching some subjects in Latin even into the early nineteenth century. One such professor was the Bohemian physician Jan Evangelista Purkyně, who established the optical principles of ophthalmoscopy in the 1820s.

After the political rebellions of 1848, Czech found its place next to German as a language of instruction at the University of Prague. In 1882, the university was formally divided into separate Czech and German faculties, the Czech Universita Karlo-Ferdinandova and the

German Karl-Ferdinands Universität. Among the appointees to the Czech University that year was a Moravian philosophy lecturer at the University of Vienna, Dozent Tomáš Garrigue Masaryk, who would one day become the first president of Czechoslovakia.[6]

By 1905, the Czech University and the German University in Prague had annual enrollments of about 3,400 and 1,100 students, respectively. Ticho was one of about 350 medical students at the German part of the Charles University. While the Carolinum continued to house the two law faculties, the philosophical and medical faculties, along with their institutes and natural science laboratories, were located farther to the south in the New City, to the southeast side of one of Prague's largest parks, the *Karlovo náměstí* or *Karlsplatz*. Ticho's clinical rotations were centered at the nearly adjacent Prague General Hospital, just to the south, which had first opened in 1791, seven years after the opening of the General Hospital in Vienna. The composition of the two university student bodies only partially reflected the changing demographics in Prague. While there were almost twice the number of medical students on the Czech side compared to the German side, the number of appointments to the medical faculties was roughly equal, about 62 and 64 positions, respectively.[7] German-speaking students like Ticho likely benefitted from the relatively more favorable faculty-to-student ratio.

During the winter semester of 1905–6, Albert Ticho's courses included pathology (gross medical and surgical) under Profs. Alfred Přibram and Anton Wölfler. Another pathology course was abruptly canceled, that of the well-known Prof. Hans Chiari, who relocated to the University of Strasbourg. Three courses were coincidentally taught by three unrelated professors with the identical surname of Pick, while a variety of other topics rounded out the schedule.[8] In the summer semester of 1906, Ticho again spent much time under Prof. Wölfler, this time in his surgery clinics and operating theater. However, the study of ophthalmology under Prof. Wilhelm Czermak constituted the greatest aggregate block of time on Ticho's schedule that semester, in the clinic, in the operating theater, and an additional course dedicated to mastering the use of the ophthalmoscope, an instrument used to examine the retina.

Prof. Czermak was a native Moravian who had succeeded Prof.

Isidor Schnabel as Professor and Chairman of Ophthalmology in 1895 when Schnabel received his appointment in Vienna.[9] He was a gifted clinician and a very accomplished ophthalmic surgeon. In 1904, after eleven years of work, Czermak had completed the "opus of his life," *Die augenärztlichen Operationen*, which Hirschberg described as the most extensive monograph in German to that time on the subject of eye operations. Like Fuchs's *Lehrbuch*, Czermak's textbook of ophthalmic surgery would be one of Albert Ticho's most frequently used reference works.

An eye clinic had first been established in Prague in 1808 by Johann Nepomuk Fischer, and the clinic was incorporated into the university in 1820. Several highly esteemed chairmen had followed. Beginning in 1882, the autonomous German and Czech medical faculties shared clinical space, medical and scientific institutes, and their library. At the time of the division of the faculties, the chairman of the Ophthalmology Department, Prof. Joseph Hasner, had taken deep offense to the assignment of half of his clinic to the Czech University. He had resigned in protest, voluntarily retiring well before his time had arrived. His assistant, Dr. Josef Schöbl, became the first Chairman of Ophthalmology of the Czech University, a post he held for two decades until his death in 1902 when he was succeeded by Dr. Jan Deyl. Deyl had initially published articles in the Czech language that were not widely read, but he later turned to English when he contributed a chapter on optic nerve diseases for Norris and Oliver's 1900 ophthalmology textbook.[10] Although Ticho attended Prof. Czermak's ophthalmology clinic on the German side, he may have also taken the occasional opportunity to observe in the "Czech" clinic of Prof. Deyl.

———◆———

During his time in Prague, a wonderful place for Ticho to study was the beautiful library within the Klementinum, a stately baroque building-complex located at the western edge of the Old City, near the banks of the Vltava. Perhaps it was here that Ticho first met the precocious philosophy student Schmuel Hugo Bergmann.

Bergmann, who was the same age as Ticho, had visited Palestine in

1910 and was an active Zionist and leader of the Bar Kochba Association of Jewish University Students in Prague.[11] After graduating in 1907 he would become a librarian at the Klementinum and in 1920 he immigrated to Palestine, becoming the first director of the National and University Library. At the Hebrew University, Bergmann would go on to become a professor of philosophy and the rector of the university. In Jerusalem, Bergmann and Ticho had the opportunity to develop a friendship that extended over several decades. Meanwhile in Prague, Bergmann had greatly influenced his childhood friend, Franz Kafka, to have a positive view of Zionism. Two of Kafka's closest friends, Max Brod and Felix Weltsch, who comprised the so-called "close Prague circle" ("*Der enge Prager Kreis*"), were also both ardent Zionists. Brod, a well-known writer and an uncanny judge of talent, remained Kafka's lifelong friend and became Kafka's posthumous literary executor. Albert Ticho, just a transient Jewish-German medical student in Prague, was not a part of the inner circle of these now well-known writers and thinkers, but his humanistic view of Zionism was likely influenced by them.

As in Vienna, Albert Ticho enjoyed the rich café-based social scene in Prague that attracted writers, artists, and philosophers. Though Ticho was very absorbed in his studies, many facets of his social life revolved around these cafés, whose patrons reflected the city's "ebb and flow of radiant optimism and dark despair," an atmosphere infused with "a gently ironic sense of black humor."[12]

Ticho could partake of many fine cultural offerings in Prague that were part of a long tradition. Mozart had lived there a century-and-a-quarter earlier, when his *Prague Symphony* and *Don Giovanni* were first performed in the city. The Bohemian capital had later been the home of the great Czech composers Bedřich Smetana and Antonín Dvořák. Gustav Mahler had performed their works alongside those of Beethoven and Wagner following his appointment as conductor in Prague in 1885. In Ticho's day, Brno native Leoš Janáček wrote and produced operas that were performed in Prague in the Czech language.[13]

In the midst of the Czech renascence and facing the upheavals of urban renewal, some of the Jews of Prague sought to preserve their culture and heritage. The Josefov District was then completing a slum clearance project as part of an initiative to model the city after Paris. The district was still inhabited by the owners of numerous religious institutions, the employees of the small prayer-halls, middlemen, and old-clothes dealers.[14] Just outside the Josefov District, a semblance of the Eiffel Tower overlooked the city from Petřin Hill as an emblem of modernity. Niklasgasse, the narrow central street through Josefov, was widened and renamed Pařížká. Ticho may have visited one of the local synagogues or the Old Jewish Town Hall that held regular evening events next door. Even in those days these were well-known tourist attractions. The Altneuschul was among the oldest synagogues in all of Europe, the combination of "old" and "new" reflected in its name had inspired the name of Herzl's novel, *Altneuland*.[15] Next door the Town Hall's clock tower featured traditional Roman numerals but a second clock affixed to the roof bore Hebrew letters and clock hands that ran counter-clockwise, just as Hebrew is read from right to left. During Ticho's second semester in Prague in May 1906, the Jewish Museum, established for the many unused artifacts that were saved from the demolitions, opened in the Josefov District. The museum had been established mainly through the work of another one of Ticho's classmates, a philosophy and history student Salomon Hugo Lieben, who had just graduated that spring and published his first studies on the history of Prague Jews.

———◆———

Albert Ticho left Prague in July 1906. During the subsequent summer vacation, he had the opportunity to use some of the medical knowledge he had accumulated. On July 22, 1906, while visiting his family in Boskovice, a fire engulfed a basement bakery in the city's *Judenstadt*. Albert's thirteen-year-old brother Alfred had been walking in the hills overlooking Boskovice with his friend, Ernst Ultmann, the baker's son. Here they heard the blast of the fire brigade's trumpet and soon discovered that smoke that was rising from the basement bakery of the Ultmann family! As the firemen rushed in, a can of kerosene exploded, causing severe burns and injuries to over twenty people and several deaths. Albert was among those who rushed over and helped the injured patients. Some of the first-aid measures he employed included the smearing of egg yolks and ointments onto the burned skin of the victims. Albert's treatments and decisive manner were credited with saving many lives, including the life of the trumpeter who had sounded the alarm.[16]

Returning to Vienna in September for the 1906–7 winter semester, Ticho again moved into the flat of his sister, Sarah Ticho Reiniger, and her family at Große Schiffgasse 5 in Leopoldstadt. The two major subjects of this ninth and penultimate semester were clinics in obstetrics and gynecology with Prof. Friedrich Schauta and ophthalmology with Prof. Hofrat Dr. Isidor Schnabel. Upon getting back to school, Ticho learned that Prof. Czermak had died suddenly of a stroke in Prague on September 8. Czermak would be succeeded by the dynamic forty-three-year-old Prof. Anton Elschnig, who was then an associate professor in Vienna. As Elschnig did not take up his new post until April 1907, Ticho had the opportunity for some contact with him at the Vienna General Hospital. Elschnig had achieved a meteoric rise through the ranks of the faculty in Graz and then Vienna. On the basis of over forty publications and a textbook on the examination of the eye, he had achieved the rank of associate professor in 1900. In Ticho's day, medical students in the Austrian-Hungary universities studied the latest editions of Elschnig's textbook to learn the basic techniques of eye examination. Elschnig was a brilliant clinician, master surgeon, writer, and teacher, and his lectures and surgical demonstrations were immensely popular.[17] Ticho quickly developed a great respect for the young professor, who would go on to an illustrious career in Prague that stretched over decades.

One of the most historically important clinical presentations in the history of ophthalmology ever to take place at the Vienna Medical School occurred in the midst of Ticho's studies in Prof. Schnabel's ophthalmology clinic. This was a live presentation of a patient who represented the first successful corneal transplant in a human being. On December 14, 1906, Dr. Eduard Konrad Zirm, a Viennese native and alumnus of the Vienna Medical School and Eye Clinics, presented this patient to the medical faculty in Vienna. A decade earlier in Vienna, Prof. Ernst Fuchs had reported a series of thirty penetrating grafts with disappointing results.[18] Fuchs came to realize that human corneas were far superior to the rabbit corneas as donor material, and he recognized that a permanent healing of the transplant occurred as opposed to gradual substitution of the graft by host tissue.

Dr. Zirm and his patient, Alois Glogar, were already famous, as the doctor's report had been published earlier that year. Glogar had been blinded by caustic injuries to both corneas. Zirm had operated on both of Golgar's eyes on December 7, 1905 at the District Hospital in Olomouc (Olmütz), Moravia. It was a hospital where a department of ophthalmology had not even existed until it was established by Zirm in 1895, and it must have been remarkable to Ticho that this milestone had occurred just a few miles from his hometown. The professors and medical students who observed Glogar could see that one of the corneal grafts had remained clear for a full year following healing, resulting in greatly improved though not perfect vision in that eye.[19] There is little doubt that Albert Ticho was quite impressed with this great accomplishment and that it only fueled his desire to excel in his clinical ophthalmology rotation and be in a position to pursue a career in this specialty.

As Ticho's last semester of medical school approached, he moved from his sister's home in Leopoldstadt across the Danube Canal to a flat at Berggasse 39 in Alsergrund (Ninth District). The building, only a block from the canal but much closer to the General Hospital, was divided into three main parts with Ticho's section being the most modest and farthest removed from the street. At the ground level, a fine restaurant may have fronted the street at that time as it does now over a hundred years later. Above this storefront there were four floors of modestly upscale flats, two to a floor, and these were reached by a broad stairwell. Outside, off the sidewalk and on the right of the building, an arching entrance opened into an enclosed, open-air carriage-path that led to a garage straight ahead. Down this path, passing by the entrance to the second wing of the building to the left, Ticho would access the main entrance of the hindmost third wing. His flat was on the second floor, apartment number 14. Although there was room for a roommate, it is not known if he had any to share the expenses and he may have lived there alone. During this last semester, Ticho took a wide variety of courses, including two gross pathology labs, one from future Nobel laureate Dr. Karl Landsteiner. The most important course for Ticho was "Diagnosis and Treatment of Eye Diseases" under Prof. Otto Bergmeister, who would eventually take Ticho as his assistant.[20]

Several months passed between the end of Ticho's last formal courses and his graduation the following spring. Much of this time was spent preparing for arduous examinations. Many days were spent observing in the ophthalmology clinics of tenured professors. As Ticho later listed Prof. Elschnig in his curriculum vitae, it is very possible that he briefly returned to Prague for a short stint in Elschnig's clinic. It was a relatively tumultuous time at the university for Italian students and for Jewish students who affiliated with the Zionist Kadimah fraternity. One bloody clash between German fraternities (Alemannians) and the Kadimah fraternity took place toward the end of February 1908. "The Alemannians occupied the entrance of the university to deny admission to the Kadimah and shouted 'Down with the Jews' and 'Off with them to Zion!' The brawl ended with the collapse of a large stone ramp by the university entrance, which left sixty people injured."[21]

Just about one week later, Albert Ticho's graduation ceremonies at the University of Vienna took place in the Main Ceremonial Hall (Großer Festsaal) of the University on March 1, 1908. University rector Prof. Richard Paltauf, a pathologist, led the procession of the faculty bearing an ornate, four-and-a-half-foot silver scepter dating to the early seventeenth century. Above them waved a more recent addition to the tradition, the banner of the university first used at a ceremony held in honor of the surgeon Theodor Billroth in 1892. The dean of the Medical Faculty, Prof. Rudolf Chrobak, addressed the graduates, and each among them, including Ticho, laid a finger upon the scepter and took an oath. After the conferral of the degrees, one of Ticho's classmates expressed words of gratitude (in Latin) for the degrees conferred. After some final words and the recessional, Ticho exited the university with his medical school degree in hand.

The following month, Ticho returned to Boskovice to spend the Passover holiday with his parents and family. On the surface, everything about the evening seemed happy and festive. But during dinner, Albert's mother took him aside. Laura Ticho told her son that she had been feeling ill for some time, and Albert undoubtedly turned the discussion to probing questions about her symptoms, recognizing the seriousness of her complaints. Immediately after the holiday Laura went to Vienna to be examined by specialists. They confirmed Albert's fear that she was suffering from advanced cancer. Albert's sister, Sarah, took their mother to a spa to try to reverse the progress of the disease. But it was much too late, and shortly thereafter, on June 14, 1908, Laura Ticho died at the relatively young age of fifty-four, survived by her husband and thirteen children.[22]

Albert observed the traditional periods of mourning even as his work was to become ever more demanding. With his graduation and his mother's death, Albert perhaps felt less tied to his home town of Boskovice, and he still had many members of his family close by in Vienna. These included Uncle Phillip and Aunt Bertha Ticho, their teenage daughter, Anna, and her young brother, Rudolph.

—◆—

There were potentially several clinics in Vienna where Ticho might have been able to secure a position as an assistant. The two most prestigious of these were at the Vienna General Hospital, one under Prof. Fuchs and the other under Prof. Schnabel. There were other positions in German universities within the Austrian sphere, including those in Prague, Innsbruck, and Graz. There were also several peripheral, university-associated hospitals in Vienna with ophthalmology clinics.[23] With some chronological uncertainties, drafts of two curricula vitae in Ticho's handwriting summarize his early career highlights, showing that Ticho very briefly worked as a junior assistant in Clinic II under Prof. Ernst Fuchs and also first worked outside of ophthalmology at the Rudolf Foundation Hospital (*k. u. k.* Rudolf-Stiftung-Spital, or Rudolfspital) in Landstraße, Vienna's Third District. He described working as an assistant, then a "secondary physician," and then in the Department of Surgery. In this same hospital, Ticho then began a four-year term as assistant to Prof. Dr. Otto Bergmeister, chairman of the Ophthalmology

Department. There seems to have been an elevation of his status to "first assistant" on February 1, 1910.[24]

Ticho's appointment as Prof. Otto Bergmeister's assistant was a fine accomplishment. A native of Silz in the Tyrol, the sixty-three-year-old Bergmeister had spent his entire professional career in Vienna. After graduating from the University in 1870 and training under von Arlt, he remained at the university and steadily advanced through the ranks of the faculty. He eventually achieved the distinguished political, honorific title of Hofrat. Bergmeister's main research interests had involved the embryology of the mammalian eye. The eponym "Bergmeister's papilla" is still used to describe both normal embryonic structures in the eye and also a developmental anomaly that may rarely be seen even in the adult human eye. In the fetus, glial sheathing cells from retinal nerve fibers form the so-called "primitive epithelial papilla of Bergmeister" as they turn into the stalk of the optic nerve at the site of the future optic disc. This usually disappears before birth but occasionally it persists.[25] Otto Bergmeister's son, Dr. Rudolf Bergmeister, also wrote about congenital eye defects. He may have visited his father's clinic during the time that Ticho worked there as an assistant but it does not seem that they established a relationship. Rudolf was eight years older than Ticho, graduating from the Vienna Medical School in 1899 and working in the University's Second Eye Clinic through the end of 1909. Rudolf published widely on several topics in ophthalmology, including tumors and tuberculosis. He worked as an ophthalmologist at the Wilhelminenspital in Ottakring (Vienna's Sixteenth District) and qualified for an associate professorship in 1915.[26]

Bergmeister and his staff were excellent teachers, and the 860-bed Rudolf Foundation Hospital was a busy and productive place for Dr. Ticho to train. Construction of the hospital in Landstraße was begun in 1858 on the orders of Emperor Franz Josef to honor the birth of his son, the Archduke Rudolf. In 1864, the emperor, empress, and six-year-old crown prince had attended the laying of the hospital's cornerstone and its dedication. The hospital was built in a romantic historicist style with smoothly stuccoed facades, varied fenestrations, a dramatic roof line, and a richly ornamented main entrance. Functionally, the hospital had been planned along the lines of French hospital organization and, for the first time in the German-speaking world, employed the principles of the so-called "pavilion system." The street fronting the hospital had been named Rudolfsgasse, although following World War I the street was renamed Juchgasse after the late-nineteenth-century Viennese artist Ernst Juch. A directory of Vienna residents for 1910 lists the hospital address at Rudolfsgasse 25 as Ticho's residence.[27] Here or possibly just a block to the east of the hospital at Rudolfsgasse 21, Dr. Albert Ticho took up his residence.

In the midst of busy and relatively happy times, Ticho experienced another loss – Dr. Isidor Schnabel – a respected and beloved professor. On a Friday morning in early December 1908, word was received that Professor Schnabel had suddenly collapsed on his way to his clinic at the General Hospital. Unconscious, Prof. Schnabel had been brought into a room of the surgical clinic where, in spite of all efforts, he died within a few minutes. Prof. Schnabel lay dead at age sixty-four. Later that day at the university, Prof. Fuchs read a eulogy honoring his departed colleague, including reference to his many scientific contributions and teaching.

While Albert Ticho was immersed in Vienna's superb medical environment, his young cousin, Anna, was immersed in its art scene. Anna's father, Phillip Ticho, had moved the family into comfortable lodgings at Franz Josephs Kai 21 in the Innere Stadt (First District).[28] In 1909, at age fifteen, Anna was formally enrolled by her parents in an art school under the directorship the German painter Ernst Nowak. Anna was inspired by the exciting environment of the arts in Vienna, from the rich collections of Old Master drawings in the famous Graphische Sammlung Albertina (Albertina Museum) to the exhibitions of contemporary artists of the Vienna Nouveau Art movement such as Gustav Klimt. Anna was only seventeen when her father (and Albert's uncle), Phillip, died in 1911 at the age of fifty-six.

Around October 29, 1911, soon after his Uncle Phillip's death, Albert moved back in with the Reinigers in Leopoldstadt at Große Schiffgasse 5. The reasons are not clear, as he was still working at the Rudolf Foundation Hospital.[29] Perhaps his immediate duties in the hospital lessened as he progressed through the assistantship to be managed by a more junior assistant. Perhaps the terms of his lease near the Rudolf Foundation Hospital had expired, or perhaps he simply wished to be closer to his cousin, Anna, with whom he had fallen in love.

Anna Ticho was quite serious about her art studies and spent countless hours in the city's museums and galleries. Even so, she did not undertake more advanced art studies. In Vienna, the foremost institute for such an education was the Academy of Fine Arts (Akademie der bildenden Künst Wien) to which many of the most ambitious young art students applied. Among the prospective artists who applied to the Academy in 1908, three became particularly well known in history: Egon Schiele and Oskar Kokoschka, who were accepted, and eighteen-year-old Adolph Hitler, who was not.

Hitler's rejection and subsequent experiences during his five years in Vienna had a profound effect upon this erstwhile art student. Throughout Vienna, anti-Semitic tabloids and pamphlets were available at newsstands and in local coffee shops. The mayor of Vienna in those days, Karl Lueger, was an avowed anti-Semite, a member of the Christian Social Party that espoused anti-Semitism in its political platform. Lueger's library, examined after his death, was found to be full of anti-Semitic hate literature. One item was a caricature depicting a group of Polish Jews at the Oswiecim (Auschwitz) railroad station leaving for Herzl's Jewish state, an eerie foreshadowing of much more tragic events to come. Yet, even as Vienna's politicians used anti-Semitism to their advantage, assimilated Jews had reached powerful positions in society beyond the realms of academia. Several had been ennobled by the emperor, particularly for contributions in the area of banking and commerce.[30]

Ticho had encountered anti-Semitism at various times during his studies in Vienna, and this continued as he neared the completion of his training. One professor offered him a staff position on the condition that he would convert to Christianity. The professor explained that two of his assistants were Jews and that he could not add yet another Jew on his staff. Ticho respectfully declined the offer, pointing out that his father would be deeply hurt. The professor countered with the suggestion that

Albert should forsake his legal and given name of Avraham. Telling the professor that he was called Albert by his family and friends was still insufficient, and he was informed that it would take an official name change to secure the position. As the story goes, Albert Ticho's agitated response closed the discussion: "You know, you are such a lovely man, perhaps I'll just go ahead and open my office right across the street from yours and give you some serious competition."

The oft-repeated family anecdote was told with a dramatic ending. In response to this bitter and disappointing interchange, an older colleague, a certain Dr. Stern (possibly pathologist Dr. Karl Sternberg), reportedly gave Ticho this momentous advice: "Leave these goyim [gentiles] and these anti-Semites. Why put up with this abuse? The Lemaan Zion Eye Hospital in Jerusalem is looking for a doctor to run the clinic. Why don't you apply?"[31] Ticho discovered that an advertisement had appeared in Zionist periodicals, placed by a Jewish benevolent society of Frankfurt am Main, the Palästinensischer Hilfsverein, which was also known by its Hebrew sobriquet, "Lemaan Zion." It seems that Ticho first contacted Hugo Bondi, the sole member of the society's board who resided in Vienna, but it was made clear that an interview in Frankfurt would be required to secure the position.

At this critical point in his life, the young Dr. Ticho took some pages directly out of Herzl's novel, *Altneuland*. Herzl had described a generation of young, Jewish-Viennese men of the middle classes who had "entered the 'liberal' professions en masse" resulting in a "surplus of trained men who could find no work but... could not, like their Christian colleagues, slip into public posts." Herzl's fictional Friedrich Löwenberg, an assistant lawyer earning forty gulden a month, is shown a newspaper advertisement by a friend that leads him via Trieste to Palestine (en route to the South Pacific). At the Western Wall in Jerusalem he meets the eye specialist Dr. Eichenstamm, who emerges two decades later in the story as the President of the New Society of Palestine; his daughter is also an oculist and then head of one of the greatest eye clinics in the world.

Ticho now aspired to establish his own clinic. Answering the advertisement of Lemaan Zion would help this dream become a reality.

Thus he would heed the call of the motto that Herzl had placed on the title page of *Altneuland,* "*Wenn Ihr wollt, dann ist es kein Märchen –* If you will it, it is no fable."[32]

CHAPTER 5

FEBRUARY *1912*

FRANKFURT AM MAIN

למען ציון לא אחשה ולמען ירושלם לא אשקוט...

*For the sake of Zion I will not be silent,
For the sake of Jerusalem I will not be still...*

Isaiah 62:1

Albert Ticho had found his Jewish religion and his Hebrew name of Avraham to be liabilities when he sought out career opportunities in Vienna. They would be assets when he went to Frankfurt am Main for interviews with leaders of Lemaan Zion, who four years earlier had established an eye hospital in Jerusalem. The organization, whose official German name was the Palästinensischer Hilfsverein, had been founded in 1888 by two leaders of modern Orthodox Judaism in Germany, Rabbi Azriel Hildesheimer of Berlin and his disciple Rabbi Marcus Horovitz, who later ran the organization from Frankfurt. Through their efforts, Lemaan Zion funded many different activities, principally medical services in Jerusalem; but they also funded Jewish settlements themselves elsewhere in Palestine.[1]

From Jerusalem, the German-born Rabbi Zelig Azrael Hoisdorf was also involved with the Lemaan Zion Society, whose chief goal was to help recipients of services become productive and independent, a practical philosophy that differed from the system of traditional monetary distributions known as *halukka*.[2] Rabbi Horovitz died in 1910, and Rabbi Nehemiah Anton Nobel, another of Hildesheimer's disciples, had taken his place as the Rabbi of the Orthodox Börneplatz Synagogue and several benevolent organizations associated with it.[3] Other members of the Lemaan Zion board may have been involved in interviewing Ticho but Rabbi Nobel likely had the final decision about whom to hire as the new director of the Lemaan Zion Eye Hospital.[4] Ticho was likely unaware of competition for the position but he knew that he would have to make a good personal impression upon Nobel to get the appointment.

The distance from Vienna to Frankfurt was about 374 miles, less than a day's travel from Vienna by train via the Oostende-Vienna line. The exact dates of Ticho's round-trip journey to Frankfurt are not known, but sometime around February 1912 he departed Vienna from the Western Railway Station (Westbahnhof) located in Rudolfsheim-Fünfhaus (Fifteenth District) on the city's Gürtel thoroughfare.[5]

The train's first stop was in the Upper Austrian provincial capital of Linz, the "hometown" of Adolf Hitler during his teens (1905–1908). From Linz, Ticho's train proceeded to the Bavarian border and arrived at the German border town of Passau, where Hitler had also lived as a young child (1892–1895).[6] As Ticho traveled to Frankfurt, he had time to reflect upon the passage in the book of Isaiah from which Lemaan Zion took its name: "For the sake of Zion I will not be silent, for the sake of Jerusalem I will not be still; 'til her victory emerge resplendent and her triumph like a flaming torch."[7]

Passing through northeast Bavaria, Ticho's train then followed the left bank of the River Main and reached Frankfurt, the largest city in the Prussian province of Hesse-Nassau. Crossing to the northern right bank of the Main over one of the new iron bridges, the train pulled into Frankfurt's Central Railway Station that was located just to the west of the city center. Operated by the Prussian State Railways, the terminus was at the time the largest in all of Europe and the third largest in the world. Disembarking from the train, Ticho stepped out into the majestic hall containing eighteen tracks that was covered by three arching iron-and-glass ceilings. Outside, the eastern façade of the station faced in the direction of the city center and, just beyond it, the area of the former

Judengasse (Jews' Alley) very near to Ticho's destination that day. Ticho could check the time of his arrival in Frankfurt by the large clock that loomed above the entryway of the Central Station's façade. The clock was embellished with two symbolic carved figures, Day to the left and Night to the right. Upon the roof was a monumental statue of Atlas supporting the world on his shoulder, assisted by two more allegorical figures – Iron and Steam.

Electric trams headed in all directions from the large square in front of the main railway station. The most direct route was also the most scenic. Along the right bank of the Main, Ticho passed by the elegant houses on a street that was appropriately named Schöne Aussicht (Beautiful View) passing several notable landmarks connected with modern liberalism – the home of the philosopher Arthur Schopenhauer, a bust of the playwright Gotthold Lessing, and the adjacent Municipal Library.[8] Beyond the library, the Rechneigrabenstraße led to Börneplatz. Some years after the ghetto walls had been torn down, Judengasse was renamed as Börnestraße in honor of journalist and author Juda Löb Baruch, a champion of Jewish civil rights who had, however, converted to Christianity and changed his name to Ludwig Börne. Ticho now stood at the south end of Börnestraße in the Börneplatz, the city square that had once served as the Jewish market at the southern edge of the ghetto. A three-acre Jewish cemetery that had served Frankfurt's Jewish community from 1180 to 1828 stretched out to the north, hidden by the Börneplatz Synagogue and the adjacent modern buildings.

As Ticho gazed northward down Börnestraße from the center of the square, he could see the modern buildings on either side. All of the original buildings of the Jewish ghetto had been pulled down and replaced, with the exception of the five-story house of the Rothschild family. Just a few buildings past the Rothschild house was the Main Synagogue, the third "Hauptsynagoge" that had been built on this site (1462, 1711, and 1860 respectively), now the home of Frankfurt's liberal Reform Movement whose leaders were generally apathetic to Zionist causes. This Börnestraße Main Synagogue had been designed by Frankfurt architect Fritz Kaysser and would be destroyed during Kristallnacht in November 1938.[9]

While the Reform Hauptsynagoge was to the left of the Jewish religious spectrum, a major synagogue on the right was the "secessionist" Orthodox synagogue (Israelitische Religions-gessellschaft or IRG) that had been led by Rabbi Samson Raphael Hirsch from 1851 until his death in 1888. Hirsch had rejected political Zionism as did his son-in-law, Rabbi Solomon Breuer, who succeeded him. In place of the old IRG Synagogue on Schützenstraße, Breuer's beautiful New Synagogue (Neue Synagoge), completed in 1907, was now the largest in all of Frankfurt.[10]

Ticho's presence in Frankfurt was specifically to interview at the Börneplatz Synagogue with Rabbi Nobel and Lemaan Zion for a clinical position in Jerusalem. It is possible that he did not take notice of other nearby synagogues in the city. At the time of Ticho's visit, no other Jewish religious leader in Frankfurt had embraced Zionism as strongly as Rabbi Nobel. Even Nobel, however, had left the Zionist movement in 1906 for reasons that are not entirely clear. For many years thereafter Nobel refrained from supporting Zionists in public, only rejoining Zionism after World War I, when he took part as a delegate of the Mizrachi Movement to the Twelfth Zionist Congress in Carlsbad. Insights into Nobel's character, oratory skills, and philosophy come through in various letters of the philosopher Franz Rosenzweig, who came to see Nobel in Frankfurt in the spring of 1919, soon after Rosenzweig's release from the German Army and the completion of his major work, *The Star of Redemption*.[11]

Similar to Ticho's home town of Boskovice, Frankfurt had a recognizable pattern of neighboring synagogues, one being more liberal and the other more conservative. Of course compared to Boskovice, the synagogues of Frankfurt, and even others in the outlying districts, were designed for much larger congregations. Even in the large main hall of the smaller Börneplatzsynagoge there was originally seating for over a thousand people between the main floor and the surrounding gallery. Just before World War I about 29,000 Jews lived in Frankfurt out of a total population of about 425,000 (6.8 percent). In terms of Jewish population, Frankfurt was Germany's second city after Berlin, where the proportion of Jews was similar, about 150,000 out of a total population of 2.1 million (7.1 percent).[12]

The modern Zionist Movement had emerged as Albert Ticho entered his late teens and young adulthood, but until his visit to Frankfurt he had not concerned himself very much with Zionist activities. Throughout these years, the literature of Zionism – its books, newspapers, and pamphlets – were pervasive in the cities of Brno, Vienna, and Prague, where Ticho had studied and trained as a specialist. Even though the young ophthalmologist was prepared to immigrate to Palestine and to embark upon his chosen career in the Holy City of Jerusalem, he really had not fully embraced Zionism as such. It seems likely that Ticho's chances of selection depended upon not only his professional qualifications, but his Jewish religious practices and his stance toward Zionism. Rabbi Nobel was now waiting to assess these issues.

———◆———

The Börneplatz Synagogue had been designed by Siegfried Kusnitzky in the style of the Italian Renaissance and had been built of red sandstone. An elegant copper-plated dome crowned the southwest corner of the building that jutted into the square. Inside the synagogue, the elevated cantor's dais was situated in the center of the sanctuary hall in view of the main floor, and the women's balcony (*ezrat nashim*) surrounded the hall on three sides. At the front of the hall all eyes would be drawn to the elegant two-story apse that featured the Holy Ark (*Aron Kodesh*) with an eternal light suspended from the apex of the towering semi-dome. Unlike the nearby Hauptsynagoge, there was no organ or other elements that were alien to Orthodox Judaism.

A portrait of Rabbi Nobel from around 1912, reveals a robust, stocky man of about forty-plus years with dark penetrating eyes, framed above by a broad forehead with a receding hairline and below by a quizzical smile and a dark, short, and thin beard.[13] He is posed in a stylish three-piece suit with satin-trimmed lapels and a watch-chain leading to his left vest pocket. Though seated, Nobel's balanced pose seems to indicate a readiness to stand at a moment's notice. Perhaps he was dressed just so and rose to greet Ticho when the young doctor called upon him in search of a position. In their meeting, Nobel certainly outlined the responsibilities and expectations of a director of the Augenklinik (eye clinic) that had been without an ophthalmologist for almost two years. He also likely reviewed the activities of the personnel employed by Lemaan Zion, both past and present.

Ticho learned that several doctors had been hired by Lemaan Zion during its twenty-two-year history while a local board or "Committee" ran the operations under the Prussian-born former journalist Mordecai Adelman, who also ran a retail clothing business on Jaffa Road.[14] Previously in Europe, Adelman had published numerous articles in *Ha-Melitz* and *Ha-Magid*, and he had served as Peretz Smolenskin's assistant in editing *Ha-Shahar*. While doing literary work in Paris, he befriended Eliezer Ben-Yehudah, and together they engaged in one of the first Hebrew conversations in modern times. The two immigrated separately to Palestine in 1881 and remained close friends throughout their lives. Adelman had first been employed by the Frankfurt Jews as the director of a Jewish orphanage in Jerusalem, and following his new assignment in 1888, he had established a general medical clinic and pharmacy in the Old City.[15]

During his interview and later from Adelman, Ticho learned more about the doctors and staff who had run the Lemaan Zion clinics in Jerusalem. In 1890, the Palästinensischer Hilfsverein sent Dr. Albert Feuchtwanger of Munich to Jerusalem. He worked mainly in the new Jewish neighborhoods outside the Old City and supplemented his income with private practice until he returned to Germany in 1894.[16] Adelman also hired Dr. Moshe Wallach to attend the Lemaan Zion clinic within the Old City. Wallach, originally from Cologne, Germany, had immigrated to Palestine in 1890 under the sponsorship of the Amsterdam Center for the German and Dutch Communities, and initially worked at the Bikkur Cholim Hospital in the Old City under the German-Lutheran physician Dr. Adelbert Einszler.[17] Wallach later founded Shaare Zedek Hospital that opened outside the city walls in 1902.

After Feuchtwanger's departure from Lemaan Zion, Ukrainian-born Dr. Gershon Krishevsky was appointed as the clinic's medical director. Krishevsky and his brother Moshe had immigrated to Palestine together to work as pharmacists. Both Krishevsky brothers returned to Europe to study medicine, passed their medical examinations in Istanbul, and returned again to Palestine. Moshe left for Egypt while Gershon followed in 1902 when Moshe fell ill. Soon thereafter Lemaan Zion sent Dr. Yehoshua Friedman to Jerusalem, where he also helped establish the School for the Blind.[18]

Pharmacists at Lemaan Zion, such as Binyamin Gavrielovitch, also served as medical assistants. In 1906, the Lemaan Zion pharmacy in Jerusalem dispensed 12,945 prescriptions (many without charge), and the majority of visits to the general medical clinic were related to eye complaints (13,419 out of a total of 23,699).[19] Acknowledging the prevalence of eye diseases and the problems of access to eye care, increased efforts at fundraising were undertaken, and in 1908, the Palästinensischer Hilfsverein established the Lemaan Zion Eye Hospital and Augenklinik near Meah Shearim, opposite the Hungarian Houses.

The first director of the new the Lemaan Zion Eye Hospital was Dr. Moses Erlanger of Lucerne, Switzerland, who directed the clinic for two years (1908–1910). Erlanger had studied medicine at University of Zurich and trained as an ophthalmologist in Berlin.[20] While recovering from a life-threatening appendicitis, he vowed to dedicate a period of service to his fellow Jews in Eretz Yisrael. After further training in Königsberg (now Kaliningrad), Lemaan Zion provided him with the opportunity to go to Palestine and fulfill his vow.[21] Through his relatively brief tenure in Jerusalem at the Eye Hospital, Erlanger had become the first Jewish ophthalmologist to practice in all of Palestine. But like Feuchtwanger, the first general physician of Lemaan Zion in the early 1890s, Erlanger came and left a bachelor.[22] In 1910, Lemaan Zion briefly held general medical clinics when Dr. Krishevsky returned from Egypt, but the doors of the eye and general clinics had been closed soon upon Erlanger's departure.[23] Another furtive attempt at opening the eye clinic occurred in August 1911 with the arrival of an ophthalmologist, a Dr. Kraus (first name unknown), who held an appointment at the government hospital in Kiev. However, Kraus apparently found the conditions unsatisfactory – either the quality of the instruments, his salary, or both – and he returned to Kiev after a few short weeks.[24]

During Ticho's interview, further details and requirements of the advertised position were explained. In addition to the heavy clinical duties, there were particular requirements of religious observance that included the wearing of a head covering (*kippah*), maintaining dietary laws (*kashrut*), and, of course, refraining from work on the Jewish Sabbath.[25] It is not known if the Lemaan Zion organization and Rabbi Nobel expected Ticho to maintain the high level of religious observance of his predecesor. Erlanger had been meticulous about every aspect of Jewish observance to the point of gathering a quorum of ten men (*minyan*) every day at the Eye Hospital in order to recite prayers of the three daily worship services. The local Jewish populace and Hebrew newspaper of Israel Dov Frumkin had lauded Erlanger's eye hospital for its pleasant Jewish character, this in contrast to the more established British Ophthalmic Hospital of Jerusalem.[26]

The subject of private patients may not have been discussed between Rabbi Nobel and Dr. Ticho. Erlanger had found limited time for private patients due to the sheer volume of patients, over 25,000 patient clinic-visits in 1909, including over two thousand new patients during the busy seven months of summer. Mordecai Adelman was able to hire additional nurses and a general physician, Dr. Aharon Yosef Yermens, to serve as an assistant.[27]

As Ticho was ultimately successful in gaining Nobel's confidence and achieving the appointment from Lemaan Zion, he was likely very careful and diplomatic in describing his personal religious observance, his political views about Zionism, and his work ethic. In the end, Ticho was selected over other candidates, including the Galician-born Dr. Aryeh Feigenbaum. Feigenbaum had also graduated from the University of Vienna, though three years after Ticho, and he had not yet fully completed his assistantship in Berlin with the renowned ophthalmologist Prof. Dr. Julius Hirschberg.[28]

Ticho had successfully completed his visit to Frankfurt, one of Europe's oldest and greatest centers of Jewish culture and religion. The synagogues would be destroyed during Kristallnacht on November 8–9, 1938; 11,134 Jews of Frankfurt would be murdered in the following years, and most of the tombstones of the cemetery would be destroyed by official decree. Because of his successful interview, Ticho would live through those events in Palestine. In the years that followed, museums and memorials were established in the area where Ticho once visited: a plaque erected on the ruined site of the Börneplatz Synagogue; later a living memorial of trees planted in a checkered arrangement; and, on the New Börneplatz (Neuen Börneplatzes), parts of the outline of the destroyed Börneplatz Synagogue were marked on the pavement.

Later in the spring, Ticho learned that the board of the Palästinensischer Hilfsverein in Frankfurt had accepted his application to serve as the director of the Lemaan Zion Eye Hospital, beginning July 1, 1912. This might have presented a problem with his mentor, Bergmeister, at the Rudolf Foundation Hospital where his contract as first-assistant ended on that same date. However, Ticho was allowed to gain full credit for his training and on May 13, 1912, he received his letter of recommendation.[29]

Plans could now be made for Ticho to travel from Vienna to Jerusalem and assume his new position. He would become the only Jewish ophthalmologist in Jerusalem and one of only two or three ophthalmologists at that time in Palestine, only the sixteenth ophthalmologist in history to practice there.

— ◆ —

After Ticho's return to Vienna, he decided to take a trip to the spas in Carlsbad with his cousin Anna Ticho and her mother, Bertha. Here Ticho applied for yet another position, that of Anna Ticho's husband. Bertha excitedly telegraphed the news to the family back in Brno, who had gathered to celebrate a religious ceremony (a *pidyon ha-ben*) for David Ticho's infant son, Robert.[30] The short telegram simply read, "Mazal Tov to everyone. Albert and Anna are engaged."

Most of the details of the courtship of Albert and Anna Ticho are not known. At this point, Anna was still under eighteen years of age and required formal permission to marry from Albert's older brother Josef, who had become Anna's guardian after her father's death. Because Albert and Anna were first cousins, Josef was initially opposed to their engagement. In spite of this, Albert and Anna planned their immigration to Palestine and their plans came to include Anna's mother. They decided that Albert would leave for Palestine in June while Anna and Bertha would follow him four months later, near to her eighteenth birthday. Any misgivings that Josef had were therefore thwarted by his brother's plans for aliyah, while Anna and her mother bided their time.

CHAPTER 6

JUNE 1912
ALIYAH

עוד לא אבדה תקותנו, התקוה הנושנה,
לשוב לארץ אבותנו, לעיר בה דוד חנה.

We never lost our hope, the ancient hope,
To return to the land of our fathers, to the city in which David encamped.

Hatikvah (original lyrics of the refrain of *Tikvateinu*) by Naftali Hertz Imber

In the middle of June 1912, Albert Ticho and his fiancée Anna entered the Südbahnhof, the Vienna terminus of the Austrian Southern Railway (Österreichische Südbahn). The large train station with its classical façade was located just three-quarters of a mile to the south and east of the Rudolf Foundation Hospital, just beyond Vienna's outer ring of roads, the Gürtel.[1] Ticho had likely used this station once or twice for short excursions to the mountains of Lower Austria and Styria, popular day-trips for Viennese residents. Today he was traveling further. Across the road, opposite the entrance of the bustling train station, the Maria Josefa Park was green and tranquil. The main entrance hall of the station was connected to a large modern concourse with several train platforms. Here Anna and Albert said their goodbyes. Albert would be making the long journey to Palestine alone, but later that fall Anna and Bertha Ticho would follow him to Palestine along the same route.

Beginning in Favoriten (Tenth District), the route of the Austrian Southern Railway that Ticho took terminated at the port city of Trieste on the Adriatic, traveling through Styria and skirting the northwest Balkan state of Carniola. A comfortable overnight express to Trieste was available to Ticho, a side route run by the Ostende-Vienna (Orient) Express, which left from Vienna in the late afternoon and arrived in Trieste just after seven o'clock in the morning.[2] This first leg of Ticho's journey ran south and then southeast to Gloggnitz, where the famous thirty-three-mile Semmering Railroad began en route to the town of Mürzzuschlag. Completed in 1854, the Semmering Railroad was a triumph of engineering in its time, the oldest of the great European mountain railways that connected Viennese tourists with Alpine lake resorts and mineral and thermal springs. Most importantly, it directly connected Vienna by rail with its port of Trieste.[3]

Seventy miles from Vienna and at an elevation of 2,930 feet, the train emerged from a mile-long tunnel at Semmering into Styria, where about two-thirds of the population spoke German and the remaining minority spoke Slovene. After a rapid descent into the resort town of Mürzzuschlag, the railway followed the picturesque valley of the Murz River to its confluence with the Mur River at Bruck. Here at the junction, the railway turned south and descended further to the Styrian plain. On the daytime routes, a mountaintop castle (Grazer Schloßberg) dominated the landscape of Styria's capital city of Graz below. On the last leg of his journey by train, Ticho passed through Leibnitz, Marburg (now Maribor, Slovenia), Carniola's capital city of Laibach (now Ljubljana, Slovenia), and on to Trieste.

At the northeastern corner of the Adriatic Sea, Trieste was situated between a mountainous coast that descended into hills and into the Bay of Trieste. Long controlled by the Habsburgs, Trieste, its suburbs, and the large Istrian peninsula to the south had been regained by the Austrian Empire in 1814 following the defeat of Napoleon. The region was then known as the Austrian Littoral (Österreichisches Küstenland). With the completion of the Southern Railway, Trieste had emerged as Austria's major seaport, a city of tremendous commercial and military strategic importance. During the nineteenth century, the city had become the fourth largest city of the Austro-Hungarian Empire after Vienna, Budapest, and Prague. While politically Austrian, the city of Trieste was ethnographically Italian with a multicultural flavor. Its distinctive dialect of Triestine (a form of Venetian) was influenced by the adjacent Slovene populations and transplanted Europeans. In those days, the bustling shipyards of Trieste were filled with workers of Italian, Slovene, and Greek origin. Combined with the constant flow of immigrants, the cosmopolitan nature of Trieste was further amplified by European expatriates such as James Joyce.

Among Trieste's population of 180,000 at the time, about 5,500 were Jewish, although almost half were not Austrian citizens. The wealthiest Austrian Jews of Trieste had long been involved at the highest levels of the city's commerce and industry – banking, insurance, and shipping – including the jewel of Triestine commerce, the Austrian Lloyd (Österreichischer Lloyd or Lloyd Austrico), which had been cofounded by Jewish banker Carlo Morpurgo. Motivated by philanthropic and pragmatic reasons, the small but influential Jewish community of Trieste was eager to assist their fellow Jews in their emigration from Europe to the Americas and to Palestine. In 1913 alone, more than 52,000 Jewish emigrants used Trieste as their port of departure on their way to the Americas. Thirty-eight percent of them came from the Russian Empire. Relatively few went to Palestine, but during the course of the Second Aliyah (1904–1914) about 10,000–11,000 Jews departed from from Trieste to Palestine, compared to about 23,000 that left from Odessa. Although among them were the one or two thousand idealistic young pioneers normally associated with the Second Aliyah, most were families with children, while nearly a quarter of them were professionals like Ticho.[4]

Located to the north side of town, the Renaissance façade of the Trieste Südbahnhof faced the Piazza del Macella that would be renamed Piazza Libertà after the First World War. Inside, the station's platforms were bathed in the natural light that penetrated the building through the glass-panelled roof. The interior architecture was embellished with Corinthian columns and sculptures of women holding laurel-wreaths and engine wheels. The contemporary journalist and author Silvio

Benco, had likened the sooty railway station's colossal, "glorious" iron trusses to the musculature of an athlete. A series of oil paintings by Eugenio Scomparini depicting the Triumph of Progress decorated the walls of the station cafè.[5]

After a long train ride, Ticho passed through the station's beautiful doorways and out into the city. It is not known if Ticho stayed in Trieste overnight or took time for sightseeing. In those days, relatively new electric trams conveyed tourists northeast up the hill to the Village of Opicina, with its obelisk commemorating the yielding of Trieste to Austria and its fine view of Trieste and its harbor. Five miles to the northwest, the seaside Miramare Castle was likewise open for tours, where guides told stories of the unfortunate Archduke Ferdinand Maximilian Joseph, Emperor of Mexico until he was overthrown and executed just three years into his reign.[6]

The street proceeding south from the railway station followed the waterfront several blocks to the Canal Grande. Just a few blocks beyond this was the Piazza Grande at the foot of the Molo San Carlo, the pier from which the steamers of the Austrian Lloyd departed for Alexandria and other destinations.[7] In one of the cafès of the Piazza, perhaps the Caffè degli Specchi at the Palazzo Stratti or in a restaurant such as the Bissaldi on the Canal Grande, Ticho enjoyed his last repast on the soil of the Austrian Empire. The date appears to have been sometime between June 20 and 25, 1912.

At this point, most of the residents of Jerusalem were unaware that Ticho would be soon arriving to reopen the Lemaan Zion Eye Hospital. As Ticho was leaving Trieste, an editorial appeared in the Jerusalem newspaper *Ha-Or* that proposed the establishment of an ophthalmological institute in Jerusalem, but it was not referring to Lemaan Zion. Rather the editorial was in response to an ambitious proposal of Jewish physicians of Jaffa to establish a central medical institute in Jerusalem to be named after Professor Max Emanuel Mandelstamm.[8] No mention was yet made of the reopening of Lemaan Zion, but on the following day, June 21, 1912, as Mandelstamm was being eulogized on the front page of *Ha-Or*, a smaller news item appeared announcing that after many months of sabbatical, the Lemaan

Zion Eye Hospital would be reopening in the coming days and that an ophthalmologist would arrive in Jerusalem that week. The newspaper reported, "The letters from the doctor have already arrived by post in Jerusalem. Already the clinic is in order and all is prepared."[9]

———◆———

No record has been discovered in the Austrian State Archives to determine which steamer of the line Ticho boarded on the afternoon of his departure; perhaps it was one of the four new steamers that had been built when the line was modernized in 1894.[10] For many years an Austrian Lloyd steamer departed from the Molo San Carlo for Alexandria every Thursday at midnight, a five-day journey. Ticho may have taken a recently added "accelerated line" that made the crossing in three days at a higher fare. On board the ship the service language was Italian, but brochures were also available in German, French, and English. From 1911 the Austrian Lloyd also served kosher food aboard the line leading to Palestine.[11]

By the first morning, Ticho's steamer reached the port of Brindisi, a town of about twenty-two thousand located on the eastern shore of Italy's boot heal. After that it was three to four more days' journey non-stop across the Mediterranean Sea to the port city of Alexandria at the western edge of the Nile delta. Founded by Alexander the Great in 331 BCE, ancient Alexandria became the largest city in the world after its founder's death, and it remained second only to Rome for many centuries thereafter. In modern times, Alexandria became Egypt's second largest city after Cairo and its most important port; before World War I it had reached a population of almost four hundred thousand, including about sixty thousand Europeans of almost all nationalities.[12]

As Ticho's steamer entered the outer West Harbor of Alexandria, the breakwaters of the island of Pharos provided shelter from the rough waters of Mediterranean. After mooring at the quay, Ticho and the other passengers disembarked and cleared customs. All of Egypt had been under British occupation since 1882 after a nationalist uprising had been defeated, but technically Egypt was still nominally a part of the Ottoman Empire. The Khedive Abbas Hilmi Paşa, the great-great-grandson of Muhammad Ali, would be deposed at the start of World War I, beginning eight years of a formal British Protectorate. Ticho's stay in Alexandria was very short, as he soon transferred to another steamer departing for Jaffa.

Leaving Alexandria, Ticho's ship made a brief stop at Port Sa'id, 140 miles to the east just beyond the opposite edge of the Nile delta and at the north entrance to the Suez Canal. Port Sa'id was a city without a real port or at least a port without any major docks. Here passengers could disembark by small boats and other passengers were brought aboard. From the deck of the steamer, Ticho might have gazed at the twenty-two-foot-high statue of Ferdinand de Lesseps that stood upon an even higher pedestal near the southern end of the western pier. It had been unveiled there in 1899 by the Suez Canal Company to mark the thirtieth anniversary of the opening of the canal for business, though an Egyptian mob brought it down in December 1956.

Leaving the canal behind, Ticho's steamer turned north along the coast of Palestine. Early in the morning of June 28, 1912, the steamer cast anchor outside a natural breakwater of rocks that formed the harbor of Jaffa, the seaport of the Ottoman *sanjak* (administrative district) of Jerusalem. The port of Jaffa was known as Joppa in ancient times, and the rocks off its coast figure prominently in the Greek myth of Andromeda and Perseus. Among several references in the Bible, Joppa is mentioned as the port that received timber from Lebanon for conveyance to Solomon's Temple in Jerusalem, and received timber yet again when the Second Temple was rebuilt under Ezra and Nehemiah.[13] Because of the dangerous reefs and silted channels, only smaller rowboats could enter into the harbor, and the rough waves made the transfer difficult. Ticho found the passage to shore somewhat harrowing as the oarsmen attempted to negotiate a narrow gap between the rocks and the breakers.[14]

Along the shore, an eight-foot-high sea wall was all that remained of the walls and towers that had once surrounded the fortified city of Jaffa. Those walls had still been standing when Napoleon Bonaparte took the city in 1799, but they had been torn down in 1870. Now, with a population of about fifty thousand, including about ten thousand Jews,

Jaffa was again experiencing a period of great transformation. Over the previous six years the Jewish population of Jaffa had almost doubled.[15] In 1908 the Palestine Office of the Zionist Organization was opened under Dr. Arthur Ruppin, and in April 1909, just a few years before Ticho's arrival, the new Jewish city of Tel Aviv had been established on the sand dunes north of Jaffa. At the time Ticho arrived in Jaffa, about one hundred buildings had been built there.[16] Among the many land purchases that Ruppin was negotiating at that time throughout the country, there was one very important local purchase, the strip of land between the new Jewish enclave and the Mediterranean shoreline.

Ticho took his first steps in Palestine just in front of the Ottoman Customs House at the south end of the harbor. He later wrote that his passage through the Passport Bureau was no easier than his harrowing boat trip through the harbor. His passport was confiscated, never to be seen again. In theory, Ticho was a subject of the Austrian Empire and special Ottoman laws governed his ability to work at the Lemaan Zion Eye Hospital, just as the hospital itself was governed through privileges granted through the German Consul in Jerusalem.

At the time of Ticho's arrival there were no Jewish ophthalmologists in Jerusalem, but the Latvian-born ophthalmologist Dr. Mayer Krinkin had settled in Jaffa just the year before; for several months, Krinkin had been the only Jewish eye doctor in the entire country.[17]

It would be several hours before Ticho took the two o'clock train to Jerusalem, the second and last of the daily trains. There was time to take a short walk about the old city, perhaps to the lighthouse just a few hundred yards southward up the hill to admire the view of the city and the harbor. Northward along the short main street that fronted the quay, just past the El-Bahr Mosque, was the Austrian Post Office where a letter or telegram might be sent. Years later the quay that Ticho walked would be renamed as the Street of the Second Aliyah Platform (Rehov Retzif Aliya Sheniya).

As the road turned to the right, away from the quay, the stalls of the Arab bazaar lined the street on either side. Then en route to the Jaffa Railway Station, Ticho entered the European-style quarter on Nagib Bustros Street. Ruppin had located the Palestine Office on this street, and his apartment was close by. Coffee shops like the Bustros Café abounded in this lively part of the city, where groups of Jews met to talk about politics and literature in a variety of languages, and Hebrew newspapers such as *Ha-Po'el* and *Ha-Ḥerut* were passed from one customer to the next. On the way to the railway station, Ticho passed the Ottoman military barracks and then the Hotel Kaminitz, owned and operated by Bezalel Kaminitz and his son.[18] This hotel was one of two major hotels run by the Kaminitz family at that time, the other being in Jerusalem. Five months later, Albert and Anna Ticho would be married in the Jerusalem Hotel Kaminitz on Jaffa Road, run by Bezalel's brother, Mordecai (Marcus), and their father Eliezer Lippa Kaminitz.

———◆———

The Jaffa Railway Station was located to the northeast of the city, just over a half mile from the Customs House. Made of local pale-colored stones, the site of the station and its tracks had been laid out at an almost right angle to sandy seashore. The relatively small, symmetrical building was spacious enough for its purposes. Beneath flat roofs, the wider and taller central hall was flanked by two smaller wings to either side. A virtually identical station awaited Ticho at the other end of the Jaffa-Jerusalem line, though one constructed of Jerusalem stone.

Ticho's trip from Jaffa to Jerusalem took about four hours – the train traveled back and forth in each direction just once daily. The fifty-four-mile narrow-gauge railway line had been completed in September 1892, representing the largest civil engineering project in the Holy Land to date.[19] Further north there were two other narrow gauge railways extending from the coast of the Levant: the Beirut-Damascus Railway and the Haifa-Daraa spur of the Hejaz Railroad. In approaching Jerusalem from the southwest through the Judean hills, the train ascended through the deep, winding Soreq and Refa'im riverbeds, wadis that turned into flash-flooded rivers in the rainy season. The highest point of the route would be reached at Jerusalem at a height of 2,181 feet above sea level. Sacred Scripture and two millennia of Jewish literature had described the physical and spiritual ascent to Jerusalem with the Hebrew word "aliyah." Ticho would complete the last leg of his aliyah in a few short hours.

Pulling away from the Jaffa station, the train passed beneath the Chelouche Bridge and through Neve Tzedek. This was a Jewish neighborhood on the outskirts of town that had been established by Aharon Shlush, the Chelouche family, and others over two decades before the founding of Tel Aviv. Here, in a pleasant house on Shim'on Rokah Street, the future Nobel Laureate, Shmuel Yosef Halevi Czaczkes, was finishing work on his first book under the penname S. Y. Agnon. Past Neve Tzedek, the train quickly skirted by Jaffa's orange groves and turned southeast toward the outskirts of Lydda (Lod), where a majestic thornapple tree was still standing, venerated as the historic look-out point for Lydda's civilians at the time of Napoleon's invasion.[20] Here the train passed through the many olive groves in the valley as it came in and out of the first station at Lydda.

Several small stations and landmarks lay ahead on the route after the train station at Ramleh: the village of 'Aqir, site of ancient Ekron and near a modern Jewish settlement of the same name; the Wadi Surar (Nahal Soreq) crossed by an eighty-two-foot bridged iron span; small stations at El-Sejed and Deir Aban; the village of Sar'a; and the village of Artuf and the nearby Jewish settlement of Hartuv; and a second crossing of the Wadi Surar between the stations of Deir Aban and Battir, the latter near the ancient ruins of Betar.[21] As Ticho neared Jerusalem he could look back at the mirror-image symmetry of his journey: Vienna–Trieste–Alexandria by train and steamship; Alexandria–Jaffa–Jerusalem by a second steamship and now another train to bring him to his new home.

It took about thirty minutes for Ticho's train to travel from Bittir to Jerusalem, ascending the Valley of Roses (Wadi el-Werd), entering the Baqa' Plateau, and passing the German Colony of the Templars.[22] Within minutes the train pulled into the station in Jerusalem. Except for the recently erected canopy that stretched between the tracks and the building and the lighter colored Jerusalem stones, the station was identical to the one in Jaffa.[23] Mordecai Adelman and the only remaining nurse of Lemaan Zion were waiting for Ticho as he disembarked from the train and took his first steps in the dusty outskirts of Jerusalem.

◆

The sun was low in the horizon as Ticho's train pulled into Jerusalem. It was late in the afternoon of Friday, June 28, 1912, and the young doctor would soon experience his first Sabbath in the Holy City. As he got off the train, Ticho was met by Mordecai Adelman, the administrator of the Lemaan Zion Eye Hospital and head of the local committee, though one of his sources of livelihood was a haberdashery that he owned on Jaffa Road. Ticho described the sixty-five-year-old Adelman as "an old man who had traveled and seen a great deal and had somewhat modern ideas."[24] Adelman was accompanied by the hospital's sole remaining nurse, whose identity has apparently been lost to history. Ticho wrote that this nurse had come to Jerusalem some years earlier from Königsberg. It is not known if Königsberg here referred to the well-known city of that name in Prussia or a smaller city of that name in Bavaria. If referring to the latter, this nurse may have been Rebecca Marx (later Brünn) whose love-story at Lemaan Zion with one of Ticho's colleagues is described later.

Ticho wrote, "Mr. Adelman immediately thought to draw our attention to the fact that both he and I were not married yet." Adelman had arranged for transportation back to the Lemaan Zion Eye Hospital for the three of them by means of a type of horse-drawn wagon known as a diligence. The "honorable old age" of the twenty-five-year-old diligence, as Ticho wrote, was "recognizable from its dirty gray color," and so this wagon had predated the establishment of the Jaffa–Jerusalem Railroad. In its prime, the diligence had traveled the challenging roads between Jaffa and Jerusalem. Now these wagons were mainly used in and about Palestine's towns and cities, whose roads were sometimes not much better.

After Ticho's luggage was loaded onto the back of the diligence, the driver helped his three passengers onto the wagon, which then departed the station northward toward the city. The Lemaan Zion Eye Hospital was a mile-and-a-quarter to the north, and Adelman pointed out in the opposite, southward direction the roads that led to Bethlehem and beyond it, Hebron. Since the opening of the railroad twenty years earlier, the last quarter-mile of the Hebron Road leading to the Jaffa Gate had been generally known as the Station Road.

Within a few minutes on the Station Road, the wagon approached the British Ophthalmic Hospital, located to the east on their right hand side. A flag with the Maltese Cross, the emblem of the Order of St. John, waved high above the building. Two square, crenellated towers vaguely suggested some military purpose (that would ultimately be fulfilled only by the Turks during World War I). At the street level, the roadside stone wall merged into the hospital's façade. Above the arched, central main entrance, triangular stonework framed the engraved name of the hospital.[25] After the diligence passed the hospital's north wing, with its trefoil club-shaped windows on the street level, and turned further east, Ticho could better appreciate the full height of the building from the rear as it hugged the slopes of the hill leading down into the Valley of Hinnom.

Permission to establish the hospital had been granted to the British on April 24, 1882, by a firman (decree) of Sultan Abdul Hamid II. The Prince of Wales (later Edward VII) had been directly involved in the negotiations and the following month, his mother, Queen Victoria, had given her royal charter to the reestablished Order of Saint John of Jerusalem that had been dissolved by Henry VIII in 1580. Adelman could recall the first temporary quarters of the hospital outside the Jaffa Gate in a building adjoining the Depôt of Messrs. Cook and Son, and that within a year,the Order of Saint John had purchased this fine stone building along the Road to Bethlehem.[26] The hospital had its own water supply and over the years the structure had been expanded from its original eighteen rooms, with a second story added to the south wing and extensive additions to the back of the building.

After receiving a royal charter, the order's secretary, Sir Edmund Lechmere, had recruited G. S. Waddell of the Shrewsbury Eye and Ear Infirmary, and over the years a series of ophthalmologists had followed (appendix 3). Arriving in Jerusalem on December 4, 1882, Waddell, the first ophthalmologist ever to practice in Palestine (serving December 1882–January 1884), was abruptly recalled to England by Lechmere, ostensibly due to illness, though the recall belied other issues such as demands for greater salary. His equally contentious replacement, John Hovelle Ogilvie of Scotland (serving 1884–1888), was recruited from the house staff at Moorfields Eye Hospital but was likewise recalled. Ogilvie was assisted for over a year by Dr. Robert Winthrop Gillman of Detroit, the son of the American Consul, who volunteered his services gratis. Fortunately for the order, the less contentious and long-serving William Edmund Cant (serving 1889–1911) came next, as did a series of competent assistants. The year before Ticho's arrival, William Ward had taken Cant's place, but a few short months of service was ended by his fatal illness at just thirty-two years of age. When Ticho arrived in Jerusalem, David Heron had been the chief surgeon of the British Ophthalmic Hospital for a full year, with Eric A. Thomson as his assistant.[27]

Early on, Adelman and other Jewish leaders were concerned about attempts of British missionaries to convert Jews to Christianity at the eye hospital, similar to activities at the Anglican Mission Hospital run by the London Society for Promoting Christianity among the Jews. This hospital had been established in the Old City in 1843 and was still located there at the time. Lechmere's early assurances to Sephardi Chief Rabbi Refael Meir Panigel (the "Hakham Bashi") had resulted in the rabbi's blessing, but the Jewish inhabitants of Jerusalem generally preferred Jewish doctors and Jewish-run hospitals.[28]

Although Heron, at the British Ophthalmic Hospital, was trusted by many Jewish inhabitants of Jerusalem, he would publicly acknowledge the effects of competition from Ticho and Lemaan Zion over the coming months. The full year of 1912 was among the British Ophthalmic Hospital's busiest ever in the inpatient department, but the annual number of new outpatient visits had reached a plateau, and returning outpatient visits had declined 29 percent from their peak during the previous six years.[29]

With the Sabbath soon approaching, there was no time for Ticho to meet Heron that day. The wagon continued quickly northward along the Station Road; it passed the junction with the road from the Templar (German) Colony of Refa'im and then it passed the two long guest houses of Mishkenot Sha'ananim ("Tranquil Abodes") that lay beyond the rocky fields. The houses, with a total of twenty-eight apartments built in 1860 and 1866, were established by Sir Moses Montefiore just south of his landmark windmill (1857) with a bequest from the American Judah Touro. They represented the oldest Jewish neighborhood ("colony") in Jerusalem outside the Old City walls. Beginning in 1891, newer homes of the adjacent Yemin Moshe were established just to the north.[30] Now turning to the east away from Yemin Moshe, the road skirted the southern side of the Sultan's Pool (Birket es-Sultan).[31] By this time of day, the crowds and the livestock from the weekly Friday cattle market had largely dispersed from the sloping north side of the reservoir. Adelman had a rather detailed knowledge of biblical sites and so he likely pointed out the rest of the Valley of Hinnom (Wadi er-Rababi) that stretched eastward and from the presumed ancient site of Topheth.[32] Just to the south, the rear of the British Ophthalmic Hospital could now be seen atop the valley's southern slope, the western sides of the building bathed in the reddish light of the setting sun.

Turning north again, the southwest corner of the Old City walls were ahead to the right, and just a quarter of a mile beyond this were the Citadel (Tower of David or El-Kal'a) and the Jaffa Gate (Bab el-Khalil).[33] From the southern end of the Citadel, a tall minaret soared upward just inside the city walls. It had been built by the Ottomans over a Mamluk mosque in the sixteenth century. At the northern end of the Citadel, the Tower of Phasael rose to an even greater height, and though named after Herod's brother and containing ancient elements at its base, this part of the Citadel was also of medieval Ottoman construction. Beyond the Citadel a breach in the walls allowed access of carriages into the Old City. This part had been taken down in 1898 when Kaiser Wilhelm II of Germany and Kaiserin Augusta Victoria visited the city. Overhead, above the outer south tower of the Jaffa Gate, Ticho took note of a recently constructed, four-sided clock that had been built in 1907 in an admixture of Arabic, Baroque, and Modern styles. Here the theme of "east meeting west" carried over to the clock's dials, which showed the time "according to both Western and Arab or Turkish reckoning."[34] By either means of reckoning, the hour was getting late and the clock confirmed for Ticho that a trip into the Old City would have to wait until another day.

The diligence passed through the large square outside the Jaffa Gate and turned onto the Jaffa Road, heading northwest for a short way and soon leaving the Old City walls behind. At this point the Jaffa Road continued past three hotels: the narrow frontage of the Hotel Fast to the left; the Hotel Kaminitz just beyond it on the right; and the Hotel Hughes a bit farther on the left.[35]

Since the middle of May, an itinerant Jewish-American eye specialist, Dr. A. Bloom, had set up an office in a wing of the Hotel Hughes to examine patients. Adelman likely informed Ticho about a recurring advertisement that had been appearing in the Sephardi newspaper *Ha-Ḥerut* almost daily since the middle of May.[36] The first few of Bloom's advertisements included an image of an eye with swollen eyelids and conjunctiva, while later ads only contained an unvarying text: "Specialist Eye Doctor Dr. A. Bloom from America who is noted for his activities in all of the cities of America and Turkey will see patients every morning from 8 o'clock until 12 European [Time] and in the evening 4–5 European [Time]." Nothing is known about the doctor beyond the advertisement in the newspaper and there is no other mention of his existence. It is tempting to identify him with the well-known pharmacist, Avraham Yehezkel Blum,[37] but the title of "Doctor" and references to his itinerant work in America exclude this. Perhaps he was an optometrist or even a charlatan. It is possible that in planning various visits about town on Sunday, Ticho and Adelman included plans for calling upon Bloom at the Hotel Hughes either during his morning office hours or soon afterward. Bloom had opened his offices at the Hotel almost directly across the street from Adelman's haberdashery and perhaps Adelman had warned Bloom in advance of Ticho's arrival. Although no permanent record of a meeting between Bloom and Ticho exists, Ticho's presence in Jerusalem definitely had an impact. Sunday was the last day that Bloom's advertisement appeared in *Ha-Ḥerut*. It seems he promptly closed up shop and disappeared.

Adelman's haberdashery on Jaffa Road had closed earlier that day. The diligence carrying Ticho and his companions turned away from Jaffa through an intersection that would be renovated by the British after the war and renamed as Allenby Square.[38] To the right across the intersection was the French Hospital of St. Louis that had relocated outside the Old City in 1874; it faced the Sultan's Gate of the Old City that had been built during the rule of the Turkish Sultan Abdul Hamid II in the 1880s. Continuing northward to his hospital, the road passed along the eastern edge of the large Russian Compound, with its hospices, hospital, and cathedral. At the northeast point of the Russian Compound to the left, two eighteenth-century gatehouses stood guard to the entrance to the Women's Hospice with carvings in archaic Russian script quoting Isaiah 62:1, the same verse that, a quarter-century earlier, the Jews of Frankfurt had used to name Ticho's medical clinic. Translated into English, the verse beginning with the words "Lemaan Zion" read: "For the sake of Zion I will not be silent; for the sake of Jerusalem I will not be still." Opposite the gatehouses to the right was Olivet House Pension, which had been owned and operated by Mr. Eno Hensman, and across an intersection beyond this was the Arab-Protestant St. Paul's Church, which would lend its name to the road during the British Mandate.

Just a bit further to the right was the Evelina de Rothschild School for Girls, renamed after its namesake's death 1866 at a time when the school was still located in the Old City. This newer building in the western New City was once the home of the Swiss banker Johannes Frutiger, who had participated with Joseph Navon in developing the Jaffa–Jerusalem railroad. In 1885, Frutiger had built the elegant two-story mansion, and like his first home in Jerusalem just to the west of the Anglican Mission, he named it Maḥanaim (after Genesis 32:2). As Ticho passed by this elegant building, he could look up at the balcony from which the Frutiger family had once enjoyed a fine view of the Old City. At the time of Ticho's aliyah, the Evelina de Rothschild School, under the management of the Anglo-Jewish Association, was the largest girls' school in Palestine, with over 550 students including over 200 in the separate kindergarten. The school's headmistress, Miss Annie Landau, a stickler for hygiene, would welcome Ticho and his coworkers to her school to examine and treat the students for the eye infection known as trachoma.[39]

The important crossroad to the side of the school, known as the Street of the Consuls (and later Street of the Prophets during the

British Mandate), curved west and south to the Damascus Gate and north and east back to Jaffa Road. Just beyond this street to the left, construction of a new hospital had been started by an Italian association (Associazione Nazionale per Soccorrere i Missionari Italiani – ANSMI). The organization had been founded by famed archeologist and Egyptologist Ernesto Schiaparelli, who had discovered the tomb of Queen Nefertari. A cornerstone for the building had been laid in 1910 but a war had broken out between Italy and Turkey on September 29, 1911, and so construction had been halted.[40] A beautiful hospital with its landmark tower would eventually emerge in this location, but for now the extensive excavations and only limited foundation work dominated the northernmost end of St. Paul's Road.

The road ahead now branched in three directions. To the left, the road followed the southern edge of Meah Shearim with its long buildings and slanted, red-tiled roofs. Established in 1874, the neighborhood of Meah Shearim was the second oldest Jewish settlement in Jerusalem outside the Old City Walls after Mishkenot Sha'ananim.[41] Along the middle road of the trifurcation that the diligence took, about one hundred yards ahead, were the Batei Ungarin (a combined Yiddish-Hebrew term for "Hungarian Houses"), established in 1891 by a group of ultra-Orthodox Jews of Slovak and Hungarian origin known as the Shomrei ha-Ḥomot (Guardians of the Wall). Over the years, Ticho would draw many patients from virtually every Jewish and Arab neighborhood of Jerusalem, and from countries throughout the Middle East.

Across the street to the right, Ticho's new home and his place of work were now seen across the rock-strewn field. The Israelis would name the modern road to the south of Ticho's eye hospital Reḥov Ḥoma HaShlishit (Street of the Third Wall). Even in those days, just to the east, along a well-surveyed line, archeologists had identified the northernmost remnants of Jerusalem's third wall, whose construction was begun by Agrippa around 40 AD and that was hastily finished by the Jews at the time of the First Revolt against the Romans.[42] After pulling up to the front gate, the driver helped unload Ticho's baggage. Ticho and his companions approached the main entrance of the Lemaan Zion Eye Hospital, which was engraved with the words "Eye Clinic" in both German (*Augenklinik*) and Hebrew (*Mirpa'at ha-'Einayim*). Ticho ended his brief written remembrance of the day of his arrival with the following: "The diligence brought us from the train station to the eye hospital, Lemaan Zion, where I had a flat. It was a small house, [two stories] high, surrounded by olive trees, and from time to time one could hear the bells of sheep and camels passing by." Like Agrippa's wall that no longer stands except for the scattered remains of its foundations, all that remains of the original building of Lemaan Zion are portions of the front wall with its arched doorway and windows. The façade bears the modern address, 48 Shivtei Yisrael Street.[43]

There is no record of how Ticho spent the next few hours as the twilight darkened and the peace of the Sabbath descended upon the Holy City. It is likely that Adelman had arranged a Sabbath meal in Ticho's living quarters or in a nearby home. Perhaps the usual Sabbath benedictions following a meal were spoken that evening, including phrases such as "the seventh day... a day on which to rest and repose in love" and "may You enable us to see Your city Zion comforted and Jerusalem, Your Holy City, rebuilt...."

For the rest of his life, Ticho would participate in the rebuilding of Jerusalem, fulfilling a dream expressed in the original wording of Naftali Hertz Imber's poem "Hatikvah": "To return to the land of our fathers / To the city in which David encamped." Ticho was familiar with these lyrics; the song's popularity had been established when it was sung in Basel to close the Seventh Zionist Congress in 1905. But as Ticho's politics or lack of politics further developed, he viewed his return outside the context of a separate Jewish state. Thirty-six years later he would see the refrain of Imber's poem changed and expanded to express the new reality of an independent State of Israel: "To be a free people in our land / the Land of Zion and Jerusalem."[44]

CHAPTER 7

JUNE–DECEMBER 1912

JERUSALEM

עמדות היו רגלינו בשעריך ירושלם.
ירושלם הבנויה כעיר שחברה-לה יחדו.

Our feet stood inside your gates, O Jerusalem.
Jerusalem built up, a city knit together.

Psalms 122:2–3

I n coming to Jerusalem, Ticho was settling in one of the world's oldest cities.[1] Ticho's spiritual and emotional connection to Jerusalem had been instilled in him since childhood; his parents and teachers made these connections through the Hebrew Bible, the Talmud, and Jewish books of prayer. His new Muslim and Christian neighbors also had their spiritual connections to Jerusalem with traditions and theology that differed from Judaism. The binding of Isaac on Mount Moriah (Jerusalem) in the Hebrew Bible was instead the binding of the abiding son (Ishmael) in the Qur'an. For Christians, the "City of God" was the scene of Jesus's crucifixion and resurrection, while for Muslims, Jerusalem, al-Quds, was the site of the Mi'raj, the Prophet Muhammad's journey into the heavens. Muhammad had tied his horse, al-Buraq, at a point that the Jews revered as the sole remnant of the Second Temple, the Kotel ha-Ma'aravi.

As a source of contention from its foundation to the present, the holy city of Jerusalem has embodied both the struggle for power and supreme spiritual guidance. Following the Jews' second mass-expulsion from Jerusalem and then following Rome's decline, Christians and Muslims had taken turns controlling the city over the ensuing centuries. Over the course of four millennia, the control of Jerusalem has been the strategic aim in at least 118 separate conflicts ranging from local religious struggles to strategic military campaigns. By the year 1912, Jerusalem had been conquered at least twenty-one times, and this number would further increase during Ticho's lifetime.[2]

The political order in Jerusalem upon Ticho's arrival reflected more "recent" history. With the exception of three different periods of Crusader occupation in the twelfth and thirteenth centuries, Jerusalem had been under Muslim control since the Caliph Umar conquered the city in 638.[3] After the conquest of Jerusalem by the Ottoman Turkish Sultan Selim I "the Grim" in 1516, the Turks had generally maintained control of the city. Selim's son, Suleiman the Magnificent, had rebuilt the complete circuit of the walls of Jerusalem upon earlier foundations.[4] Following a nine-year period of Egyptian control, the Turks retook Jerusalem in 1840, and looking westward, they instituted a system of reforms including extraterritorial concessions to foreign nations known as Capitulations or Tanzimat, a system that relied upon foreign consulates to assure privileges and protection of institutions and individuals. The Tanzimat Period would come to a close in another twenty-six months, but for now Dr. Ticho and Lemaan Zion could generally rely upon the protection of the Austrian and German Consuls.

In 1887, the Ottoman *sanjak* (district) of Jerusalem was carved off from the vilayet of Syria and became an independent mutasarriflik (subgovernorate). The mutasarrif (governor) of Jerusalem was directly appointed by and responsible to the central administration in Istanbul. Appointed mutasarrifs and military rulers of Jerusalem had traditionally held the honorific title of *paşa*, though following the revolution of the Young Turks in 1908 the title of *paşa* was reserved for officers above the rank of colonel and the grand vizier. The equivalent Hebrew term used by Eliezer Ben-Yehudah and others was *peḥa*.[5] When Ticho first

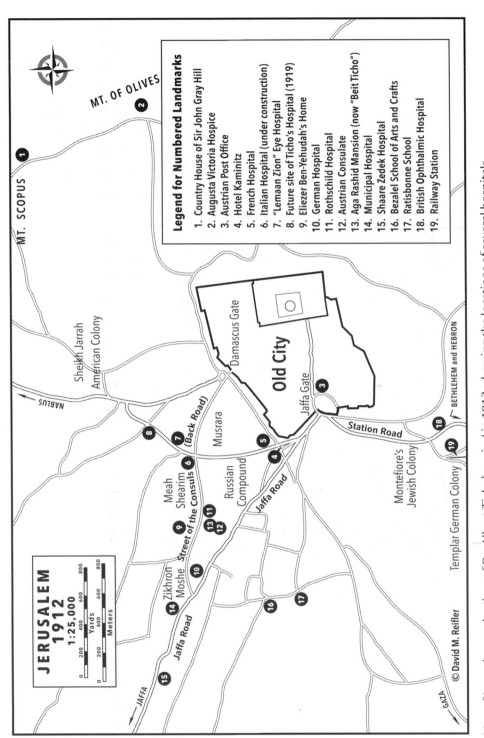

Map of Jerusalem at the time of Dr. Albert Ticho's arrival in 1912, showing the locations of several hospitals and other landmarks (graphic art by Willem Mineur)

Albert Ticho, c. 1912 (from the Ticho House Archives and *Ticho House: A Jerusalem Landmark* by Irit Salmon, 1994, © The Israel Museum, Jerusalem)

Anna Ticho, c. 1912 (from the Ticho House Archives and *Ticho House: A Jerusalem Landmark* by Irit Salmon, 1994, © The Israel Museum, Jerusalem)

Portrait drawings of Ignatz and
Laura Ticho, Albert Ticho's parents
(courtesy of Charles Ticho)

Albert Ticho's birthplace, A. J. Ticho store and family residence, Boskovice Moravia, c. 1905 (courtesy of the Boskovice Museum, Boskovice, Czech Republic)

Post-World War II commercial building that replaced the former Ticho family home and business on the main square of Boskovice, Czech Republic (photograph by the author, May 2009)

Dr. Isidor Reiniger, Albert Ticho's
brother-in-law (courtesy of Charles Ticho)

Phillip Ticho, Anna Ticho's father and Albert
Ticho's uncle (from the Ticho House Archives,
© The Israel Museum, Jerusalem)

Old Synagogue in Boskovice by Samuel Brunner, oil on canvas, c. 1915
(courtesy of the Jewish Museum in Prague)

Albert Ticho, c. 1908
(courtesy of Charles Ticho)

Anna Ticho, c. 1908 (from the Ticho House Archives and *Ticho House:
A Jerusalem Landmark* by Irit Salmon, 1994, © The Israel Museum, Jerusalem)

Rabbi Nehemiah Anton Nobel, c. 1912.
R. Nobel was the spiritual leader of the
Borneplatz Synagogue and head of the
Lemaan Zion benevolent society that sent Dr.
Ticho to Jerusalem. (courtesy of the Jüdisches
Museum Frankfurt am Main, Germany)

Prof. Dr. Otto Bergmeister, c. 1908. Dr.
Bergmeister was Dr. Ticho's ophthalmology
preceptor and mentor at the Rudolf Foundation
Hospital. (courtesy of the Collection of Pictures,
Collections and History of Medicine, University
of Vienna Medical School)

Dr. Moses Erlanger, Dr. Ticho's predecessor
at Lemaan Zion Eye Hospital, c. 1909
(courtesy of Irene Pollak-Rein)

Mordecai Adelman, c. 1912 (courtesy of
the Central Zionist Archives, Jerusalem)

Lemaan Zion Eye Hospital,
c. 1908 and 1910, respectively
(courtesy of Denise and Daniel Rein)

Sole remnant of Lemaan Zion
Eye Hospital at 48 Shivtei Yisrael,
Jerusalem (photograph by author,
January 2008)

British Ophthalmic Hospital, 1918
(from the Matson Photographic
Archive, Library of Congress,
Washington, DC)

Anna Ticho standing next to her mother, Bertha, 1912 (from the Ticho House Archives and *Ticho House: A Jerusalem Landmark* by Irit Salmon, 1994, © The Israel Museum, Jerusalem)

Nurses Rose Kaplan (right) and Rachel Landy (left) with Eva Leon (center) outside the Hadassah Nurses' Settlement House in Meah Shearim, Jerusalem, 1913 (from the Hadassah Archives, courtesy of Hadassah, The Women's Zionist Organization of America, Inc.)

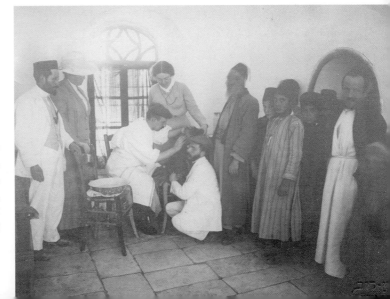

Eva Leon observing Dr. Ticho at the Lemaan Zion Eye Hospital, 1913 (from the Hadassah Archives, courtesy of Hadassah, The Women's Zionist Organization of America, Inc.)

Participants of First Trachoma Conference of Hebrew Physicians, 1914. Back row (right to left): Dr. Avraham Ticho, Dr. Aryeh Feigenbaum, Dr. Meshulam Levontin, Dr. Mordecai Borochov (Berachyahu), Dr. Moshe Neumann, and Dr. Miriam Neufach. Middle row (right to left): Dr. Aharon Yermens, Dr. Ze'ev Brünn, Dr. Sonya Belkind, Dr. Meir Krinkin, Dr. Hannah Waitz, Dr. Yisrael Biskind, and Dr. Beila Korvakov (Korvakova). Bottom row (right to left): Dr. Naftali Waitz, Dr. Aryeh Goldberg, Dr. Jacob Segal, Dr. Aryeh Pouchovsky, Dr. Aharon Mazie, Dr. Avraham Zvi Moskovitz, and Dr. Aryeh Shimoni-Mäkler. Absent from the photo are Dr. Avraham Abushadid, Dr. Jacob David, Dr. Moshe Wallach, and Dr. Gildenson. (courtesy of the Central Zionist Archives, Jerusalem)

דין וחשבון
של
ועידת הגרענת

הראשונה של הרופאים העברים בא"י.
ירושלם תרע"ד.

———

נערך והוצא לאור על ידי
מחלקת הגרענת של תחנת הבריאות העברית
(מיסודו של נתן שטרויס).

———

עם 4 טבלות.

ירושלם
הוצאת תחנת הבריאות העברית
תר ע ו.

Title page of *Proceedings of the First Trachoma Conference of Hebrew Physicians of Eretz Yisrael*, the first modern medical book published in Hebrew (5676/1915)

Austro-Hungarian Military Reserve Hospital at the Ratisbonne School in Jerusalem, 1916 (from the Matson Photographic Archive, Library of Congress, Washington, DC)

Capt. Marek Schwarz, circa 1916 (from the Ticho House Archives, © The Israel Museum, Jerusalem)

Excursion of Albert Ticho and fellow Austrian army officers to Transjordan, 1917 (from the Ticho House Archives and *Ticho House: A Jerusalem Landmark* by Irit Salmon, 1994, © The Israel Museum, Jerusalem)

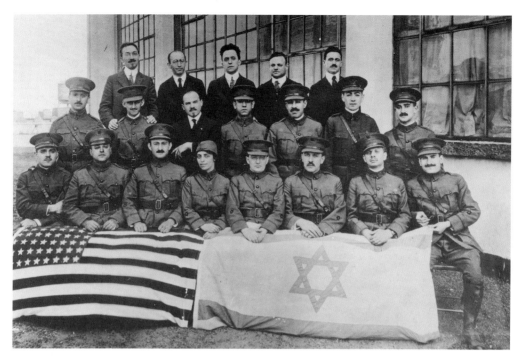

American Zionist Medical Unit (AZMU) on the eve of their departure from New York, June 1917 (from the Hadassah Archives, courtesy of Hadassah, The Women's Zionist Organization of America, Inc.)

Nurses of the AZMU and Hadassah Central Committee members, New York, June 1917 (from the Hadassah Archives, courtesy of Hadassah, The Women's Zionist Organization of America, Inc.)

Albert and Anna Ticho returning to Jerusalem after World War I, December 1918 (from the Ticho House Archives and *Ticho House: A Jerusalem Landmark* by Irit Salmon, 1994, © The Israel Museum, Jerusalem)

Medical faculty standing behind the nursing faculty and inaugural class of nursing graduates at the Rothschild-Hadassah Hospital, December, 1921. Dr. Isaac Max Rubinow and Henrietta Szold are seated in the second row. Dr. Ticho is standing in the center of the back row next to Dr. Helena Kagan. (from the Hadassah Archives, courtesy of Hadassah, The Women's Zionist Organization of America, Inc.)

Close-up view of Dr. Ticho

Dr. Ticho's private eye hospital in the Musrara neighborhood of Jerusalem, c. 1922 (from the Ticho House Archives and *Ticho House: A Jerusalem Landmark* by Irit Salmon, 1994, © The Israel Museum, Jerusalem)

Albert and Anna Ticho in the clinic of their private hospital, c. 1925. A picture of Dr. Ticho's mentor, Dr. Otto Bergmeister, is hanging on the wall behind them. (from the Ticho House Archives and *Ticho House: A Jerusalem Landmark* by Irit Salmon, 1994, © The Israel Museum, Jerusalem)

Alfred Ticho in Binyamina, c. 1930 (courtesy of Charles Ticho)

Ticho House (Beit Ticho), 2007 (courtesy of Marc Sussman)

Grave sites of Albert and Anna Ticho, Har ha-Menuhot Cemetery, Jerusalem
(photograph by the author, July 2007)

came to Jerusalem in June 1912, the city was awaiting the arrival of its new Ottoman governor, Majidi Shevket Bey, replacing a governor who had come under attacks by Jerusalem's Arab notables. Majidi Bey was the ninth mutasarrif of Jerusalem since the turn of the twentieth century, but only a few more would follow.[6]

Jerusalem was a growing city when Ticho first arrived. For centuries, the city had been mired in the provincial backwaters of the Ottoman Empire. The recent growth in the population of Jerusalem had outpaced modernization, and much of the city's infrastructure was at a practically medieval level. Electrification had been achieved in several areas of the city during the preceding decade, but many streets were still illuminated at night by oil street lamps or in some of the richer quarters gas lamps. In 1838 the city had only 11,000 inhabitants but now it had grown to a population of at least 68,000 comprised of about 8,000 Muslims, 10,000 Christians, and 50,000 Jews. Outside of Jerusalem about 15,000 Jews were concentrated in Tel Aviv and a half dozen other cities, while about 12,000 lived among forty or more rural settlements. Although about forty-four Jewish rural settlements had been established, Jews owned only about 105,000 acres, 1.6 percent of all the land.[7] Except for these Jewish enclaves, the Jews of Palestine were mostly urban dwellers and a decided minority compared to Palestine's 600,000 Arab inhabitants.

At the beginning of 1912 there were only thirty-two Jewish physicians throughout all of Palestine, including just nine who practiced in Jerusalem. About an equal number of non-Jewish physicians practiced in the city. By the middle of 1914 the numbers of Jewish physicians both within and outside of Jerusalem would double.[8] Although these gains were temporarily offset by expulsions and conscriptions during World War I, Ticho was arriving in Jerusalem at the threshold of an era when Jewish physicians would predominate in Palestine, both in numbers and in accomplishments.

Lemaan Zion was among several clinics and hospitals available to the inhabitants of Jerusalem, but old superstitions were a barrier to medical treatment even from a Jewish physician. The wearing of amulets with imagined protective and healing powers was commonplace throughout the city. Out of suspicion and fear, many Jewish inhabitants of the city tended to avoid the doctors at the non-Jewish hospitals run by the French, Germans, Greeks, Russians, and British, even the excellent British Ophthalmic Hospital near the train station. In the poor neighborhoods of the Old City, the water supply was unreliable, living conditions were crowded, and sanitation was poor. These conditions contributed to the prevalence of trachoma and other eye infections (conjunctivitis) that often reached epidemic proportions in the early summer months.

Before Jewish eye specialists had come to Jerusalem, the Jewish population had mainly turned to pharmacists, their apprentices, or other lay persons known as *yad'anim* to treat eye problems.[9] *Yad'anim* dispensed medicines such as the eyedrops prepared by Yehoshua Yonah and copper sulfate imported from Egypt by the watchmaker Yehoshua Zeigermacher. Other non-physicians providing eye care included Rav Gershon Porush, Dr. Moshe Wallach's assistant at Shaare Zedek, and Binyamin Gavrielovitch, the pharmacist at the Lemaan Zion Polyclinic. Ticho's predecessor there, Dr. Erlanger, had also correctly stressed the importance of hygiene in the prevention of trachoma in an article that he published in the newspaper *Ḥavatzelet*.[10]

With the reopening of the Lemaan Zion Eye Hospital, Ticho and Adelman rehired Erlanger's former assistant, Dr. Aharon Yosef Yermens, an observant Jew from Vilna who had embraced political Zionism.[11] Yermens and his wife, Hannah, had immigrated to Palestine in December 1890 by way of Istanbul aboard the same ship as Dr. Moshe Wallach, the founder and director of Shaare Zedek Hospital. The Yermenses had first settled in Hebron and worked for a clinic funded by the Anglo-Jewish Association of London. The following year they were joined by the doctor's mother, Chayah, who helped raised their family until her death in 1902. In 1905, Hannah Yermens had insisted that the family move to Jerusalem so that their children could receive the best available education. The Yermenses joined other highly educated individuals such as David Yellin and Yehiel Michael Pines in founding the Zikhron Moshe neighborhood. Traveling about Jerusalem on the back of his donkey, Yermens had also worked at most of the other local Jewish hospitals and maintained a private practice.

Ticho and Adelman also hired assistants who were native Jerusalemites, first Rav Zadok Creuz and later Dov Halaban. Creuz, a disciple of Rabbi Sonnenfeld and head secretary for the Hungarian community's Shomrei ha-Ḥomot, had roots in Palestine that extended five generations on his father's side and ten on his mother's. He had learned German and studied medicine sufficiently to serve as a medical assistant. Creuz was a talented musician, playing both flute and violin, and it is said "he was cheerful and made others so."[12] Halaban, who also lived nearby in Meah Shearim, was a man of short physical stature who apparently suffered from a type of congenital spinal defect. He spoke Hebrew, Arabic, Yiddish, and German, and he was familiar with the customs and psychology of both Jews and Arabs. He would remain Ticho's faithful and valuable employee over many years, serving in many capacities.

In addition to his main assistants, Ticho employed "a very well-equipped staff of nurses."[13] One of Ticho's nurses was the widow Shoshana Marx. A member of a wealthy family, she had immigrated to Palestine from Germany in 1903 under the auspices of Ḥibat Ziyon. Mrs. Marx was highly educated and certified as teacher. Soon after immigrating she had found employment at the Evelina de Rothschild School. However, she preferred her volunteer work at the Lemaan Zion Eye Hospital, caring for patients both day and night and administering their medications. As she was a woman of some means, she apparently donated her entire wages back to the hospital.[14]

Later, in the fall of 1912, when Anna Ticho and her mother Bertha arrived in Jerusalem, Anna learned to assist in the clinic and in surgery while "Tanta Bertha" supervised the kitchen. An efficient and hard-working staff enabled Ticho to see a high volume of patients in the busy general clinic – about 200 patient-visits daily, including an average of 1,130 new patients per month – with Dr. Yermens seeing about half of this patient volume under Ticho's direction. During his first twelve months Ticho saw 8,233 patients with a total of 67,239 patient visits, performing 247 major and 248 minor operations.[15]

News of Ticho's arrival in Jerusalem was widely publicized. Adelman's good friend, Eliezer Ben-Yehudah, immediately published a positive article in his newspaper Ha-Or.[16] Just two weeks later, the Sephardi Hebrew newspaper Ha-Ḥerut published an open letter addressed to Ticho stating that Jerusalem's poor could not afford the fee of one Turkish mejidi (a silver coin equivalent to two and a half English shillings, or forty pence) that had been set for an initial visit. The editor, Avraham Elmaleh, acknowledged that the doctor was seeing patients several times per week without charge but noted in erudite Aramaic that "you get what you pay for." Two days later, in the familiar front-page position of the same newspaper previously occupied by Dr. Bloom's advertising (chapter 6), Ticho's response constituted his one and only advertisement in *Ha-Ḥerut*. Here he simply stated that he would see patients without charge from eight in the morning until twelve noon *every* day of the week (except of course on the Sabbath).[17]

———◆———

Among the other news events in July of 1912 were the elections for the Turkish Parliament that briefly brought the Entente Liberale Party to power in Istanbul, four years after the Young Turk Revolution and three years since the deposition of Sultan Abdul Hamid II. Mehmed V was the sultan, but post-revolution power now lay in the hands of various members of the Ottoman government and would soon be concentrated in the hands of three *paşa*s: Interior Minister Mehmed Talaat Paşa, Minister of War Ismail Enver Paşa, and Minister of the Navy Ahmet Cemal Paşa.[18] The war with Italy over Tripoli was still ongoing and there were many external and internal pressures on the newly elected government.

On August 5, 1912, the Turkish Parliament was again suspended but Ticho may not have noticed signs of any political instability as he became acclimated to his new surroundings. He may have noticed the sound of a cannon-shot at sundown on August 14, but it was only the signal of the end of the first day of Ramadan (of the year 1330 on the Islamic calendar), a month that is the most venerated in the Islamic calendar. During the daylight hours of that entire month, observant Muslims abstain from eating, drinking any liquid, and sexual intercourse. The cannon shots would continue each night at sundown throughout that month, during which time Ticho would have fewer surgeries to perform on his Muslim patients.

That fall, the war with Italy over Libya ended, and the architects of the planned Italian Hospital, brothers Antonio and Giulio Barluzzi, came to Jerusalem to supervise the construction project a short way down the road from the Lemaan Zion Eye Hospital.[19] A beautiful building would now begin to emerge where extensive excavations had stood unattended for many months. Although there was peace again with Italy, war quickly erupted elsewhere at the edges of the Ottoman Empire. Just ten days before the war with Italy officially ended, King Nicholas of Montenegro declared war against Turkey (October 8), and the Balkan League (Serbia, Bulgaria, and Greece) followed suit nine days later. Under these less than optimal circumstances, Anna Ticho and her mother Bertha traveled from Vienna to Jerusalem by essentially the same route that Albert had taken five months earlier. Austrian steamers were continuing their transits through the Adriatic, though their schedules were occasionally disrupted.

Anna and her mother were still en route to Palestine when another pioneering woman of the arts in Palestine arrived at the train station in Jerusalem for one last time. On October 9, 1912, the train that arrived in Jerusalem at a quarter past twelve in the afternoon carried the ailing wife of Arthur Ruppin. Suffering from a post-partum infectious peritonitis ("puerperal fever"), Shulamit Ruppin was brought there by her husband in a special train car, and this was followed by an agonizing hour-long ride by wagon to Shaare Zedek Hospital far up Jaffa Road.[20] Here Dr. Moshe Wallach and his colleagues were unable to cure the infection, and Mrs. Ruppin died six days later on October 15. Many businesses and schools were closed the following day, and Ticho may have joined with many if not most of Jerusalem's Jewish physicians in the funeral procession to Shulamit Ruppin's final resting place on the Mount of Olives.[21]

Ticho would similarly be called upon to consult in difficult cases, such as that of a young medical colleague, twenty-seven-year-old Dr. Ze'ev Brünn, a Jewish-German physician specializing in tropical diseases. In 1910, Brünn had settled in Hadera, one of the most fertile breeding grounds for the Anopheles mosquitoes that transmitted malaria. Brünn himself had contracted the very disease he had been fighting in the swamps, and it seems that the great quantities of quinine he had taken resulted in a temporary paralysis of half of his face (Bell's palsy). Because of the problems he had in closing the eye on the affected side, he was sent to Dr. Ticho in Jerusalem. While under the ophthalmologist's care in Jerusalem, he met and fell in love with one of Ticho's nurses, Rebecca Marx, the daughter of a German banker. The two were married the following year.[22] It was through Rebecca, in Germany, that the writer, S. Y. Agnon, met Rebecca's sister, Esther, whom the writer later married in 1919.

◆

Before leaving Europe, Anna Ticho had spent time with her mother in Paris visiting museums and taking additional art classes. Albert's brother (Anna's cousin) Josef had overcome his initial objections to the wedding. His legal ward was fast approaching the age of majority and was now beyond his direct influence. Albert also received the blessing of his brother-in-law, Dr. Isidor Reiniger.[23] A member of the newly founded Agudas Yisrael, Isidor arranged for one of the main leaders of the ḥaredi (ultra-Orthodox) community in Jerusalem to conduct the wedding ceremony. This was Rabbi Yosef Chaim Sonnenfeld who, together with Rabbi Yehoshua Leib Diskin, had participated in founding the Hungarian Houses. Rabbi Sonnenfeld had immigrated to Palestine as a young man in 1873 with his mentor and their families, leaving their flourishing yeshiva in Kobersdorf, Hungary.[24] Like the followers of Agudas Yisrael of those days, Rabbi Sonnenfeld and the Jerusalem ḥaredi community strongly opposed political Zionism. Although Rabbi Sonnenfeld would officiate at the Tichos' wedding, the bride and groom were more inclined toward the secular world rather than an ultra-Orthodox way of life.

It appears that Anna and her mother arrived in time for the celebration of their shared birthday of October 27 – his twenty-ninth and her eighteenth. During the busy days leading up to the wedding, there was little time for Anna to devote to her art, but she very likely visited the Bezalel School of Arts and Crafts whose new retail pavilion she had first seen just outside the Jaffa Gate on her way into town.[25] Soon after her arrival in Jerusalem she would meet the school's eccentric and charismatic founder, Professor Boris Schatz. At that time, the only female student at the Bezalel School was the seventeen-year-old Russian immigrant Marousia (Miriam) Nissenholtz, who went by the fanciful name Ḥad Gadya (An Only Kid), perhaps because she felt like a young goat among the school's male student-wolves. It appears that Anna later briefly took some instruction at the Bezalel School, but never as a full-time student. In the years to come, Anna would develop her own unique style of drawing and painting that was widely acclaimed, but for now she placed her artwork aside. At that time, perhaps the most notable woman creating rich paintings of Jerusalem and environs was Lady Caroline Gray Hill, a wealthy Englishwoman who had been coming to Jerusalem for a quarter century with her husband.

On Thursday, November 7, 1912, Albert and Anna's wedding took place at the Hotel Kaminitz.[26] The Sephardi *Ha-Ḥerut* newspaper did not cover the wedding. Neither did Ben-Yehudah's newspaper, *Ha-Or*, though it contained some interesting local and international news about ophthalmology (eye examinations at the Hebrew Academy by Dr. Segal and the enucleation of Marconi's badly injured right eye by Ticho's former professor, Dr. Ernst Fuchs), and there was also a report that the first Italian nationals had begun to return to Jerusalem now that the war with Italy had ended.[27] *Ha-Or* also continued to run Dr. Moshe Sherman's advertisement announcing his office hours at the Hotel Kaminitz, hours that coincided that day with the time of the Tichos' wedding ceremony and reception. Just a week or two later, Sherman permanently closed his itinerant practice in Jerusalem to work full-time at his permanent office in Jaffa. A new doctor, Dr. Aryeh Shimoni-Mäkler, arrived in Jerusalem to take Sherman's place at the Hotel Kaminitz.[28] Unlike Sherman, Shimoni-Mäkler practiced only in Jerusalem where he advertised his specialization in eye, ear, nose, and throat diseases (EENT).[29]

In November 1912, while the Tichos were away on their honeymoon, *Ha-Or* reported that a new clinic would be opening in Jerusalem in a large building that had previously housed the British Consulate for twenty years on what is now called Ethiopian Street.[30] Other buildings in other Jerusalem neighborhoods would later house this clinic run by the Jewish Health Bureau (also called the Health "Station" or *Taḥanat HaBriyut* in Hebrew) that had been founded earlier near Haifa in February 1912 by the German-born American philanthropist Nathan Straus.[31] He subsequently decided that the Health Bureau should be located in Jerusalem, where he was also opening a soup kitchen for the destitute. Chaim Weizmann was very excited to hear about a centralized Health Bureau in Jerusalem and, as he wrote to Judah Magnes, he felt that such an institute should be incorporated into a Hebrew University.[32]

Earlier that spring, the agronomist Aaron Aaronsohn had advised Straus to appoint Dr. Ze'ev Brünn as the director of the new Health Bureau. In advance of his move to Jerusalem, Brünn gave a scientific lecture in Jerusalem in October that Ticho attended.[33] Now Brünn was busy organizing the newly established Health Bureau into three divisions, planning to direct the Malaria Division himself. Through his connections in Germany, he hired the ophthalmologist Dr. Aryeh Feigenbaum, who was still serving as Prof. Julius Hirschberg's assistant in Berlin. Although Feigenbaum had unsuccessfully competed with Ticho for the appointment at the Lemaan Zion Eye Hospital earlier that year, he too would be able to immigrate to Palestine with a position waiting for him. In January 1913, seven months after Ticho's aliyah, Feigenbaum arrived in Jerusalem and became the director of the Trachoma Division of the Jewish Health Bureau. But as that new clinic was just being organized, Feigenbaum apparently worked for several months during 1913 as an associate at Lemaan Zion, as did another ophthalmologist, Dr. Miriam Neufach, the first female ophthalmologist to practice in Palestine. Meanwhile, at the Jewish Health Bureau, Brünn hired the bacteriologist and serologist Dr. Aryeh Goldberg as the director of his Bacteriology Division.[34]

◆

In November 1912, Dr. Ticho was as yet the only Jewish ophthalmologist practicing in Jerusalem, and so the Tichos' honeymoon was important news for local newspaper publishers Avraham Elmaleh (*Ha-Ḥerut*) and Eliezer Ben-Yehudah (*Ha-Or*). On November 13, *Ha-Ḥerut* reported that the newly married Dr. and Mrs. Ticho were leaving the Holy City and traveling to Europe.[35] A different account of the Tichos' itinerary appeared in Ben-Yehudah's paper. On November 19, *Ha-Or* reported that the Tichos had left on a trip to Jericho and the Dead Sea and would return the following Tuesday, November 26. After a brief stay in Jerusalem, they would continue their honeymoon with a three-week trip to Egypt.[36] The same edition contained a notice that Dr. Jacob Segal of the Rothschild Hospital would be leaving for a study tour en route to Paris.

The road to Jericho in those days could be traveled by carriage in about four hours. At about the halfway point, the road descended the Tal'at ed-Dam (Ascent of Blood), the biblical Adummim. Continuing its descent through the wadis, the Tichos' carriage entered the plains of Jericho. Here in 1909, the German Oriental Society had excavated the terraces and winter palace of Herod at Tell Abu 'Alaikh that commanded a view of the southern Jordan Valley and the Dead Sea. A half hour down the road the "modern" village of Jericho had been reestablished in the era of the Crusades, and now in 1912 it was a small village with about three hundred inhabitants and three or four tourist hotels. A pleasant evening excursion would have been a walk northwest to the Ein es-Sultan (Sultan's Spring) near German excavations of the most ancient walls of the original Jericho at Tell es-Sultan. Albert and Anna probably took the popular two-hour excursion to the Jordan River where Christian pilgrims came to bathe. After a visit to the Dead Sea they would follow the main roads back to Jerusalem.[37]

Other than the initial journey that brought her to Palestine, the Tichos' trip to Jericho was Anna's first experience traveling into the surrounding Judean hills and deserts. Anna later wrote that "it was love at first sight," and she expressed how the experience had a profound and lasting effect upon her art, stating, "I remember my first encounter with Jerusalem as if it were today. The mountains were bare, not as they are now. There wasn't a tree on them. I remember when I stared I was drawn to the view. I was swallowing it all in with my eyes – the pure lines of the mountain, lines that return onto themselves as if they continue forever and came from the distance. It all spoke to me. I felt the loneliness of the landscape, but I couldn't draw… I never missed the landscapes I saw abroad that I had once loved so much."[38]

Other factors likely affected Anna Ticho's ability to concentrate on her art. Her first pregnancy ended with the death of their newborn child, and she would have five more miscarriages in the coming years. Ticho's assistant in the mid 1920s, Dr. Ephraim Sinai, presumed that consanguinity of the first cousins was the underlying problem and incorrectly wrote that the Tichos' children suffered from hereditary hydrocephalus (accumulation of fluid on the brain).[39] It should be remembered that relations between Ticho and Sinai were never close and often strained. Sinai was often dismayed at how very little personal conversation and information was shared between them (chapter 17).

Consanguinity was apparently not at all involved in Anna's many miscarriages. In retrospect, the true diagnosis was erythroblastosis fetalis – Rh incompatibility leading to hemolytic anemia in the baby – a condition that was poorly understood at the time. Anna Ticho's blood-type was Rh-negative and each of her unborn children had inherited the Rh-positive blood type from Albert. In each subsequent pregnancy, antibodies produced by Anna's immune system were able to cross the placental barrier and attack the red blood cells in the fetal circulation. While the main human blood type groups (A, B, AB, and O) had been identified in those days, the Rh (Rhesus) factor that is generally responsible for most cases of erythroblastosis fetalis was not discovered until 1940 by Ticho's former professor, Dr. Karl Landsteiner, who had earlier described the basic classification of blood types (the A–B–O system).[40]

Instead of devoting her time and energy to her art, Anna now entered the nursing profession. She managed all of the surgical instruments and eventually became a skillful assistant.[41] She also supervised patients who were admitted to the hospital. The Chief Surgeon at the British Ophthalmic Hospital noted some of the innovations that the Tichos had introduced, writing, "The principal aim of that hospital has been the treatment of acute ophthalmia, and for this purpose seven nurses were engaged, and the hospital administered so that not only the patients themselves were admitted as *inpatients*, but the *mothers*, also, were allowed to sleep and live in the hospital. This arrangement, in some respects a good plan, is one which we, with our small nursing staff, large operating list, and limited accommodation, could not possibly imitate."[42]

Albert's happiness and love for Anna during this time is reflected in a letter to his brother Max. Before leaving for Egypt, Albert learned of Max's engagement to twenty-two-year-old Grete-Miriam Fleishmann of Vienna. From Jerusalem he wrote a warm letter to Max offering him his congratulations and best wishes that contained the following excerpt: "According to what I hear from all sides, you let your heart choose and speak, emulating me nicely. The famous Ticho family does not look right or left, but goes like the path of a train. I hope that you will be as happy as I am, in love as I am, and will marry your love and bring her quickly to your house … I wish that what is said in this week's Torah portion comes true, 'May they be like fish, multiplying in the land,' that the match will be healthy, lucky, and comfortable and will serve as the base for the building of a Jewish home." The biblical quotation places the writing of this letter during the week of December 5, 1912.[43]

After the Tichos returned from their honeymoon in late December or early January 1913, *Ha-Ḥerut* reported that they had indeed been to Europe.[44] Perhaps they attended Max and Grete's wedding. Wherever their honeymoon had taken them, the Tichos had likely celebrated their first Hanukkah as a married couple with the traditional lighting of the Hanukkah menorah. In future years Albert would assemble one of the largest collections of antique menorahs held in private hands, a collection that was subsequently bequeathed in its entirety to the Israel Museum.

CHAPTER 8

JANUARY 1913–FEBRUARY 1914
SCHOOLCHILDREN AND VISITING NURSES

הצרי אין בגלעד אם-רפא אין שם,
כי מדוע לא עלתה ארכת בת-עמי.

Is there no balm in Gilead? Can no physician be found?
Why has healing not yet come to the daughter of my people?

Jeremiah 8:22

Soon after returning from their honeymoon, Anna and Albert Ticho experienced their first spring together in Jerusalem. It was mid-January 1913, more than a month before the last snow fell in the city, and yet the Jewish National Fund proclaimed that spring had arrived and that trees were available for planting by volunteers willing to pay three rubles for the privilege. The signs of spring typically came early in Palestine where the almond trees were among the first trees to blossom. On January 23, Ben-Yehudah devoted the entire front page of his newspaper, *Ha-Or*, to the planned activities of Jerusalem's schoolchildren marking the celebration of Tu B'Shvat, the Jewish Arbor Day. While the Tichos were busy at work in their clinic, fourteen schools participated in the first organized, city-wide celebration of Tu B'Shvat in Jerusalem.

Meeting points for processions to the western outskirts of the city included the main Jewish hospitals, the Rothschild Hospital on the Street of the Consuls and the new Bikkur Cholim and Shaare Zedek Hospitals along the Jaffa Road. At a vineyard on the road to Motza, activities included the planting of trees and the singing of Hebrew songs. The symbolism of this modern pilgrimage was rooted in an ancient, brief Talmudic discussion about the "New Year of the Trees," but it was now developing as a new Zionist tradition. As recorded in his diary, Theodor Herzl himself had planted a cypress tree (with the help of Arabs) in this field near Motza on November 2, 1898.[1]

Even as Ben-Yehudah devoted so much attention to the Tu B'Shvat celebrations, he continued to report the latest news from Istanbul and London about the war in the Balkans.[2] With Bulgarian forces poised for attack on Adrianople (now Edirne, Turkey), Grand Vizier Mehmed Kamil Paşa convened the Turkish Parliament to debate an ultimatum of the Balkan League. Ben-Yehudah wrote that he was certain a decision would be made "out of love for the homeland and to secure the future." That day, after four months of fighting in the First Balkan War, and without consulting Ben-Yehudah, Ismail Enver Paşa and a group of coconspirators forced their way into the cabinet chamber, shot dead the War Minister, Nazim Paşa, and forced the Liberal government's resignation at gunpoint.[3] Although the previous grand vizier, Mahmud Shevket Paşa, was restored to power, he would himself be assassinated just a few months later.

In Jerusalem, the coming of warmer weather meant that Dr. Ticho again began to see greater numbers of patients with acute eye infections, especially younger schoolchildren. Most of these were simply acute cases of "pink-eye" but many also had the classic signs of trachoma, progressing through stages of discharge and acute swelling around the eyes, and the development of tiny bumps or so-called "granules" on the conjunctiva, the membranes lining the inner eyelids. In advanced stages the eyelids, and even the surface of the eyeball, could become scarred. In the early years of Ticho's career, the causative organism of trachoma, *Chlamydia trachomatis*, had not yet been identified, but microscopic evidence of infection had been observed and experimentally reproduced.[4] The organism was so small that it was incorrectly presumed by many to be a virus. Ticho appreciated the infectious and contagious nature of trachoma, and he also recognized cases of trachoma that were admixed with other bacteria that were more easily identified under the microscope, including the gonococcus that caused "blenorrhea" and the Koch-Weeks bacillus that caused "pink-eye."

From the time of Napoleon's military campaigns in Egypt, these infections had often been lumped together under the terms "Egyptian ophthalmia" or "military ophthalmia." Ticho would later comment on the historical concurrence of mixed conjunctival infections among the soldiers in Napoleon's armies. Following several decades of recurring epidemics in Europe, the ancient Greek word, trachoma (meaning "rough" and alluding to the granules), had been reintroduced and was often used interchangeably. Referring to the granules, a modern Hebrew word for trachoma, gar'enet, had been coined in Palestine by Ticho's contemporary, Dr. Aharon Mazie, who has been widely recognized as the father of modern Hebrew medical terminology.[5]

As the earliest signs of spring were appearing in Palestine, the cruise ship *Franconia* of the Cunard Line set sail from New York on January 18, 1913.[6] Two of the passengers were American nurses who were bound for Jerusalem, where they would come to personally assist Ticho and his colleagues with a different type of war, the "War against Trachoma." Their activities represented the first project in Palestine for the American Zionist organization the "Daughters of Zion" (later known as Hadassah) that had had emerged from several women's study circles and was growing. Seven initial signers of an invitation to a national organizing meeting on February 24, 1912, had included Henrietta Szold, and this had attracted over thirty women to the vestry rooms at New York City's Temple Emanu-El. The first year of subsequent meetings had featured lantern slide presentations of grievous medical conditions in Palestine, and one of the first presenters was socialite Eva Leon, who had worked with several of Jerusalem's midwives. By year's end, with 122 members and $542 in dues collected, the Daughters of Zion had decided to establish a social welfare program in Palestine modeled after Lillian Wald's Henry Street Settlement Visiting Nurse Service.[7]

It had been almost a year since Nathan and Lina Straus had visited Palestine and established a soup kitchen and the Health Bureau in

Jerusalem. It had been a year marked by personal family tragedy. Nathan's brother and sister-in-law, Isidor and Ida, had died aboard the ill-fated *Titanic*, and it seemed that the tragedy only intensified the Strauses' philanthropic activities. Mr. Straus now planned to establish a total of twenty-one soup kitchens, and he was working with the Empress of Germany to establish a Jewish medical society for tropical research.[8]

In December 1912, the Strauses had approached Henrietta Szold with an offer of funds to underwrite the travel expenses and the initial establishment of a nurse in Jerusalem. At a board meeting on January 1, 1913, Szold convinced the Daughters of Zion to support a nurse in Jerusalem for the final twenty months of a two-year term. Eva Leon then announced that she had secured an additional commitment for $2,000 per year from non-Zionists friends in Chicago, and so the organization committed to hiring a second nurse for a term of eighteen months.[9] One of Straus's conditions was that both nurses needed to be hired and be ready to leave for Palestine with Mr. and Mrs. Straus by January 18. Among twenty-one applicants that Szold personally interviewed, two were selected, nurses Rose Kaplan and Rachael Diane Landy. After brief stops in Europe, the *Franconia* arrived at Alexandria, whereupon the Strauses and their group went to Cairo. Aware of his benefactor's arrival in Egypt, Dr. Ze'ev Brünn came to meet with the Strauses, and though they stayed behind, Brünn returned to Palestine with the American medical missionaries.

Accompanied by Brünn and Leon, Kaplan and Landy arrived in Jerusalem on the evening of February 11, 1913.[10] The two nurses differed in age, appearance, and temperament, but they had become good friends during the long journey. Forty-five-year-old Rose Kaplan was the older of the two – shorter, stout, and dark-haired, cautious and more serious in disposition. Kaplan was a native of Saint Petersberg, Russia, who had come to the United States in her mid-twenties. She soon began training as a nurse at New York's Mount Sinai Hospital and after graduating in 1894, went on to have a very broad experience in general and public health nursing. In contrast, twenty-seven-year-old Rachel Landy was tall and blonde, fun-loving and free-spirited. Born in Sirvintai, Lithuania, she came to America at age six, whereupon her father, a scribe, teacher, and book-dealer, Americanized their last name from Landsman to Landy.[11] Raised in Cleveland, Ohio, where she attended public schools and nursing school, Rachel Landy had worked with the famous Dr. George Crile before moving to New York and working at the Harlem Hospital and Dispensary, where she had risen to the position of assistant superintendent of nurses. It turned out that the district nursing goals of Hadassah and the talents of the nurses professionally intersected with Ticho's position in the community, and therefore much of nurses Kaplan and Landy's work very soon came under his supervision.

Upon their arrival, Eva Leon publicly expressed the goal of establishing a nurses' training school in Jerusalem, something that Henrietta Szold would describe as "the ultimate object" of the Hadassah organization.[12] After World War I, Ticho would participate in realizing this dream, serving on the faculty of the Nurses' Training School, and also directing a staff of newly immigrated ophthalmologists-educators. Leon and the nurses visited Ticho and watched as he demonstrated techniques of examining and treating children with trachoma.[13] Meanwhile a settlement house that served as the nurses' home and clinic was established in Jerusalem's Orthodox Meah Shearim neighborhood, opposite the Hungarian Houses, and thus very close to Ticho's hospital. Here, on a stone wall above a wrought iron gate, just outside a courtyard with a fragrant lemon tree, Eva Leon and the nurses hung a sign in both Hebrew and English that read: "American Daughters of Zion / Nurses Settlement / Hadassah." On March 23, 1913, Kaplan and Landy accepted their first maternity patients at their settlement home, and with the help of Dr. Ticho they soon also began to take on trachoma cases that were so rampant.

The two Hadassah nurses had expected much help and guidance in their mission from the Jewish Health Bureau, but Dr. Brünn, who was supposed to supervise their work, was otherwise occupied. In February, Brünn took other members of Straus's medical team to Tiberias to help fight a cholera epidemic, and the following month he was preoccupied with a "War against Malaria," finding that promised help from German researchers had evaporated. (Among other affronts, this had led to very frosty relations between the physicians of the Jewish Health Bureau and

German researchers.) At the beginning of April, Brünn left Palestine for a three-month stay in Europe, in part to garner further support for the newly established Pasteur Institute in Jerusalem. Dr. Feigenbaum, whose Trachoma Division was just getting established at the Health Bureau, later recalled that the two nurses (whom he nicknamed Short and Tall) "were like lost souls, wandering through Jerusalem, not knowing what to do." Ticho, more established in the community, took the nurses under his wing. Ticho's collaboration helped the nurses overcome initial suspicion and skepticism of Jerusalem's residents.[14] Through work at their clinic, general home visits, and their supervision of midwives, the two Hadassah nurses became an accepted and even beloved part of the community.

In the summer of 1913, under Dr. Ticho's supervision, Nurses Kaplan and Landy began to systematically examine and treat patients in thirty-one Jewish schools in Jerusalem, both "in the city" (within the Old City walls) and in the Jewish neighborhoods outside of the Old City (appendix 4).[15] Although Ticho was the primary supervisor for the two Hadassah nurses, there was overlap at about a dozen schools that both he and Dr. Feigenbaum visited. Ticho saw many Arab children in his clinic, but his visits did not include nearby Arab schools. For his part, Dr. Feigenbaum visited at least four local, predominantly Arab schools.[16]

Under Rabbi Yehiel Michel Tykocinski, the Eitz Hayim Talmud Torah had two branches that Ticho visited, one in the Old City and one in the Mahane Yehuda neighborhood.[17] The rabbi had a great reputation for his knowledge of mathematics and astronomy, and Ticho found the rabbi to be an interesting and lively conversationalist. Ticho and Rabbi Tykocinski's relationship therefore continued over many years, and the rabbi would come to Ticho with complaints and questions about his declining vision.[18] The other leading figure of Eitz Hayim was Rabbi Ze'ev Wolf Shachor, who had done much to develop the Mahane Yehuda neighborhood where the newer Eitz Hayim Talmud Torah was located.[19] Perhaps the largest religious school in Jerusalem that Ticho visited, however, was the Talmud Torah of Meah Shearim, nearer to Lemaan Zion and the Hadassah Nurses' Settlement House.

Just to the west of Meah Shearim in the adjacent Zikhron Moshe neighborhood, Ticho and the nurses visited the more progressive and secular Lämel School that was easily identifiable as a Jewish institution. The school building's stone façade featured a clock with Hebrew letters above two windows in the shape of the Tablets of the Covenant and another circular window just below this featuring the six-pointed Star of David. Beneath these windows, the keystone of the school's main entrance showed a palm tree symbolizing righteousness (Psalm 94) and a well symbolizing the Enlightenment against a backdrop of a peaceful settlement. In 1903, under Principal Ephraim Cohen-Reiss, the school had moved to this location on what was then an otherwise barren hill. About two years later, Ticho's assistant, Dr. Aharon Yermens, moved from Hebron with his family to be close to this school and, along with other highly educated individuals ("*maskilim*") such as David Yellin and Yehiel Michael Pines, Yermens participated in the establishment of the Zikhron Moshe neighborhood. In the ethnically mixed Abyssinian neighborhood many of the most gifted students who pursued advanced secular studies attended the Ezra Seminary. Among these older students of the seminary, Ticho and his nurses would find a relatively low incidence of trachoma.

Throughout Jerusalem – in Meah Shearim, Zikhron Moshe, the Abyssinian neighborhood, the Jewish Quarter of the Old City, and elsewhere – Ticho and his assistants undertook the daunting project of systematically treating trachoma in the schools. Their efforts were augmented by Feigenbaum of the Jewish Health Bureau, whose ardent Hebraism led him to adopt a hyphenated Hebrew-German surname, "Teëni-Feigenbaum" whose redundant parts both had the meaning of "fig." Two additional local physicians were engaged by the Trachoma Division of the Health Bureau for this work: the aforementioned ophthalmologist Dr. Miriam Neufach, and the private-practice EENT specialist Dr. Aryeh Shimoni-Mäkler (chapter 7) who had recently moved his offices out of the Hotel Kaminitz and a little farther down Jaffa Road.[20]

Ticho directed the daily treatment of children by Neufach and Shimoni-Mäkler in three of the thirty-one schools. In all, thousands of

Jewish children were treated in the schools. Those children with active trachoma were treated on a daily basis by the assistants while Ticho reexamined active cases at two-week intervals. Mass examinations were performed at three-month intervals. For their part in the "War against Trachoma," Ticho and his assistants visited different types of Jewish schools in Jerusalem that included several residential orphanages. Most, however, were day schools (and workshops), from which students returned to their homes every evening, and the unhygienic conditions perpetuated the infections.[21]

In August 1913, Ticho began to formally record observations and data about the mass school treatments as his part in the "War against Trachoma" (appendix 4). He used a medical record form that Feigenbaum instituted at the Jewish Health Bureau.[22] Ticho found that the highest incidences of trachoma were in the religious schools of the Old City, especially those of the Persians (82 percent) and the Yemenites (57 percent), where the children would sit on the ground or unfinished floors, two to four children learning from the same book. In the secular schools, where hygienic conditions were better, the incidences of trachoma were lower ("only" 25 to 30 percent), even though these institutions similarly drew students from "the poorest of the Sephardi, Yemenite, and Kurdish strata." Comparable differences were seen among Ashkenazi kindergarten students who showed twice the incidence of trachoma in the kindergartens of the Old City as compared to cleaner kindergartens elsewhere.[23]

Antibiotics would not be discovered for another quarter century and so in addition to promoting hygiene, Ticho and his assistants relied upon topical applications of caustics such as mercury bichloride ($HgCl_2$ or "Sublimate") that was not much more effective than copper sulfate.[24] In more stubborn cases they used aluminum acetate ("Lenicet").[25] As was the standard in those days, Ticho would also mechanically express conjunctival granules, using ointment to help the massaging and a bare or cotton wool-covered glass rod ("grattage"). Sometimes he would even use his own finger nails (Cuignet's method) in children afraid of the sight of surgical instruments. Surgical procedures sometimes consisted of a partial excision of the conjunctival fold that required ether anesthesia in younger children or topically applied dry cocaine and adrenaline solution in older children.[26]

One of Kaplan's first reports of their work under Ticho's supervision was read by Henrietta Szold at the Hadassah Chapter meeting in New York on September 8, and the following spring Kaplan reported their work to the American Nurses Association.[27] Referring to Ticho as the "oculist" and "specialist" who supervised their work, Kaplan stated, "The patients at each school are treated daily, and are reëxamined every two or three weeks. *All* the pupils (in this case not only the patients, but all the children) are reexamined every two months. In light cases, treatment lasts for three months. It takes a year or longer to cure an old case, of course sometimes they cannot be cured." The work of Ticho and his assistants became well known both in Europe and in America through the medical literature. Separate reports of Feigenbaum and Ticho appeared in German periodicals published in Berlin, and their papers were cited by prominent American ophthalmologists such as Drs. Casey Wood and Harry Friedenwald.[28]

In the years before World War I, Ticho and the nurses were able to cut the incidence of trachoma in the schools in half. Even though Ticho and his colleagues valiantly fought this battle in the "War against Trachoma" and could claim some success, it was the widespread improvements in hygiene and introduction of medicines such as sulfanilamide that later won the war.[29] As Ticho concluded, "I came to recognize that these people did not lack the will, the time, or the effort in order to be healed, if only they were made to understand the nature of the disease. And thus mass treatment of trachoma in a specified area will be found to be suitable among the local Jewish population, something that is also true from the viewpoint of the school; since the treatment will have lasting value only when the home and the family cease being a source of the infection."

Besides trachoma, other public health battles were simultaneously undertaken by the physicians in Jerusalem. During the early weeks of 1913, two deaths from rabies were reported in the city, deaths that would have been preventable if treatment with the standard series of rabies vaccines had been available. Bites of all stray animals were suspect and, in such cases, physicians advised immediate travel to Cairo for treatment.[30] The management of animal bites changed when Dr. Aryeh Beham arrived in Jerusalem to head a newly established Pasteur Institute. Beham had studied laboratory and tropical medicine in Hamburg, Germany. He had just been released from a Russian jail and expelled for Zionist activities.

After arriving in Jerusalem in early March, Dr. Beham was a key participant in organizing the Association of Hebrew-Speaking Physicians in Jerusalem (Agudat Rof'im Medabrei 'Ivrit), emulating the Association of Hebrew Physicians of Jaffa and Environs that had been established in January 1912. The founding of the association was an initiative of "four Aryehs" (Drs. Beham, Feigenbaum, Goldberg, Shimoni-Mäkler) plus Drs. Ze'ev Brünn and Miriam Neufach.[31] Ticho apparently initially resisted the founding of this association that seemed to separate itself from the larger medical community, and perhaps he was the particular physician who had protested that he was a "cosmopolitan." A contentious first meeting was followed later that month by an acceptable compromise, and the emphasis upon physician membership of "Hebrew-speakers" was hailed by Eliezer Ben-Yehudah. Notably, the Orthodox Dr. Moshe Wallach protested that he was "German" and he did not join until the group came to his defense in a case of alleged malpractice. Ticho's participation in Agudat Rof'im was evident the following spring when he would work with three other members on a committee in organizing a historic conference on trachoma in Jerusalem in cooperation with their colleagues in Jaffa and elsewhere in Palestine (chapter 9).[32]

In the summer of 1913, other conflicts were attracting more headlines in Jerusalem's newspapers than "wars" against various diseases. The Second Balkan War erupted when Bulgaria attacked its former allies, Serbia and Greece. Closer to home, escalating tensions between Arabs and Jews were also sowing the seeds of wars to come. In late July, there were reports of domestic skirmishes between the hired Shomerim (guards) of the Jewish Rehovot settlement and Arabs of the neighboring village of Zarnuqa. Accounts of the violence and the prolonged legal proceedings were perceived and reported differently in

Palestine's Hebrew- and Arabic-language newspapers.[33] Jewish writers like Dr. Shimon Moyal and his wife Esther had attempted to bridge this gap by translating anti-Zionist articles from Arabic into Hebrew and publishing their own conciliatory responses. Their friend Nissim Malul likewise advocated the development of close relationships and assimilation with Arabs, including learning the Arabic language. Ticho likely sympathized with Malul's contention that "national consciousness is achieved by activities, not by the language spoken by the people."[34]

Over the years, Ticho learned only enough Arabic to help him treat his Arab patients, though, as he had promised Eliezer Ben-Yehudah, he put more effort into learning to speak modern Hebrew. Even so, Ticho's personal, primary language was German, a language that was still competing with Hebrew among Zionists in Germany and in Palestine. Although not envisioned by Theodor Herzl, modern Hebrew was now poised to be incorporated as a "constitutive element" of mainstream Zionist ideology.

———◆———

Having lived in Jerusalem for over a year, Ticho regularly made his way all about the city to Jewish orphanages, schools, and workshops. Each of the secular day schools in the city were supported by one of three main Jewish philanthropic societies centered in Europe that aimed to safeguard the human rights of Jews around the world and to economically strengthen their communities: the Alliance Israélite Universelle (Kol Yisrael Ḥaverim), founded by French statesman Adolphe Crémieux in 1860; the Anglo-Jewish Association; and the Hilfsverein der deutschen Juden (Aid Society for German Jews, Ḥevrat Ezra shel Yehudei Germania, or "Ezra"), founded in Berlin in 1901 by Dr. Paul Nathan.[35] The prestigious Ezra Seminary was the flagship of the several schools run by the Hilfsverein that since 1910 had also included the Lämel School. Although the benefactors of these benevolent societies met their goals of helping fellow Jews in need, they sometimes viewed their support through the prism of the nationalistic and colonial aspirations of their respective homelands. At a local level in Palestine, this was expressed through the teaching of secular subjects in the language of the country from which the various schools' charitable endowments originated – France, England, and Germany. Ticho could speak French fluently with Alliance Principal Albert Antebi and his successor, or English with Miss Landau and her staff at the Evelina de Rothschild School. When he visited the Hilfsverein-run Ezra Seminary and the Lämel School, he was proud that the German language was increasingly being used for instruction of secular subjects.

By 1914, the Hilfsverein ran about thirty schools all over Palestine, ranging from kindergartens to two seminaries, one for teachers and one for rabbis.[36] The Hilfsverein was also planning to use German as the language of instruction at the Technion, a technical college that was being built on the slopes of Mt. Carmel in Haifa. Plans for the "Technikum" had been conceived by Paul Nathan and funded by large grants from Jacob Schiff of New York and heirs of Russian tea merchant Wolf Wissotzky. Zionist leaders outside of Germany such as Chaim Weizmann correctly surmised that the Kaiser's government was encouraging the Hilfsverein to Germanize instruction at the college, thereby making it "a *Stützpunkt* [point of support] of Germany in Palestine." Unlike the planned Technikum, the Hilfsverein schools were technically outside of consular protection as they had become officially recognized as Ottoman schools in 1913. Even so the German Consuls in Jerusalem, Haifa, and Jaffa, kept Berlin closely informed about developments in the "Language War."[37]

In June 1913, members of the senior class of the Ezra Seminary had been among the Jewish students of Jerusalem and Jaffa who sent a letter of protest about the use of German to the Board of Directors (Kuratorium) of the Technion that was dominated by non-Zionist Hilfsverein members.[38] This was one of the opening salvos of the "Language War" that would erupt into broader protests and strikes in the late fall of that year. One of the leaders among the students was twenty-three-year-old Eleazar Lipa Sukenik, a future archeologist who would later excavate the fields adjacent to Ticho's eye hospital in search of Jerusalem's Third Wall.[39]

At a meeting in Jaffa in August 1913, the Hebrew Teachers Association issued the following resolution: "The principles of national education demand that all subjects of instruction shall be taught in the Hebrew language, and this meeting pledges that the members of the Teachers Association will fight with all their energy against the teaching of secular subjects in a foreign language." Teachers and prospective students were called upon to boycott the Technion, and that fall the Lämel School in Jerusalem became a particular focal point in Palestine's "Language War." Since coming under the management of the Hilfsverein der Deutschen Juden in 1910, Principal Cohen-Reiss had acquiesced to the demands of the Hilfsverein for greater instruction in German and a de-emphasis of Hebrew for secular subjects. From the 1880s onward, much to the chagrin of Jerusalem's rabbis, the Lämel School had a long tradition of teaching secular subjects in Hebrew and presenting Hebrew language plays in its auditorium. Only the previous spring, Cohen-Reiss had enjoyed immense popularity and had been feted with great pomp and circumstance by the Jewish community on the occasion of his twenty-fifth anniversary as the director of the Lämel School, though Eliezer Ben-Yehudah bristled at the fact that children performed skits in German.[40]

On November 7, students from the Ezra Seminary and Ezra Vocational School demonstrated in the square of the Bukharan neighborhood against the Kuratorium's decision on language instruction at the Technikum. The rallies grew in size and the following week about one thousand people attended a rally in the field adjacent to Beit ha-'Am in the Zikhron Moshe neighborhood, where issues about the language of instruction at the Lämel School were added to the list of grievances. Here, Dr. Shimoni-Mäkler was given the honor of opening the speeches, and he emphasized two objectives of the large gathering: a declaration of protest and a proposal of means to meet the "evil" language policies of the Ezra.[41] Later at the same dais and now representing Jerusalem's Association of Hebrew-speaking Physicians, both Dr. Mäkler and Dr. Beham were among those who spoke.

The next few weeks brought a further escalation of the conflict. On December 10, 1913, students and teachers marched in protest through the streets of Jerusalem. After some windows were broken at the school, Cohen-Reiss called in the Turkish police to break up the demonstration.

The teachers and students went on a more prolonged strike. Most of the students and teachers went over to a newly established Hebrew Teachers Seminary (Beit Midrash la-Morim ha-'Ivri) while the Ezra Seminary was forced to close its doors.[42] The disruptions at the Ezra schools are reflected in Ticho's writings – the collection of trachoma data at these schools extend only through November 1913, while at almost all of the other schools the collection of data continued through January 1914.

The "Language War" continued into 1914 and the strikes, and the opening of Hebrew schools supported by the Teachers' Association began to have their effect. Pressure to adopt Hebrew in all spheres of education gained support from Jewish leaders around the world and sometimes from unexpected quarters. In February, aboard Baron Edmond de Rothschild's yacht in Haifa Harbor, Arthur Ruppin and the Sears and Roebuck magnate, Julius Rosenwald, discussed the matter in German and French. The two wealthy philanthropists allowed Ruppin to telegraph the Technion's Board in Berlin and add their voices in support of instruction in Hebrew. Later that month, the Technion's Board offered a compromise – it would begin instruction in Hebrew immediately in some fields, and by the end of four years the remaining subjects would also be taught in Hebrew. Modern Hebrew language emerged triumphant throughout the Jewish public schools of Palestine.[43]

Around this time, Ticho began to prepare a manuscript for submission, his first published medical article. Written in German, the paper would be presented first in its original German to a group of his colleagues in Jerusalem in April 1914, and it would be published in Berlin in November 1914 (chapter 9).[44] Although the paper was read in German and first published in German, Ticho's colleagues Teëni-Feigenbaum and Shimoni-Mäkler would see to it that it would also be published in Hebrew. Although Ticho was a somewhat reluctant soldier in the "Language War," his contribution became part of a milestone publication, the first modern medical book published in Hebrew.

CHAPTER 9

MARCH–AUGUST 1914
THE EVE OF WAR

הבאת אל-אצרות שלג ואצרות ברד תראה.
אשר-חשכתי לעת-צר ליום קרב ומלחמה.

Have you entered the storehouses of snow,
Or seen the storehouses of hail,
Which I have put aside for times of trouble,
For a day of war and battle?

Job 38:22–23

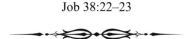

During his frequent visits to schools in the Old City, Ticho would often stop at the Austrian Post Office located just inside the Jaffa Gate and opposite the Citadel.[1] It was the oldest of the foreign post offices in Jerusalem, first established in the Armenian Quarter in 1853 and moved near the Jaffa Gate in 1859, just off the commercial Sueikat 'Allan street leading to David's Street. Looking up above the entryways of the two-story post-office building with its small central balcony, there was signage across the façade in Italian and French as well as German, while below there was a rectangular veranda enclosed by a railing that stood several feet above the sloping street. The German-language newspapers that Ticho received through the Austrian post enabled him to stay in touch with world events, and he would correspond with friends and family in Europe who still lived in the corridor between the

Austrian capital and his hometown, Vienna, where his older sister Sarah was busy with seven children and where two older brothers Josef and Max were both practicing law; Brno where brothers Jacob, David, and Heinrich ran the A. J. Ticho business; and the town of Boskovice where his father Ignatz still lived and where younger brothers Nathan and Paul were establishing their own clothing business.[2]

Just outside the Old City along Jaffa Road, the German and French Post Offices were housed in more modest buildings that had each opened in 1900. The German Post Office was the closer of the two, only about a hundred yards away from the Jaffa Gate. In order to send personal letters to family or acquaintances and reports back to Frankfurt am Main, Ticho could use one of several foreign post mailboxes that were fixed to the walls on Jerusalem's main streets. After many years of uninterrupted service, these mailboxes would be replaced with Turkish-only mailboxes, in October 1914 (chapter 10).[3]

In the late winter of 1914, mail through the Austrian postal service included a photographic postcard from Venice that showed his brother Josef and bride Elsa (née Herzog) feeding pigeons in Saint Peter's square on their honeymoon. Albert and Anna had traveled to Europe for the wedding and likely joined the newlyweds and other siblings on holiday in Venice. It was good to see that Josef was happy and that Elsa seemed such a suitable match. She had a solid middle-class background coming from an affluent family involved in buying and selling antiques. While the Tichos were abroad for their brief trip, the Lemaan Zion Eye Hospital was staffed by Drs. Aryeh Feigenbaum and Aryeh Shimoni-Mäkler. Meanwhile the local committee, comprised of Mordecai Adelman, Rabbi David Feinstein, and Rabbi Yosef Gershon Horwitz, published announcements soliciting financial support of the institution. Fundraising efforts continued through the spring.[4]

Upon their return from Europe, Ticho also received a letter in excellent German from a well-known American ophthalmologist and Zionist, Dr. Harry Friedenwald, who hoped to visit Ticho as part of a working tour in the late spring.[5] Ticho wrote back that he would be happy to provide a place for Friedenwald to work and study at his eye hospital and that he would also look forward to entertaining his family socially.

Later that spring, after a busy day of work in his clinic, Albert
Ticho set out from Lemaan Zion for an early evening walk to the
Jewish Health Bureau. At Dr. Ze'ev Brünn's request, Ticho had
agreed to cohost a conference on trachoma in Jerusalem that would
be open to all of the country's Jewish physicians. The original idea
for this conference had been proposed in 1913 by Dr. Elias Auerbach
of Haifa in a weekly German medical journal. The support of Ticho
and Jerusalem's Association of Hebrew-speaking Physicians prompted
Brünn to send out a preliminary announcement to Jewish physicians
throughout the country and the response had been very positive. Ticho
was a member of the official organizing committee along with three
physicians from the Health Bureau: Drs. Brünn, Shimoni-Mäkler, and
Teëni-Feigenbaum.[6] The committee meetings apparently took place at
the Jewish Health Bureau that was perhaps still located at that time on
Abyssinian Street (chapter 7). Among the stately homes and institutions
here, the Jewish Health Bureau was performing the important public
health role that Nathan Straus had envisioned for it. The building also
housed the Germans' International Health Bureau, with whom relations
were more than a bit strained. Since the previous summer, space had
also been provided for Dr. Aryeh Beham, who directed Jerusalem's
new Pasteur Institute, and since that time at least five lives had been
saved in documented cases of rabies infection. As Ticho arrived at the
Jewish Health Bureau, he could look at the nearby home of Eliezer
Ben-Yehudah whom he had visited during his first days in Jerusalem.[7]

During the committee meeting, a date for the historic three-
day conference in Jerusalem was set for Tuesday, March 31, 1914,
through Thursday, April 2, 1914, therefore ending nine days before the
beginning of Passover. Although the official language of the conference
was to be Hebrew, presentations could be given in foreign languages,
most notably German. Therefore plans were made to have secretaries
for both Hebrew and foreign languages. The organizers planned for the
first and last day of the conference to take place at the Jewish Health
Bureau, while the middle day (Wednesday, April 1) would take place
at Lemaan Zion, and the afternoon session there would include surgical
demonstrations by Drs. Ticho and Teëni-Feigenbaum. In just a few

months, twenty-four physicians would convene in Jerusalem for the historic meeting, brought together by two nascent physician groups and two medical institutions (the Jewish Health Bureau and Lemaan Zion). Such conferences would someday be commonplace in Jerusalem, but this conference was the first of its kind in Palestine. The two physician organizations of Jaffa and Jerusalem would eventually merge and one day evolve into the Israel Medical Association. Educational activities of the societies – of the Health Bureau and the Hadassah organization – would be carried forward by major universities.

In keeping with the aspirations of the medical societies and the Health Bureau, the Zionists were steadily moving closer to their dream of a Hebrew University that was first launched in 1901 when the Fifth Zionist Congress in Basel passed a resolution in favor of the project. In the summer of 1913, the Zionist Congress in Vienna had authorized the formation of a commission for the founding of the Hebrew University with Dr. Chaim Weizmann as its head.[8] That fall, one of the first advocates for locating the university on Mount Scopus was Nahum Shimkin, a Zionist leader and ophthalmologist of Odessa. In early 1914, Zionist leaders and only a few land developers learned that a choice piece of land on Scopus – very suitable for a university – was available for purchase.[9]

—◆—

The Jewish holiday of Purim that year marked two anniversaries for Hadassah and for the two nurses that the American organization had sent to Jerusalem – two years since the organization's inaugural meeting at Temple Emanu-El in Manhattan and just one year since Kaplan and Landy opened the doors of the Hadassah Nurses' Settlement to patients in Jerusalem. A professional milestone for Hadassah would be recorded for posterity when Kaplan's report on their work in Jerusalem was read in St. Louis the following month at the Annual Convention of the American Nurses' Association.[10]

As the Orthodox neighborhood of Meah Shearim observed the day before Purim with the traditional Fast of Esther, Arthur Ruppin was celebrating a day or two early. On that day (March 11, 1914), Ruppin signed an agreement to purchase the Mount Scopus estate of Sir John Gray Hill on behalf of the Board of the Hebrew University. Negotiations had commenced in earnest with the seventy-five-year-old Gray Hill a few weeks earlier through the aspiring land developer Benjamin Ibry. With Gray Hill's return to England, the provisional negotiations were concluded between Ruppin and Gray Hill's nephew, Sir Arthur Norman Hill. In the midst of the war, the property in the end came into the Zionists' hands through the beneficence of the Jewish-Russian philanthropist, Yitzhak Leib Goldberg.[11]

With a possible foothold on Mount Scopus the Zionists looked to a bright future, but they also went looking for their ancient roots in and around the Old City. At this same time, archeological excavations were being undertaken on the southeastern spur of land adjacent to the Ottoman Old City walls, known as the Ophel. It was land that Baron Edmond de Rothschild had privately purchased four years earlier. Baron de Rothschild engaged Jewish-French Egyptologist Raymond-Charles Weill to excavate the site. His archeological campaign of 1912–13 marked the first time that a Jewish archeologist had conducted such work in Palestine under Jewish patronage.[12]

The Zionist movement regarded the Bible as "the most important source book in the process of national revival," and art was another means of depicting an ancient narrative that showed a connection between the Jewish people and the land.[13] Boris Schatz, founder of the Bezalel School, had invited the well-known painter and journal illustrator Abel Pann from Paris to teach, and drawing upon authentic local colors the artist produced the first of many biblical scenes in his paintings and pastel drawings. Pann probably had an influence upon at least one of Anna Ticho's paintings, a watercolor portrait of a Jerusalem boy, signed and dated 1917. The work preceded the conquest of Jerusalem by the British and predates sketchbooks that were produced later during the Tichos' wartime sojourn in Damascus (chapter 14).[14]

Many Arab writers and leaders viewed the Zionists' use of archeology and art as propaganda, pure and simple – further tools to help the Jews disenfranchise and displace fellahin from their land. But at that time some Arab notables such as Mayor Hussein Salim al-Husayni expressed more moderate views. In March 1914, perhaps with individuals such as the relatively apolitical Albert Ticho in mind, al-Husayni offered these moderate impressions of Zionists in the Egyptian press: "I am certain that the idea of founding a Jewish state in Palestine does not occur to any reasonable and rational Zionist, as people say. The Zionists come to this country to live. They are educated, cultured people; they do not inflate their importance and they are united amongst themselves. It is not just or humane that we should hate or despise this people. On the contrary, we should imitate them and learn from their activities, which can give us a good and appropriate lesson...." However, he went on to say that "despite all this, we must keep an open eye on them, for if we continue in our way and they in theirs, then all our lands will pass into their possession.... Our fellah is poor and impoverished, and the poor man is liable to surrender his land to keep himself alive. Therefore, the Government must pass a new law concerning the sale of land in Palestine, setting up known conditions and limiting them according to our position in the country."[15] Meanwhile Ticho continued to see increasing numbers of Arab patients in his practice, from the fellahin of the countryside to members of the *a'ayan*, the notable urban Muslim families such as the Husaynis.

As Ticho and his colleagues on the organizing committee prepared for their conference, Jerusalem was in a run-up for elections to the Ottoman Parliament and the Municipal Council. However, all of the members of the committee were Ashkenazi Jews who, as part of the Second Aliyah, had just recently immigrated to Palestine from Central and Eastern Europe. None of them were Ottoman citizens, and they were therefore still foreigners in their adopted country. Raghib al-Nashashibi, from Jerusalem, the leading candidate for the Parliament, declared, "If I am elected as representative I shall devote all my strength, day and night, to doing away with the threat of the Zionists and Zionism." The more moderate Mayor of Jerusalem, Hussein Salim al-Husayni, who had succeeded his father to the position in 1910, had the support of the city's Jewish voters.[16]

In January, an editorial in the Sefardi newspaper *Ha-Herut* noted the mayor's efforts to provide lighted and clean streets and described him as a "wise, intelligent, and progressive man and a lover of Israel." The writer went on to say, "If Hussein al-Husayni will remain in office, there is no doubt that he will try to introduce further important improvements for the good of the city and its enhancement."[17] Though it would not come to pass under al-Husayni's next and last term of office, there were plans for further electrification of the city and the construction of a streetcar line running southward toward Bethlehem.

On March 31, 1914, the same day that Mayor al-Husayni's comments were published in *Ha-Ḥerut*, the city of Jerusalem hosted the first medical conference to draw participants from several different areas of Palestine. That Tuesday morning, the opening session of the First Trachoma Conference of Hebrew Physicians of Eretz Yisrael took place at the Jewish Health Bureau (appendix 5). Ze'ev Brünn welcomed twenty-four physicians (twenty-one men and three women) and also local teachers and principals who had been invited as guests. Fifteen of the physicians were from Jerusalem, six from Jaffa-Tel Aviv, and one each from Rehovot, Yavne'el, and America. The latter, Dr. Israel Biskind, was in the process of immigrating to Palestine and his "temporary" return to Cleveland, Ohio, after the conference would be lengthened to a period of four years due to the outbreak of World War I. These physicians represented approximately half of the total number of Jewish physicians in Palestine at that time. Several physicians who could not attend sent letters or telegrams, including Dr. Auerbach, who had first proposed the idea of the conference, as well as Dr. Eliakum Waizbard of Rishon le-Zion, Dr. Hillel Yaffe of Zikhron Ya'akov, and Dr. Eliyahu Cohen of Safed.[18]

After opening the meeting in the name of the organizing committee, Brünn asked for a vote of acclamation to elect Dr. Aryeh Pouchovsky of Tel Aviv as chairman of the conference and Dr. Aharon Mazie as vice-chairman. Drs. Aryeh Shimoni-Mäkler and Jacob Segal were elected as secretaries for Hebrew (the official language of the conference) while Drs. Aryeh Leib Goldberg and (Avraham Zvi) Herman Moscovitz of Jaffa were elected as secretaries for foreign languages.[19] The three-day conference was divided into morning and afternoon sessions for a total of six sessions.

The presentations on the first day ended with Dr. Hillel Yaffe's paper on the treatment of trachoma by lower-level medical assistants, presented in abstentia by Dr. Segal. In the discussion period, Ticho pointedly stated, "Only specialist nurses are qualified to be assistants to a doctor [in the treatment of trachoma]. We use [lesser trained helpers] only in emergencies in all of the varied, personal ways that the lecturer suggests." Ticho also raised some criticism in another discussion period following Dr. Mazie's paper, stating, "The lecturer blames dust as the means of transmission of the infection. It is impossible to agree with this opinion, since dust is only capable of causing inflammation, but it is not a reason for [gonococcal-type] microbial infection."[20] The afternoon session closed with microscopic demonstrations by Drs. Goldberg and Teëni-Feigenbaum that illustrated the different bacterial forms seen in the various eye infections, including the intracellular Prowazek-Halberstädter bodies of trachoma.

That evening, the participants of the conference and their spouses met at 8:30 p.m. in the beautiful and spacious hall of Jerusalem's "Shulamit" Conservatory of Music on Abyssinian Street. Like its sister institution in Tel Aviv, the school had been named in memory of its founder, Shulamit Ruppin (chapter 9). The Tichos took the short carriage ride to the conservatory from their residence at Lemaan Zion in the direction of the Italian Hospital that was still under construction.[21] Just past the Italian Hospital, their carriage turned onto the so-called Back Road, also known as the Street of the Consuls even though various consulates had moved away (including the American consulate, under Rev. Dr. Otis Glazebrook).[22] On the Back Road, the Tichos' carriage passed a field to the right where just about fifteen years earlier, the visiting Kaiser Wilhelm II and his entourage had temporarily erected a large encampment of tents.[23] Beyond this to the right was a parsonage for the head of the German Protestant community, the new German secondary school, and the Jewish Weingarten Orphanage. To the left on the south side of the Back Road was the School for the Blind that was founded in 1902 by the writer and publisher Avraham Moshe Luncz, who had himself suffered blindness at the age of twenty-three. Next door to the School for the Blind was the Rothschild Hospital that had moved to this location from the Old City in 1888, the first Jewish hospital in Jerusalem to be established outside the city walls.[24]

At the conservatory, nurses of the Jewish Health Bureau handled the tickets and they collected the admission charge of two and a half francs per person. With a picture of the school's founder, Shulamit Ruppin, hanging upon the wall in the hall, the conference attendees and guests were entertained with performances of song, violin, and piano. In particular, the conference proceedings later noted a fine song by the director of the conservatory, Mr. Sakhna'i.[25]

The second day of the conference (April 1, 1914) was held at the Lemaan Zion Eye Hospital, and only Ticho and Teëni-Feigenbaum presented lectures and surgical demonstrations that day. In the morning, Teëni-Feigenbaum presented his methods of diagnosing and recording statistical data based upon his forms, which Ticho had also adopted. Then Ticho presented a lecture entitled "The Course of Trachoma and Its Treatment." Following a luncheon that was supervised by Ticho's mother-in-law, the afternoon session consisted of several surgical demonstrations, also by Ticho and Teëni-Feigenbaum (appendix 5). That evening, the physicians gathered to discuss the idea of founding a general association of physicians throughout Palestine and the first steps to take vis-à-vis the matter of the government's approval. There seems to have been a formal, concurrent meeting of Jerusalem's Association of Hebrew-speaking Physicians. One of Ticho's suggestions at this meeting was to establish in cities one or even a few kindergartens that were entirely free of trachoma.[26]

On Thursday, April 2, 1914, Brünn opened the final day of the conference at the Jewish Health Bureau with a lecture entitled "The Organization of the War against Trachoma." He cited the studies of Teëni-Feigenbaum in Jerusalem and drew comparisons with those of Dr. Hermann Kuhnt in Prussia, and another study of a network of tent hospitals in Egypt.[27] Ticho was the first to comment on Brünn's paper, stating, "Experience shows that it is impossible to force every school to conduct a systematic treatment of their students. Here in Jerusalem, for example, there are religious schools that don't want this. In regard to the question of removal of sick students, it is necessary to direct the teachers to send home any children that have secretion of pus; after some days, when the secretion ceases, it is possible to permit them to return. In my opinion, the lecturer's suggestion to fix the principles of treatment is very important, since most of the treatment of trachoma is in the hands of a physician but is often given over to a paramedic. I also support his suggestion to establish education about trachoma."[28] Dr. Hannah Waitz, the first woman physician to practice in Palestine (though she was then retired), was among the other discussants that followed Ticho.[29]

Following Brünn's paper and the discussion of it, Ticho next presented the paper that summarized his own experience treating trachoma in the schools of Jerusalem, which he had undertaken at the behest of the Daughters of Zion organization and had been accomplished mainly through his supervision of Nurses Kaplan and Landy (appendix 4). Ticho stated that daily treatments of trachoma patients by a physician would be much better, but he emphasized that intelligent and well-trained nurses could be entrusted to daily treatment under supervision of a doctor. That afternoon, after Dr. Pouchovsky formally closed the conference proceedings, Ticho spoke on behalf of the participants thanking the chairmen and the secretaries for "their adroit and successful handling of the proceedings of the conference." Dr. Mazie then offered words of encouragement, stating, "Allow me, honored colleagues, a little side discussion. You may be equivocating lest your work in the conference and your efforts in the future toward eradicating trachoma serve to increase emigration from Palestine to America. However, we greatly trust that trachoma is not our only connection to the land. And I say to you, go with this wisdom and bring blessing to the Yishuv [the Jewish settlement]."[30]

That night, Albert and Anna made their way to the Old City to attend a "parting banquet" for the conference at the Amdursky (Central) Hotel, located just inside the Jaffa Gate opposite the Citadel. The owner, thirty-seven-year-old Yerahmiel Amdursky, had followed his father, Yosef, into the hotel business and moved the hotel to this site after his father's death in 1895.[31] As recorded in the proceedings, "Spirits were merry and at times festive. Warm words were spoken and they raised a glass for the success of the War against Trachoma and to Jewish scientific breakthroughs. There was no lack of jokes and jovial school songs. At a late hour in the night, the colleagues departed from one another with hearts full of mutual hopes and blessings that they would be able to participate in the [future] Second Trachoma Conference." Sometime during the conference, an iconic photograph was taken for posterity that included twenty of the twenty-four participants of the First Trachoma Conference.[32]

Ticho would have the opportunity to welcome other visitors to Lemaan Zion in the spring of 1914. As the First Trachoma Conference was concluding on April 2, American Ambassador Henry Morgenthau was arriving in Jaffa Harbor and American Vice-Consul Samuel Edelman had gone out into the harbor to personally greet Morgenthau aboard his ship. Although Morgenthau was not a Zionist, he took an interest in visiting several *moshavot* ("colonies") with Arthur Ruppin, who respectfully greeted Morgenthau at the quay. Escorted by Edelman and Ruppin, Ambassador Henry Morgenthau took a tour of Jerusalem that included visits to several hospitals and schools. As recorded in his diaries, Morgenthau visited Miss Landau at the Evelina de Rothschild School and then Lemaan Zion on Monday, April 6. Further details of his visit with Ticho have not been discovered. Later that week on Thursday, just before Morgenthau's departure from Jerusalem, Adelman brought the ambassador for a visit to the B'nai B'rith Lodge, where a record number of thirty-five members had convened.[33]

American support for the Jewish community in Palestine was becoming increasingly important. Lobbying efforts were led by both Zionist and non-Zionist Americans, both Jews and Christians. The immediate pre-war period was a very optimistic time for Ticho and the medical community in Jerusalem. Soon after the conclusion of the trachoma conference, Ticho received correspondence from Henrietta Szold who had been making plans for sending a third nurse to Palestine and for the establishment of a training school for nurses. Nathan Straus had offered further aid. Szold wrote to Ticho that she had plans for a maternity hospital with a social service department. This new phenomenon of "American Orientalism" would become critical to the survival of the Yishuv during World War I.[34]

On June 22, 1914, Ticho welcomed Dr. Harry Friedenwald of Baltimore to the Lemaan Zion Eye Hospital. Although the two ophthalmologists had corresponded by mail, this was their first personal meeting as Friedenwald's first visit to Palestine three years earlier had preceded Ticho's arrival. Just three weeks earlier, Friedenwald had departed from America with his wife, Birdie, and their seventeen-year-old son, Jonas, aboard the S.S. *Moltke*. Their first stop in the Near East was Egypt, where they toured the pyramids and visited with ophthalmologist Dr. Max Meyerhof, who had written extensively about eye infections. Ostensibly the family's tour of Egypt and Palestine was a family "vacation," but Friedenwald's plans were closely connected to Zionism and ophthalmology. He privately hoped to reinforce his son Jonas's interest in both Zionism and medicine, and his son fulfilled these hopes in both areas, becoming a distinguished professor of ophthalmology at Johns Hopkins while maintaining a life-long support of Zionism.[35] In addition to social activities and meetings with Jewish leaders, Friedenwald's busy itinerary included clinical and surgical work and the study of endemic eye infections. Through the State Department and Ambassador Morgenthau, Friedenwald had been assured that, although it would be impossible to obtain a medical license, the Turkish authorities would not oppose his short-term practice in Palestine for humanitarian purposes.

Friedenwald spent the last week of June in Jerusalem examining cases at Lemaan Zion and assisting Ticho in surgery, while also finding time to visit other institutions in the city, such as the British Ophthalmic Hospital directed by Drs. Heron and Thomson. Ticho took his visiting American guest to several schools where they could corroborate Ticho's findings that the highest prevalence of the earlier stages of trachoma was seen in the youngest students. Friedenwald was also introduced to Nurses Kaplan and Landy, and he was especially pleased that he had advised his longtime friend Henrietta Szold to adopt their mission as Hadassah's first specific project. As he wrote to Szold, "I feel sure in stating that the work done in combating trachoma under the excellent supervision of Dr. Ticho is of great value, that the nurses you have sent to Jerusalem have done good work, and that you have reason to be satisfied that you sent them...the example of excellent and conscientious and intelligent service is also not to be underestimated."[36]

While Friedenwald was still spending time with Ticho in his clinic, news arrived in Jerusalem of the assassination of Archduke Franz Ferdinand and his wife, Sofie, in Sarajevo on June 28 by the Bosnian Serb nationalist Gavrilo Princip. The Archduke had unwisely chosen a solemn anniversary day for his visit, one that the Serbs had observed for over five centuries – their historic defeat by the Turks at the Battle of Kosovo. Immediately following the assassination, a tense peace momentarily prevailed in Europe, and in Palestine life went on as usual.[37] The Friedenwalds left Jerusalem in early July for the Palestinian countryside, the doctor undertaking similar work and studies of trachoma in Rehovot, Haifa, Safed, and Tiberias. Ticho, however, continued to work in his clinic, drawing patients from throughout Palestine..[38] After about a three-week working tour, Dr. Friedenwald returned to Jerusalem to organize his data and again work at Lemaan Zion.

The following year, Friedenwald summarized his medical work and observations in a paper presented to the American Ophthalmological Society that included statistical data on trachoma from Jerusalem and the other cities and settlements that he had visited.[39] He gave detailed synopses of the papers that Ticho and Feigenbaum had presented at the trachoma conference in April 1914 and expressed his gratitude to Ticho and other physicians with whom he had worked and who had assisted him in his research. Friedenwald reported that (excluding his work in Jerusalem) he had performed over two thousand eye examinations, half of them in schoolchildren, finding a 54 percent incidence of active or terminated trachoma. Friedenwald also noted, "The trachoma work of Dr. Ticho and Dr. Feigenbaum in Jerusalem has been helped in no small measure by means furnished from America, but especially by the intelligence and devotion of American graduate nurses sent to Jerusalem and maintained there by the Hadassah Society...."

On August 1, 1914, after a pleasant and restful Sabbath afternoon together, Ticho and Friedenwald walked to the Wailing Wall in the Old City, now more often called the Western Wall (Kotel ha-Ma'aravi, or simply the Kotel). With them were Friedenwald's son, Jonas, Nurses

Rose Kaplan and Rachel Landy, and Dr. Jacob Segal. Together they reached the Kotel, part of the retaining wall of the ancient Second Temple and thus the holiest accessible site to religiously observant Jews. As darkness fell, Ticho and his party lingered at the holy site while a crowd began to gather. A traditional day of mourning and fasting had begun known as Tish'a B'Av (the ninth day of the month of Av).[40] Now in front of the Kotel, a number of elderly Jews sat on the ground reading prayers by the light of small candles and lamps. Jewish watchmen (*shomrim*) stood behind them on guard. The observance of this fast had been established in ancient times to mark five calamities in the history of the Jewish people including the destructions of both Temples 656 years apart.[41] The moon was bright that night as Ticho and his group listened to the plaintive notes of the poetic lamentations (*kinot*), among them a mournful poem that recalled ten martyred rabbis who were tortured and executed by the Romans.

This year, Tish'a B'Av marked the beginning of another major crisis for the Jews in the Holy Land. Three days earlier, Austria-Hungary had declared war against Serbia, but on Tish'a B'Av the conflict broadened when Germany declared war on Russia and prepared to invade the lowlands en route to Paris. For this reason, August 1, 1914, would be remembered as the "official" date that World War I began. Within three more days, France and Great Britain were at war with Germany and Austria-Hungary.[42] The First World War would again bring severe suffering to the Jews of Palestine – mass expulsions, starvation, and deaths.

In Europe, there were many who greeted the news of war enthusiastically. Adolf Hitler wrote, "Even today, I am not ashamed to say that, overpowered by stormy enthusiasm, I fell down upon my knees and thanked Heaven from an overflowing heart for granting me the good fortune of being permitted to live at this time."[43] On August 1, 1914, Hitler joined a huge crowd in a main public plaza in Munich to celebrate the German proclamation of war, and two days later he enlisted in a Bavarian regiment of the German Army. During the war that followed, Ticho would come face to face with another infamous oppressor of the Jews, the cruel and ruthless Turkish general, Cemal Paşa.

During the weeks prior to the outbreak of war, Ticho had made one of his periodic visits to the Weingarten Orphanage. Just next door, inscribed high upon the lintels of the German parsonage, Ticho could read the German Gothic inscription, *"Wünschet Jerusalem Glück."* Ticho likely recognized this verse from Psalms (122:6) that has been translated into many languages from the original Hebrew: *"Sha'alu shalom Yerushalayim"* (Pray for the peace of Jerusalem). Now a war of worldwide scope would first bring war and misery to Jerusalem and, in its wake, a new geo-political world order.

CHAPTER 10

AUGUST–DECEMBER 1914
MOBILIZATION

...החלצו מאתכם אנשים לצבא

Let men be picked out from among you for a campaign...

Numbers 31:3

As Ticho said farewell to the Friedenwalds on Monday, August 3, 1914, the outbreak of war was already disrupting life in Jerusalem. Leaving their hotel early that day, the Friedenwalds had to make their way to the train station on foot while their baggage was carried by porters. The Turks had already commandeered horses, camels, donkeys, and mules, and throughout the city Ticho would find carriages with empty harnesses standing in the middle of the streets where the Turks had left them. In Jaffa, the Friedenwalds found that almost all of the ships had stopped sailing, but with Arthur Ruppin's help they changed their booking for a French ship bound for Marseilles and continued home over a far more circuitous route than planned.[1]

Although Turkey was not yet at war, it had quickly announced a general mobilization throughout Anatolia, Syria, and Palestine. On August 5, a special edition of Ben-Yehudah's newspaper *Ha-Or* carried a notice of the days that week on which all male Ottoman citizens between twenty-three and thirty-three years of age were to report for military service. There was an outward appearance of neutrality in this

115

mobilization, but three days earlier a secret Treaty of Alliance between Germany and Turkey had already been signed in Istanbul. While the Ottoman empire remained officially neutral for another three months, five European empires were now at war.[2]

Foreign banks operating in Jerusalem, among them the Deutsch Palästina Bank that handled accounts for the Lemaan Zion Eye Hospital, tried to calm the fears of the city's residents. Beginning on August 6, Deutsch Palästina, along with the Anglo-Palestine Company and Crédit Lyonnais, took out reassuring ads in *Ha-Or* and *Ha-Ḥerut*. In spite of the reassuring ads, there was a scarcity of money, and as a precaution Dr. David Heron at the British Ophthalmic Hospital stopped admitting inpatients on August 9. As it turned out, virtually all of the foreign banks would stop functioning by the end of the month. Compounding the banking crisis that affected all segments of the economy, reduced shipping traffic and hoarding resulted in a scarcity of necessary goods. On September 6, Dr. Heron telegraphed the Chancery of the Order in London reporting that the British Ophthalmic Hospital was without funds.[3] With the disruption of traditional sources of European aid and, foreseeing impending economic disaster, Arthur Ruppin also sent desperate cables requesting aid. His calls were echoed by American Consul Dr. Otis Glazebrook and the American Ambassador in Istanbul, Henry Morgenthau. Through the U.S. State Department and the organizing efforts of American Jews led by Louis D. Brandeis and others, supplies and much needed funds in gold reached Palestine beginning in early October. As the war went on and conditions worsened, a total of thirteen American warships came to Palestine with aid. This aid, and other donations to individuals and institutions, enabled the Jewish community in Palestine to survive.[4]

To combat the spreading of famine among Jerusalem's population, an organization was founded called Meḥayeh (Revivification) that raised funds locally for its food kitchens (*batei tavshil*). Ticho's name did not appear on the lists of contributors, but he was very generous that year in providing winter jackets for soldiers. Food was also distributed to up to four hundred persons daily at so-called Bread and Tea Houses. The leaders of the Eitz Ḥayim schools in Mahane Yehuda, Rabbi Ze'ev Wolf

Shachor and Rabbi Yehiel Michel Tykocinski, established the Bread and Tea House in Mahane Yehuda, and their daily presence there helped reduce the embarrassment of poor and hungry people that depended on charity for sustenance.[5] The cost of providing a month's food for thirty persons was estimated at about 200 francs. Ticho continued his *pro bono* work, but as the economy deteriorated his operation of the Lemaan Zion Eye Hospital, always especially busy in the summertime, was becoming more and more challenging.

The Ottoman government in Istanbul rotated its provincial civil servants and military commanders frequently, and so Ticho had already seen several of these men come and go since his arrival. In August 1914, Jerusalem's governor was Majidi Shevket Bey and the local military commander was Zakey Bey, the latter being a liberally minded man who was favorably inclined to the Jews. It was said that Zakey Bey was of Jewish ancestry, a member of the Dönme (a Turkish word, meaning convert), Muslim followers of the seventeenth-century false messiah and apostate Shabbatai Zevi, who for generations had secretly continued Jewish observances. Most of the Turkish leaders in Palestine reflected Istanbul's unannounced preference for the Germans, but Zakey Bey seemed to maintain a more neutral stance. During the run-up to Turkey's entry into the war, he was said to convey "an atmosphere of tranquility and assurance" to Jerusalem's residents.

In mid-August, Zakey Bey called upon all Jerusalemites to unite, regardless of nationality and religious beliefs, in order to cope with the crisis that the city was facing.[6] A few weeks later, he cordially received a delegation of leaders of a proposed Jerusalem Merchants Association (David Yellin, Albert Antebi, and Avraham Yehezkel Blum), and he supported this association that pledged to provide food and support for all residents of the city regardless of ethnicity and race. Zakey Bey's favorable attitude toward the Jews was also demonstrated when he approached Arthur Ruppin with an offer to sell the Moroccan Quarter adjacent to the Kotel for a sum of £20,000, which the Jews however could not afford at the time. It was proposed that the money from the sale could be used to relocate the Muslim families and create a public garden in front of the Wall.[7]

With the outbreak of the war, Ticho was called for service in the Austrian Army but Zakey Bey and leaders of all of the communities in the city prevailed upon the Austrian consul to allow Ticho to remain in Jerusalem. The evidence generally supports the belief that Ticho received a reservist or consultant's appointment in Jerusalem and that an active commission was received only after his forced evacuation to Damascus in December 1917. A letter in Ticho's own handwriting from Damascus dated December 31, 1917, indicates that he was assisting the Austrian medical corps as a civilian but that he would likely soon receive his commission. While Ticho treated several soldiers at Lemaan Zion, his wartime practice in Jerusalem was overwhelmingly devoted to civilian patients. However, a photograph dated April 1917 shows Ticho in military uniform among a group of fifteen Austrian soldiers who appear to be on a sociable hike out into the hillside country (chapter 13).[8]

Although Ticho had received a special dispensation to remain at his work in Jerusalem, the prospect of military mobilization loomed over most of his colleagues. A warning had been published that reminded all physicians and pharmacists that they were obligated to active military service, and they should report without delay to receive their commissions as army captains and first lieutenants, respectively. The reminder ended with the words, "Brothers, beware of your souls." The published warning took on an added meaning for Ticho when, in mid-September 1914, Istanbul announced its decision to cancel the capitulations effective October 1.[9] Foreign citizens would no longer enjoy the extra-territorial protection of their consulates, and eventually many Jews in Palestine considered either applying for Turkish citizenship ("Ottomanization") or leaving Palestine, perhaps entailing military service in their countries of origin. The inhabitants of Jerusalem tended to take the news of the cancellation of the capitulations in stride as compared to other parts of the Ottoman Empire. On Saturday September 12, Majidi Bey and Zakey Bey both sought to reassure the populace with combined celebrations of the Sultan's birthday and the abrogation of the capitulations.[10] Leading citizens were invited to a reception by the governor at the municipal building and then most went on to a late-morning feast with Zakey Bey at the military residence. At three in the afternoon, formal celebrations commenced at the public garden on Jaffa Road.

———◆———

As troops were rapidly mobilizing in Europe and somewhat more slowly in the Ottoman Empire, twenty-one-year-old Alfred Ticho, the youngest of the ten Ticho brothers, arrived in Palestine.[11] When the war broke out, Alfred was on summer vacation from the University of Vienna, where he was studying agronomy, and was making his way to Jerusalem. His timing and choice of vessels was apparently good, as the family stories reflect no detours or delays in his journey. Like Alfred Ticho, David Ben-Gurion and Yitzhak Ben-Zvi (the "Benim") were also on vacation at this time from studies in Istanbul, and they were likewise en route to Palestine when the war broke out. Unlike Alfred, the Benim were detoured to Alexandria, then detained off-shore in Jaffa harbor, and only after sailing to Beirut could they make their way back to Jaffa and then Jerusalem.[12]

Much in the spirit of the Zionist Workers Movement, Alfred Ticho had come to Palestine ostensibly to tour agricultural settlements and to plan his immigration, though the outbreak of the war would delay this for another two years. More than any of the Ticho siblings, Alfred had shown a love of Zionism from an early age. He had been an active member of the Maccabi Jewish youth organization that stressed vigorous exercise in preparation for aliyah (immigration). Among his friends he was nicknamed "Schperke" (Sportsman).[13] Filled with enthusiasm and dreams of farming the land in Palestine, he had dropped his studies of law at the University of Vienna after just one year in favor of agronomy, much to his father's chagrin. Back in Boskovice for the summer, Alfred's younger sister Irma had prepared Alfred's baggage and tearfully saw him off on his trip. Her letters would soon beg him to come back.

At the outbreak of the war, Albert Ticho's male siblings ranged in age from the youngest Alfred at twenty-one to the oldest Jacob at thirty-nine, and so each of the ten Ticho brothers were potentially eligible for military service. Alfred apparently fulfilled his duty to register for military service in the Austrian Army while visiting his brother Albert in Jerusalem. According to recorded anecdotes, Alfred followed his older brother Albert's advice to feign infection with trachoma by applying raw onion to each eye before reporting. Under questioning of a doubting physician, the red-eyed Alfred claimed that he had contracted trachoma before coming to Palestine (specifically in Mährisch-Schönberg, Moravia, now Šumperk, Czech Republic). Even though Alfred was granted a medical deferment, he was compelled to return to Vienna. After his return, he underwent subsequent army examinations, first in Vienna and then in Boskovice, but qualified for a temporary military deferment as an essential agricultural worker. Alfred was then even able to arrange for his brothers Victor and Paul to come and work for him and avoid the army.

In Boskovice, Nathan Ticho was excused from the army when doctors noted that he had astigmatism in one eye, and Paul Ticho obtained a temporary release since their factory was producing military supplies. At least three other brothers did end up serving in the Austrian Army: David Ticho, a co-owner of the A. J. Ticho business in Brno; Josef Ticho, the second-oldest brother who had a successful law practice in Vienna; and eventually Victor Ticho, who was later captured by the Italians while fighting in the Alps and spent a long time as a prisoner in a camp in Sardinia.[14]

Sergeant David Ticho's military experience during his deployment in Romania was not altogether unpleasant. Serving as a quartermaster in the Austrian Army, David enjoyed living well, able to select the best available food and drink for himself. However, Capt. Josef Ticho was deployed to Eastern Galicia where he came perilously close to losing his life. When the Russian Army overran the city of Lemberg (L'viv, Ukraine) on August 26, 1914, Josef's unit fell back to a position near the town of Jarosław (now in Poland), sixty miles to the west of Lemberg and twenty-five miles north of the fortress city of Przemyśl (now also in Poland).[15] Making his way through enemy lines to the already besieged Przemyśl, Josef joined the defense of the city that was to last for nearly six months. Joseph's postcards to his family were carried out of Przemyśl by airplane, the first air-mail flights by plane in history. During the fighting, Josef was later severely wounded in the chest and one arm. He was able to return to Vienna to recuperate and, when he was well enough, he was given a desk assignment in Vienna at the Ministry of Defense.[16] Josef continued to have difficulties using his injured hand and was assigned a certain Corporal Hypta as aide-de-camp, who happily served Josef and his family, rather than being sent to the front lines.

———◆———

On Friday, September 25, 1914, the newspaper *Ha-Or* reported that Dr. Ticho had been called to serve in the Austrian Army and that he would be setting out on his way the following day. It was further reported that Dr. Ticho had ten brothers, and (erroneously) that all of them were already serving Austria in the field of war. But after *Ha-Or* had gone to press that day, it was Dr. David Heron, the chief surgeon of the British Ophthalmic Hospital, and not Ticho who closed the doors of his hospital, and it was Heron who left for Alexandria via Jaffa the following morning.[17] It seems that this was the moment that Zakey Bey and others intervened with the Austrian consul on Ticho's behalf, and that *Ha-Or* had conflated Dr. Heron's story with that of Dr. Ticho's, or perhaps even with that of his younger brother, Alfred. Two days earlier *Ha-Or* had similarly reported that Dr. Jacob Segal of the Rothschild Hospital had been called to serve in the Medical Corps of the opposing French Army, but this story turned out to be true. Eliezar Ben-Yehudah never reported the story of the British Ophthalmic Hospital's closure or Heron's departure, but in the next edition following the Sabbath, the following announcement from Lemaan Zion was reported in Ben-Yehudah's newspaper: "The Honorable Dr. Ticho, eye doctor of the Eye Clinic 'Lemaan Zion' is not leaving. The hospital will remain open to receive patients and the doctor will answer all inquiries every day as before – The Management."[18]

On the same day that Dr. Heron was preparing to leave Jerusalem, Maurice Wertheim arrived in the city with Arthur Ruppin. Wertheim, a wealthy heir to his father's cigar manufacturing business and Ambassador Morgenthau's son-in-law, stayed as a guest of American

Consul Dr. Glazebrook for almost three weeks. While at the American Consulate, Wertheim and Ruppin conferred with the Governor Majidi Bey and several foreign consuls while establishing committees for the distribution of $50,000 that soon arrived at Jaffa on the U.S. battleship *North Carolina*.[19] After the Jewish High Holidays, Ruppin was joined by his committee cochairs – Aaron Aaronsohn for Northern Palestine and Ephraim Cohen-Reiss for Jerusalem. The *North Carolina* finally laid anchor at Jaffa Harbor on October 6, 1914; a sub-committee for Jerusalem's distributions had by that time been selected that included Ticho's colleagues Drs. Naftali Waitz and Aaron Mazie.[20] The Jerusalem branch of the American Relief Fund set up a local office in a building in front of the Evelina de Rothschild School. Later, the Joint Distribution Committee would use the school building and its grounds to distribute food and supplies that were sent from America.

Like other institutions in Jerusalem, the operations of the Lemaan Zion Hospital suffered from the loss of key employees to the military, such as Dov Halaban. The hospital was likewise hurt by the early disruption of money transfers, but eventually its financial situation stabilized as many private, direct contributions came to it from Germany and America. Apparently Ticho did not immediately receive direct assistance through the American Relief Fund as distributed by Cohen-Reiss and his committee. The following year, however, Lemaan Zion would be among the thirty-five institutions that received direct distributions from the American collier turned supply ship, the U.S.S. *Vulcan*.[21]

As the American Relief Fund was getting organized locally, the cancellation of the capitulations went into effect on Thursday, October 1, 1914, immediately following the Jewish fast day of Yom Kippur (Day of Atonement). Jerusalem's incoming and outgoing mail by foreign post officially ceased, including the Austrian post that was Ticho's main line of communication with his family. Just before the cessation of foreign postal services, Ticho received off-printings of his first publication that had been based upon his trachoma work with Nurses Kaplan and Landy. Ben-Yehudah had warned that the post office closings were "the first tangible evidence of absolute rule of the government" and that a new era had begun "in which it would not be possible any more to predict the great ramifications in regard to our empire."[22] While religiously observant Jews of Jerusalem fasted and prayed in their synagogues, the upper façade of the Austrian Post Office, that had for years displayed very large-lettered signage in multiple languages, was painted over with dark red paint. Later that day, workers of the several foreign post offices removed their many mailboxes from the walls of the city streets and porters loaded them and returned them to their now closed offices. As Ben-Yehudah noted, these events caused a "part of the life of Jerusalem to evaporate... The power of a free and emancipated Turkey," he wrote, "was prominently apparent to every eye."

The following day, the Turks were already placing new mailboxes throughout the city in the former places of the foreign mailboxes. Home mail deliveries became undependable in spite of promises by Jerusalem's Turkish postmaster to the contrary. With the absence of funds and the lack of resources, the Misgav Ladakh Hospital became the first local Jewish hospital to suspend its operations while other institutions likewise seemed on the verge of closing. In Jaffa, the arrival of the anti-Zionist Caimakam (District Governor) Beha-ed-Din and a fanatic Islamist military governor, Hassan Bey el-Bassri, presaged worse times yet to come. Noting the frequent appearance of "Zion" in the Jewish prayer book, Beha-ed-Din viewed all Jews as foreigners and separatists. Unfettered by the capitulations, he had Hebrew signposts and street plates taken down and prohibited Jews from immigration, land purchases, and possession of weapons. Avraham Elmaleh described the gloomy outlook of Palestinian Jewry, writing, "The threat of extinction hovered over the Yishuv."[23]

———◆———

On October 31, 1914, Turkey formally entered the war on the side of the Germans and the Austrians, causing the almost immediate closure of all institutions under the management of the Russians, French, and British. In the name of the Sultan-Caliph Mehmet V, a *fatwa* for *jihad* (a proclamation of a worldwide holy war) was issued by Essad Effendi, Sheikh ul-Islam. In Jaffa, Hassan Bey seized upon the opportunity to print a pamphlet urging every devout Muslim to kill the infidels, Christians and Jews alike. At this point, the Turkish rulers of Jerusalem were less fanatical, but they carried out the expulsion of physicians who were citizens of enemy states. With his hospital closed, and because he was a French citizen, Dr. Avraham Abushadid of Misgav Ladakh was exiled and left for Alexandria. Other physicians who were expelled to Alexandria, Egypt, included Dr. Naftali Waitz and Dr. Meshulam Levontin of Tel Aviv.[24] The exiled Dr. Abushadid stayed in Alexandria and established a small hospital there under the auspices of the local Jewish community's Medical Committee.

When Dr. Ze'ev Brünn returned to Europe to serve in the German Army, Dr. Aryeh Goldberg was asked to become the acting director of the Jewish Health Bureau and, along with all his fellow workers, he was conscripted into the Ottoman Army. Throughout Palestine during the war, fourteen or fifteen Jewish physicians, comprising about a quarter of all Jewish physicians in the country, would serve in the Turkish Army. From Jaffa and Tel Aviv, Drs. Moshe Sherman, Aryeh Pouchovsky, and Mordecai Berachyahu (along with nurses, sanitarians, administrators, and a cook) went down to Gaza and re-opened an abandoned Anglican Mission Hospital as a hospital for Jewish soldiers of the Turkish Army. Overall, relatively few Jews actually became Ottoman citizens after Turkey's declaration of war, representing only a small fraction of the fifty thousand Russian Jews who had immediately become enemy aliens. Inhibited by a tax that was placed upon Ottomanization and the prospect of conscription, many of these Russian Jews did little more than "flaunt red fezzes and patriotic expressions while praying silently for an Entente victory."[25]

Austria-Hungary was allied with Turkey, and so Ticho made no move to change his citizenship. Ticho had developed a friendly relationship with the new Austrian General Consul, Friedrich Kraus, who had arrived from Kiev to assume his new post in February 1914.[26] However, many of his colleagues quickly became targets of the Ottoman authorities, and many were faced with a choice between conscription or deportation. The effect upon medical manpower and the confiscation of medical supplies and equipment resulted in a growing health care crisis in Jerusalem. For physicians like Ticho who remained in Jerusalem, the work load and responsibilities further increased.

Dr. Moshe Wallach came almost daily from the Shaare Zedek Hospital to the Rothschild Hospital to help with the administration, until the Rothschild building was completely taken over by the Turks and used as a military hospital. Equipment and supplies were stripped from the British Ophthalmic Hospital and its local caretakers were evicted. The hospital was then used to store munitions. Several Jewish hospitals – the Shaare Zedek Hospital, the Bikkur Cholim Hospital in the Old City, and the Lemaan Zion Eye Hospital – that had previously been under the protection of the German Consulate were allowed to remain open.[27]

Ticho's workload further increased in early November, when a new epidemic of a virulent eye infection broke out in several areas in Palestine. Ticho diagnosed these cases as gonococcal conjunctivitis (extragenital gonorrhea caused by the species of bacteria *Neisseria gonorrhea*).[28] Most of these cases were seen among Yemenite Jews who had made their way to Palestine via Egypt just before the outbreak of the war. The patients came from Jerusalem and Jaffa, but also from settlements at Hadera and Rehovot.

Conscriptions, voluntary departures, and forced expulsions that began in late 1914 resulted in an acute shortage of nurses and physicians, but it provided some opportunities for a young woman physician – Dr. Helena Kagan – who would become one of Albert Ticho's closest coworkers during and after the war. The twenty-five-year-old Dr. Kagan had first arrived in Jerusalem with her widowed mother, Miriam, in May 1914.[29] A native of Tashkent, Uzbekistan, Dr. Kagan had received her medical degree in Bern, Switzerland, in 1910 at the young age of twenty-one and completed specialized training in pediatrics in 1913. In coming to Palestine, Dr. Kagan had had fulfilled the dying wish of her father to visit Palestine, but she and her mother aimed at permanent settlement. Unable to find employment in Tel Aviv, and even actively discouraged by Dr. Aryeh Leiba Pouchovsky, the Kagans moved on to

Jerusalem where together they purchased a home on Abyssinian Street. Still finding it difficult to make a living, she approached Dr. Kamal Bey al-Husayni, the nephew of the city's mayor, who was working as the assistant director at the Municipal Hospital. With the expulsion of citizens of hostile countries, Dr. Husayni intervened in several ways with the help of his uncle: He loaned Dr. Kagan one hundred napoleons and got her a job as a nurse at the Municipal Hospital, while also arranging a certificate for her mother forbidding her to travel for health reasons.[30]

Dr. Kagan had arrived in Jerusalem about six weeks after the trachoma conference but as the country's first pediatrician and working with Ticho, she would become very skilled in the treatment of children with this disease. It would be another year before Kagan would begin working with Ticho and Nurse Rachel Landy. Meanwhile Dr. Kagan took on greater medical responsibilities at the Municipal Hospital under the hospital director, Dr. Photios Efklides. With the outbreak of the war, one of Dr. Kagan's duties was the teaching of nursing to Jewish and Arab girls.

Dr. Kagan's nursing instruction was part of a broader home-front effort in Jerusalem, the founding of a local Red Crescent Society (*Cemiyet Hilal-i* in Turkish; *Ha-Sahar ha-Adom* in Hebrew) that was prominently based in the Russian Compound. With the approval of Zakey Bey, Jerusalem's Red Crescent Society also established a Jewish subdivision. Hussein Salim al-Husayni (soon to be ousted from his position as mayor) served as the local society's honorary president and Albert Antebi as his deputy, while Dr. Aharon Mazie initially headed the administrative duties.[31] Like other Jewish physicians, Ticho was called upon to give first aid courses that were offered by the Hebrew Ottoman Red Crescent Society at the Jewish Health Bureau most evenings beginning in early December.

For a short time, the Russian Compound also served as a training site for a local Jewish militia that Zakey Bey had allowed Ben-Gurion and Ben-Zvi to organize. However, under increasing pressure from Ottoman censors, Eliezer and Hemda Ben-Yehudah had decided to leave for America, and on December 3, 1914, they published their farewell to their friends and acquaintances, wishing all of their readers a speedy return to peaceful times and a blessing "to see you soon."[32]

As the days passed during the month of December, the gloomy skies over Jerusalem brought the usual winter rains. With their eyes on Egypt and the Suez Canal, the ruling triumvirate of the Ottoman Empire saw the winter rainy season as a time for a military foray southward through the Negev and Sinai Deserts. The appointment of Cemal Paşa to lead this campaign also brought about many improvements in infrastructure, such as macadamized roads between Damascus and Nablus, and likewise between Amman and Jericho. Roads between Hebron and Beer Sheva were improved throughout that year, and under the German engineer Heinrich Meissner, a new narrow-gauge railway line was completed from al-Mas'udiya (just northwest of Nablus) via Lydda to Beer Sheva.[33] Further southern extensions into the Negev and partially into Sinai would be completed in the spring and summer of 1916.

However, Cemal's continued presence in Palestine and Syria over the next three years would have terrible consequences for the local Jewish population. Under Cemal's harsh rule, Ticho was personally threatened with arrest and expulsion on several occasions. He was able to keep his hospital open for nearly three years, just ten days shy of the British conquest of Jerusalem.

Chapter 11

November 1914–December 1915
Year of the Locusts

יתר הגזם אכל הארבה
ויתר הארבה אכל הילק
ויתר הילק אכל החסיל.

What the cutter has left, the locust has devoured;
What the locust has left, the grub has devoured;
And what the grub has left, the hopper has devoured.

Joel 1:4

It was mid-November 1914 when Ahmet Cemal Paşa, one of the ruling Ottoman Triumvirate and Minister of the Marine, received his appointment as Field Marshal of the newly formed Fourth Army. His first mission was to organize an offensive against the British and their fortified positions at the Suez Canal. In his role of defending the home-front, he became the virtual ruler of Syria and Palestine. Traveling overland through Anatolia and Syria with German chief staff officers, including Col. Werner von Frankenberg and Lt.-Col. Freiherr Kress von Kressenstein, Cemal arrived in Damascus on November 18, 1914, and established his headquarters at the Palace Hotel. In preparing the details of the Suez campaign, he summoned several civilian and military officials to report to him, including two chief officials of Jaffa who shared his contemptuous attitude toward the Jews: the governor,

Beha-ed-Din, and the military commander, Hassan Bey. These two local rulers gained Cemal's approval for a series of edicts that culminated in their order expelling all Jews of Jaffa-Tel Aviv who were of foreign nationality. The steamship *Vincento Florio* that was anchored in the Jaffa Harbor was to be their mode of transportation to Egypt.

During the day of "Black Thursday," December 17, 1914, and into the late evening, the Italian steamer was able to take on only about five hundred of the exiles, and in the confusion many families became separated. Zionist reports would confirm the brutality of Turkish policemen and soldiers in Jaffa who "beat and arrested men and women, old persons and children, and dragged them to the police buildings." The boatmen who took the exiles out into the darkness of the evening were no less cruel, striking their victims and threatening them with knives.[1]

The following day in Jerusalem, as Ticho and his staff looked across the fields to the east of the Lemaan Zion Eye Hospital, a column of Turkish soldiers could be seen in the distance traveling south on Nablus Road toward the Damascus Gate – two regiments of the Fourth Army's Tenth Infantry Division that were on their way to Beer Sheva (and ultimately to the Suez Canal a month later). The long column of approximately twelve thousand soldiers followed a route through the city that took them past the Damascus Gate, then through the new city, and finally past the Jaffa Gate where the Bezalel School director, Boris Schatz, had erected a ceremonial archway adjacent to his school's retail pavilion, the Beitan Bezalel.[2] From there the army proceeded southward in the direction of Hebron and beyond that to Beer Sheva. Finally around sundown on that evening of December 18, Cemal Paşa arrived for his first visit to Jerusalem as the Field Marshal of the Fourth Army, and a brief reception was held outside the Damascus Gate in his honor. Having tarried several hours in Nablus, the Turkish commander had made his entry to Jerusalem on the eve of the Jewish Sabbath, and therefore most of Jews who had gathered there to greet him had already returned to their homes.

The skies were once again overcast when Jerusalemites returned to welcome Cemal Paşa outside the Old City walls on Sunday, December 20, 1914. Albert and Anna Ticho's private conversations that weekend likely included the worrisome topics of government edicts, expulsions, and the reports of the rough treatment that Jewish deportees had received three days earlier in Jaffa. As he walked to the Damascus Gate, Ticho hoped to hear some encouraging words from Palestine's new overlord, but he would be very disappointed. Cemal addressed an enthusiastic crowd of Muslims who had gathered before the flag of the Empire and before the Alam, the sacred Muslim standard that had been brought to Jerusalem from the Muslim Holy City of Mecca. Cemal was heard to say that Zionism was a "revolutionary and anti-Turkish movement which must be eradicated." He then made a point of waiting to receive the welcome of the Jewish community until first praying at the Mosque of Omar with the flag-bearer. The elderly sheikh who had come from Mecca would not survive to see the battle, dying that week in Jerusalem of an apparent heart attack.[3]

A light rain began to fall but Ticho and the crowds continued to wait for Cemal's return to the Old City's northern entrance. After Cemal emerged on the opposite side of the Old City at the Zion Gate (Bab El-Nabi Da'oud) and after he had prayed at the nearby Tomb of the "Prophet David," he left the company of the Sharīf and returned by way of carriage. Among those who returned with Cemal to receive the greetings of Jerusalem's Jews were the city's Ottoman civilian and military governors who would be soon be dismissed – Majid Bey and Zakey Bey. Close by his side now were Chief of Staff Werner von Frankenberg and 'Ali Roshen Bey, an Albanian native who would replace Zakey Bey in command of the Jerusalem garrison and the official Mufattish Manzil ("residence of the inspector") in reference to his role in conscriptions and mobilization.[4] The official welcome of Cemal Paşa by the Jewish community was given by the Turkish-speaking David Yellin, who noted that Cemal had just prayed at David's Tomb, and Yellin therefore recited appropriate verses in both Hebrew and Arabic from the book of Psalms, which according to Jewish tradition had been authored by King David himself. In the name of the Jewish people, Yellin wished the Ottoman Army success and victory. After Yellin's welcome, Cemal expressed in Turkish his satisfaction with the reception; a translator was requested to express thanks to the Jews in his name and on behalf of the army under his command.[5]

The St. Paulus Hospice stood before Cemal's entourage outside the Damascus Gate; it resembled a medieval castle with mixtures of Mamluk and Western architecture, its serrated stone railing upon a high rooftop mirroring the Old City ramparts.[6] Like the Roman Catholic Dormitio Abbey on Mount Zion, both the German-Catholic St. Paulus Hospice and the German-Lutheran Augusta Victoria Hospice on the Mount of Olives had been built in the wake of Kaiser Wilhelm II's 1898 visit to Jerusalem, and both structures seemed to have had design input from the Kaiser's military advisors.[7] Ticho watched as the entourage passed further on in their wagons toward Olivet and the Turkish Army's advance headquarters at the Augusta Victoria Hospice. Some months later, Ticho would trek up to these headquarters in order to meet Cemal Paşa and plead his case to remain at his work in Jerusalem.

During Cemal Paşa's reception, members of a local Jewish fraternity stood to either side of the Damascus Gate. They were members of the local branch – or *masu'ah*, meaning beacon or torch – of the (Order of Ancient) Maccabeans, an order that had been founded in England. Eliezar Ben-Yehudah's son, Itamar Ben-Avi, reported that with the departure of the official entourage, the members of the *masu'ah* broke out in "their song." It is possible that Ben-Avi was referring to the militant words of the *Song of the Maccabees*, the fraternal order's hymn that had been written in the late nineteenth century by their own High Commander, Ephraim Ish-Kishor. As the event coincided with the last day of Hanukkah, the eight-day "Festival of Lights," it is also possible that they sang the much older traditional hymn of *Ma'oz Tsur* (Rock of Ages) that, with the exception of its final stanza, was written in the fourteenth century. This hymn recalls various periods of servitude and exile that the Jewish people have endured over the centuries and praises God for redemption from each of them.[8]

The previous evening, Jews throughout Jerusalem and worldwide had lit the final candles of the holiday menorah in celebration of the ancient Hasmonean victory and the rededication of the Second Temple over two thousand years in the distant past. Now the embodiment of a new oppressor had stood directly before Ticho and his coreligionists. There were many loyal supporters of the Ottomans among the Jews of

Jerusalem but there were also growing numbers of clandestine opponents – all rightfully feared that a new period of darkness had begun. After describing the events of that day, just one final, abbreviated edition of the newspaper *Ha-Or* (literally meaning "The Light") would appear in its last brief flicker of publication and then forever be extinguished.[9]

———◆———

Before leaving Jerusalem, Cemal Paşa established various headquarters of his army including headquarters for 'Ali Roshen Bey at the Notre Dame Hospice that also housed the headquarters of the Turkish Medical Corps. The hospice building that had been vacated by the French Assumptionists would be known as the Manzil (the Residence), and until today the section of road between it and the Old City walls is popularly known among elderly Arabs of Jerusalem as Aqbet al-Manzil. The advanced, well-equipped operating rooms of the adjacent St. Louis Hospital served the Ottoman Fourth Army until the British conquest of Jerusalem in December 1917.[10] Cemal also appointed Beha-ed-Din as his chief political advisor for all of Palestine. The outgoing Governor Majid Bey departed the city, and although Zakey Bey remained in Jerusalem, he was relieved of command.

The Ottoman administration was now decidedly unsympathetic to the Jews; anti-Zionist programs that had been instituted in Jaffa would now be enforced in Jerusalem. The nascent Jewish-Ottoman militia that Zakey Bey had authorized was declared illegal, and its two main leaders, Ben-Gurion and Ben-Zvi, were arrested.

When Cemal returned to Damascus, Arthur Ruppin boldly undertook a five-day journey there in an unsuccessful attempt to gain an audience with him. Ruppin arrived in Damascus on Christmas Day but he was able to get only as far as seeing Cemal's chief of staff, Colonel von Frankenberg. Some five days later, on December 30, Cemal gave the administratively impossible order requiring all Jews to become Ottoman subjects within three days, and those who had not done so by then would be immediately expelled with their families from the country.

Many Jews in Jerusalem and throughout Palestine now finally began to apply for Ottoman citizenship.[11] Others voluntarily sought passage to Alexandria on the United States warship *Tennessee* that would leave Jaffa at the end of December and continue to shuttle refugees to Alexandria free of charge into the new year. Many of the refugees came from Jerusalem and a second daily train from Jerusalem to Jaffa was reactivated to handle the increased traffic. Others came from the north, such as the Russian-born Dr. Jacob Norman and his wife who returned to Boston after a three-year sojourn working in Metula. During January 1915, about seven thousand Jews left from the port of Jaffa for Alexandria. By the end of 1915 the total figure of those expelled and those who had left of their own volition amounted to almost twelve thousand.[12]

Ticho was concerned that the name of his hospital (literally meaning "For the Sake of Zion") might make him a target of the irascible Beha-ed-Din. On January 8, 1915, just before departing Jerusalem to lead the Suez Canal Offensive, Cemal Paşa summoned over thirty Jewish notables to his headquarters, but it is unknown whether Ticho was among them. Before coming to a final decision on planned expulsions, Cemal granted a private audience to Albert Antebi, who, by means of diplomatically expounding the groups' case in Turkish, succeeded in persuading the Ottoman commander to soften his stance toward the Jews in general. While the threat of expulsion hovered over him, Ticho still tried to maintain the routines of his practice and his work with the Hadassah nurses in Jerusalem's schools, the latter having finally yielded statistically encouraging results. In January 1915, he wrote to Dr. Friedenwald in Baltimore that the incidence of trachoma among the three thousand schoolchildren under his care had been reduced by half, from 28 percent to 14 percent.[13]

Soon after writing to Dr. Friedenwald, Ticho learned that the forty-seven-year-old Hadassah nurse, Rose Kaplan, was very ill. Nurse Kaplan was apparently suffering from breast cancer and although an initial surgical procedure had been performed in Jerusalem, more treatment had been recommended. Kaplan's personal health crisis came at the time of the imminent expiration of her contract with Hadassah and in the midst of disrupted communications with the Hadassah Central Committee. She therefore bid farewell to Ticho and her many acquaintances in Jerusalem and departed for Alexandria in January. Although she hoped to help care for refugees in the camps, Kaplan instead soon made her way back to America.[14] Rachel Landy now took sole charge of the Hadassah Nurses' Settlement House and under very trying circumstances she continued her work in the schools and midwife home-visiting services.

Meanwhile, Ticho was completing a manuscript on vernal conjunctivitis, an allergic eye condition that was best known in those days as vernal catarrh, or, in German, *Frühjahrskatarrh*. He submitted his work to a prestigious ophthalmologic journal in Stuttgart, Germany, and it would be published that spring. In this article, Ticho also described combinations of vernal catarrh and infantilism and cases of familial spring catarrh. In those cases not combined with active trachoma, he used therapeutic, tight fitting clear glasses of H. Bayer with good results. Later that year, an English translation appeared as the lead article in the *American Journal of Ophthalmology*.[15] As described in Ticho's paper, vernal conjunctivitis was much rarer than the various forms of infectious conjunctivitis that he saw in his clinic, just 0.155 percent of his clinic patients seen over his first thirty-one months in practice. In these cases, flattened, paving-stone-like elevations were seen on the inner lining of the eyelids, and pale, uneven nodules were seen on the membrane of the eyeball itself, just peripheral to the clear cornea. These small, pale nodules were often referred to by the eponym "Trantas's dots." Among his twenty-six patients, all but five of the patients were Arabs or Sephardi Jews. The others were four Russian-Jewish immigrants and one girl born in Jerusalem's German Colony.

From time to time – in times of relative peace and in the trying times of war – Ticho returned to writing on medical topics. Drs. Feigenbaum and Shimoni-Mäkler were also busy at work in the midst of the war, editing the proceedings of the previous year's trachoma conference which included Ticho's contributions and a glossary of Hebrew medical terms. Dr. Aharon Mazie continued to expand this glossary into a full Hebrew lexicon of medical and scientific terminology (completed by Dr. Shaul Tchernicovsky and published posthumously in 1932).

In mid-January 1915, Cemal Paşa set out on his unsuccessful First Suez Offensive, his Ottoman Fourth Army unable to capture the canal. The army instead retreated to Beer Sheva, where Cemal reorganized his Desert Force and established an advance desert headquarters. He then returned to Jerusalem to reestablish his own headquarters and plan his next offensive. After his return to Jerusalem, Cemal ordered the expulsion of Ben-Gurion and Ben-Zvi from the Ottoman Empire, though they both would languish in jail until late March before their actual deportation to Egypt.[16] One of Ticho's greatest fears was realized when the Turkish commander personally ordered his expulsion from Palestine. Looking to appeal this decree, Ticho turned to Dr. Wallach who had been allowed to remain in Jerusalem and to keep the Shaare Zedek Hospital open and operating.[17]

Early the next morning, Wallach arrived at Lemaan Zion in a carriage to take Ticho to Cemal's advance headquarters at the Augusta Victoria Hospice on the Mount of Olives. The roads at the northern outskirts of the city probably took them past the former residence of the Anglican Bishop where Cemal himself had taken up residence, onto Nablus Road passing the villa of the American Colony, and then eastward past the traditional site of the tomb of Simon the Just, the High Priest of the Second Temple in the time of Alexander the Great.[18] Beyond this they passed the Sheikh Jarrah Mosque and neighborhood, the site of the tomb of Husam al-Din al-Jarrahi, the twelfth-century physician of Saladin. After Sheikh Jarrah, the road crossed the Wadi el-Joz (Valley of the Nuts), the flat upper part of the Kidron Valley, to Mount Scopus past the summer home and gardens of the late Sir John Gray Hill – the future site of the Hebrew University.[19] The final ascent up the northern slope of the Mount of Olives led to Cemal's advance headquarters.

The twenty-acre compound of the Augusta Victoria Hospice had been a gift of Sultan Abdul Hamid II to the Augusta Victoria Foundation on the occasion of Kaiser Wilhelm's visit to Jerusalem in 1898. It had been designed by architect Robert Leibnitz in a medieval style to resemble other Hohenzollern castles of Germany's Rhineland. Two bronze statues of the Kaiser and Kaiserin, dressed in medieval garb, graced the hospice's courtyard. After three years of construction, Prince Eitel Fritz and his wife, dressed in twentieth-century garb, had dedicated the building in April 1910.[20] The massive complex included a malarial convalescent home, a hostel for German pilgrims, and the Himmelfahrtkirche, the sumptuous Evangelical Lutheran Church of the Ascension. As the Germans intended, the building dominated the fairly barren horizon to the east of the Jerusalem. On clear days, the church's bell tower that rose almost two hundred feet into the air could be seen from the banks of the Jordan River twenty miles further to the east.[21] The civilian uses of the Augusta Victoria Hospice were short lived. Its commanding view of the city, spacious grounds, and its modernity – complete with sanitary plumbing and an electrical system powered by a diesel generator – made the compound very desirable as a military command post. It is certain that many military specifications had been incorporated into the designs of the hospice, including a searchlight set atop the tower that could be seen many miles out at sea as well as far across the other side of the Jordan – something that would have been quite extraordinary for simply "a place of rest for tired missionaries."[22]

As Wallach and Ticho entered Cemal Paşa's office, the Turkish commander cried out to Dr. Wallach, "Here comes the devil to cancel the edicts." Dr. Wallach persisted and explained to Cemal about Ticho's important work and his service to the citizens of Jerusalem without heed to religion or nationality. He pointed out that the British Ophthalmic Hospital had been closed for months and, aside from the various facilities of the Jewish Health Bureau, Lemaan Zion was the only eye hospital that was operating anywhere in Palestine at the time; Dr. Feigenbaum and the Health Bureau would not open an eye hospital until the following year.

Ultimately rescinding the order of Ticho's expulsion, Cemal was possibly more persuaded by the ophthalmologist's potential usefulness to Turkish military efforts and the unique nature of his practice. During a twelve-month period approximately covering the first year of the war, Ticho saw 3,266 new patients and performed 515 major operations and 830 minor operations, and several of these cases increasingly involved war-related casualties. During approximately the same twelve-month period, Ticho recorded 102,576 outpatient visits, an average daily patient load of 256 patients.[23]

Ticho soon had other reasons to be concerned about the possibility of even worse Turkish reprisals against himself and his fellow Jews based upon the reports about Turkish massacres of Armenians. Mass murders of Armenians had begun in the Van province in the spring of 1915; these murders were decried by the Allies as crimes against humanity and civilization.[24] By September 1915, more than six hundred thousand Armenians had been massacred and another four hundred thousand had perished as a result of the brutalities and privations of forced southward marches into Syria and Mesopotamia (statistics that have continued to be disputed by the Turks). There was always the fear that the Jews might suffer the same fate and become the victims of what later became known as genocide, later still as ethnic cleansing.

Ticho was also perhaps wary about the existence of a Jewish fighting force within the British Army known as the Zion Mule Corps. Under the command of a British officer, Lt.-Col. John Patterson, the Zion Mule Corps was a transportation supply unit comprised mainly of Russian Jews who had been exiled to Egypt from Palestine. Its senior Jewish officer was Capt. Josef Trumpeldor, who had, like Ticho, immigrated to Palestine in 1912 but had suffered expulsion from his *kevutzah* (collective farm) in the Galilee. Trumpeldor had originally been trained as a dentist, but as a soldier he had lost an arm in the Russian army during the Russo-Japanese War. Following his expulsion from Palestine to Alexandria, Trumpeldor had befriended Russian Jewish war correspondent Vladimir Jabotinsky, who was urging Jews to take up arms alongside the British, French, and Russians against the Germans and Turks.[25]

Though his own father had opposed the idea, Dr. Meshulam Levontin was among the 650 men who enlisted in the British Army as part of the Zion Mule Corps and among 562 of them who were sent to the Gallipoli front. With Trumpeldor, he was one of eight Jewish officers leading the five hundred or so Jewish soldiers. Dr. Levontin received an appointment as the corps' medical officer on April 15, 1915, and although he was not considered a member of the British Medical

Corps per se, he became the sole Palestinian Jewish physician to serve in his profession with officer rank in the British Army during World War I.[26] Similarly, Ticho would later become the sole Palestinian Jewish physician to serve as an officer in the Austro-Hungarian Army.

When the Zion Mule Corps left Alexandria for Gallipoli on April 18, 1915, its members believed they were being dispatched to the Sinai Front to fight for the liberation of Palestine. On April 25, the British Army's Twenty-Ninth Division landed instead at Cape Helles, the southernmost tip of the Gallipoli peninsula, and the Zion Mule Corps, under Lieutenant-Colonel Patterson, landed at W Beach. That day also, about fifteen miles to the north along the Aegean side of the peninsula, the Turkish commander, Mustafa Kemal, issued his famous order to his infantry: "I do not expect you to attack, I order you to die. In the time which passes until we die, other troops and commanders can come forward and take our places."[27] The British campaign was long and disastrously unsuccessful, but the credible performance of the Zion Mule Corps had opened the prospect of Jewish military participation in the British-led conquest of Palestine.

Meanwhile, units of Austrian soldiers were also present in Gallipoli in support of their Turkish allies, among them Jewish Zionists such as artillery officer Marek Schwarz who would become a close friend of the Tichos. A native of Tarnopol in eastern Galicia, Captain Schwarz had previously fought in the Balkans and served at the War Ministry in Vienna before volunteering for service in Palestine.[28] He arrived in Jerusalem in August 1915 along with contingents of the Austro-Hungarian artillery – twenty-four cm mortars of the *k.u.k.* Motor-Mörser-Batterie No. 9 and fifteen cm howitzers of the *k.u.k.* Haubitzbatterie No. 36. These were forces that had been recruited from both the German and Hungarian portions of the empire and so their units were designated as "*k.u.k.*" (*kaiserlich und königlich*, or Imperial and Royal). Austrian headquarters were maintained in Istanbul under General Joseph Pomiankowski.[29] In Palestine, Captain Schwarz kept close contact with Zionist leaders such as Jacob Thon and David Yellin, helping to facilitate their communications with Central Europe while also representing their interests to the Austrian command, and often helping to mitigate harsh Turkish actions against Jews of the Yishuv.

As two ships bearing the Zion Mule Corps were crossing the Mediterranean Sea northward, the American collier U.S.S. *Vulcan* was steaming eastward toward Jaffa. It had left Philadelphia on March 14, 1915. As the British were landing at Cape Hellas, the *Vulcan* arrived at Jaffa Harbor around April 25 carrying supplies for the U.S. warships *Tennessee* and *North Carolina*, but also nine hundred tons of flour and other food – representing an expenditure of about $150,000 – for the beleaguered inhabitants of Palestine.[30] Two Jewish-American overseers who traveled aboard were Louis Levin, a noted social service worker and brother-in-law of Henrietta Szold, and a young dentist, Samuel Lewin-Epstein. This aid from three American Jewish organizations and private donors was coordinated by the newly formed Joint Distribution Committee. American Consul Dr. Otis Glazebrook also became personally involved in the distribution of the food among the various communities. He also conveyed $100,000 in gold to David Yellin that ultimately found a hiding place in the home of Dr. Helena Kagan.[31] The arrival of this aid was most timely as a plague of locusts was beginning to wreak havoc upon the Palestinian countryside.

—◆—

Toward the end of the rainy winter season in February 1915, areas of new vegetation provided food and shelter for newly hatched desert locusts (*Schistocerca gregaria*). The locust larvae soon developed into nymphs or "hoppers," but this particular year their crowded feeding areas outside of Palestine triggered a cascade of metabolic and behavioral changes. Because of this crowding, great numbers of solitary locusts transformed from ordinary appearing grasshoppers to a gregarious form of locust with swarming, destructive behavior. Most scientists deduced that these locusts came from the south. However, John Whiting was convinced that the locusts had originated from the north and east, for 2,500 years earlier the prophet Joel had described the invading locust as the "northerner."[32] Some of the first swarms of locust were spotted in Palestine at the Ain Fara gorge bordering the Wilderness of Judea, just a few miles east of Jerusalem. The swarms of locusts had flown overhead in such thick clouds as to obscure the sun.[33] As in the days of Joel, this modern plague of locusts would be among the most widespread and devastating in many generations. Throughout that spring and summer, the locusts eventually spread to virtually all of Palestine and Syria, from the Taurus Mountains in the north to Palestine's borders with Egypt to the south.

The first locusts were seen in the skies of Jerusalem at noontime on March 1, 1915. For several days, a sudden darkening of the bright sunshine would be followed by a shower of the insects' dark excretions that fell thick and fast, covering the white macadam roads of the city beneath them. The black swarms at times reached an elevation of hundreds of feet above the ground, while at other times they came down quite low. There were occasional flocks of migrating storks that also flew over Jerusalem that time of year. They feasted well on the locusts but the numbers of storks were insufficient to stem the onset of the disaster. Evidently seeking greener and less populated districts, the flying locusts did not settle in Jerusalem that week, though they did settle in surrounding areas such as Bethlehem and the Valley of Roses, which lay on the train route north and east of the Betar ruins (chapter 6). It is from these directions that the armies of the locusts' offspring would later attack Jerusalem by ground. In spite of communal and outside relief efforts, deaths in Jerusalem from starvation began to be seen, as the cost of flour rose to fifteen dollars a sack and potatoes sold at six times their ordinary price.[34]

From the many different areas of Palestine, reports of locust swarms and their widespread egg-laying began to reach the governing authorities. Cemal Paşa took prompt and vigorous action, appointing a "Central Commission to Fight the Locusts" under the titular presidency of the new governor of Jerusalem, Midhat Bey. Although he had first threatened the agronomist Aaron Aaronsohn with hanging, he instead appointed the outspoken agronomist in charge of fighting the locusts on March 27, 1915. From the Turkish military standpoint, Cemal's appointment of Aaronsohn was a blunder of sorts for he was unaware that Aaronsohn had been assembling an anti-Turkish spy ring, known as Nili. The word "Nili" was an acrostic taken from Samuel's retort to

Saul, "*Netzaḥ Yisrael lo yishkar*" meaning "The Eternal of Israel does not deceive."[35]

The commission, officially attached to the headquarters of the Fourth Army at Jerusalem, was charged with fighting the locust plague throughout the *sanjak* of Jerusalem and the Vilayets of Beirut and Damascus. As Aaronsohn made his way around the country, he took note of Turkish military positions and troop movements and conveyed the information to the British. Not waiting for British help, groups of Arabs in Palestine and Syria were simultaneously planning their own anti-Turkish revolution. The conspirators included the Mufti of Gaza, Arif al-Husseini, and his son Mustafa. Both of them would be hanged in public early that summer outside the Jaffa Gate.[36]

At Aaronsohn's recommendation, a proclamation was issued on April 19, 1915, requiring every city-dwelling male, ages sixteen to sixty years, to collect eleven pounds of locust eggs or to pay an exemption fee of one Turkish pound ($4.40). This rule was so rigorously enforced that about eight hundred persons paid the tax, while the others either gathered the required amount or purchased them from peasants who brought them in secretly for sale. It seems almost certain that Ticho would have paid the tax rather than go out digging for locust eggs. Although great quantities of eggs were dug up and destroyed, far greater numbers hatched, and when the larvae, already about an inch long, reached the Plain of Rephaim at the southern outskirts of Jerusalem, hundreds of men, women, and children gathered in lines to meet them. Many tactics were employed, including flagging the locusts into dense columns and driving them into tin-lined boxes sunk into the earth or into sacs hung at the end of portable ramps. In spite of these efforts, the locust armies moved northward by ground through the German Colony and Yemin Moshe. They next invaded the Mamilla neighborhood and completely covered the walls of the American consulate before moving on to the walls of the Old City.[37]

It is not known if Ticho went down to the Jaffa Gate to see the incredible sight of swarms of locusts climbing the walls of the Citadel and completely filling its dried moat, but such reports of this scene undoubtedly reached him quickly. The images again evoked the words of Joel, who had likened the locusts to warriors who "scale a wall like fighters." The Arabs also likened the locusts to warriors, calling them *djesh Allah* (Allah's army).[38] There was little nourishment for this army of larvae within the confines of the walls that Suleiman the Magnificent had built, and they left most of the Old City unscathed, never reaching the Temple Mount. The maturing larvae marched northward through the less densely populated western suburbs and, veering south around the Old City they also traveled north through the Kidron Valley.

On May 28, having attained the stage of pupae with their rudimentary wing sacs, the locust swarms reached the foot of the Mount of Olives. Here they attacked the beautiful garden of Gethsemane that is most famously associated with the last days of the life of Jesus, the place where he last prayed with his disciples before his crucifixion.[39] The garden was then "in its full summer bloom" but was laid bare within about a day, and it could not be certain whether even the heartiest of the olive trees, some of them one thousand years old, would survive. The relentless northward migration of the army of maturing insects brought them at last to the northern suburbs and the neighborhood of the Lemaan Zion Eye Hospital.

Written details of the hospital's encounter with the locust pupae have not been preserved, but it is certain the insects infested the grounds and climbed the building's walls. As in some areas of Jerusalem, perhaps some of the locusts penetrated into the building by eating through wooden doors and windows.[40] The Tichos and their staff may have made some efforts to combat the locusts or perhaps resigned themselves to only watch as the pupae devoured their garden before heading further northward, leaving a mostly defoliated Jerusalem behind them.

———◆———

Throughout his career, Ticho would treat members of all faiths from the very poor to the very rich and powerful. This continued during the war, when he also dutifully supported the Ottoman Red Crescent, consulted in cases of military casualties, and treated some members of the Turkish high command. In September, Mumtaz Bey, aide-de-camp of War Minister Enver Paşa, came to Ticho from Istanbul to undergo

surgery. The nature of the illness is not known, but after the Suez Canal
Offensive, Mumtaz Bey had apparently returned to the Turkish capital
after a tour in Southern Palestine where he had supervised conscriptions
of fellahin and Bedouins, and, according to several of them taken
prisoner by the British, he had harshly carried out their march into
battle. Ticho's apparently routine operation was successful, but it is
likely that the high-ranking Turkish officer received upgraded quarters
as he convalesced at Lemaan Zion for a few weeks. Soon after Mumtaz
Bey transferred to the Grand New Hotel so that he could continue to see
Ticho as an outpatient, the Syrian Patriarch was similarly hospitalized
at Lemaan Zion to undergo surgery.[41]

Even as Ticho was treating military and religious leaders from far
and wide, he continued to devote time to schoolchildren in Jerusalem,
but he would soon be without the assistance of Nurse Rachel Landy.
Landy had remained in Jerusalem even after her employment contract
with Hadassah had expired in the summer. As reported to the Hadassah
Central Committee, she had "kept to her post" though she had requested
and received ongoing supervision from Dr. Helena Kagan, and after
some months of working together, Dr. Kagan was "prepared to assume
charge."[42] Since the summer, Ticho had therefore begun to work with
Dr. Kagan; he was the first male Jewish physician in Palestine to work
with Dr. Kagan on an equal, collegial basis. The two doctors also
developed a friendship that would last their lifetimes. Late that summer,
Landy was recalled by the Hadassah Central Committee; the concern
and health of Landy's parents in Cleveland were cited as the reasons.
After distributing supplies that she had received from the *Vulcan*, she
closed the settlement house but decided to remain in Jerusalem until
her ship was about ready to leave from Jaffa. At the specific request of
Hadassah, Drs. Kagan and Ticho continued the medical work with the
help of two or three probationers that the nurses had trained.[43]

The Red Crescent Ball in mid-September presented Dr. Kagan and
the Tichos with a pleasant opportunity to socialize with Nurse Landy one
final time before her departure. Involving all of the faith communities
of Jerusalem, the event took place on a Saturday night between the
Jewish High Holidays. This was the largest evening event to date for the

local branch of the Red Crescent Society and took place in the garden of the Manzil, the Notre Dame Hospice that had been commandeered by the Turks.[44] The garden of the Manzil was decorated beautifully that evening: "Tents and stands, settees and chairs, benches and boards stood here and there, and the bright and pleasant light of the electricity poured upon everything." The attention of the crowd was directed to a large and beautiful stage, draped in red and white and decorated with the flags of three empires; smaller lights were shaped into a picture of a star and a half-moon. According to estimates the number of guests who arrived by special invitations was close to 1,500 persons.

The Tichos and their friends were exposed to a wide variety of entertainment that evening: sonatas for piano and violin by Mozart and Anton Rubenstein, and Turkish, Arabic, and Hebrew songs performed by local students and school choirs. It is not known if Anna was impressed with the drawings of the artist Mr. Horodski of the Bezalel School, who quickly rendered drawings of the three emperors of the Triple Alliance (Sultan Mehmed V, Kaiser Wilhelm II, and Kaiser Franz Joseph I). Horodski's last picture of Cemal Paşa was reportedly the most precise and flattering, receiving thunderous applause. Cemal had seen the grouped arrangement of the three emperors' portraits before, but he was now envisioning himself as a potential successor to Mehmed V. That evening the less detailed image of the figurehead sultan contrasted with his own more focused visage. Three months later, Cemal sent word to the Russians via an Armenian emissary that, with Allied help, he would be prepared to seize the Ottoman throne for himself. Although the Russians accepted his plan, the French rejected it.[45]

Appropriately for all of the guests at the Red Crescent Ball, but perhaps especially for Rachel Landy, the last song played by the military band was entitled "The Farewell." Soon after the ball, Landy departed for America, via Egypt and Italy.[46] Her ship, *Cretic*, departed Naples on October 10, and she safely arrived in New York two weeks later.

When Landy met with the Hadassah Central Committee the following day, she delivered a letter from Dr. Kagan requesting support for the establishment of a small polyclinic for female diseases. This was approved at a later meeting, and in January 1916, the Hadassah Central

Committee further authorized funding for a polyclinic for women's and children's diseases. With the funds from Hadassah, Kagan and Ticho rented a free clinic for women and children in two small rooms in Meah She'arim opposite the Cohen Mill, initially with morning clinic hours three days per week. In covering the opening in late January, the newspaper *Ha-Ḥerut* acknowledged Hadassah's three years of operations in Jerusalem treating trachoma in the city's Jewish schools and also extending its midwife services to the city's poor women during the confinement of their labor and delivery.[47] As an emerging sign of the acceptance of female physicians, Kagan's directorship of the polyclinic was reported in a very matter-of-fact fashion.

Around the time that Landy's ship arrived in New York, her friend, Rose Kaplan, was heading back to the Middle East. Kaplan had exhausted all available treatments for cancer in New York and had regained her strength through the summer. She convinced the Hadassah Central Committee to re-engage her for service in Alexandria and began a harrowing journey, surviving the sinking of the ill-fated *Athinai*. Kaplan ultimately reached Egypt in early December, and for over eighteen months until her death she selflessly cared for thousands of young refugees in Alexandria using many of the methods that she had learned during her time with Ticho in Jerusalem.

As Nurses Landy and Kaplan were making their journeys across the Atlantic, some of the last swarms of locusts, now red in color, were seen in the skies of Jerusalem, at first flying past the city without descending. Eventually locusts landed in various parts of the city, covering trees and devouring their foliage. As late as December 1915, Aaron Aaronsohn would see a swarm of flying locusts in the skies near Zikhron Ya'akov. This particular swarm was quite large, about six miles long and a mile across. Soon thereafter, Aaron Aaronsohn resumed work as the director of the locust control program after he first arranged the release of his jailed friend (and clandestine coconspirator), Avshalom Feinberg.[48] While the "year of the locusts" would end as the swarms of immature insects failed to lay eggs, food shortages continued in Jerusalem with an increasing number of deaths from starvation.

CHAPTER 12

1916

BROTHERS IN ARMS
AND IN DISTRESS

כלו בדמעות עיני חמרמרו מעי
נשפך לארץ כבדי על שבר בת-עמי
בעטף עולל ויונק ברחבות קריה.

My eyes are spent with tears, my heart is in tumult,
My being melts away over the ruin of my poor people,
As babes and sucklings languish in the squares of the city.

Lamentations 2:11

Food shortages in Jerusalem during the war affected all segments of society, at both an individual and institutional level. Although Ticho's inpatient services became increasingly expensive he managed to continue his work, including his daily free clinics. As wheat and flour grew more scarce and expensive, starving people came out into the streets calling out for bread, their cries often deteriorating into a "miserable, ceaseless whimper of hunger." Deaths from starvation were being seen in Jerusalem on a daily basis.[1] In early January 1916, Arthur Ruppin went to Transjordan to make mass purchases of wheat, but his activities were soon interrupted when he and four Zionist colleagues were placed before a military tribunal in Jerusalem. The three-week trial ended in early February with the acquittal of all of the defendants, but Ruppin thereupon transferred the directorship of the Palestine Office to Jacob Thon, who had agreed to accept Ottoman citizenship. The trial ended just before Enver Paşa's well-publicized visit to Jerusalem that was followed by his further tours of the Sinai Front and the Hejaz with Cemal Paşa and Emir Faisal. German diplomatic pressure, reinforced by Enver Paşa's visit, may have helped forestall Ruppin's expulsion from Palestine.[2] When Ticho was arrested by the Turks in November 1917, he would likewise benefit from the intervention of foreign diplomats (chapter 13).

The war and Turkish persecutions were continuing to deplete the number of Jews in Palestine. According to a census of Jews carried out by the Zionist Office, the Jewish population of Jerusalem had declined to twenty-six thousand by the middle of 1916 – a reduction of about 50 percent over less than a two-year period. The number of Jewish physicians there had likewise declined due to emigration, expulsion, or military service. Ticho was one of the few Jewish physicians with a substantially civilian practice who remained in Jerusalem during the middle years of the war.[3] Dr. Helena Kagan was directing the polyclinic in Meah Shearim in addition to her work at the Municipal Hospital. Dr. Aryeh Feigenbaum established the Jewish Eye Hospital and "Eye Clinic A" in Zikhron Tuvia at the former Russian Post Office on Jaffa Road (nowadays known as "the Armenian Building" at Jaffa Road 19), and he also supervised "Eye Clinic B" of the Jewish Health Bureau in the Old City. Dr. Aaron Mazie worked for the Red Crescent at the Russian Compound, and Dr. Aryeh Beham for the time being continued his work as a civilian for the Pasteur Institute. Beham's Zionist politics led to his arrest and trial for the publication of "illegal articles."[4]

Several of Ticho's Jewish medical colleagues had remained in Palestine and had accepted Turkish citizenship, entering the Turkish Army early in the war. Two of these physicians had previously served in the Balkans: Jerusalemite Dr. Moshe Neumann, who served in Afula and later became involved in espionage against the Turks; and Moshe Krieger, who served the Turks more faithfully at the Sinai Front.[5] At sixty-one years of age, Dr. Menachem Stein had been conscripted into the Turkish Army and came to Jerusalem from Jaffa to work at the Municipal Hospital. Also in Jerusalem, Dr. Aryeh Goldberg continued his work as interim director at the Jewish Health Bureau while Dr. Aryeh Pouchovsky was stationed for a time at the Russian Compound. Previously, Dr. Pouchovsky and his colleagues at the Jewish Field Hospital in Gaza had been denied the right to wear Turkish military uniforms but this policy changed as the war progressed. Ticho may have worn an Austrian uniform in a reservist's capacity in Jerusalem.

As the war continued, one of the most serious medical problems in Jerusalem was epidemic typhus, an example of a zoonosis, a disease transmitted between animals and humans. The causative agent of louse-borne typhus, *Rickettsia prowazekii*, is a very small (1.0 x 0.3 μm) round/oval bacterium whose active form lives within a host cell (in medical terms, an "obligately intracellular coccobacillus"). It also possesses an extracellular dormant form that remains infectious in louse feces for months. The intermediary between humans and the germ, *R. prowazekii*, is the human body louse, *Pediculus humanis corporis*, that spends its entire life cycle in the clothing of the human victim. The louse bites its human host four to six times a day for a blood meal, its only source of food. When the lice are infected with the typhus fever germ, its fecal material loaded with *Rickettsia* get scratched into the itchy feeding site and the germ finds its way into the bloodstream, leading to high fevers and often death. The epidemic disease is associated with unhygienic conditions that prevent bathing and washing of clothes in hot water.[6] The root causes of these conditions – war, poverty, displacement of populations, and crowded jails – were all present in Jerusalem at the time. Even a non-infested care-giver may be bitten and contract typhus. A few years later, during her time working as a nurse in Damascus, Anna Ticho would become seriously ill with the disease.

An outbreak of typhus in the Old City's central prison in February 1916 forced its partial evacuation.[7] Epidemic typhus had affected the outcome of wars through the end of the nineteenth century; for example, typhus killed hundreds of thousands of soldiers in Napoleon's army during his Russian campaign. An estimated three million deaths from typhus occurred in Russia during World War I, the Bolshevik revolution,

and its aftermath. In early 1916, an outbreak of typhus had spread
rapidly through the Turkish Army at the Sinai Front, reaching a peak
in March. The periodic influx of soldiers into Jerusalem from the front
presented challenges to controlling the typhus epidemic. In Jerusalem,
many public announcements were made by the health ministry about
hygiene, and toward the end of April, Dr. Beham lectured about typhus
at the Hebrew Teachers Seminary.[8] The Municipal Hospital where Dr.
Kagan worked became a center for the treatment of typhus and other
infectious diseases.

The care of typhus patients by medical personnel was a potentially
dangerous undertaking, especially at Jerusalem's Municipal Hospital.
Contracting typhus in his work there, Dr. Menachem Stein succumbed
to the disease at the end of April. So did a pharmacist, a secretary, two
nurses, and one male orderly. Finally, the director of the hospital, Dr.
Photios Efklides, a Turk of Greek origin, likewise contracted typhus
and died a few days later.[9] Ticho would have the sad opportunity to
attend two funerals for his medical colleagues within a week's time.
Following Dr. Efklides's demise, it fell upon Dr. Kagan to serve as the
hospital's acting administrator for several months.

Dr. Helena Kagan's performance so impressed a visiting Turkish
medical delegation that the young doctor was granted the first official
medical certificate given to a female physician in the history of the
Ottoman Empire. Around this time, however, Dr. Kagan cared for an ill,
incarcerated leader of Ha-Shomer, Yisrael Shochat. The improvements
in Shochat's unhygienic surroundings infuriated the newly appointed
hospital director, Dr. Munir Bey, a Lebanese Arab who had converted
from Christianity to Islam. Dr. Munir Bey and his pharmacist brought
complaints against Dr. Kagan, and she was soon dismissed.[10]

———◆———

Skirmishes continued along the border with Egypt throughout the spring
of 1916. At the end of April, German commander Kress von Kressenstein
and his Ottoman soldiers captured the better part of a British cavalry
regiment and its commander at Katia. On May 5, over 250 British
prisoners were brought to Jerusalem by train and were paraded up Jaffa

Road to the pro-Turkish, patriotic shouts of the crowds along the way. After treatment at the Russian Compound and their dispersal to various detention sites, they were returned to the train station the following day and boarded onto special trains that took them to Damascus. Jerusalem would see more movements of military troops that month. The Austro-Hungarian Consulate notified Ticho and others in the local community that a contingent of the Austro-Hungarian Army would be arriving the following Tuesday morning. Consul Kraus was specifically urging all Austro-Hungarian nationals in Jerusalem to come out and welcome the arrival of their brothers-in-arms.[11]

On the morning of May 9, 1916, Ottoman, Austro-Hungarian, and German flags flew above municipal offices, homes and businesses in Jerusalem and large crowds turned out to greet their countrymen. Like the artillery regiments that had arrived the year before, these units had been recruited from both the German and Hungarian portions of the empire and so their units were likewise designated with the prefix *k.u.k.* The key fighting unit among the newer arrivals was the mountain howitzer division, the *k.u.k.* Gebirgshaubitzdivision von Marno that had been formed from Alpine regiments Nos. 4 and 6 and was named after its commander, Maj. Adolph von Marno. This artillery unit would go on to fight along the southern front throughout the rest of the war. Another well-known unit was the Austrian Army band that became very popular among Jerusalemites through their frequent performances, including performances at the showing of silent movies.[12] Finally, a key unit that arrived that spring belonged to the Medical Corps – the *k.u.k.* mobile Reservespital under the command of Capt. Hermann von Schrötter. The "Austrian Reserve Hospital" was not involved as a *Feldspital* at the front but was rather established at the rear, first in Jerusalem until December 1917 and thereafter in Damascus until the end of the war. Ticho would join this unit in Damascus where he would receive a full commission and assignment to the Reservespital. For the time being, Ticho's own description of his position indicates that he was a "consulting oculist of the German, Austrian and Turkish troops."[13]

The four hundred Austro-Hungarian soldiers that arrived in Jerusalem that May included about ten Jewish soldiers. The unit apparently traveled via the Hejaz Railroad as far south as Amman and came to Jerusalem via Jericho. Accompanied by Turkish soldiers and a military band, Mayor Zi'ah Bey and other dignitaries went out to the south of the city to greet the Austro-Hungarian soldiers. Here by the side of the railway station, the Austro-Hungarian military band played the Kaiserhymne, the imperial anthem that had been composed by Joseph Haydn. Consul Kraus and his deputy were among those who sat in a wagon at the head of the procession that returned to the city. The Turkish military band also joined the procession and played an Austro-Hungarian march.

Enthusiastic crowds watched as the army made its way from the train station to the Jaffa Gate and then through the New City to the Damascus Gate. Jewish Ashkenazim, especially those of the Austro-Hungarian community, went out with their wives and children to see their countrymen; students of the Ashkenazi Jewish schools went out waving their flags. It is very likely that Albert and Anna Ticho both went out toward the Damascus Gate to greet the soldiers. Perhaps Anna was among those who decorated the soldiers with flowers placed upon their headgear and their chests. Although Hebrew-lettered signs had been banned, banners were written in Latin letters saying, "The Jewish Austro-Hungarians greet their brothers with the blessing, '*Berukhim ha-Ba'im* [Welcome].'" Passing through the Damascus Gate and into the Old City, the soldiers made their way to their headquarters at the Austrian Hospice. While the main Austrian contingent occupied the Austrian Hospice, some of the units were headquartered and housed farther away in the western outskirts of the city at the Ratisbonne School, which sometimes would be called Ratisbonne Hospital during the middle years of the war.[14]

After the military procession, the local branch of the Order of Ancient Maccabeans quickly sent out invitations to all ten of the newly arrived Jewish soldiers and their commanding officers, inviting them to attend a reception at the Hebrew Teachers Seminary the following evening. At the reception of May 10, the Moravian-born Ticho was among those invited to speak on behalf of the Jewish community, as was Dr. Aryeh Feigenbaum who was a native of Galicia. It was reported that the seven Jewish soldiers and their commanding officers who were able to attend the reception sat at a table adorned with wreaths of flowers, bottles of Carmel wine, sweets, and fruits of the land.[15]

Dr. Aryeh Goldberg's wife presented all of them with Bezalel-crafted silver brooches, personally attaching the gifts to the soldiers' clothing. Toasts were made to the good health and fortune of Kaiser Franz Joseph and Sultan Mehmed V, though neither would live to see the end of the war that would result in the dissolution of their empires. (Kaiser Franz Joseph would die later that year at the age of sixty-seven, and Sultan Mehmed V would die in July 1918 at the age of seventy-three, just four months before the end of the war.) Led by their officers, a few of the soldiers made some grateful remarks, and the reception concluded with the words "*le-shana ha-ba'a bi-Yerushalayim*" (next year in Jerusalem) and the singing of "Hatikvah." When the initial reception concluded at eight o'clock, Albert and Anna Ticho were among the smaller group that joined the soldiers for a banquet that was held in the courtyard of the Lämel School.

At receptions or soon thereafter, Ticho learned that the chief of the new Austrian Reserve Hospital in Jerusalem was the son of one of his medical school professors, Prof. Dr. Leopold von Schrötter (chapter 3). Like his father, Dr. Hermann von Schrötter was a graduate of the University of Vienna Medical School. He had trained in his father's clinic as an internist with a special interest in tuberculosis and was among the first to introduce instruments into the pulmonary bronchi. The younger von Schrötter went on to do much research in human physiology at high altitudes and in deep diving. In 1894 he designed an oxygen mask with which the meteorologist Artur Berson set an altitude record of thirty thousand feet in a balloon. In 1901, von Schrötter worked with Berson in establishing yet another altitude record in the balloon *Preussen*. Before coming to Jerusalem, von Schrötter's military experience had included service during the Balkan Wars of 1912–1913. In addition to his previous medical writings on high-altitude physiology, he had published on various military medical subjects.[16]

Ticho visited von Schrötter immediately after the company's arrival in Jerusalem and he was quickly recruited as a consultant, even before the first Austrian casualties were brought to Jerusalem from the Sinai

Front. Here von Marno's artillery corps were part of a set attack upon the British fortifications at Romani about twenty-three miles east of Port Sa'id. The combined forces under the command of von Kressenstein included German machine gunners in support of the Turkish and Arab regiments.[17] The attack upon the British stronghold began on August 3, 1916, but after two days of fighting, the joint forces were once again repelled by the well-prepared British and their allies, who went on a week-long counter-offensive, gaining territory further east of Romani. The fighting that week was a turning point in this theater of the war; the Turks and their allies were now on the defensive. Palestine and Syria eventually would be lost to them during the next two years.

———◆———

As a consultant oculist with the Austrians, Ticho did his share in caring for the casualties from the battles in northern Sinai, and he developed a cordial relationship with Captain von Schrötter. The Reserve Hospital at Ratisbonne was on the western outskirts of the city, less than a mile to the south and west of the Lemaan Zion Eye Hospital, and in making his rounds, Ticho would often make his way there on foot. In the later decades of the twentieth century, Ben Yehudah Street and then its pedestrian mall (midriḥov) would serve as a route between the two points beyond the Jaffa Road, but in those days Ticho would have walked westward along a lane that eventually led past a large stone building, a Christian girls' orphanage by the name of Talitha Kumi. This orphanage had been founded and operated by the Deaconess Order that served the nearby German Hospital, built in the 1860s according to the designs of architect Conrad Schick. Toward the top of the tall gabled façade, the name of the institution appeared on a large sign just below a clock and just above a central archway leading to a small balcony. Seventy-five years later, the sign, clock, and archway would be saved from the building's demolition and preserved along with one of the chimneys as a ground-level monument. As Ticho walked by, he would have had to look upward to see the sign "TALITHA KUMI." The words in Aramaic meaning "Little girl, arise" were taken from the Christian Bible and a story of miraculous resurrection.[18]

Turning south, but before reaching the Ratisbonne School, Ticho would pass another Jerusalem landmark – two nearly identical buildings of the Bezalel School of Art and Crafts. The buildings had been constructed by a wealthy Arab notable around 1888, and their exteriors featured roughly dressed Jerusalem limestone trimmed with lighter-colored stone around the edges and between the stories. High arched windows of the central façade were embellished with rounded pilasters. This was the second location of the school since its establishment. In 1905, Professor Boris Schatz had secured approval of the idea for an arts and crafts school in Jerusalem at the Seventh Zionist Congress. Under a Berlin-based board of directors headed by Prof. Otto Warburg, the school had first opened the following year near the Abyssinian Church.[19] In 1908, Schatz had moved the school to this site on the western edge of the New City after the buildings and grounds had been purchased by the Jewish National Fund. Before the outbreak of the war, the school had grown to comprise about five hundred students and teachers who worked there in more than thirty fields.

The war had caused reductions in enrollments and teaching staff at the Bezalel School but the school remained a cultural center. Albert and Anna Ticho had been to the school to view the exhibits in the large central hall of the southern building. The previous fall, Cemal Paşa had also paid a pleasant, two-hour visit to the school accompanied by Jerusalem Governor Medhat Bey as well as Zakey Bey and Albert Antebi. Cemal had been impressed with the monumental painting *The Eternal Jew* by the late painter Shmuel Hirszenberg, and he had even posed for a picture with his entourage, which was taken by Ya'akov Ben-Dov, a photographer who was known as "HaFotograf."[20] However, at another visit, Cemal had reacted quite strongly to Theodor Herzl's portrait (decried to Schatz as "Your Messiah") and this had prompted his order of Professor Schatz's expulsion.

Walking just a block or so further south along the road (later named Shmuel HaNagid Street by the Israelis), Ticho would reach the grounds of the Saint Peter of Sion School that is now better known as the Ratisbonne Monastery. The primary school for boys had been established in 1876 by a converted French Jew and Catholic priest, Father Marie-

Alphonse Ratisbonne. Alphonse's older brother, Theodore Ratisbonne, was baptized in 1827 at the age of twenty-four and Alphonse decided to likewise convert after having a vision of Mary in the church of Saint Andrea delle Fratte in Rome. Encouraged by his brother, Alphonse, Theodore Ratisbonne founded the congregation of Our Lady of Sion between 1843 and 1852. For several years, Father Ratisbonne operated a crowded school in the Old City. He later purchased the grounds of an isolated hill outside the city walls from an Orthodox Christian. After a central building had been constructed, he engaged a Parisian architect, M. Doumet, to draw up plans for an expanded school, which he wanted to be large in order to accommodate many children, and to be beautiful in order to inspire them. The curriculum that was taught by a staff of professional teachers included eighteen different areas, and the languages taught there included French, English, Arabic, and Hebrew. However, the school of Saint Peter of Sion had been closed down in November 1914; its many foreign-born teachers were expelled from Ottoman territories.[21]

The building that lay ahead of Ticho featured a beautiful three-hundred-foot-long façade that had been constructed in an Italian Renaissance-Baroque style with Romanesque elements. Atop a hill, it faced the Old City and a developing New City. The façade of the central building that Ratisbonne had first built was framed on either side by long loggias and one-story buildings that were open to the front through a series of elegant arches. At right angles beginning from each end of the façade, both the northern and southern extensions of the building (built between 1884 and 1891), rose to two stories in elegant contrast to the central, one-story buildings. The Austrian Army utilized several large halls in the basement of the building, which included a kitchen, dining facilities, and classrooms. Clinical facilities and hospital beds seem to have been concentrated in the school's north wing.

While the Reserve Hospital cared for the wounded, it was also a place of social gatherings. Here Dr. Feigenbaum could play the viola in string quartets and other ensembles. On Friday, August 18, Ticho had attended formal celebrations of Kaiser Franz Joseph's birthday at the Austrian Consulate that included a performance by the Austro-

Hungarian military band. The celebrations continued that night at the Ratisbonne School, and although the Sabbath had begun, it is likely that the Tichos attended that evening, where it is said that the band played on until midnight.[22]

Beginning in the early summer of 1916, von Schrötter supported Ticho's requests to the Foreign Ministry that he be allowed to purchase special instruments and supplies from the company Carl Reiner and Lieberknecht, Ltd., in Vienna.[23] The Austro-Hungarian Consulate in Jerusalem had followed with a communiqué noting several reasons to support Ticho's request: (1) The importance of his eye hospital for the region where more than half of the population suffered from eye disease; (2) the fact that a significant part of these people belonged to the Austro-Hungarian colony; (3) that Dr. Ticho was treating members of the Austro-Hungarian and German Military; and (4) that the Sanitätschef of the Reservespital was not able to supply these instruments to him.[24] After giving its approval, the Foreign Ministry sent official notice that their comptroller had handled the payment of 52 K (crowns), 80 h (heller) and that the package would soon be en route by military courier via Istanbul.[25] Although Ticho had requested that his brother, Advokat Max Ticho in Floridsdorf (Vienna's Twenty-First District), handle the payments, it seems that his brother was not involved in this transaction or subsequent ones. On August 26, 1916, Consul Kraus personally conveyed Dr. Ticho's reimbursement to the Foreign Ministry.

Between August 1916 and May 1917, Ticho made at least four more requests for authorizations to purchase more instruments and supplies. As before, all of the orders were placed to Carl Reiner and Lieberknecht with the approval and help of Austrian Consul Kraus and the Foreign Ministry. As in the first instance, the packages arrived by military courier via Istanbul. Because of the strict wartime procedures, many of the associated communications and receipts came to be preserved in Vienna in the Haus-, Hof- und Staatsarchiv.[26]

The instruments and supplies that Ticho received from Vienna during the middle years of the war enabled him to maintain a high level of medical and surgical care. Until the time of the Turco-German-

Austrian evacuation of Jerusalem in December 1917, his inpatient surgical work remained brisk and steady. Ticho's own reports show his continued involvement in the war effort. For example, in November and December, four German soldiers were hospitalized for eye surgery and at least two of them had prolonged hospitalizations well into the new year.[27]

———◆———

As more Austrian soldiers arrived in Jerusalem, Albert Ticho's youngest brother Alfred also decided to come to Palestine, though not as a soldier. At the beginning of 1916, Alfred was managing a large farm outside of Vienna that was considered essential to the war effort. Brother Victor Ticho worked for Alfred for a time, but upon losing his military deferment, Victor went off to fight in the Alps. The Italians had declared war on Austria-Hungary in May 1915 and had severed diplomatic relations with the Sublime Porte that August.[28] As the spring of 1916 approached, the Austrians planned a counteroffensive over the Asiago plateau that in turn led to several battles for control of the Isonzo River. During one of the battles, Victor was captured by the Italians and sent to a prisoner-of-war camp in Sardinia where he languished for the rest of the war. On the opposite side of the conflict, some Italian prisoners of war were put to work on the very farm that Alfred managed.

In spite of his work and a university diploma as an agronomist, Alfred once again found himself in jeopardy of losing his military deferment. During a visit to Boskovice he was ordered to report to the garrison in Brno. Hoping to serve in Palestine instead of Europe, Alfred applied to a special unit of the Medical Corps that had been established to fight typhus, but his application was rejected.[29] When the garrison's sergeant gave Alfred an additional two weeks to report, Alfred returned with several large parcels of hard-to-find food items and liquor. His quartermaster brother, Sgt. David Ticho, had located additional delicacies for Alfred to give to the sergeant, who extended Alfred's military exemption through the end of the war. In spite of this exemption, Alfred made the risky decision to make his way to Istanbul and then on to Palestine. Perhaps his university diplomas and certificates helped him gain transit documents from the Turkish Ministry of Agriculture, but somehow he made his way to Palestine and found work at the Mikveh Israel Agricultural School.

—◆—

During the spring and summer of 1916, Jerusalem's physicians were seeing an increasing number of patients with cholera, a disease characterized by profuse, watery, and bilious diarrhea.[30] Physicians readily recognized cholera, as no other illness produced such severe dehydration in a matter of hours where death could therefore occur quickly. As reported by the Municipal Health Bureau in Jerusalem that summer, there were at least four times the number of cholera cases and cases of deaths from cholera as there were for corresponding illnesses and deaths from typhus.[31] Responding to a request from the Municipal Health Bureau, Ticho participated in the public health efforts to control the epidemic.

Cholera was an ancient disease, but it was not until 1817 that Thomas Sydenham distinguished "cholera the disease" from "cholera the state of anger." The water-borne character of cholera had been demonstrated by the mid-nineteenth century, and soon thereafter, the causative organism had been microscopically identified by Filippo Pacini in the stools of his patients; he designated the "vibrating" bacterium as *Vibrio cholerae*.[32] Doctors of Ticho's era were likewise familiar with the organism's live microscopic appearance: a curved bacillus with a single flagellum that gave rise to rapid and erratic, helical movements.

In addition to the word "cholera" (meaning a bilious flow), the root of the ancient Greek word for bile had found its way into many languages, incorporated as an element into words such as "melancholy" and "cholesterol." The Greek term for the disease had entered the Hebrew language (*kolera*), but an approximate transliteration (*holir'a*) meaning "bad illness" was often used instead.[33] This was the spelling preferred by the Sefardi newspaper *Ha-Ḥerut*. On July 23, 1916, *Ha-Ḥerut* carried a front-page announcement from the municipality's chief physician, Dr. Tzedek Bey, stating that there were two locations where cholera vaccinations were being administered. It was reported that

Ticho was providing cholera vaccines daily without charge between the hours of 2 and 4 p.m. at the Lemaan Zion Eye Hospital while Dr. Aryeh Beham was giving vaccines daily at the Pasteur Institute between 9:30 a.m. and 12:30 p.m. The following day, the Jewish Health Bureau likewise announced that they also were giving cholera vaccinations for a nominal fee of 2½ *grush* at Eye Clinics A and B (in Zikhron Tuvia and the Old City).[34]

Other signs of competition for public service or perhaps public attention can be found in other news items published in *Ha-Ḥerut*. During the middle years of the war, Jewish medical institutions undertook the publication of disease and treatment statistics. First came Dr. Beham's reports for the Pasteur Institute, then Dr. Goldberg submitted his reports for the Jewish Health Bureau that also included statistics for the Trachoma Division and the Jewish Eye Hospital. Perhaps not to be outdone, Ticho also published five monthly reports describing the activities of the Lemaan Zion Eye Clinic and the Eye Hospital for the months of August through December 1916 (appendix 6). During these five months, there were 73,100 patient visits to the Lemaan Zion Eye Clinic. The published data show that 161 patients were hospitalized, resulting in a total of 2,164 "patient-days" of treatment and support. Monthly statistics of the number of Jewish and non-Jewish inpatients were generally provided as were the locations of the patients' places of residence. About half of Ticho's inpatients came from Jerusalem and the others came from various places in Palestine, Syria, and Transjordan. Overall, about 58 percent of the inpatients were Jewish; the rest were Muslims and Christians. During this five-month period, Ticho performed 317 major surgeries and 334 minor surgeries. Except for the report of the September activities, each report listed several types of operations that were considered major. These included at least twenty operations for cataracts, seventeen for glaucoma, and six surgeries of the tear drainage system (lacrimal sac and duct). The most common operation, however, was expression and curettage of the conjunctiva for trachoma (chapter 8).

Ticho's reports to the Hadassah Central Committee reveal further information about the incidence of trachoma among schoolchildren during this same period.[35] That fall, Ticho noted increasing numbers of students with this disease. The previously reported pre-war incidence of 28 percent had declined to just over 11 percent by June 1916 (354 cases among 3,132 children), but by November 1916 the incidence rose to about 14 percent (437 among 3,121 children), since as many as 40 percent of newly admitted students had signs of active trachoma.

Meanwhile Ticho's public reports published in *Ha-Ḥerut* described some interesting cases that reflected the prevailing circumstances of famine and war. In his report for September, Ticho noted eight cases of general blindness associated with starvation or malnutrition (so-called "nutritional amblyopia"); all were Jewish (both men and women) and all but one were between the ages of fifty and seventy-six.[36] Ophthalmologists had long recognized nutritional amblyopia but there was controversy whether other factors such as tobacco and alcohol were causal or coincidentally encountered findings.[37] There were also several cases of severe conjunctivitis of extragenital gonorrhea and a case of diphtherial infection (Loeffler's bacillus). Ticho commented on the seasonal variations of his outpatient practice, noting a dramatic decline in clinic visits as the annual pink-eye epidemic of Koch-Weeks bacillus abated in the late fall. In December, Lemaan Zion handled "only" about six thousand clinic visits, less than a quarter the number seen during of the peak month of August.

———◆———

A period of relative quiet followed the battles of early August on the Sinai Front. That fall Dr. von Schrötter's German counterpart, Maj. Dr. Carl Hegler, turned his attention to organizing medical meetings at the Reserve Hospital for German-speaking physicians who were working in Jerusalem or out in the field. Dr. Hegler had served as Professor of Medicine in Hamburg before the war with several medical publications to his credit.[38] His physician-wife, "Mrs. Dr. Hegler," had accompanied her husband to his field hospitals at Beer Sheva and 'Uja al-Ḥafir (near present-day Nitzana, Israel) but she is not mentioned in the proceedings of the Reserve Hospital meetings.

Summaries of the evening presentations by Ticho and other

physicians at Ratisbonne appeared in a series of published proceedings, called *Referierabenden*, with Dr. Klein of Munich serving as secretary; the first of these publications gives a record of the meetings of both November 22 and December 14, 1916.[39] In the November 22 presentation, Ticho presented a new case of a twenty-year-old Sephardi Jew who suffered from (infectious) Koch-Weeks conjunctivitis superimposed upon (allergic) vernal catarrh, possibly the first reported case of the simultaneous occurrence of both conditions. Ticho was able to place the unusual case into perspective by citing his previously published papers on vernal conjunctivitis.[40] That evening Dr. Aryeh Goldberg of the Jewish Health Bureau and Dr. O. Stross of the Reservespital also gave presentations. At the meeting of December 14, 1916, Dr. Ticho presented a case of ophthalmomyiasis (larval fly infestation of the eye) that was subsequently submitted elsewhere as a formal case report and published in the fall of 1917, just a few months before the conquest of Jerusalem by the British.[41] In addition to Ticho, the report listed physicians who presented or contributed to discussions that evening: Drs. von Schrötter and Stross; three of the "four Aryehs," Drs. Goldberg, Feigenbaum, and Mäkler (minus Dr. Beham that evening); and one other physician, Dr. Canaan.

Dr. Tawfiq Canaan was a well-known Christian Arab physician of Jerusalem who had received a commission as a captain in the Turkish Army immediately after the outbreak of the war. He had returned to Jerusalem from the Sinai Front where he served as the head of the medical laboratories at 'Uja al-Ḥafir. Dr. Canaan was practically fluent in German and in fact he published prolifically in this language. Before the war the young Dr. Canaan had worked at the German Hospital and at Shaare Zedek Hospital before assuming charge of the polyclinic for the Municipality of Jerusalem, and he had then gone on to study tropical medicine and microbiology in Hamburg.[42] For many years following the war, Dr. Canaan and Ticho remained on friendly terms, even in times of tense Arab-Jewish relations. After 1948, the two physicians, just a year apart in age, would reside in opposite sides of a divided Jerusalem.

———◆———

Officially relieved of the Palestine Office directorship, Arthur Ruppin had come to Jerusalem to prepare his work on Syria's economy.[43] When Ruppin's *Syrian als Wirtschaftsgebiet* was finished that summer, a French translation was prepared for Cemal Paşa, who was dismayed that the work did not laud his contributions to Syria's economic progress. He immediately sent Ruppin into exile on eight days' notice. Ruppin arrived in Istanbul in September 1916 and remained in the Ottoman capital through the end of the war.

As Ruppin was disengaging from his official activities in Palestine, other Jewish intermediaries, such as the banker Haim Valero, became involved in government-sanctioned grain syndicates. In October 1916, Cemal ordered fifteen thousand kilos of wheat brought to Jerusalem daily by the military from Horen, Karak, and Salt in Transjordan and delivered to civilian municipal authorities. He also increased the price of wheat by 50 percent, imposed severe penalties for hoarders and offered a percentage reward of recovered wheat for those who turned in black marketeers.[44] The following month, November, *Ha-Ḥerut* still reported, "We hear the call, 'Bread! Bread!' from thousands of starving families of the Children of Israel whose bitter situation leaves them unable to buy even a slice of bread." The article, however, gratefully acknowledged the efforts of the American Joint Distribution Committee that helped distribute wheat and flour to Jerusalem's Jewish community.[45]

As Ticho was becoming more involved with the Reserve Hospital and his Jewish-Austrian brothers-in-arms, he also became increasingly active in organizing medical relief for his brothers-in-distress. In the autumn of 1916, Ticho and other Jerusalem physicians organized relief efforts known as the Medical Assistance Committee for Jerusalem's Poor.[46] In October 1916, Dr. Aryeh Beham wrote to Dr. Thon about a plan to aid the impoverished sick who were forced to remain at home because of a lack of hospital space. The Palestine Office's acting director warmly endorsed the plan. He had already received word from America about plans for a medical relief unit to be known as the American Zionist Medical Unit (AZMU). Therefore Thon felt that the Jerusalem physicians should be funded for this "temporary medical service" until the AZMU would arrive. In addition to Drs. Beham and Ticho, the executive committee included Drs. Helena Kagan, Aryeh Feigenbaum, and Aryeh Goldberg; they worked out a plan of trilateral monthly contributions from the German Hilfsverein ("Ezra"), Hadassah, and the Jewish Health Bureau. Beginning in mid-January, related notices began to appear regularly in *Ha-Herut* announcing the availability of free medical care at Lemaan Zion and at both of the Jewish Health Bureau eye clinics in Zikhron Tuvia and the Old City.[47] The announcements eventually directed patients according to their specific neighborhoods, and Ticho's clinic at Lemaan Zion was cited as taking patients from several areas to the north and west of the Old City.[48]

CHAPTER 13

JANUARY–DECEMBER 1917
THE ROAD TO DAMASCUS

… ה' מתיר אסורים.
ה' פקח עורים…

The Lord sets prisoners free;
The Lord restores sight to the blind.

Psalms 146:7–8

emal Paşa was especially proud of the improved roads and railways
that provided lines of military transport and communication
within Palestine. These routes linked Palestine with adjacent areas of
the Ottoman Empire: to the south with the Sinai Front, to the north
with Syria, and to the east with Amman and the Hejaz Railroad. Meir
Dizengoff was among the contractors, improving the main road from
Jaffa to Latrun and using many young Jewish men who received military
exemption in lieu of their work. In addition, many Jewish soldiers were
removed from their military units, disarmed, and put to work on the
roads and railways under very harsh conditions. Aaron Aaronsohn's
brother, Alexander, had been among those taken from his army unit and
assigned to the working corps, building the road between Safed and
Tiberias. Damascus Governor Hulusi Bey, an engineer by profession,
was persuaded (under threat of execution by Cemal) to expedite the
completion of the most northern segment of the road to Damascus that

began in Kuneitra (now in the occupied Golan Heights).[1] As the war in Palestine turned in favor of the British, the railways and roads to Damascus would become routes of retreat for the Turkish-German-Austrian forces. The Tichos would be a part of one stage of this prolonged retreat just in advance of the British conquest of Jerusalem.

In early 1917, the British were continuing their slow advance through the Sinai Peninsula while the Turks maintained a natural defensive line that extended from their stronghold at Gaza to Beer Sheva, i.e., from the Mediterranean Sea to the foot of the Judean Hills. Under Gen. Archibald Murray and Gen. Charles Dobell, the British made their first attack on Gaza on March 26, 1917. The First Battle of Gaza turned out to be the best chance the British would have to break the Gaza–Beer Sheva defensive line without committing major forces to the region. Dobell was on the verge of capturing Gaza but his last-minute decision to withdraw instead handed victory to the Turks. Captured British soldiers were again brought to Jerusalem and paraded through the streets; wounded soldiers were triaged at a Casualty Clearing Station outside the French Hospital.[2]

Immediately following the ill-fated British attack, Cemal Paşa ordered the civilian evacuation of Gaza, and then on April 6 he ordered the evacuation of Jaffa and Tel Aviv. Most of the ten thousand Jewish deportees headed first for Petah Tikvah before being forced to migrate further north. Meir Dizengoff became head of the Immigrant Committee and the Organization for the Assistance of the Exiles and Refugees. In Damascus he assumed the role of *Raish Galuta* (Exilarch or Leader of the Exiles). While Jewish refugees were still on the move, a second British attack upon Gaza on April 17–19 likewise ended in a Turkish victory. Dizengoff's Immigrant Committee was established in Damascus in May, and following Ticho's relocation to Syria at the end of that year, Ticho would be invited to join the committee, which included several notable leaders of the Yishuv.[3]

In the wake of the mass expulsions, apprehension spread among the Jews elsewhere in Palestine. The mood was also affected by news that the United States had entered the war against Germany with a formal declaration signed on April 6, 1917. The United States never declared war upon Turkey, but American-Turkish diplomatic relations were severed on April 20. This further complicated the delivery of American aid to Palestine, impacting many of Ticho's activities, from his work with the Medical Assistance Committee to his trachoma work in the schools. News of the expulsions were soon known throughout the world, and official criticism was forthcoming from governments on both sides of the world war. The entry of the United States into the war also delayed the deployment of the AZMU to Palestine. Despite America's quasi-neutrality toward the Turks, Cemal Paşa accepted an offer by members of the American Colony to care for the wounded, and he assigned the commandeered Grand New Hotel to them for this purpose as a hospital.[4]

Civilian life was in disarray along the coastal plain following the evacuation of Jaffa and Tel Aviv, though following the Second Battle of Gaza, relative calm prevailed militarily along the southern front and to the east. It was around this time that Ticho joined a group of Austrian soldiers on a trek into the countryside that may have been mainly for recreational purposes. An annotated and dated photograph of April 1917 shows Ticho in uniform among a group of fifteen Austrian army officers who all appear relaxed and refreshed, holding walking sticks in different poses – variously standing, kneeling, seated, or semi-reclining – at a summit in the region of Mount Küra, east of the Dead Sea.[5] About half of Ticho's companions here are wearing one or more medals of honor high above their left breasts.

One of these soldiers in the picture may be Lt. Eugen Hoeflich, a decorated Jewish-Austrian soldier who arrived in Jerusalem in 1917 and was stationed for several months at the Austrian Reserve Hospital.[6] Ticho is among the others without medals though he would receive several during active service in Syria the following year (chapter 14). At the site of the photograph or nearby, the party visited the town of el-Kerak (the ancient Kir-Hareset or Kir-Moab) where a huge Crusader castle, partially in ruins, housed military barracks. The view from the top of the castle included the Dead Sea that stretched out more than two thousand feet below them some miles further to the west, and the Mount of Olives, far in the distance to the north.[7]

———◆———

Like no other British leader, Prime Minister David Lloyd George aspired to the conquest and acquisition of Palestine for the British Empire, and included in this vision was the development of a Jewish homeland there. Gen. Sir Archibald Murray, who had brought the British Army to the gates of Gaza publicly proclaimed his support of a "new Jewish State under British or French aegis [that] would become the spiritual and cultural centre of Jewry throughout the world."[8] However, as Lloyd George's government envisioned expanded British hegemony in the Middle East, it sought support of both Zionist and Arab nationalist movements leading to conflicting and vague promises. The Arab Revolt that had been proclaimed by Hussein bin Ali of Mecca in June 1916 finally yielded some tangible results with the capture of Aqaba on July 6, 1917, by Sheikh Audu ibu Tayi and with the assistance of T. E. Lawrence. The following month, the formation of the first battalion of the Jewish Legion (the Thirty-Eighth Battalion of the Royal Fusaliers) was announced in London.

By the summer of 1917, the war in Palestine had entered a strategic pause. The British expeditionary forces regrouped and Gen. Murray was replaced with Gen. Edmund Allenby, a cavalry officer who had distinguished himself in France. Allenby arrived in Cairo on June 28 to lead an expanding Egyptian Expeditionary Force, poised to begin its conquest of Palestine in earnest. A new Desert Mounted Corps was created and with Allenby's permission, Lawrence went to the Hejaz and returned to Aqaba with Emir Faisal and his Arab Bedouin followers. From here Faisal continued his raids upon telegraph lines, the Hejaz Railroad, and Ottoman garrison towns.

Ticho was likely unaware of specific military developments far to the south as he continued his work that summer as a consultant-oculist to the Austrian Army. In early July, one interesting patient that was referred to him was a twenty-five-year-old Austrian soldier who had just arrived in Jerusalem with a serious eye problem. The soldier had been born with a benign tumor of the surface of that eye and this had become infected as he was in transit to Palestine. Ticho found that the infecting organism was a rod-shaped bacterium grouped in pairs ("diplobacilli") known as *Moraxella lacunata*. On July 7, Ticho took his young Austrian patient to the operating room at Lemaan Zion and closely followed him postoperatively. Noting that the eye had healed nicely within just one week of the operation, the soldier was soon returned to active duty. Ticho later wrote about this patient in the German medical literature, though the article was not published until after the war.[9]

Like the British, the Turks and their German allies also began to reorganize their military forces, and some of the changes became apparent even in Jerusalem. The Yildirim (or Thunderbolt) Army Group was established, which supplanted Cemal Paşa's semi-autocracy in Palestine (and eventually Syria).[10] Gen. Erich von Falkenhayn arrived in Palestine to take command of the Yildirim while Cemal was on a tour of military and industrial facilities in Germany. In place of the Fourth Army, Turkish deployments in Palestine also included the new Seventh Army under the Turkish hero of Gallipoli, Mustafa Kemal (later known as Atatürk), and the new Eighth Army under Gen. Kress von Kressenstein. Both of these armies were placed under von Falkenhayn's Yildirim that the Germans called Army Group F. On September 26, Enver Paşa moved the advance headquarters of Cemal's Fourth Army north to Damascus. Over the objections of Kemal and the now subordinated Cemal, the Germans had been placed in charge of the final defense of Palestine, but they would retreat in the face of superior British forces and relentless attacks, aided by Nili-supplied military intelligence and some cunning diversions. The British attacks began at Beer Sheva on October 31 and, following a late charge of the Australian Fourth Light Horse Brigade, the desert water town was in British hands by that evening. In the Third Battle of Gaza on November 7, 1917, Allenby finally captured the city for the British. It was at this point that the *k.u.k.* Reserve Hospital withdrew from Jerusalem to Damascus, with a smaller facility in Daraa and a convalescent center in Zahle.[11] As the Austrians withdrew from Jerusalem, Allenby quickly moved north to take Jaffa just nine days later on November 16, 1917. He now turned his sights upon Jerusalem. He hoped to deliver the Holy City to Prime Minister Lloyd George for Christmas.

As yet, the Jewish population of Jerusalem was unaware of the publication of a letter of November 2, 1917, written by the British foreign secretary to Walter Rothschild.[12] In response to the Balfour Declaration and coming so soon after the discovery of the Nili spy ring, the Turks reacted very harshly to the civilian Jewish population, placing Jewish leaders in Jerusalem and elsewhere in Palestine in great peril. At Zikhron Ya'akov, seventeen-year-old Sarah Aaronsohn had been arrested and tortured, but she had mortally wounded herself with a pistol before divulging secrets. The physician who faithfully stayed by her side for the next three days while she lay dying was none other than Dr. Hillel Yaffe, the veteran physician of the Jewish settlement who was one of those who had called for the 1914 trachoma conference and whose paper had been read in abstentia. One of the Nili leaders, Joseph Lishansky, was captured by the Turks eleven days later and eventually transferred to a jail in Jerusalem and thence to Damascus. Ticho's colleague Dr. Moshe Neumann, a former attendee of the 1914 trachoma conference, would also be incarcerated as a Nili operative.[13] In just a few months, Ticho would be in Damascus and witness the various sentences that the Turks meted out to Lishansky, Neumann, and their coconspirators (chapter 14).

◆

On November 17, the British reached the outskirts of Jerusalem while on that same day General von Falkenhayn left Jerusalem and reestablished his headquarters in Nablus forty miles to the north. The half hearted defense of Jerusalem was left to Ali Fuad Paşa, the commander of the Turkish forces in the district, and Ismail Izzet Bey, the city's last Ottoman governor.[14] Four days later, Allenby's infantry captured Nebi Samwil, the traditional site of the Tomb of the Prophet Samuel, which lay just four miles northwest of Ticho's hospital. From the hilltop of Nebi Samwil, the British could view Jerusalem and above it to the east, the tower of the former military headquarters at the Augusta Victoria Hospice.[15]

In the final few days of Turkish rule in Jerusalem, Izzet Bey sought to carry out Cemal Paşa's threat to expel Jews from Jerusalem on a broad scale. Under his direction, the Turkish police sought the arrest of many Jewish leaders of the city. Around November 29, the Turkish police arranged a sham meeting of Jerusalem's leaders to discuss the rationing of wheat, and it was here that Ticho was arrested. When Anna Ticho visited her husband, he quipped, "Anna, bring me my slippers please...I'll need them."[16] Anna Ticho urgently sought assistance for her imprisoned husband. The Austrian Consul Kraus had apparently already evacuated the consulate in Jerusalem in concert with the Austrians' military retreat. The role of savior fell to de Ballobar, much to the Tichos' good fortune.

Antonio de la Cierva Conde de Ballobar held deep sympathies for the Jews. His father, Placido de la Cierva, at one time a military attaché in Vienna, had met and married there a Viennese Jewess, Maria Luisa Levi (or Lewita), and Antonio had been born in the Austrian capital. From Spain's position of neutrality and personally representing the interests of a dozen countries in Palestine, the thirty-two-year-old Spanish Consul had assumed an important role in wartime Jerusalem. At his consulate and home near the Abyssinian Church and near the former home of Ben-Yehudah, he continued to host sumptuous meals for the city's elite and ruling class even in the midst of prevailing famine. Calling upon his personal relationships with Field Marshal Erich von Falkenhayn and his aide de camp, de Ballobar was able to bring diplomatic pressure upon Izzet Bey at the highest levels of the Turkish government in Istanbul. He was able to secure Ticho's release within twenty-four hours of his arrest.

In his diary, Conde de Ballobar recorded the following description of Ticho's arrest and his own role in the Ticho's release:

> November 30, 1917... Now we are in the peak mania of anti-Semitic persecution, because the governor does nothing but arrest all of the Jewish notables left and right: Doctor Thon, head of the Zionists, Astruc [Administrative Director] of the Rothschild Hospital, Doctor Ticho, Farhi of the Alliance Israelite, Barouchan and Doctor Schatz of Bezalel, and also the Franciscan Dragoman and other Christian notables, and even a Muslim from Jaffa. For this matter I went to interview Major Schrenger at the Hospice of St. Paul, who sent my information to Field Marshal

Falkenhayn. The Field Marshal immediately answered, thanking me repeatedly for my efforts on behalf of the Germans and Austrians, informing me that he is directly telegraphing Count Bensdorff [*sic*] so that he will immediately send a consular functionary from his country [Germany] and another Austrian to Jerusalem, to be at my service, without any connection to the English. I liberated Doctor Ticho and I was allowed to send the thirty-five North American detainees to Damascus by car instead of their walking on foot. Bravo for Major Schrenger for allowing me to do this![17]

It is clear that the main condition of Albert Ticho's release was that he would leave Jerusalem along with the Austrian Army. Before Albert and Anna Ticho left for Damascus, he met with Dr. Helena Kagan, authorizing her to use the building and the ophthalmological equipment of the Lemaan Zion Eye Hospital as well as his private apartment for additional medical services. Kagan later wrote about her reaction to Ticho's departure in her memoirs: "On the night that he left a new sign was hung above the entrance to the hospital; on it was written 'Hadassah Hospital.' I decided to use the name Hadassah as a reminder of my prior work with Hadassah." The story has become a part of Hadassah folklore.[18]

According to the second-hand account of journalist Pierre van Paassen, the Turks demanded that the Austrians train their artillery upon the Temple Mount and the Mosque of Omar. Although van Paassen fought in the war, he was at this time stationed far away in Europe on the western front, and he did not visit Palestine for the first time until August 1926.[19] The actual first-hand details of the account had been purportedly given to van Paassen by the Jewish-Austrian artillery officer Capt. Marek Schwarz. However, van Paassen's embellishments cited the crazed Turkish orders as having been given personally by Cemal Paşa before he "left for Megiddo to make his last stand before Damascus." As Cemal had left Jerusalem many months before and was not at the Battle of Megiddo, this part of the story or perhaps all of it seems to be a fabrication. Another inconsistency in the account was the defiance of orders by Captain Schwarz, who purportedly had "ammunition for a forty-eight-hour intensive bombardment...[but] rather than destroy Jerusalem, quietly spiked his own guns and walked into British lines." It is not known if this walk into British lines was for the purposes of surrender or escape. A brief biography of Schwarz confirms that he was among the last retreating forces from Jerusalem that made their way to Damascus and that he did not surrender to the British.[20] Ticho also described Schwarz's presence in Damascus and their continued friendship. Despite these inconsistencies, van Paassen's story of supposed Turkish disregard for Jerusalem's Muslim holy places and their salvation by Ticho's good friend continues to resurface from time to time.[21]

With the help of fellow Jews and sympathetic foreigners such as the Conde de Ballobar, several highly sought-after Jewish leaders were able to evade capture by the Turkish police. Dr. Feigenbaum was not so fortunate, and Ticho's outspoken Zionist colleague was arrested on December 7 and subjected to harsh treatment as an enemy. He was forced to march on foot all the way to Jericho, a distance of twenty miles, then on to Salt and Daraa, where he was boarded on a train to Damascus, in all an eight-day trip. Other prisoners who were transferred to Damascus via Jericho were Alter Levine, an imprisoned businessman, poet, and purported spy, and his Arab friend Khalil al-Sakakini.

Soon after Albert and Anna Ticho left Jerusalem, Hussein Salim al-Husayni was reinstated as Jerusalem's mayor, ostensibly to surrender the city to the British. In a tale that has achieved legendary proportions, al-Hussayni's seven successive attempts to surrender to the new rulers of the city came to involve a cast of characters that included leaders of the American Colony, a Swedish photographer, Dr. Moshe Wallach, and finally several British soldiers and officers that led up the chain of command to Gen. Allenby.[22]

Allenby's conquest of Jerusalem began a new era for the Holy City. It ended 730 years of Muslim rule over the city, of which the final centuries had been under the rule of the Ottoman Turks. A war was still raging nearby, and the complete defeat of the Turks and their surrender would take another eleven months. Ronald Storrs was installed as the military governor of Jerusalem and quickly brought martial law and order to the city. The prewar population of Jerusalem had been about 80,000 and had declined to about only about 55,000 by the end of the war; about 27,000 were Jews, half the prewar population. The return of Jewish exiles and new immigration was a priority set by the newly formed Zionist Commission (Va'ad ha-Tzirim le-Eretz Yisrael) under the chairmanship of Dr. Chaim Weizmann. The Zionist Commission was entrusted with coordinating institutional services to the Yishuv throughout Palestine. Under British control, financial support of civilian hospitals and clinics resumed and restaffing commenced. Nathan Straus's Jewish Health Bureau increased its operations and Dr. Aryeh Feigenbaum returned as head of its eye department. Albert and Anna Ticho received news about momentous events in Jerusalem only from afar: The ceremonies wherein the twelve cornerstones of the Hebrew University had been laid before a crowd of almost six thousand guests; the arrival of the AZMU in Jerusalem later that summer.[23] While fighting with the Turks and their allies still raged just miles away to the north and to the east of Jerusalem, the Tichos would participate in the ongoing war in Damascus on the opposite side of the conflict.

———◆———

The exact route that the Tichos took out of Jerusalem is unknown, but in reaching the Hejaz Railroad through either the Jezreel Valley or the Transjordan branches, they certainly passed through Daraa in southern Syria, a city that is identified with the biblical Edrei, the ancient capital of Bashan.[24] The former route, heading north from Jerusalem, would have taken them through Nablus and possibly Haifa; areas that were still controlled by the Yildirim forces of von Falkenhayn. The latter route included the middle portion of the north-south line of the railway that extended from Damascus to Medina, areas that were under the control of Cemal Paşa's Fourth Army, albeit with sporadic raids of Bedouin Arab rebels. The Tichos likely took this latter route, first by carriage through Jericho and then on to Amman under protection of the Turkish VIII Corps's Forty-Eighth Infantry Division.

Even with their hasty departure from Jerusalem, Ticho was nevertheless able to bring some diagnostic and surgical instruments, and a few medical books. He also carried an uncompleted manuscript concerning his aforementioned treatment of an Austrian soldier with an eye tumor. Ticho had already prepared a summary of the operation in which he had removed the oval, white tumor with its "scaly keratinized surface" extending over the cornea and the sclera.[25] In his manuscript, Ticho's treatment was reminiscent of the Christian biblical story of Ananias who had laid his hands upon the blinded Saul of Tarsus, "…and immediately there fell from his eyes as it had been scales and he received sight forthwith…."[26] Occurring in the year 34, four years after the crucifixion of Jesus, Saul was traveling from Jerusalem to Damascus in the company of members of the Sanhedrin, commissioned to destroy the small community of Christians that had been formed there. Recent theories about Saul's call (the Pauline "conversion") include a claim that he was a Roman agent and that the episode of blindness was contrived. Other theories suggest that Saul's blindness may have been the result of injury from lightning, in particular a side flash that produced thermal injuries to the surfaces of both of his corneas but sparing the underlying Bowman's membrane.[27] As written by the physician-evangelist Luke, the "laying on of hands" by Ananias seems to have been the removal of corneal keratinized surface material.

Arriving by train at the Qadem Station in the southern sector of Damascus, Albert and Anna Ticho were likely near the place where Saul (soon to be known as the Apostle Paul) is said to have experienced his blindness. Traveling north by tram to the central Marjeh Square, they passed a gate of the Old City known as Bab al-Jabiya that led to the ancient Straight Street where Paul's miraculous cure was said to have taken place. Ticho's road to Damascus had begun with orders that came from a German major in Jerusalem's Hospice of St. Paul. As Allenby was entering Jerusalem 135 miles to the southeast, Ticho was entering Damascus to continue his work of healing eyes and restoring vision. Here Ticho would also finish his manuscript describing the interesting case of the scaly eye lesion that he had successfully treated. Ticho's case report, a relatively minor contribution to the literature, published after the war, received far less attention than the case of Ananias's cure of Saint Paul as published by the physician-evangelist Luke in the Acts of the Apostles some eighteen centuries earlier.

CHAPTER 14

DECEMBER 1917–NOVEMBER 1918
WAR AND PEACE

... עת מלחמה ועת שלום.

...A time for war and a time for peace.

Ecclesiastes 3:6

A lbert and Anna Ticho's arrival in Syria in December 1917 came as the war was reaching its final stages. In less than a year's time, a peace would be declared that would establish a new order in the Middle East. The Egyptian Expeditionary Force of General Allenby that was now threatening to conquer Syria had been preceded in ancient times by the campaigns of Thutmose III during the fifteenth century BCE. Even by the time of Thutmose III, Damascus had been in existence and continually inhabited for several centuries. Sheltered by the Anti-Lebanon Mountains and supplied by the Barada River, the wider oasis plateau around Damascus held traces of settlements dating back to 9000 BCE.[1] Some eight millennia later, Aramean settlers began to transform Damascus into a center of commerce and governance. They built portions of the Tora Canal that began upstream within the Barada Gorge, thereby controlling the spring torrents of the river, extending the fertile season to the entire year, and expanding farmable areas into the steppes. The Bible describes the rise of the Aramean Kingdom (around 965 BCE) and its subsequent struggle for Samaria with the

176

Northern Kingdom of Israel. Over the centuries, lands once ruled by the Arameans and by the Israelites had fallen to a series of conquerors: Assyrians, Babylonians, and Persians from the east; Macedonians and Romans (and later Crusaders) from the west; and Muslim Arabs from the south.[2]

At the beginning of the First World War, Damascus had a population of over three hundred thousand people, the second largest city of the Ottoman Empire after Istanbul.[3] This included about three thousand or more Turkish soldiers garrisoned there, and by the beginning of 1918, the military presence had grown. By Ottoman standards, Damascus was a modern city with over 1,400 electrified streetlamps and an electric tramway that crossed the city's central Marjeh Square. The square had been built over the Barada River and was bounded by several administrative buildings, including the Town Hall, the Criminal Court and Police Headquarters. Within the plaza there was a tall, bronze colonnade that had been erected in 1905 to mark the completion of the Damascus-Mecca telegraph line. From this square, one arm of the tramline extended to the northwest up to the al-Salihiye neighborhood at the foot of Mount Kassyun, while the other arm extended southward along the western wall of the Old City to the Midan quarter. Toward the Old City the tram crossed Cemal Paşa Avenue (now Sharia Nasr) at the Bab al-Nasr Gate that is no longer present. The grand improvements to this boulevard had been a favorite project of Cemal Paşa who entrusted its construction to his local chief army engineer, Gedaliah Wilbushevitz, and his senior gardener, Baruch Chizik, both Jews conscripted into the Turkish Army and assigned to Syria.[4]

Like Wilbushevitz and Chizik, the Tichos likely sought lodgings in the Jewish Quarter of Damascus that was located in the southwestern portion of the Old City. Although the Jewish Quarter was crowded, lodgings could be found in one of the modest hotels, such as the Hotel Gordon that housed Jewish exiles, refugees, and those who had come to Damascus to help incarcerated loved ones. Three of Ticho's medical colleagues, each one a former participant of the trachoma conference, were languishing in Damascus jails at that time – Dr. Aryeh Feigenbaum, Dr. Moshe Neumann, and Dr. Sonia (Alexandra) Belkind, whose husband, Menahem Mendel Henkin, was likewise imprisoned for his connections to Nili operatives.[5]

For a short period of time, Dr. Neumann shared a jail cell with Joseph Lishansky, but while the doctor was given a short prison term Lishansky was sentenced to death. To their good fortune, Dr. Belkind and her husband were also soon released from jail. Through his connections with one of the head Turkish military judges, Marek Schwarz was able to secure the release of several prisoners where incriminating evidence was not so strong. Likewise, Dr. Feigenbaum apparently managed to escape his lice-infested jail through bribery, using some gold coins that Dr. Helena Kagan had been able to smuggle to him while he was on his long journey by foot to Daraa. Upon his escape, Feigenbaum made his way south to a refugee camp in Kfar Saba where lice infestation was no less a problem. Here he helped his friend Dr. Yaffe fight a typhus epidemic. Managing to cross British lines, Feigenbaum was able to make it back to Jerusalem by the spring of 1918 and reopen the Jewish Health Bureau's eye hospital with funds that were again coming from abroad.[6]

Meanwhile in Damascus, Ticho had been able to connect with other Austrians who had entered military service for their homeland, including Daniel Auster, a native of Galicia and a graduate of the University of Vienna Law School, who had likewise immigrated to Palestine before the war. Auster was serving as an officer in the Austrian Army, but following his transfer to Damascus he had continued to serve as a liaison between Dr. Arthur Ruppin in Istanbul and the Jewish communities in Syria and Palestine.[7] Before dawn in the early morning hours of December 16, 1917, Ticho and Auster were among those ordered to go to the Marjeh Square to witness the execution of Joseph Lishansky and Naaman Belkind, the two Nili spies who had been sentenced to death by hanging for espionage. In the plaza, two tripods of sturdy poles had been erected that would each hold a hangman's rope.

Ticho had been well aware of previous hangings of deserters and conspiritors outside of the Jaffa Gate in Jerusalem and elsewhere in Palestine. Damascenes had likewise witnessed previous public hangings, such as those of May 6, 1916, when mass executions of

Arab notables had been carried out simultaneously both on the Marjeh Square in Damascus and on the Burj Square in Beirut. The Arab Revolt that was proclaimed by Emir Hussein one month after that event would later give those victims an aura of martyrdom in the cause of Arabism.[8] However, opinions about Joseph Lishansky in particular were far from unanimous among the Zionists at the time. After escaping from the Turkish blockade of Zikhron Ya'akov on October 1, Lishansky had turned to some old friends (and rivals) in Ha-Shomer who at first hid him but then decided to kill him. On October 9, the day that Sarah Aaronsohn had died of a self-inflicted gunshot wound, Lishansky was shot twice by his Ha-Shomer protectors-turned-captors and left for dead. Lishansky survived and escaped, only to be captured eleven days later. The extent of his confessions under torture has been disputed, but he may have bitterly pointed a finger back at Ha-Shomer. Twelve other purported Nili members were transferred to Damascus and given sentences that ranged between one and three years in prison, while another thirty were sent to serve in the army.[9]

Large crowds had gathered for the public executions in the pre-dawn hours that Sunday morning in Damascus. When Lishansky was brought into the square, Ticho may have heard him call out in Hebrew, "Hello, Jews. I am going to my death!" Refusing to be calmed by his Turkish guard, Lishansky spoke next to Arab onlookers in Arabic decrying the contemptible, corrupt Ottoman regime and lauding the British conquest of Jerusalem that the Turks had given up without a battle. After the hangman performed his duties around nine o'clock that morning, the bodies of both Lishansky and Belkind were left on display. Auster had brought a camera to the square and he photographed the grisly scene for posterity.[10] Eventually, the controversial Lishansky would come to be seen as a martyr among the Zionists. Just months following the Israeli Knesset elections of 1977 (the so-called "*Mahapakh*" or "Revolution"), Lishansky's reputation was rehabilitated by new evidence, and so the government allowed his remains to be reinterred with state honors in Jerusalem on Mount Herzl. In December 1982, the Israel Postal Authority Philatelic Service included Lishansky's portrait among a group of martyrs described in Hebrew as *harugei malkhut*, i.e., executed by (a hostile) government. Showing that history tends to repeat itself, the most recent martyr included among the *harugei malkhut* as cited by the Israel Postal Authority in 1982 was Israeli spy Eli Cohen, who was publicly hanged in Damascus on May 18, 1965.[11]

◆

In the face of their dislocation and with the backdrop of ongoing military tribunals in Damascus, the Tichos turned to Capt. Hermann von Schrötter at the newly reestablished Austrian Reserve Hospital. The medical unit was now known as the *k.u.k.* Sanitätsanstalten für Syrien (Royal and Imperial Health Institutes for Syria).[12] Although the exact location of this facility has been obscured over time, it was apparently located just outside the Old City in the northeast sector (Bab Touma), at or near the German Hospital, perhaps at the commandeered French or English hospitals along the road to Aleppo. Two other main hospitals had been functioning in Damascus at the outset of the war – the Markaz Hospital in the central city and the Qadem Hospital at the city's southern outskirts. Other facilities that had been pressed into medical service during the later years of the war included the Hamidie and Baramkie military barracks and residential homes near the three northeast hospitals (appendix 7).[13]

On December 30, 1917, von Schrötter instructed Ticho to begin organizing an eye clinic at the new Reserve Hospital. The next day he wrote to a friend back in Vienna, "As a private doctor, I have been busy since yesterday establishing an army eye clinic, and with my improvements I have been nominated as [a fully commissioned] Army Eye Doctor. I could stay because the Commander here wishes it so.... Today we are invited to a New Year's Eve party with the medical officers, which is being held in the Medical Club." During his service in Syria, Ticho would receive several decorations: The Iron Cross Second Class; the Austrian Red Cross with Decoration; the Prussian Red Cross; and the Turkish Iron Half-Moon (Gallipoli Star).[14] Ticho also wrote that he was fortunate to have the friendship of the Austrian artillery officer Capt. Marek Schwarz. Among the last Austrian soldiers to evacuate Jerusalem, Schwarz was now stationed in Damascus, and, like

Daniel Auster, he continued his communications with Zionist leaders in Istanbul on behalf of the local Jewish population.[15]

Ticho also worked on behalf of the refugees in Damascus, joining the Immigrant Committee that had been established under Meir Dizengoff's leadership.[16] The committee included several other notable Jewish personalities: Dr. Jacob Thon, acting director of the Palestine Office; educators David Yellin of Jerusalem and Bezalel Yaffe of Tel Aviv; Joseph Sprinzak, secretary of Ha-Po'el ha-Tza'ir, who would later serve as the first head of the Israeli Knesset and then acting president after the death of Chaim Weizmann; and the aforementioned Gedaliah Wilbushevitz, the Turks' chief military engineer in Damascus.[17]

Ticho was fairly busy in his position as a military ophthalmologist and with his community service. He still found time to put the finishing touches on his manuscript describing the case of the scaly, cystic eye tumor that he had successfully treated in Jerusalem the previous July. The report included illustrations of the histology rendered by Captain von Schrötter and a clinical illustration prepared and signed by yet another comrade (a certain T. Jodel) bearing the date of October 25, 1917. Submitted from Damascus, the manuscript would be published in Wiesbaden, Germany, soon after the war ended.

Anna's experience as her husband's assistant had prepared her well for work as a nurse at the Reserve Hospital. Later on, Anna's service was interrupted when she contracted typhus and was bedridden for some time. As she was convalescing, Anna began to pass the time making sketches, and soon she was sketching landscapes of the environs of Damascus.[18] She would only later develop her skills in this medium to a masterful level in her sketches of Jerusalem and the Judean hills. Some of Anna's sketchbooks from this period survived and a few of the sketches from this period were published in a retrospective of her career.

While the Tichos were able to become somewhat settled in Damascus, several of their friends and colleagues were redeployed closer to the front lines. Their friend Dr. Moshe Krieger, who had previously seen action at the Sinai Front, was sent from Damascus to Nazareth, continuing his road-weary tour of several months. He wrote to the Tichos from Nazareth in March 1918, happy to have seen the Sea of Galilee and Mount Carmel for the first time during his tour, but missing the friends that he had made in Damascus. He thought that he would soon be redeployed to Tulkarem (just ten miles north of the front at that time). In closing, he also gave greetings to their mutual friend, Marek Schwarz.[19]

Dr. Krieger was likely still in Nazareth on March 1, 1918, when Gen. Liman von Sanders Paşa arrived there to replace Gen. Erich von Falkenhayn as the commander of the Yildirim forces in Palestine. The Turkish General Staff had also given him authority over the Fourth Army based in Damascus.[20] Cemal Paşa had returned to Istanbul. Sanders had first come to Turkey in December 1913 as chief of the German military mission, and he had subsequently earned the honorific title of *paşa* through his able command of the Turkish Fifth Army in the defense of the Gallipoli Peninsula. Just one week before von Sanders's arrival in Palestine, Jericho had fallen to the British. Soon after he had taken command, two separate attempts by the British to take Amman were repelled, one at the end of the month of March and one at the end of April.[21] Several casualties from the Turkish-German side were certainly seen and treated that spring at the rearguard hospitals in Damascus that included Ticho's Austrian unit.

———◆———

As Ticho was treating war casualties and others in Ottoman-controlled Damascus, medical relief missions were also arriving in British-controlled southern Palestine. On March 13, 1918, a contingent of the American Red Cross sailed from New York to Palestine heading for the horn of Africa. Included among them was the Jewish surgeon Dr. Jacob Norman and the widowed bacteriologist Agnes Goldman, who was described as a nurse. After a detour to Ceylon, the medical team headed for Palestine via the Suez Canal, arriving in Jerusalem in June. Meanwhile, a second American Jewish physician, Maj. Dr. Solomon Lowenstein of New York's Mount Sinai Hospital, traveled separately to Jerusalem, arriving just before the mission's celebration of the Fourth of July.[22]

As the Red Cross mission was leaving New York in March, Supreme Court Justice Louis D. Brandeis likewise succeeded in obtaining authorization from the American and British governments for deployment of the American Zionist Medical Unit (AZMU). The World Zionist Organization in Copenhagen had first explored the feasibility of a Jewish medical relief mission to Palestine in the spring of 1916 but found itself unable to recruit available physicians from neutral countries in Europe, who were turning their attention to overwhelming medical needs much closer to home. The United States, as yet neutral in the war, was considered to be the only possible source of organized medical help for Palestine's Jewish community. The request had reached American Zionist leaders, including Justice Brandeis and Dr. Harry Friedenwald. Eventually the American Zionist leadership had turned to Henrietta Szold and the Hadassah Women's Zionist Organization to help organize and administer the medical mission. Hadassah's successes in Palestine before the war, through their nurses and local physicians like Drs. Ticho and Kagan, were well remembered. The AZMU was thereby created, but deployment was delayed when America entered the war in April 1917.

On June 12, 1918, the AZMU left from New York City bound for England aboard the S.S. *Megantic* ("Ship 19" among of a large convoy of ships). On board the *Megantic* the AZMU staff consisted of most of the contingent – physicians, nurses, dentists, a pharmacist, medical assistants, and administrators. Some of the AZMU administrators and physicians took separate routes to Palestine while some would not make it at all. At the last minute, Medical Director Dr. Isaac Seth Hirsch determined that he was unable to join. His replacement, Dr. Isaac Max Rubinow, had ongoing commitments and he would not arrive in Palestine until March 1919.[23] The medical advisor of the AZMU was Ticho's friend and ophthalmologist-colleague, Dr. Harry Friedenwald, who would also serve as the acting director of the Zionist Commission in Chaim Weizmann's absence. Together, Drs. Friedenwald and Rubinow would sail from New York for England in late January 1919 and arrive in Palestine only at the end of February.

There were three American eye, ear, nose, and throat (EENT)

specialists aboard the *Megantic*, Drs. Joseph Krimsky, Isak Alcazar, and Solomon Reina.[24] In the course of his recruiting efforts, Dr. Hirsch had, at certain points, offered the first two the position as chief of the EENT department. In regard to these dual appointments, Henrietta Szold noted that Dr. Hirsch had "vacillating ways in engaging the doctors… always on with a new love before he was off with the old."[25] Just days before sailing, Szold negotiated an additional clause in Dr. Alcazar's contract in which he "resigned all claims to the Chiefship in favor of Krimsky" (and thereby membership in the "Medical Board") with the proviso that the two EENT specialists would share approximately equal length of rotations between Jaffa and Jerusalem. The AZMU arrived in Liverpool after a twelve-day voyage and was warmly welcomed with much ceremony in England. Dr. Alcazar swallowed his pride as Joseph Krimsky received special honors given to him as a department chair and member of the Medical Board. However Alcazar would later complain about the lack of fulfillment of the rotation clause in his contract. Upon the arrival of the AZMU in Eretz Yisrael, Dr. Reina was dispatched to Tiberias in a small unit that was under the leadership of the orthopedic surgeon Dr. Henry Keller.[26]

En route through Europe, the AZMU's administrative duties were handled by Adolph Hubbard and Alice Seligsberg, the Unit's Hadassah representative. The head administrator, Eliyahu Lewin-Epstein, had traveled ahead. After crossing the English Channel, the AZMU traveled to Paris where the two administrators and engineer Louis Cantor formally presented the AZMU's plans to Baron Edmond de Rothschild. The baron agreed in principle that the Meyer de Rothschild Hospital would be given to Hadassah and renamed as the "Meyer de Rothschild-Hadassah Hospital, under the management of AZMU." He authorized his son, Maj. James de Rothschild, then serving with the Zionist Commission in Palestine, to draw up a contract when they arrived in Palestine. Leaving Paris, the AZMU contingent traveled through southern Europe by train and then boarded a ship in Taranto, Italy, bound for Egypt. They arrived in Alexandria on August 11, 1918, and were greeted there by Dr. Chaim Weizmann.

Weizmann had been extremely busy that summer. He had orchestrated a historic cornerstone-laying ceremony for the planned Hebrew University on Mount Scopus that took place on July 24 before close to six thousand guests. General Allenby himself had brought Weizmann in his Rolls-Royce and Lord Balfour had cabled greetings.[27] With Allenby's staff of officers looking on, representatives of all sections of the Jewish people and the local populace had symbolically laid twelve cornerstones representing the twelve Israelite tribes, including "a teacher, an artisan, an agricultural worker, a child, and an Arab." Jerusalem's rabbis laid a foundation stone "in the name of Jerusalem" together with the Anglican Bishop and Mufti Kamil al-Husayni. Although Spanish General Consul de Ballobar mused about the seemingly reluctant participation of the mufti, most other British and Jewish leaders continued to find him to be a man of great dignity and courtesy who professed a desire to bring the communities together.[28] Ticho and Mufti Kamil al-Husayni's friendship would be renewed after the war.

On August 18, members of the AZMU crossed the Suez Canal in the midst of a sandstorm. They made their way quickly by train to Lydda (Lod) and then on to their assignments in Jaffa and Jerusalem. In the late summer and early fall of 1918, considerable work was undertaken to bring the venerable Rothschild Hospital building into useable condition. Located on the Street of the Prophets and first dedicated in 1888, the building had been taken back from the Turks with virtually no useable plumbing, lighting, or heating systems.[29] With work still in progress, the hospital was quickly opened and functioning. The Zionist Commission now planned the rededication ceremony that was scheduled in early November, a symbolic time connected with the first anniversary of the Balfour Declaration.

—◆—

While American relief efforts were getting started in the midst of a very hot summer, the front lines to the north of Jerusalem remained fairly static. Overall, the Palestine theater was relatively quiet as afternoon temperatures in the Jordan Valley sometimes rose to over 130° Fahrenheit. Although the resources of the Turkish Army were being stretched thin and morale was declining, Allenby's forces were also depleted by required transfers of several infantry divisions and battalions to France. Allenby reorganized his forces, which now included several Indian Army infantry regiments from Mesopotamia and two of the three Egyptian-based Jewish Legion battalions (the Thirty-Eighth and Thirty-Ninth Royal Fusiliers). Col. John Patterson's Thirty-Eighth Battalion arrived at the front lines near Nablus (Shechem) in mid-June and remained there until mid-August, engaging in nightly forays from their high ground into the enemy-controlled valley, activities that Lt. Vladimir Jabotinsky appropriately termed "small warfare."[30]

In the fall, the "small warfare" ended and one of the last great cavalry operations in the history of warfare turned the tide of the entire war decisively in favor of the British. On September 16, Allenby began with diversionary attacks east of the Jordan that included raids by the Arabs and T. E. Lawrence upon the railroads between Daraa and Amman. The Jewish Legion advanced upon e-Salt while Arab forces advanced on Amman. On September 20, Allenby's decisive blow was delivered at the Battle of Megiddo, wherein the British rapidly swept across the Jezreel Valley. A surprised von Sanders was chased from his headquarters at Nazareth, and he attempted to organize a fighting retreat. By the following day the British had reached the shores of the Sea of Galilee and the upper Jordan River.

By September 25, the rail station of Samach at the southern shore of the Sea of Galilee fell to the British, as did Haifa and Acre on the Mediterranean coast. As Liman von Sanders withdrew his headquarters to Damascus and then further northward to Aleppo, the German-Turkish armies began their evacuation of southern Syria and Damascus. Virtually all remaining Austrian fighting and medical units participated in this retreat through the Barada Gorge to Rajak and then 170 miles further north to Aleppo.[31] As the chaos of war in Syria enveloped the Tichos, British-occupied Jerusalem was undergoing more peaceful transformations. On October 17, 1918, Maj. James de Rothschild formally signed papers that transferred the management of the Rothschild Hospital to the Americans and agreed to the renaming of the facility as the Rothschild-Hadassah Hospital.

Less than a year earlier, the Tichos had left Jerusalem just days in advance of the city's multiple "surrenders" to the British on December 9, 1917. Likewise, just days after the Tichos had left Damascus, that city was also "surrendered" to different parties on October 1, 1918, including the Australian Light Horse, (possibly) a regional Hashemite commander, and, later that day, Lt.-Col. T. E. Lawrence.[32] To help restore order, Lt.-Gen. Harry Chauvel organized an official military procession on October 2; yet another victory parade marked the formal entry of Emir Faisal on October 3.

By the time Aleppo fell on October 25, the Tichos and their Austrian medical unit had already crossed the Amanus Mountains, passing through or near the railway terminus at Dörtyol, about twenty miles north of the port city of İskenderun (Alexandretta). Early in the war, British cruisers had harassed this area of the Levantine coast, blowing up bridges and disrupting Turkish railway and telegraph lines of communications. The Turks had managed to keep control of the region throughout the war with military reinforcements and improvements in the railways and roads. They had also carried out mass deportations of thousands of local Armenians that they viewed as a strategic threat.[33] Retreating further west across the coastal plain that lay south of the Taurus Mountains, the Tichos reached the city of Adana, which had likewise been entirely cleansed of its large Armenian community.

The Tichos appear to have been in Adana when a defeated Turkey signed an armistice with the Entente on October 30, 1918, on the deck of the HMS *Agamemnon* at Lemnos Island in the harbor of Mudros. The following day, as the armistice went into effect, Liman von Sanders turned over command of the Yildirim forces to Mustafa Kemal Paşa, although the "Lightning Group" would be dismantled just seven days later and Kemal would also soon leave for Istanbul. If Ticho was not among the German officers who heard the von Sanders's farewell address at the Adana train station, he would have had the opportunity to read its written publication. The German general cited months of tenacious defense that "gave proofs to the far superior enemy of the devoted bravery of the Osmanic Army, and of the German and Austrian troops fighting in unison with them." Although many high-ranking officers quickly made their way westward across Anatolia, many

German and Austrian soldiers faced delays due to shortages of coal for the trains and deteriorating conditions that would lead to an outbreak of a cholera epidemic.[34]

While the Tichos were thus waiting in Adana, news came of the resounding defeat of the Austro-Hungarians at the Battle of Vittorio Veneto at the hands of the Italians. An armistice between Austria-Hungary and the Entente had been signed at Padua on November 3. That same day, the Italians took possession of Trieste as troops disembarked from the torpedo ship *Audace* tied up at the Molo San Carlo, Ticho's point of emigration six years earlier.[35] Austria-Hungary was now also out of the war and it would officially cease to be an empire with the abdication of Emperor Karl I eight days later. By this time an independent Czechoslovakia had been proclaimed in Prague that included Ticho's homeland of Moravia. However ethnic Germans also declared a short-lived Republic of German Austria that sought to include German enclaves of the former empire, including Brünn (Brno) where Ticho had gone to school and where Anna had been born. Tomas Masaryk, one of the cosigners of Czechoslovakia's Declaration of Independence and very well liked by the Jews, would be elected as the first president of the new country.

Decommissioned from military service, Ticho sought to return to Palestine with Anna but he found that direct sea and land routes were blocked. With permission of the French, the British had landed at Alexandretta (İskenderun) and had temporarily taken possession of the city. Final divisions of the former Ottoman Empire would be based upon many prior, often conflicting agreements among the victorious allies, such as the Sykes-Picot Agreement that had been concluded in January 1916 but held secret for two years. Spheres of influence were already reflected in the military administrations that were being instituted throughout the region. Jerusalem, Nablus, and Acre and their surrounding former Ottoman *sanjak*s were being reorganized by the British into the Occupied Enemy Territory Administration–South (OETA–S), one of four administrations of the occupied territories.[36] The Tichos were forced to begin their journey home in a circuitous route.

On November 3, 1918, as the Tichos were miles away to the north, a dedication ceremony of the Rothschild-Hadassah Hospital took place in Jerusalem. The small balcony at the front entrance on the Street of the Prophets served as the main stage for the ceremony that included representatives of the principle parties: Eliyahu Lewin-Epstein representing the AZMU, Maj. James de Rothschild representing his father and his family's legacy gift; Dr. Abraham Hilkowich representing the medical staff; and the former director of the hospital, Dr. Jacob Segal, who presided as master of ceremonies. A wide array of dignitaries were also present: Maj.-Gen. Arthur W. Money, the military governor of OETA–South; Col. Ronald Storrs, the military governor of Jerusalem; Col. Garner, the head of the Medical Corps; Spanish Consul Count de Ballobar, who still represented American interests in Jerusalem; representatives of the American Red Cross; representatives of Jewish dignitaries throughout Palestine; and naturally local clergy of various religions. Dr. Segal, still wearing a French military uniform, delivered a silver key prepared by students at the Bezalel Art School to Lewin-Epstein, who gave an address in Hebrew, and Lewin-Epstein in turn passed the key to Maj. James de Rothschild, who thanked him in Hebrew and in English. The Mufti of Jerusalem invoked blessings in Hebrew (!) and Arabic.[37]

The rededication ceremony took place only six weeks after the arrival of the AZMU in Jerusalem. A few notable positions were opened to some of Ticho's colleagues who had practiced with him in Jerusalem before the war. Out of ninety beds in the rededicated hospital, twenty-four beds were assigned to Dr. Jacob Segal, who headed the Internal Medicine Department, and twenty-four beds were assigned to Dr. Helena Kagan, who headed the new Department of Pediatrics. Chairmanships and beds assigned to the American physicians included: Drs. Samuel Druskin and Abraham Hilkowich for Obstetrics and Gynecology with twelve beds; Dr. David Satenstein for Dermatology and Syphilology with ten beds, and Dr. Joseph Krimsky for the Department of Ophthalmology. At the time, Ticho had no notion that he would eventually succeed Dr. Krimsky as Hadassah's Chief of Ophthalmology.

CHAPTER 15

NOVEMBER–DECEMBER 1918
RETURN TO ZION

...וקבצתי אתכם מכל-הגוים

ומכל-המקומות אשר הדחתי אתכם שם נאם-ה'

והשבתי אתכם אל-המקום אשר-הגליתי אתכם משם:

...And I will gather you from all the nations
and from all the places to which I have banished you – declares the Lord –
and I will bring you back to the place from which I have exiled you.

Jeremiah 29:14

The withdrawal of the Austro-Hungarian Empire from the World War on November 3, 1918, effectively brought an end to Dr. Albert Ticho's military career. The Tichos were far from the military ceremonies in Padua, and they were also far from the rededication ceremonies of the Rothschild-Hadassah Hospital that took place that same day in Jerusalem. Instead, Albert and Anna Ticho languished in Adana in southeastern Turkey where the remnants of their mobile hospital unit were located. This coastal region, long known as Cilicia and called Çukurova by the Turks, was surrounded on all sides by the Taurus Mountains.[1] According to the secret British-French Sykes-Picot agreement of 1916, the Syrian regions surrounding Damascus and Aleppo and also northern Iraq had been designated as a zone of French "influence," while Cilicia and the entire Lebanese coast (the "Littoral"

of Syria including Beirut) had been designated as part of a zone of direct French "control."

The formal assumption of the French occupation from the British had officially been set to take place on November 1, 1918, although final arrangements for the French coastal zone had only been negotiated between Clemenceau and Lloyd George in Paris in mid-September. The newly appointed Gen. Jules-Camille Hamelin had only six weeks to assemble an army of occupation and move it into Syria and Cilicia.[2] In Adana, deactivated Germans and anxious Turkish civilians were likely concerned about how much initial control a few hundred French officers might have over thousands of Armenian French Legionnaires who would begin their return to Cilicia in mid-November via the ports of Mersin and İskenderun (Alexandretta). The withdrawal of Turkish and foreign military troops began to accelerate, and by the time General Hamelin entered Adana in mid-December, the Turkish forces and their former allies had long since withdrawn. The Tichos once again became attached to a mass migration of retreating and defeated armies.

Farther west, an allied fleet of sixty ships was entering the Dardanelles to occupy the former seat of Ottoman power. The triumvirate of Turkey's rulers who had promulgated their empire's war and brutal civilian repression – Talaat, Enver, and Cemal – along with their close relations, had already fled from Istanbul across the Black Sea aboard a German ship.[3] The Black Sea would also serve as an evacuation route for Albert and Anna Ticho in a circuitous journey that would take them from Adana to Odessa and then back home to Jerusalem. The first part of the journey northward across Anatolia was taken in the company of fellow Austrians and Germans, demobilized soldiers that may have included other Jewish-Austrian friends such as Capt. Marek Schwarz and medical comrades-in-arms such as Dr. Hermann von Schrötter. Overall, the Tichos' journey back to Jerusalem would take about two months.

During this period of hasty evacuation from Adana, the trains were said to be very short on fuel, prompting many to consider alternate routes.[4] In spite of this, the Tichos were able to begin their journey by train, bypassing the steep and winding roads that ascended into the

Taurus Mountains. North of Adana, these mountains formed a long
ridge of snow-capped summits that reached altitudes of nine thousand
feet. The Tichos' train followed the course of the narrow-gauge railroad
through a ravine leading northwest to a point just east of the Cilician
Gates, one of the main passes through the Taurus Mountains. Recent
wartime improvements in infrastructure were apparent as the Tichos
ascended into the mountains through several tunnels and over several
viaducts that had been completed by the Germans and Turks. Over
the centuries, the armies of Alexander the Great and the Crusaders
had traveled southward through these mountain passes. In the reverse
direction, St. Paul had traveled northward through the Cilician Gates on
his missionary journeys to the Roman province of Galatia.[5] In ancient
and medieval wars – the campaigns of Alexander, the Romans, the
Byzantines, and the Crusaders – the Cilician Gates formed a great and
strong defense with their opposing eight-hundred-foot-tall precipices
that were separated by only thirty or forty feet. In the days of modern
warfare however, cannons on the Tekir summit – an even higher
stony plateau overlooking the Cilician Gates – controlled access to
the mountain road below and the mouth of a flattened vale farther to
the northeast. This was the glen of Pozanti (also known as Bozanti or
Pendosis) that widened into a well-watered and relatively flat valley.

The Turks had built a key railway station house at Pozanti, and it
was here that the Tichos and their companions likely changed their
means of travel from train to car, unloading the trucks and automobiles
from the remnants of their motorized divisions, and continued on the
main road. The Tichos' convoy traversed the last short mountain road
north of Pozanti that led through yet another pass. They now emerged
beyond the northern slopes of the Taurus Mountains and onto the
treeless Lycaonian plain. Far to the west, the level expanse faded into
the horizon, interrupted by great volcanic mountains that rose abruptly
at various points of the compass. Just to the north and east there was
the snow-covered double-cone of Mount Hasan, the second highest
mountain of central Anatolia, which rose to an altitude of over ten
thousand feet. Even further to the north, the landscape was dominated
by the snowcapped Mount Erciyes, another dormant volcano and the

highest mountain of central Anatolia at almost thirteen thousand feet. Just north of Mount Erciyes, the Tichos and their companions came to the city of Kayseri (called Caesarea in ancient Roman times) and further north they crossed the southern portion of the Kizilirmak River, the longest river in Anatolia. Here the river flowed to the west and southwest before turning north and east in its broad arch toward the Black Sea. The Tichos' northward path was now more direct, but they once again passed through mountain passes that emerged near the Black Sea coastal city of Samsun. As the Tichos emerged into the narrow band of lowlands with their many farms, they could look up at the northern slopes of the coastal mountains, which were also far less barren than the highland plateau that they had successfully traversed.

Near the city of Samsun, two rivers and their deltas emptied into the Black Sea – the Kizilirmak ("Red") River to the west and the smaller Yesilirmak ("Green") River to the east. According to ancient myths, the Yesilirmak delta had been home to the Amazons, females warriors who had one of their breasts removed in order to shoot easily with bow and arrow. Within a year of the Tichos passing through Samsun, the area would again gain prominence as the base and staging area for the forthcoming Turkish War of Independence led by Mustafa Kemal (Atatürk). However, the remnants of the Turkish Ninth Army had not yet assembled in Samsun, and the Tichos found a quieter port from which to continue their journey. In Samsun, the Tichos found passage on a coal steamer bound for Odessa, where it was thought that the Germans still had influence.[6] After passing close to the Crimean ports of Yalta and Sevastopol, however, the Tichos arrived at Odessa only to enter yet another unstable military zone.

———◆———

The region surrounding Odessa had once been known as Novorossiya (New Russia), and first came under Russian control during the Russo-Turkish War of 1789–1792. In 1794, Empress Catherine gave her approval to found a new port city there, and the Duc de Richelieu, who had fled the French Revolution and served in Catherine's army, served as the city's governor between 1803 and 1814. Jews began to arrive in 1819 when the city was made a free port, and surviving numerous pogroms, their numbers generally increased throughout the nineteenth century. By the census of 1892, the Jewish population of Odessa had reached about 112,000 or about 33 percent of the population.[7] The city had its own Jewish hospital and a fine eye department, whose director, Dr. Nahum Shimkin, was a leading Zionist. Pogroms (1881 and 1905) and the war had initiated mass migrations to the Americas and to Palestine. Immigration rates would again increase, and in the midst of continued political turmoil, Dr. Shimkin was among those who chose Palestine as his destination.[8]

Only after the Tichos arrived in Odessa did they learn of the general armistice of November 11, 1918. They also learned that Charles I of Austria had abdicated the following day (or as he put it, "withdrew from affairs of state"). Peace had not yet come to the coastal areas of Odessa or in adjacent lands of Ukraine that had come under the temporary control of a German-backed, former tsarist general, Pavlo Skoropadskyi. Skoropadskyi formed a short-lived, anti-Bolshevik government in Kiev known as the "Ukrainian Federation," which was overturned by rebels who formed an insurrectionary government called the "Directory." Meanwhile, on November 26, the British cruiser *Agamemnon*, accompanied by British and French torpedo boats, arrived in Odessa. With the French in the lead, the Allies landed forces in Odessa and neighboring Black Sea ports, though they were insufficient to effectively intervene in Russia in support of anti-Bolshevik White forces.[9]

Somehow in the midst of the turmoil, the Tichos were able to make their way from Odessa to Istanbul. Again their trip by sea covered a distance of over 350 miles until they reached the confluence of the Black Sea with the Bosporus. Here the Tichos might have gazed at the steep bluffs that overlooked both sides of the straights, a ruined medieval Genoese castle on the Asiatic side. The trip down the heavily patrolled Bosporus led to Istanbul, and their ship would have likely found a mooring place on one side or the other of the waterway known as the Golden Horn. The traditional Old City of Istanbul, or Constantinople, occupied the peninsula to the south, and a relatively new pontoon bridge, built by the Germans before the war, now stretched across the Golden Horn to Galata to the north. These areas comprised much of the European side of Istanbul east of the Bosporus.

Rising up before the Tichos, on the higher ground of the Old City, the famous landmarks of the Old City included the Topkapi Palace at the Seraglio Point (Sarayburnu), the Hagia Sophia, and the Sultan Ahmed (Blue) Mosque. Had the Tichos been able to reach Istanbul across Anatolia by train, they would have arrived at the Teutonic-styled Haydarpaşa Gari, the Istanbul railway terminus on the opposite Asian shore of the Bosporus. Even if the Tichos could have crossed Anatolia by train, it is doubtful that they could have arrived any earlier than the British and French troops who entered Istanbul in mid-November 1918.[10] When the Tichos arrived at the end of the month, Allied troops were already occupying sections of Istanbul and were setting up an Allied military administration.

Arriving in Istanbul, the Tichos now hoped to make their way back to Palestine. They sought out Arthur Ruppin at the Zionist Office; Ruppin had recently remarried and was also preparing to leave Istanbul with his wife, Hanna.[11] The expulsion of German and Austrian civilians was already underway, and many of the remaining eight hundred Germans were awaiting departure aboard the ship *Corcovado* that had been secured for this purpose. For the Tichos, however, the *Corcovado* was heading in the wrong direction. With the help of their friend Marek Schwarz, they instead were able to book passage back to Palestine, finding accommodations aboard the French collier (coal barge) *La Gaule* provided by the French Navy. Schwarz would be among the passengers.[12] The ship was described as being a "coastal vessel" and so a relatively prolonged journey along the southern shores of Anatolia and along the shores of Levant was expected. According to Ruppin's diary, the *La Gaule* departed Istanbul for Palestine on December 4, 1918, with 410 passengers.[13] Ruppin had considered the journey eastward but he was also worried that the Tichos' route and accommodations would be very taxing for Hanna, who was then seven months pregnant. Passage for refugees to Palestine on this ship was initially restricted to men, but an exception was apparently made for Anna Ticho.

Once aboard the *La Gaule*, the Jewish refugees informally renamed their vessel as the *"Geula,"* a Hebrew word meaning redemption.[14] By mid- to end-December, 1918, the *"Geula"* reached Beirut. Here the ship took on supplies and a few more Jewish immigrants who were members of the local Maccabee Zionist Organization. There was no additional room for women or children, but one of their members, a nurse by the name of Shulamit Yedid-Halevy (later Cantor), was brought aboard the vessel and hidden on deck behind a stack of camp beds. Spirits were high as the *"Geula"* departed Beirut, and together the Jewish passengers enjoyed an evening of song and celebration. Apparently at this point, the young female stowaway was discovered, and the captain began to turn his ship around toward Beirut. After convincing arguments by Shulamit's cousin and others, Anna Ticho prevailed upon her husband to vouch for the young nurse and to vouch for her fare. In doing so, Dr. Ticho was able to convince the captain to travel on to Palestine and not return the young woman to Beirut. The ship turned again toward Palestine and disembarked at Jaffa at the end of December 1918 (or possibly very early January 1919).

The Tichos' return to Palestine occurred at the threshold of the so-called Third Aliyah (1919–1923). This next wave of Jewish immigration would not reach its climax for many months, yet the ingathering of Jewish exiles and a reorganization of society had already begun months earlier under the British. The depopulation of Jerusalem that had occurred during the war was being reversed, and the occupying military administration busily proceeded with its plans to improve the city's infrastructure. During the Third Aliyah, about thirty-five thousand new immigrants would arrive in Palestine, mainly from east European countries. A prominent symbol of the Third Aliyah, the ship *Ruslan* with 650 new immigrants, would sail from Odessa and arrive in Jaffa many months later on December 19, 1919. Among its passengers were four ophthalmologists, Drs. Hayim Yassky, Shoshana (Rosa) Seidel, Judith Kozlov (Kosloff), and Yaakov Cohen (Kohan or Kagan).[15] The previously mentioned Dr. Nahum Shimkin would soon follow. All of these physicians, including Ticho, would face many challenges in starting afresh in British-occupied Palestine.

Arriving safely in the Holy Land, the Tichos went straight on to Jerusalem. It is not known where the Tichos initially stayed upon their arrival, perhaps with Helena Kagan and her mother or at a local hotel. After Shulamit Yedid-Halevy found employment with the AZMU, she was able to move into their nurses' quarters at the Hotel Hughes. The Tichos' close friend Marek Schwarz took up residence on the ground floor of a three-story house on Jaffa Road near the Russian Compound. Another tenant with Schwarz during that time was Moshe Shertok (later Sharett), who had served as an officer in the Turkish Army and who would one day become the first Foreign Minister and the second Prime Minister of the State of Israel. Later that spring, Ze'ev Jabotinsky and his friend Shlomo Salzman rented the flat on the second floor of that same house in anticipation of the arrival of their families from Russia.[16]

By this time, in the late spring, the Tichos had reestablished themselves very near to the Lemaan Zion Eye Hospital. The old clinic building and their former residence had been commandeered by the British Army during the war, and stables for the cavalry had been added to the property.[17] Dr. Ticho quickly worked to reestablish his clinic, although initially he was short on resources. During the war, his brother, Alfred, had arranged the sale of Albert's gold in Vienna and transferred the savings to an intermediary in Lucerne, Switzerland. Austria's misfortunes in war, combined with hesitation on the exchange of Austrian crowns for Swiss francs, had wiped out the value of these savings, and they became almost as worthless as the remaining Turkish money in Albert's wallet. Further support from Germany was no longer available. The activities of the Palästinensischer Hilfsverein had been permanently disrupted, and the German economy was in collapse. Before the war, for example, the German mark had been worth twenty-four cents, but it had fallen to two cents by the end of 1919 and a period of even much worse hyperinflation would follow.[18] Fortunately at this time, the Tichos' extended family came to their aid; Albert and Anna proceeded to rebuild their lives.[19]

With financial help and based upon his previously earned reputation,

Ticho was able to reopen his practice, establishing a new clinic and hospital on St. George's Road, less than two-tenths of a mile further north along the road that led between the Hungarian Houses and the former Lemaan Zion Eye Hospital. Meanwhile, there were other hospitals and clinics in the city where ophthalmologic services were available from colleagues and competitors. Dr. Aryeh Feigenbaum had reopened the Jewish Health Bureau's Eye Hospital in the spring of 1918, and it was receiving funding support through the Joint Distribution Committee and Nathan Straus among others.[20] At the war-damaged British Ophthalmic Hospital, Capt. William Gowans of the Royal Army Medical Corps could see only outpatients, as did his successor Capt. Thomas Findlater. Later, on June 30, 1919, the first inpatients were admitted under the care of the new Surgeon-in-Charge, Lt.-Col. John C. Strathearn, who had been an assistant surgeon to Dr. Cant at the hospital before the war.[21]

At the Rothschild-Hadassah Hospital, Dr. Joseph Krimsky was chairman of the eye department that provided full outpatient and inpatient care. The AZMU was adding hospitals and clinics in Palestine's largest towns and cities where there was a significant Jewish population. In Jerusalem, "Hadassah" Hospital had already established a nurses' training school. Because of her nursing skills and ability to teach in Hebrew, Shulamit Yedid-Halevy was hired by the AZMU's acting medical director, Dr. Benjamin Roman. Ticho would also soon begin to teach at the Nurses' Training School, which was the first such school anywhere to teach nursing in the Hebrew language. However, Ticho now gave his full attention to the new clinic and eye hospital that comprised his private practice. The inpatient portion eventually grew to contain about twenty inpatient beds, and once again the Tichos established a comfortable residence above the clinic. Located a bit further north on St. George's Road, the area would acquire notoriety between 1948 and 1967 as the Mandelbaum Gate border checkpoint in a divided Jerusalem.[22]

CHAPTER 16

JANUARY 1919–FEBRUARY 1922
UNDER NEW MANAGEMENT

... והסרתי מחלה מקרבך:

...And I will remove sickness from your midst.

Exodus 23:25

Thirteen months had passed since Dr. and Mrs. Ticho had joined the hasty retreat of the Turks, Germans, and Austro-Hungarians from Jerusalem. All three empires of the once-allied army now lay supine in defeat and dissolution. There had been two imperial abdications in Central Europe, and it would not be long before the last figurehead Ottoman sultan in occupied Istanbul would follow. Trading one empire for another, Jerusalem was now under the control of the British as part of the Occupied Enemy Territory Administration (OETA) South. The country was under new management, although the British were following the "Laws and Usages of War" in its attempts to administer Palestine along Turkish lines.[1] The Rothschild Hospital was also under new management by the Americans, with new satellite operations throughout Palestine. These were administered by the American Zionist Medical Unit (AZMU) under the auspices of Hadassah and the Zionist Commission in Palestine that had been formally recognized by the British.

Soon after arriving in Jerusalem, Ticho paid visits to colleagues

Jacob Segal and Helena Kagan, who were now the chairpersons of the Internal Medicine and Pediatrics Departments at the flagship Hadassah Hospital. Ticho learned that his friend and colleague Dr. Harry Friedenwald would soon be en route to Palestine to serve a six-month tour as Acting Chairman of the Zionist Commission. The Zionist Organization of America also had appointed Friedenwald as Medical Advisor to the AZMU and a member of its Executive Committee. As a member of the Zionist Commission he was also given authority to collect and prepare material and data for the eventual creation of a Medical Department of the Hebrew University. Both Dr. Friedenwald and AZMU Medical Director Dr. Isaac Max Rubinow were aboard the S.S. *Nieuw Amsterdam* bound for England when it sailed from New York to England on January 23, 1919. From England, Friedenwald and Rubinow went on ahead to Palestine, arriving in Jaffa on February 24 and in Jerusalem three days later in the company of Eliyahu Ze'ev Lewin-Epstein. This was coincidentally just one day after Allenby presided over the official reopening ceremonies of the British Ophthalmic Hospital.[2]

Upon their arrival in Jerusalem, Lewin-Epstein took Friedenwald and Rubinow for a tour of the renovated Rothschild-Hadassah Hospital and then to the AZMU's administrative offices at the Hôtel de France. Later that day, Friedenwald visited Dr. and Mrs. Ticho at their new clinic and Friedenwald brought news that Ticho had been invited by Rubinow to discuss working for the AZMU. The following week, Ticho called upon Rubinow at the Hôtel de France, where he found the director well briefed about Ticho's previous work with Dr. Kagan and his mentoring relationships with Hadassah's first nurses before and during the war.[3] Although Ticho was now fully engaged in his private practice, he offered to substitute for Dr. Joseph Krimsky in the eye clinic when necessary.

One of Krimsky's longest absences from Jerusalem occurred that spring when he was appointed to participate in an extended tour of Jewish settlements, an "Expedition for the Survey of Sanitary Conditions." Led by the Haifa physician Dr. Hillel Yaffe, this expedition was a collaborative effort organized by the AZMU and local physicians: Drs. Krimsky and A. M. Hilkowich of the AZMU; their public health worker Dr. Samuel Schmidt; and local Jerusalem physicians Drs. Aryeh Beham and Aryeh Goldberg. The AZMU's collaboration was seen as an important effort to appease local and established non-AZMU physicians. Several of these local physicians formed the leadership of the newly reorganized Medical Society in the Land of Israel (Ha-Histadrut ha-Refu'it be-Eretz Yisrael), and they were among the AZMU's harshest critics, though Ticho was not among them.[4]

Ticho's reestablished private practice was not publicly touted by the Zionist Commission, perhaps because he was outside of the Zionist mainstream or perhaps because the practice was still relatively small. The clinic and small hospital were not mentioned in the regional guidebook the Commission published in 1920.[5] On the other hand, Ticho's work for the AZMU and his commitment to his private practice were both mentioned in reports that were sent to Henrietta Szold in New York, and his business relationship with the AZMU was described as being on a "friendly footing." As Krimsky's one-year contract would soon expire, Rubinow clearly thought that Ticho would be an excellent choice to succeed Krimsky as the full-time chairman of the Eye Department. Only the issue of Ticho's private practice was considered to be an obstacle.[6] However, by the summer of 1919, Friedenwald had prevailed upon Rubinow to hire Ticho as Krimsky's successor on very exceptional terms that included Ticho's retention of his private practice. These conditions were offered with much trepidation by Rubinow, who had a background of socialist philosophies and activities.

The Russian-born Dr. Isaac Max Rubinow had immigrated to America in 1893. He obtained an MD degree from New York University Medical School and had worked in the poor Jewish neighborhoods of New York City's Lower East Side. He enrolled in Columbia University studying economics, statistics, sociology, and political philosophy, receiving a PhD in 1914.[7] He was a founding member of the American Socialist Party, and he had been a leading activist in the social insurance movement in America, a movement that he had seen collapse. In response to internal and external pressures, the American Medical Association had dismissed him from his committee work on social insurance. Rubinow hoped that his ideas that had failed to take hold in America could be implemented through the AZMU and that they would resonate with a socialist-leaning population in Palestine. He cited comparisons of the AZMU to "the history of rural medicine in Russia, the famous system of *Aamakaya Meditzina*."[8] Rubinow envisioned a socialist society where private practice would be replaced by salaried service in the framework of public health organizations. His appointment as medical director of the AZMU offered him "an opportunity to head an organizational experiment in socialized medicine."[9] As the AZMU expanded its services to the Jewish population throughout Palestine, centralized management and medical services were based upon a national hospital and clinic network. It was a management system in which private practice was seen as an impediment.

In spite of his socialist background and philosophies, Rubinow was also a pragmatist in matters of administration and finance. One of the issues that he quickly faced was the forthcoming expiration of the one-year contracts for American physicians, virtually all of whom held key positions. These included all of the AZMU eye, ear, nose, and throat specialists. Rubinow asked Krimsky to stay on but the latter had declined; Isak Alcazar was not asked to stay, perhaps due to the latter's many complaints about various breeches of his contract by the AZMU (though it appears his complaints were justified). Rubinow wrote to Miss Szold, "I am almost assured of Dr. Ticho's willingness to join us, and I do not think that we would have any difficulty with Dr. Feigenbaum if we needed him. Dr. David, whom you might have met on your visit to Palestine, is also anxious to join us – though his terms are rather stiff. One or two men have already come in from Europe."[10]

All three of the AZMU's eye, ear, nose, and throat specialists returned to America in July 1919: Drs. Krimsky, Alcazar, and Reina. The following spring, Dr. Josef Fleischner, who had practiced briefly in Palestine before the war, returned to become the sole otolaryngologist of the AZMU. He settled in Jerusalem, and as a fellow Czechoslovak citizen, he was quickly befriended by Ticho. Dr. Fleischner's stay, however, was again short-lived as he returned to Prague in December 1920, ostensibly because of the illness of his father. A salary dispute may also have been a factor in his decision. Years later, as Germany prepared its invasion of Czechoslovakia, Fleischner returned to Palestine for a third and final time, finding employment with Ticho (chapter 19).[11]

Friedenwald had previously pointed out that the original salary scale had been somewhat extravagant, especially for "the elect and favored," and that this had stimulated excessive greed for salaries that were entirely out of proportion to the resources of the country. He had recommended that the AZMU should try to employ local physicians at relatively lower salaries instead of engaging expensive American physicians.[12] However, for experienced local physicians, the ban on private practice represented an obstacle to joining the AZMU and was also a source of complaints from those who joined under the original ban. As Rubinow wrote, "The local physicians pleaded that, as the Unit was a temporary organisation, they could not afford to abandon private practice altogether; they might find it hard to re-establish themselves when the Organisation was disbanded."[13] As a compromise, Dr. Rubinow offered Dr. Ticho an exception that allowed him to continue his private practice while turning over the monetary proceeds of his practice to the AZMU. Thus Dr. Albert Ticho was hired as the first local physician to be the head of Hadassah's Eye Department. Like other full-time AZMU physicians, Dr. Ticho was given two weeks of yearly vacation and two and a half sick days per month; he was eligible for a pension and worker's compensation insurance.

Dr. Ticho's hiring, however, resulted in a "domino effect" in which the exception he received to engage in private practice was soon extended to five other local physicians. As Dr. Rubinow wrote to Miss Szold, "The appointment of Dr. Ticho with a right to private practice was the first break in our system. That was done by Dr. Friedenwald as an exception in view of Ticho's professional standing, but exceptions are very hard to keep up in Palestine." Dr. Rubinow further cited subsequent contract negotiations with Dr. Helena Kagan, who was granted the right of free private practice and a raise in salary to forty pounds per month; he also noted that Dr. Jacob Segal, "considering himself a higher man professionally than Dr. Kagan," demanded fifty pounds and private practice, giving a larger salary than either Dr. Biskind or Dr. Roman.[14] Local physicians to whom Rubinow made concessions included Dr. Meshulam Levontin in Tel Aviv and ophthalmologist Dr. Ya'akov David in Tiberias.

In addition to the pool of well-established local physicians, an influx of new immigrant physicians also helped to maintain staffing of the AZMU, even as the original medical contingent left and returned home to America. The newer immigrant physicians were given less favorable contracts and eventually served as leverage when the AZMU sought to eliminate the private practices of their senior staff. One of the first physicians who immigrated to Palestine after the war was Czech ophthalmologist Dr. Erich Raubitcheck, who arrived in June 1919 with his pediatrician wife, Else.[15] They worked unhappily in Safed until their request for a transfer to Jaffa was fulfilled. For a time, Drs. Ticho and Raubitcheck were the only ophthalmologists employed by the AZMU, and although their careers never fully intersected, they remained in contact and on very cordial terms throughout their lives (chapter 19). In Jaffa, Dr. Raubitcheck was temporarily assigned two assistants in succession, Dr. Judith Kozlov (Kosloff), who had studied medicine in Kharkov and ophthalmology in Russia, and Dr. Yaakov Cohen, who had trained as an ophthalmologist in Moscow.[16] As mentioned (chapter 15), both Kozlov and Cohen had come to Palestine in December 1919 on the *Ruslan*, and both subsequently transferred to Jerusalem under Ticho. Rubinow had discovered that it was much easier to transfer more junior staff members who did not have private practice obligations in a fixed location. Although Rubinow often transferred junior physicians where needed, he also recognized that "continuous changes are not very desirable." Dr. Shoshana (Rosa) Seidel, for example, another ophthalmologist who arrived on the *Ruslan*, was promply hired by the AZMU for work in Haifa, but she practiced in that same city for most of her long career.[17]

Rubinow's desire for the AZMU to provide basic welfare services for the Yishuv followed precedents that had been addressed by Hadassah prior to and during the war through their visiting nurses and supervising physicians, who included Drs. Ticho and Kagan (chapters 8–10). Accordingly, Rubinow established an administrative division for the medical supervision of schools known as the Department of Hygiene.[18]

The arrival of Yaakov Cohen as Ticho's assistant and the hiring of additional nursing staff made it possible for Ticho to re-establish his trachoma work in Jerusalem's schools; and others, such as American dermatologist Dr. David Satenstein, likewise undertook public health work with Jerusalem's schoolchildren and their families.[19] Satenstein was followed by Dr. Mordecai Boruchov (Berachyahu) and his wife, Anna, who was also a dermatologist-physician who was of great help with the examinations of schoolgirls.[20] The organization of the Department of Hygiene in 1921 shows two main divisions of the department under Mordecai Borochov, with Ticho as a full-time appointee as head of the Department of Ophthalmology and Dostrovsky as a part-time appointee as head of the Department of Dermatology, with assistants, nurses, and the appointments of physicians in the satellite hospitals of Jaffa, Haifa, Tiberias, and Safed.[21]

In addition to his public health assignments with the AZMU, Ticho began to teach students in the Nurses' Training School. He gave about five hours of lectures in ophthalmology per week to the nursing students. The other physician-faculty members were Jacob Segal (Internal Medicine), Helena Kagan (Pediatrics), Mordechai Berachyahu (Hygiene and Infectious Diseases), Israel Biskind (Surgery), and Aryeh Dostrovsky (Dermatology). Dostrovsky later became Professor of Dermatology at the Hebrew University Hadassah Medical School and, some decades later, Dostrovsky and Ticho would author a paper together describing a novel treatment for leprosy.[22]

AZMU nurses who served as instructors included the Head of Nursing, Anna Kaplan, who was one of two remaining nurses from the original group of twenty-two nurses that sailed from New York in June 1918 aboard the S.S. *Megantic*. Kaplan had survived a severe case of influenza and had stayed a few extra months in England to convalesce. Another main nurse-instructor was Shulamit Yedid-Halevy, whom the Tichos had befriended after she stowed away on the *La Gaule* (chapter 15). Yedid-Halevy had been instrumental in assuring that this first group of nursing students received much of their education in Hebrew.

—◆—

Albert Ticho was very much at the center of the AZMU's internal issues of staff salaries and assignments, issues that arose in the context of wider health-care delivery systems in Palestine at that time. For example, the AZMU, its administrators, and its medical staff (including Ticho) were affected by pressures and criticisms arising from outside of the organization, especially from local, non-AZMU physicians. These physicians had amalgamated the medical societies of Jaffa and Jerusalem and formed the aforementioned Histadrut that planned to operate in three areas: (1) professional continuing education; (2) protecting professional interests and rights of its members; and (3) emphasizing the Jewish-national character of the organization. Most of the Medical Society's leaders were very critical of the AZMU and its director. They attacked Rubinow in public addresses, in the press, and sometimes in the courts. In his letters back to Henrietta Szold, Rubinow wrote that these pugnacious leaders included "the famous clique of the doctors, Beham, Goldberg, Feigenbaum, Sherman, Fuchovsky [Pouchovsky], who are biding the time when I will retire and they can get hold of the Unit and its budget to their own advantage. I should want to keep up this work until it is safe from their scheming."[23]

In contrast to the Zionists' campaign for the exclusive use of Hebrew ("rak 'Ivrit") Rubinow was practically illiterate in the language and relied heavily upon English and sometimes Russian. He repeatedly clashed with the administrator of the Kupat Ḥolim, Jacob After, and the Labor Federation's newspaper, *Ha-Po'el ha-Tza'ir*, at one point called for a boycott of the AZMU and urged them to "go home back to America."[24] Another important critic of the AZMU was the vice chairman of the Zionist Commission, Menachem Ussishkin, who was determined to bring the AZMU fully under local Zionist control. He sought to impose a mandate that all internal and external communications be done in Hebrew. The AZMU director soon recognized that Ussishkin's stance was far more popular on a local level and, in an attempt to compromise, promised that the Unit would "endeavor to further the use of Hebrew in the Unit" and to make the official language of the Unit "primarily Hebrew and secondarily English." Rubinow's relations with the Zionist Commission became further strained when a confidential cablegram from Szold to Rubinow about confrontations with Ussishkin became public.[25] Nevertheless, Rubinow held firm on the question of independence of the AZMU from the Zionist Commission and he even sought to absorb the Zionist Commission's system of local clinics known as the Ezrah Meditzinit.[26]

Against this background of external opposition to the AZMU and internal dissension among the staff, a surprise party was held at the Rothschild-Hadassah Hospital on February 24, 1920, ostensibly to celebrate the anniversary of Dr. Isaac Rubinow's arrival in Palestine. The party was the idea of the Unit's chief surgeon Dr. Israel Biskind, and AZMU financial officer Robert Kesselman served as the master of ceremonies.[27] The "humorous" barbs and criticisms that were aimed at the guest of honor were designed to express the discontent among several of the medical staff members. As the criticisms continued, Drs. Ticho, Segal, and Kagan remained silent. Over the next two weeks, Rubinow held a series of separate, private meetings with members of the medical staff, identifying the different factions within his ranks: those who supported the transfer of the AZMU to the control of the Zionist Commission as Ussishkin had proposed; those who opposed transfer yet sought to force Rubinow's resignation; and only one strong supporter in the person of Dr. Kagan, who urged Rubinow to fight a petition drive aiming to force his resignation that she and Ticho had refused to sign.[28] When Rubinow accompanied Helena Kagan to Jaffa for her previously planned trip to Europe, Rubinow's medical staff was meeting back in Jerusalem to plan their strategy for the first meeting of an advisory Medical Council to be held the following day. A full-scale revolt was in the works, and it seemed to Rubinow that Histadrut leaders were being kept closely informed.

———◆———

Even as the AZMU medical staff squabbled internally with the administration and among themselves, the leadership of the Yishuv squabbled over the issue of self-defense concerning Jerusalem and points farther distant. Between September and December 1919, British forces had withdrawn from the Upper Galilee zone of the OETA that had been assigned to the French. Four Jewish settlements (Metula, Kfar Giladi, Tel Hai, and Hamara) were exposed to armed Bedouin raids in a lawless frontier area. The Jewish defense of the region, led by Joseph Trumpeldor, was undermanned and scantily armed. During the last week of February 1920, Jabotinsky sparred with Ben Gurion and others over the feasibility of defense, the existential implications of retreat, and even the "political value and political influence of martyrdom."[29] During this time, AZMU surgeon Dr. George (Gershom) Garry arrived in Kfar Giladi as the sole physician in the area. On Saturday morning, March 1, 1920, about two hundred armed Shiite Bedouins surrounded Tel Hai, and warning gunshots of alarm from Tel Hai were heard just over a mile away in Kfar Giladi. The reasons for the subsequent violence will forever remain in doubt, but when Trumpeldor and his company of nine men reached Tel Hai, a deadly firefight broke out.[30] By the time Dr. Garry arrived at Tel Hai several hours later, five Arabs and five Jewish settlers were dead and ten Jewish settlers, including Trumpeldor, were severely injured. Trumpeldor died of his wounds en route to Kfar Giladi, though others survived and were evacuated to Metula and Sidon. Garry reported the following words were spoken by the mortally wounded Trumpeldor: "It does not matter. It is good to die for one's country." Jabotinsky, until then a doubter of the influence of martyrdom, eloquently eulogized Trumpeldor and his companions in *Haaretz* and later in his poem, "Song of the Prisoner of Acre."[31]

The massacres at Tel Hai further polarized Jews and Arabs in Palestine as political developments in Syria were unfolding. The following week, Faisal was declared King of the Arab Kingdom of Syria by the Syrian National Congress. Although Faisal's "Greater Syria" included claims to Lebanon and, most importantly for the Jews, Palestine, his reign and these territorial claims would soon be overturned by the victorious Allied Powers at the San Remo Peace Conference. One of Faisal's supporters was twenty-five-year-old Amin al-Husayni, the half brother of Mufti Kamil al-Husayni. Amin spent the rest of March in Damascus, returning to Jerusalem on April 1, becoming a key figure in a violent clash there between Arab nationalists and Zionists.[32]

On the Zionist side of the equation, leaders such as Ze'ev Jabotinsky and Chaim Weizmann wrote about their fears of imminent Arab riots in the face of standing military orders for a passive reaction. In Jerusalem, Jabotinsky openly began organizing Jewish self-defense.[33] In March 1920, in advance of the Muslim Nebi Musa festival, Jabotinsky recruited about two hundred men in Jerusalem, several of them quite young but many among them former soldiers. Jerusalem was divided into four "military sectors," and Ticho's private hospital was among four first-aid stations that were set up in various Jewish neighborhoods of the New City. Many of the religious Jewish inhabitants of the Old City rejected Jabotinsky's organizing efforts, and they ignored Dr. Aryeh Mäkler's efforts to organize a first-aid station among them. It has been noted that these preparations were the first example of self-organized military medical units in the history of the Yishuv.[34]

During the first week of April 1920, the beginning of Passover coincided with the Easter weekend (on both the Orthodox and Western Latinate calendars) and the Muslim Nebi Musa festival. On Friday morning, April 2, while Jabotinsky's followers watched over Jews making their way to the Kotel, organized processions of Christians thronged the Via Dolorosa and the traditional organized Nebi Musa procession passed David Street on the way to the Haram forecourt. Here Muslims listened to speeches by the Mufti Kamil al-Husayni and his young half brother, Haj Amin. On Sunday, April 4, the main procession of the Muslim pilgrims – including many from Hebron – coming to Jerusalem from the shrine of the prophet Musa (Moses), stopped on Jaffa Road just opposite the Jaffa Gate. Here inflammatory speeches were given by Arab notables, including Aref al-Aref, the editor of the popular nationalist newspaper *al-Suriyya al-Janubiyya* (the Southern Syria) and Jerusalem's mayor, Musa Kazim al-Husayni. The crowd responded with cries (in Arabic), "We will drink the blood of the Jews" and "Palestine is our land, the Jews are our dogs!"[35]

A riot ensued just inside the Jaffa Gate, allegedly provoked by Jewish spectators. Violence flared off and on for three days. The Zionists noted that Governor Ronald Storrs had early on deployed only a small fraction of the available police into the Old City, a force mainly consisting of Arabs. Once the riots began, Storrs confiscated Jabotinsky's pistol and prevented his volunteers from entering the Old City that was being ransacked. Ticho undoubtedly treated a number of casualties at his private hospital, but with the exception of one patient, no specific record remains extant. Nearby at the Rothschild-Hadassah Hospital, Pinhas Rutenberg coordinated volunteers in all capacities after Jabotinsky's arrest. Ticho's friend Marek Schwarz had been present with others for Jabotinsky's "last meal" before he surrendered himself to the British. In the end, the riots resulted in five Jews and four Muslims killed. The tally of wounded civilians was 211 Jews, 21 Muslims, and 3 Christians. Two Jewish girls were raped.[36]

A continued debate has ensued ever since the Nebi Musa riots as to whether they could be characterized as a pogrom against the Jews. The Zionists quickly applied this term, as they perceived the British military inaction as the collusion of an official power with those perpetrating organized slaughter.[37] Regardless of the definition, the riots presented a clear argument for the transition from military occupation to civilian mandate, as was sanctioned just a few weeks later at the San Remo Peace Conference.

Meanwhile, Jabotinsky had already been tried before a military court for the possession of an illegal firearm and subversive activities. During the trial, Isaac Rubinow testified that he was present when British Governor Storrs and Jabotinsky discussed the Haganah's possession of arms, among the proofs that the organizing of the self-defense was done openly with full knowledge of the British. Jabotinsky was sentenced to fifteen years imprisonment and hard labor; Mayor Musa Kazim was likewise sent to Acre Prison and dismissed from his post. Aref al-Aref and Haj Amin al-Husayni, who had fled to Syria, were initially sentenced to ten years imprisonment in abstentia. At the second Palestinian Congress of May–June 1920, the latter two exiles were chosen as leaders of the first Palestinian political party in history, the Palestinian Arab League.[38]

The Nebi Musa riots perhaps accelerated Britain's governmental transition of Palestine to a civilian mandate. Jews had experienced British inability or unwillingness to defend them from attack, and the Haganah was further developed as an underground organization.

Ticho and many other Jews, however, avoided the charged rhetoric of the Zionists who labeled the Nebi Musa riots as a pogrom, and he dismissed the rhetoric of Muslim Arabs who decried Jewish incitement that injured religious feelings of an indigenous population. A believer in Arab-Jewish coexistence, Ticho avoided the opposing, inflammatory vocabularies and narratives of a growing conflict.[39]

On June 20, 1920, a dinghy conveyed the new high commissioner, Sir Herbert Samuel, from the S.S. *Senator* to the quay at the Port of Jaffa. After he was helped ashore, Sir Herbert was greeted with a seventeen-gun salute and was rushed away by car to Jerusalem. One of his first acts as high commissioner that summer was the granting of amnesties to those convicted in the Nebi Musa riots, including Jabotinsky and Haj Amin al-Husayni. Samuel's early actions also included the establishment of Hebrew as an official language and resetting the annual number of Jewish immigrants.[40]

There is little or no evidence to support Pappe's statement that Ticho served as Sir Herbert's "private physician." The Armenian physician, Dr. Vahan Kalbian, served as the primary physician to each of the high commissioners during the Mandate. Ticho was likely not present at the first formal reception for the new commissioner on June 22 given by General Bols at Government House on Mount Scopus. This reception was another key event that marked the end of the OETA and the start of Sir Herbert's civilian administration. At the reception, General Bols made an attempt to reconcile Jewish and Muslim leaders, as he stood flanked by Menachem Ussishkin and Mufti Kamil Husayni. Bols tried to get them to shake hands but Ussishkin's refusal to do so was viewed as an unforgivable snub, a grudge that was carried by Kamil's successor as mufti, Haj Amin.[41] Ticho's later attempt to repair the breach between Mufti Haj Amin and the Zionist Commission was rebuffed (chapter 17).

Other than the high commissioner, the highest ranking Jewish member of the British administration in Palestine was Attorney General Norman Bentwich, who had arrived in 1918 while the war was still ongoing. He was joined by his wife, Helen, toward the end of the year after the war had ended. The Tichos came to know the Bentwiches rather well. In July 1920, Drs. Ticho and Helena Kagan joined the Bentwiches in paying a social visit to Mufti Kamil Husayni at his home.[42] Unlike his much younger half brother, Haj Amin al-Husayni, who had led the mobs in the riots just a few months earlier, Mufti Kamil al-Husayni was relatively friendly to the Jewish community and remained so until his death in 1921. Even when the more extremist Haj Amin al-Husayni succeeded his brother as mufti in 1922, Ticho remained a trusted family friend and medical advisor involving matters that often went well beyond the scope of ophthalmology.[43]

Around the time of Herbert Samuel's arrival in Palestine, a group of Jewish and Arab physicians in Jaffa attempted to improve professional and personal relations between their respective groups. On June 28, 1920, twenty-six physicians (fourteen Jews and twelve non-Jews) of Jaffa-Tel Aviv gathered to form the "International Society of Physicians."[44] The effort was relatively short-lived but, for a time, it spawned similar organizing efforts among physicians and pharmacists throughout Palestine. In Jerusalem, principally through the efforts of Drs. Tawfiq Canaan (Arab Protestant) and Vahan Kalbian (Armenian), the physicians' organization met in the auditorium of the YMCA in Jerusalem on Monday evening, November 22, 1920. Ticho was among forty physicians representing "all religions and races" who participated in the proceedings, which were conducted in English and translated into various languages.[45] The physicians' efforts had a synergistic effect upon the country's pharmacists who also aimed to organize themselves and officially raise their standards above those of so-called *yad'anim*. The following Saturday night, Ticho was among several physicians who were invited to a government-sponsored event that welcomed organizing pharmacists to Jerusalem. The pharmacists soon convened at the Amdursky Hotel for the "First Annual Meeting of the International Society of Pharmacists." Drs. Canaan and Kalbian again represented the International Society of Physicians, with others representing Jewish medical groups. Just two weeks later, the leaders of the Pharmacists' Society received a memorandum from the director of the Department of Health announcing the government's "intention to start a Government School of Pharmacy in Palestine." It was, however, a promise that was never kept. [46]

◆

Preceding the arrival of the high commissioner, members of the Histadrut ha-Refu'it reestablished a professional bulletin such as one that had been briefly published by the Jaffa group before the war. In April 1920, under the editorship of Dr. Aryeh Feigenbaum, the journal *Harefuah* aimed to advance the development of medicine and Hebrew as their professional language but it also provided a platform to present the Histadrut's side of its conflicts with the AZMU and the Zionist Commission. This inaugural issue contained articles on sanitation issues connected with immigration by Dr. Yaffe and sanitation issues of Yemenite Jews in Palestine by Drs. Beham and Goldberg. Both of these issues had been studied by the joint expedition of the AZMU and non-AZMU physicians that had been placed under Yaffe's leadership. Elsewhere in the issue, Beham noted that the local physicians had much difficulty in being included in the expedition that was in fact their idea in the first place. Even harsher criticism was directed at all of the Americans involved for the lack of effective follow-up actions in delivering relief of the situation, criticism aimed specifically at Dr. Friedenwald and the Zionist Commission on the one hand and Dr. Rubinow and the AZMU on the other hand.[47]

Ticho was not involved in the inauguration of the Medical Society's bulletin but he did participate in some of the relatively large medical meetings at Hadassah along with Drs. Biskind, Segal, and Roman.[48] On May 13, 1920, about thirty-five members and guests attended the hospital's "grand rounds" where three of Dr. Biskind's presented patients were victims of the riots. Ticho presented "a case of albinism, one of secondary glaucoma and [corneal] pannus that was cured by a plastic operation, and he gave an interesting lecture on a neuroglioma of the eye." None of Ticho's patients presented that day had been victims of the riots but he was soon called to testify in court about the case of his patient Eliyahu Kramer, an employee of a pharmacy on Jaffa Road, who had been a victim of the rioting on April 4. As Ticho did not recall any details of visits or treatments his testimony was not very helpful.[49]

Toward the end of the spring of 1920 a surprising resolution emerged from Hadassah's Advisory Medical Council that recommended the prohibition of private practice. Much to Ticho's chagrin, it was a resolution that Rubinow immediately endorsed. However, the implementation of the resolution was delayed by Rubinow's departure from Palestine in June 1920. Rubinow was ostensibly leaving to attend the annual Zionist Conference in London, and once in London, he was successful in procuring additional funds for the AZMU. In writing to Miss Szold, he did not reveal that he had developed a romantic, extramarital relationship with his Russian secretary, who had left her job. Leaving Palestine would defuse conflicts among Zionists in Palestine, but it would also allow him to sort out his personal issues. He took the opportunity to extend his trip into a prolonged vacation to be with his wife and three adolescent children who waited in America.[50] Before leaving Palestine, Rubinow had accepted the medical staff's request for representation on the Executive Committee, but the election of representatives was delayed for many months as the medical staff squabbled about the private practice issue.

When Dr. Rubinow informed Henrietta Szold that he needed to take an extended vacation, Szold set out for Palestine "to see why the doctors quarreled interminably among themselves, why the Yishuv hated them, and what could be done about it." Arriving in Palestine in June 1920, Szold initially took up residence in Helena Kagan's home while the doctor was yet in Europe.[51] Soon, however, Szold took on the responsibilities as Acting Director of the AZMU, dealing with the Zionist Commission, the Histadrut ha-Refu'it, and the disgruntled members of her own medical staff, many of whom sought either parity of salary with the original "elect and favored" or an opportunity to engage in private practice like Dr. Albert Ticho and the new tier of the "elect and favored." Reflecting on her entry into these controversies, Szold would later write, "I came modestly in my private personal capacity. I had received no Mandate from the American organization. Here it was expected that a word of mine would decide long-standing disputes between the Unit and the community, and still more aggravated disputes between the members of the Unit, and between its physicians and its Director. At the end of two weeks I was a wreck. I was ready to flee back to America. I wondered bitterly whether I had devoted twenty years of my life to an ideal that had turned out to be a will-o-the-wisp.... That period has passed."[52]

In some respects, the squabbles surrounding the AZMU were a microcosm of the broader social and political experimentation of the Yishuv as it built up pre-state institutions. Henrietta Szold and others aspired to merge their health care delivery system with the planned Hebrew University, and in 1920, the Zionist Organization in London had just begun to probe the possibility of medical and scientific institutes in Palestine, including a medical library. In May 1920, Schmuel Hugo Bergmann, a person well known to Ticho from his days in Prague, was appointed to the directorship of the National Library in Jerusalem. Not unlike others working in Zionist causes in Palestine, Bergmann was involved in squabbles about the control of the library holdings, mainly with representatives of the local B'nai B'rith Jerusalem Lodge.[53] To her great credit, Henrietta Szold was adept in dealing with the quarrels between the administration and the medical staff. She also was adept in working with a new civilian administration that was instituted by the British under High Commissioner Sir Herbert Samuel.

Herbert Samuel's wife, Lady Beatrice Samuel, joined Sir Herbert in Jerusalem about six months after his arrival.[54] Lady Samuel would also prove to be a good friend and a supporter of Szold's Nurses' Training School. When Palestine made the full transition from a military administration to the civilian British Mandate, Samuel and his Department of Health Director, Col. George Wykeham Heron, turned to Miss Szold and the AZMU for a continuing health care system for the Jewish population of Palestine. Still dealing with financial and local political crises, Miss Szold began formulating even longer-range plans for the organization, but in her estimation, the experiment of private practice within the AZMU would need to be terminated at the earliest opportunity.

After an absence of over five months, Dr. Rubinow returned to Palestine on November 24, 1920.[55] He brought his family with him, and Miss Szold felt that their presence had "a good influence." Rested and ready for battle, Rubinow immediately became embroiled in the controversies of local politics when he sought to implement the "absorption" and concurrent closure of Nathan Straus's Jewish Health Bureau by the AZMU. The Bureau's debts were high, its financial issues were very complex, and, other than its Eye Division, Rubinow saw that its work was inefficient and not useful. In comparison to the Bureau's small "one-horse" laboratory, the better equipped laboratories of the Rothschild-Hadassah Hospital were now performing twenty times the number of analyses. Although the pending closure of the Bureau and the permanent layoffs of over twenty employees caused "general indignation throughout the land," Rubinow dug in his heels and, with Nathan Straus's acquiescence, succeeded in eliminating the now outdated "white elephant." The addition of the vigorously recruited New York bacteriologist Dr. Israel Kligler to the AZMU staff at this time only further placed the chapter of the Nathan Straus Jewish Health Bureau in the rear-view mirror. Now the Bureau's only vestige was a down-sized eye hospital privately run by Dr. Feigenbaum in a smaller rented building.[56] Feigenbaum, at this point, was still unwilling to give up his own private practice and work for the AZMU, and this decision would impact Rubinow's forthcoming negotiations with Ticho.

———◆———

Henrietta Szold was relieved that Rubinow had returned to take care of so many thorny issues. She looked forward to her sixtieth birthday, which would be celebrated in Palestine on December 21, 1920. A large party was being planned for her at the Hôtel de France, where her many coworkers and acquaintances would be invited. The Tichos were present at the celebration, joining other senior medical staff and their spouses, enjoying the party that went late into the night. At one point, a large birthday cake with 61 candles was placed before the respected (and for many, beloved) cofounder and matriarch of Hadassah. As a birthday gift, Anna Ticho presented Szold with one of her better portraits to date, one of a young yeshiva boy with sidelocks that she had painted before the war.[57] This would not save her husband from a forthcoming ultimatum from Rubinow, who now turned his full attention to the issue of contract negotiations with his senior medical staff.

In addition to the already existing wages, pension, and insurance benefits, the bargaining processes yielded gains by the medical staff on four key points: participation of physicians in defining terms of employment; institutional funding of continuing medical education; sabbatical leave every six years, at half pay; and tenure after one year of employment. The major concession by the medical staff was their acceptance of a ban on private practice. Dr. Rubinow had explained the decision on private practice and other issues at two separate meetings of the medical staff, one for English speakers and one for Russian speakers.[58]

Seeing that Ticho was committed to continuing his private practice, Rubinow had offered Ticho the position of "consulting oculist without remuneration," a position that Ticho initially accepted. The arrangement assured Ticho of the continued availability of four beds that would enable him to operate on cases that he could not handle at his private hospital. Rubinow noted, "While the position thus created presents a certain novelty for Palestine, it is one of great dignity in Europe and America. The duties in connection wherewith will not be heavier than you are willing to assume." Just after New Year's Day 1921, Ticho learned that Rubinow had offered the position of chief oculist of the AZMU to Feigenbaum. Not knowing yet if Feigenbaum had accepted (he had not), Ticho hastily withdrew his acceptance of the consultant's position.[59] Then, learning that Feigenbaum had declined in favor of private practice, Ticho reconsidered and accepted an appointment as Consultant Ophthalmologist of the Rothschild Hospital without remuneration. His appointment was confirmed by Rubinow on January 31, 1921, who noted that the vacant, full-time chairmanship of the Eye Department could not be left open indefinitely, and he further suggested that it would soon be offered next to Dr. Nahum Shimkin, who was then en route from Europe to Haifa. At that same time, the AZMU Executive Committee reached a historic, formal agreement with the full-time medical staff considered to be the world's "first formal adoption of the salaried physician model."[60] The agreement of January 29, 1921, stated that "private practice would be prohibited to all members of the medical staff as of March 1, 1921, and the salaries of the six members who had enjoyed the privilege of private practice were adjusted to compensate them for the loss of the privilege."[61]

After these meetings, Dr. Rubinow's detailed summary of the

sessions was distributed to each member of the medical staff. The letter included the following comments on the issue private practice: "It is a matter of deep satisfaction to find that the problem of private practice did not create as much discussion as might have been expected. I am sure that is due not only to the physicians accepting the fait accompli, but also to the growing conviction that the decision was not a caprice on the part of the Executive Committee or the Director, but the result of a deep conviction of the incompatibility of complete devotion to the medical needs of the country and the disturbing influence of private work. It is significant that with one or two exceptions, little resistance has appeared against this rule on the part of the physicians who have had this right to private practice, and who are abandoning it in accordance with the instructions of the Committee and the negotiations conducted between the Committee and the individual physicians."[62] Of course Ticho was the principle, if not the sole exception to the "little resistance" reference. However, as there was not a suitable and available full-time chairman for the Eye Department, Ticho would retain his private practice but also remain a member of the AZMU for approximately fourteen more months, serving as consulting oculist, supervisor of ophthalmic medical care in the schools, and faculty member of the Nurses' Training School.

———◆———

Two well-known episodes of Arab disturbances coincided with significant events during Ticho's final months working for the AZMU as a consultant (March 1921–April 1922). Neither of the episodes seem to have permanently soured his relations with Arab acquaintances and the many Arab patients in his private practice. On May 1, 1921, militant Arabs had begun rioting in Jaffa. The violence spread to other places over the following week and resulted in the deaths of forty-seven Jews and forty-eight Arabs, with many wounded on both sides.[63] Most of the Arab casualties resulted from clashes with the British who were attempting to restore order. Among the murdered Jewish victims was Yosef Haim Brenner, one of the pioneers of modern Hebrew literature. High Commissioner Herbert Samuel had declared a state of emergency, imposed press censorship, and called for reinforcements from Egypt.

On May 6, 1921, as the Arab riots were being quelled, Ticho was confirmed as a member of the B'nai B'rith Jerusalem Lodge. The main speaker at the meeting that evening was David Yellin, a lodge member and its former president who was then serving as deputy mayor of Jerusalem and head of the Va'ad Le'umi. Yellin gave an update of the situation and attempted to calm those present.[64] High Commissioner Samuel attempted to make peace with Arab notables and, meeting with them in Ramleh, he announced that Jewish immigration would be suspended. Immigrants within sight of the shores of Palestine were not allowed to land. The previously amnestied Haj Amin al-Husayni was appointed as Mufti of Jerusalem (or Grand Mufti).[65]

Ticho's relations with his Arab patients remained excellent. One of his Arab patients was the Bedouin sheikh Mithqal al-Fayez, chief of the powerful Banu Shakr tribe that owned much of the land around Amman and south of it. During the war he had sided with the Turks and had been slow to join the Arab revolt. In the autumn of 1921, the sheikh underwent eye surgery in Ticho's private hospital and remained in the hospital for some time during his convalescence. Following his recovery, the sheikh paid Ticho a handsome fee and, in addition, he gave Ticho a beautiful Arabian horse as an expression of his satisfaction and gratitude. In the coming years, al-Fayez would be one of Emir Abdullah's closest friends and chief allies as the former rose to power in Transjordan.[66] Emir Abdullah and his family would also become Ticho's patients.

Soon after Sheikh Mithqal al-Fayez had recovered, another Arab riot took place in Jerusalem. The timing of these riots coincided with the graduation of the first class of students from the Nurses' Training School after three years of study that had begun at the time of the hospital's rededication. The school's historic commencement ceremony had been scheduled to coincide with the celebration of Balfour Day on November 2, 1921. Because of the many rumors of planned Arab disturbances, Henrietta Szold was advised to postpone the ceremonies, initially for one week.

Miss Szold's worst fears were realized when on Balfour Day 1921,

Arab mobs ran out of the Old City of Jerusalem, burning and pillaging as they went, while the British military police failed to intervene effectively. Two days later, a large funeral procession of an estimated eight thousand people listened to the eulogies outside the Rothschild-Hadassah Hospital. They then marched in silence from the compound behind the stretchers on which four *tallit*-draped bodies were borne. The funeral procession's route to the Mount of Olives first passed the Italian Hospital and then paused just beyond Dr. Ticho's private hospital, where a British Army company was waiting. From this point onward "only" several hundred were allowed to continue on to the cemetery. When a month of mourning was declared, the graduation exercises were at first rescheduled for December 2, though the ceremony actually took place on December 7, 1921. The graduation certificate retained the November 2 date.[67]

The graduation ceremony took place at the hall of Bet Aminoff on Jaffa Road, which was the new nurses' home. The graduation of twenty-one nurses approximated the number of the twenty-two American nurses that had originally sailed with the AZMU for Palestine in June 1918. Only two of those original nurses remained, including Nurse Anna Kaplan, the head of the school, who led the nurses into the hall. Rubinow wrote that the graduation of the first class of nurses from the Training School was "the greatest event in the history of the Unit during the year 1921," and he noted that it was recognized by the entire population of Eretz Yisrael as of national importance. He further noted with pride that detailed accounts of the event appeared in the press locally, in America, and elsewhere.[68] Among all of his colleagues and in spite of his consulting status on the AZMU staff, Ticho received the honor of addressing the first graduating class of nurses on behalf of the medical faculty.

The graduation of Hadassah's first class of student nurses coincided with another milestone for the AZMU: its further transition into a permanent medical institution. This process had begun in a subtle fashion with the initial hiring of just a few physicians and nurses who were permanent residents of Eretz Yisrael, and it continued when other local physicians and nurses were appointed to fill vacant positions of departing Americans and the many new positions created by the greatly expanding operations. Now, following decisions made at the Twelfth Zionist Congress of September 1921 in Carlsbad Germany, the AZMU was further transformed into an independent medical organization that would function autonomously in Palestine, though it would remain subordinate to Hadassah in America. The American Zionist Medical Unit was renamed as the Hadassah Medical Organization (HMO). The disappearance of the word "American" was welcomed by Henrietta Szold and others, as was the great reduction in its financial dependence upon the Joint Distribution Committee.[69] Further steps toward local autonomy would take place in the coming years with the appointment of local medical directors and the participation of Hadassah with the planned Hebrew University. Although the establishment of a medical school would take some time, the goals of its establishment were, in the mind of Miss Szold and others, at one with Hadassah's aims. Hadassah would keep its base in Jerusalem while elsewhere in Eretz Yisrael the HMO soon began a process of "devolution" in which institutions it had built for the Yishuv would be handed over to local control.

———◆———

As Hadassah's consulting oculist, Ticho continued work in the schools of Jerusalem, and he occasionally traveled a bit further. This was exemplified by his trips to the Negev region, where the prevalence of trachoma in children was very high and where work crews were also known to suffer from various eye problems. In 1920 Ticho had found that the incidence of trachoma was 98 percent among the children in an Arab school in Beer Sheva. In the late fall of 1921, soon after the graduation ceremonies of the Nurses' Training School, Ticho had planned a trip to the region to visit Arab schoolchildren suffering from trachoma and to examine Jewish work crews. Ticho's trip was postponed due to the Arab riots that had also delayed the graduation ceremonies at the Nurses' Training School. On December 10, 1921, just three days after the riot-delayed graduation ceremonies, Dr. Ticho finally made his way again to Beer Sheva at the special request of the British governor of the region, Kenny Levek. After visiting a crew of *ḥalutzim* (pioneers) that were working on a military cemetery, Dr. Ticho went to the Arab school. Ticho's report to the AZMU (submitted in German and translated into Hebrew) is a fine example of his outreach to disadvantaged Arab populations.[70]

Governor Levek was personally present at all of the examinations of the schoolchildren and assisted him until sunset along with a certain Dr. Ghazalle and the schoolchildren's teacher. Later that evening, Dr. Ticho and Mr. Levek invited story and travel writer Arthur Holitscher to join them in visiting the group of thirty-five *ḥalutzim*, including fourteen Yemenite and Sefardi workers, who were working on a military cemetery. The event in Beer Sheva was apparently not mentioned in Holitscher's subsequent books about Palestine,[71] but Ticho wrote:

> The governor stayed there more than an hour and while leaning over a cup of tea discussed with us the matter of the urgency of the cooperative work of Jews and Arabs. Among the rest of his words he related that in the beginning of November he visited villages close to Ruhama and warned them to be quiet on November 2 (Balfour Day). They answered me that they had learned to recognize the diligent workers and the settlers to protect them, since they very much respected them and it never occurred to them to harm them…. In the evening we arranged in the club [for the mixed] Mohammedan-Christian-Jewish [audience], a presentation that extended until midnight, and Jews and non-Jews tried to elevate the spirits as much as possible.

Later in his report, Dr. Ticho recommended that the Jewish workers and others be provided with gloves and protective eye glasses because of the large number of infections of the hand and diseases of the eyelid. His superior, Dr. Rubinow, was able to help implement these suggestions through the Department of Labor of the Zionist Executive when he recalled the existence of a special fund for the protection of *ḥalutzim* against eye diseases.[72]

Mr. Holitscher and Dr. Ghazalle were invited to the evening social event at Mr. Levek's home where they met local Arab notables, including the acting mayor, Abu Atef Effendi, and members of the community.

Dr. Ticho wrote that Abu Atef Effendi read a letter of thanks from the inhabitants of Beer Sheva for his treatment of eye diseases that he had extended gratis to the community and that the mayor presented him with a silver cup, the work of the Bezalel School. Ticho wrote, "The following inscription was engraved on the cup: 'Shalom from the Arabs of Beer Sheva to Dr. Ticho as a sign of gratitude for returning our eyesight.' The speech of the representative of the city was translated word for word into French by Dr. Ghazalle, and I answered in French (Dr. Ghazalle translated into Arabic)."

In Dr. Ticho's response to his British and Arabic audience, he emphasized that the objective of his work was "only the treatment of the sick without regard to race or religion." He expressed to them that this was a personal philosophy that had guided his practice of medicine since his arrival in Palestine a decade earlier. The original French and the Arabic translation were not recorded, but the contents of Ticho's remarkable address were preserved in the report that he submitted to the AZMU:

> When I came to Palestine ten years ago, I saw how one patient was distinguished from another according to religion and race – how the Jewish medical institutions treated only Jews, how Muslim ones only Muslims, and how patients of other religions were turned away – and I resolved to make amends; and in the course of ten years I made an effort to ensure that our hospital and clinics would be open to all people without distinguishing by religion and race. Indeed the work in Beer Sheva is not only my work but also that of the AZMU in which capacity I came and so I am here as [one of their] comrades. Particularly worthy of praise for this is Governor Kenny Levek, who, through his conduct, showed exceptional concern for eye treatment and the development of this place.... Afterward, I expressed my hope that the government, the doctors, and the inhabitants will work together hand in hand to improve the sanitary conditions in Beer Sheva and in all of the land.

During his last months of service with Hadassah, Ticho continued volunteering in the schools and teaching at Hadassah's Nurses Training School. He also continued his inclinations to engage in clinical research and writing on medical topics. Perhaps he also found additional motivation from activities of his chief rival, Dr. Aryeh Feigenbaum. Feigenbaum had likewise turned to private practice following the closure of the Jewish Health Bureau, while also serving as the founding editor of the Histadrut's Hebrew-language medical journal *Harefuah*. Feigenbaum published articles in this journal and also in the German literature.[73]

Meanwhile, Ticho was preparing the first, or at least among the first, medical scientific articles to originate from the Hadassah Medical Organization. The two articles he wrote drew on clinical material encountered in 1921 at the AZMU-managed Rothschild-Hadassah Hospital, but of course a medical school or university affiliation did not exist. In May 1921, the dream of a medical school was being highlighted by Albert Einstein in America, including a speech he made in New York City to a group of eight hundred Jewish physicians. "The Medical College," Einstein declared, "will undoubtedly be the most important department of the university, as we Jews have always excelled in this particular branch of science." In March, Mary Fels, a Philadelphia Zionist and soap heiress, had pledged $600,000 to purchase yet additional land on Mount Scopus for the planned university. Also at that time, Dr. Nathan Ratnoff of New York was leading the American Jewish Physicians Committee in raising $500,000 for a projected medical school.[74]

Ticho's clinical work at this time showed the rudiments of future academic work of a higher level. His medical articles were published the following year, one in Germany, the other in Great Britain. The first was on the surgical treatment of glaucoma, a condition of elevated pressure in the eye that, when left unchecked, leads to visual loss. Ticho reported his results with the Elliot operation, in which aqueous humor (the clear fluid in the front chamber of the eye) is given an escape route beneath a thin "bleb" of conjunctiva (the membrane covering the white of the eyeball). Ticho had adopted this operation just before the war but, even then, it had already become the most popular surgical method of treating chronic glaucoma. One of the potential problems with the operation was the passage of bacteria into the eye through the thin conjunctival bleb. This could occur even several months or years after the operation. Reports of catastrophic infections had appeared in the literature, with incidences ranging from 2 percent to as high as 18 percent.[75] At the time of his report, Ticho was very aware of the high incidence of acute conjunctivitis in Palestine, but he hoped that the operation could still be employed in his practice with an acceptable rate of complications. In fact Ticho achieved good results, and he published his experiences in the German literature under the title "*Beitrag zur Elliot-Operation*." Ticho sometimes performed this operation a number of times in the same eye.[76]

The second major article that Ticho prepared during his last year with Hadassah again reprised the subject of endemic trachoma in Palestine. It appeared in *The Lancet* in September 1922 and was coauthored by Dr. Kligler, who was recruited to add further analysis and discussion. The core of the article was the calculation of the incidence of trachoma among 6,069 Jewish schoolchildren in Jerusalem during May and June of 1921. Ticho recapitulated the fact that the prevalence of trachoma was higher in the southern parts of the country, in settlements further removed from the cities, under conditions of poverty and malnutrition, and that trachoma in Palestine was especially a disease of young children that diminished in extent among the later age groups. Again he noted that the greatest numbers of fresh cases were found in the kindergarten and lower classes, whereas in the higher classes there were fewer fresh cases and more of the chronic, cicatrixed (scarred) forms. In his part of the article, Kligler reviewed Ticho's past accomplishments in reducing the incidence of trachoma among Jerusalem's schoolchildren from 31.3 percent in 1913 to 13 percent in 1916. The post-war incidence had risen to 21.7 percent in 1919 and was only slightly less at the time of their study. Kligler hoped to implement pilot projects in sections of Jerusalem that would concentrate on educating families on matters of hygiene and nutrition. He concluded that such projects might "lead to a newer and more effective method for the complete eradication of this disease."[77]

———◆———

In February 1922, Rubinow again revisited with Ticho the issue of "the necessary reorganization of the ophthalmological department" – the vacancy in the position of chief oculist and Ticho's position as consulting oculist. Rubinow noted that possible reforms were soon forthcoming as an Investigating Commission was due to arrive, and that, in any event, Rubinow might not stay on in Palestine beyond the final year of his contract.[78] Knowing that Dr. Feigenbaum was close to coming to terms and would likely give up his private practice, Rubinow made one final offer to Ticho to take the Ophthalmology Department chairmanship. Ticho declined, and so Dr. Aryeh Feigenbaum became the new head of the Ophthalmology Department at the Rothschild-Hadassah Hospital. This also occurred following the formal transition of the AZMU to the Hadassah Medical Organization as mandated by the 1921 Zionist Congress in Carlsbad, and so it is technically correct to say that Dr. Feigenbaum was the first chairman of Ophthalmology of the Hadassah Medical Organization (appendix 8).

Feigenbaum proved to be an excellent successor as chairman, bringing an equal measure of clinical experience, surgical abilities, and teaching skills. His literary skills actually surpassed Ticho's, especially in Hebrew. He had been the editor of the well-known trachoma conference proceedings before the war (chapter 11), and he was the founding editor of *Harefuah*, the journal of the Histadrut ha-Refu'it be-Eretz Yisrael. With Feigenbaum's acquiescence, Rubinow urged Ticho to retain his consulting status, with an even greater allotment of beds if needed.

For over two years, Ticho's negotiations with Rubinow had revealed his competitiveness with Feigenbaum, but there is evidence that Ticho did stay on in a consulting role for a period of time. Rubinow wrote, "I understand that you have expressed your willingness to remain consultant oculist of the Rothschild Hospital with a certain number of beds. I am also informed both by Dr. [Alexander] Salkind and Dr. Feigenbaum that you seem to think six beds excessive. Of course, if you do, I have no doubt that Dr. Feigenbaum will be glad to get a larger number of beds. Will you be kind enough to drop me a line stating how many beds you would want definitely assigned to you?"[79] The six beds offered turned out to be more than was needed. In fact, only one extraordinary case during the 1929 riots has been uncovered that documents a subsequent instance of Tichos's consultation at the Hadassah hospital (chapter 18). Ticho's active association with the AZMU and the HMO had come to an end.

Eventually Feigenbaum's abilities and the close affiliations of the HMO with the Hebrew University would lead to a distinguished academic career. He would be the first dean of the pre-faculty of the Hebrew University and its first professor of ophthalmology. Ticho, on the other hand, concentrated on building a thriving private practice from which he personally achieved a widespread reputation throughout Palestine and the Middle East. He continued to treat the poor and rich alike, both Arabs and Jews, and the fees paid by his more affluent patients enabled him to keep his fees low and often provide care without charge. He also continued publishing articles in the medical literature from time to time.

Rubinow would soon leave Palestine, proud of his accomplishments and acknowledging without apologies that he had quarreled with practically all segments of Jewish society there. After returning to America he became the director of the Jewish Welfare Society of Philadelphia, followed in 1928 by his concurrent appointment as executive director of both the Zionist Organization of America and the United Palestine Appeal.[80] He eventually served as an advisor to President Franklin Roosevelt on Social Security. Before he left Palestine, Rubinow succeeded in having the HMO enter formal agreements with the Kupat Ḥolim Klalit, the General Sick Fund of the Labor Federation of Hebrew Workers (or Histadrut). The HMO partially underwrote Kupat Ḥolim expenses for medicines and medical equipment and provided hospitalization for workers at a reduced rate. Kupat Ḥolim also adopted the model of the salaried physician, further institutionalizing the socialization of health services in Palestine.[81]

Rubinow departed Palestine without finalizing negotiations that he had begun with Ticho, but leaving records behind on the subject. Five years later, Ticho revisited the matter with HMO Director Dr. Ephraim

M. Bluestone (chapter 17). About three decades passed until some of the restrictions on private practice were eased in the mid-1950s in the State of Israel. By this time Aryeh Feigenbaum was just retiring as chairman of the Ophthalmology Department while his colleague, Avraham Ticho, was entering the last years of his practice.

CHAPTER 17

1922–1928
SOMEWHAT QUIETER TIMES

. . . והארץ שקטה ממלחמה.
. . . And the land had rest from war.
Joshua 11:23

With his departure from the Hadassah Medical Organization in the spring of 1922, Ticho turned full attention back to his private practice. St. George's Road adjacent to his clinic had just been given its official Mandatory-period name by the Pro-Jerusalem Society that Governor Ronald Storrs had founded in 1918, chaired by his civic advisor, Charles Robert Ashbee. A total of eighty streets were named (or numbered for naming) in the New City and forty-six streets were named in the Old City. As was the case for other Jerusalem streets, the naming of St. George's Road was set in three official languages with "attention to the three traditions, Christian, Moslem, and Jewish." The first exception to the "traditionalist" street-naming was Allenby Square at the foot of Jaffa Road where a new clock tower was being planned by the Society.[1] St. George's Road was named for the Anglican church just to the north of where Ticho established a new hospital. The continuation of the road southward was given the name St. Paul's Road, reflecting the name of the Arab Protestant church across from the Italian Hospital. Continuing southward past the newly named Street of the Prophets, St.

Paul's Road passed between the Hungarian Houses and the old site of the Lemaan Zion Hospital on its way to Allenby Square. Together, the two connecting roads of St. George and St. Paul formed the boundary between two neighborhoods north of the Old City: to the east Musrara; to the west Meah Shearim and the Hungarian Houses.[2]

Ticho's new private hospital and clinic at the outskirts of the Musrara neighborhood was described in one memoir as a "stylish and beautiful stone house." The hospital was strategically located from a demographic standpoint, sandwiched between the traditional Jewish neighborhoods to the west and southwest, and the mixed but predominantly Arab neighborhoods to the east and southeast. The Arab physician, Dr. Tawfiq Canaan, also made his home in Musrara and considered Ticho among his friends. The two had met soon after Ticho's arrival in Palestine in 1912 and each had married that same year.[3] South and eastward, across the fields from Ticho's private hospital, Henrietta Szold rented an old Arab house that she shared with her friend and fellow American Sophie Berger who was also working for the Hadassah Medical Organization (HMO). Soon after Ticho's resignation from the organization and Rubinow's return to America, Szold once again temporarily took charge of the HMO. More Americans became part of Szold's English-speaking circle of friends when in June 1924, Judah Leon Magnes was appointed to head the still embryonic Hebrew University. Magnes and his family initially took up residence in Musrara in old Arab house nearer to Herod's Gate.[4]

The particular geographic location of Ticho's clinic and hospital at the border zone between neighborhoods was significant, as was the demographics of his patient population. At the Rothschild-Hadassah hospital on the newly renamed Street of the Prophets, 80 percent of Dr. Feigenbaum's patients were Jewish and only 20 percent were Arabs.[5] At the British Ophthalmic Hospital on Hebron Road, the vast majority of patients seen by Dr. John Strathearn and his assistants were Arabs. As Dr. Ticho resumed his private practice, he initially saw Jewish and Arab patients in approximately equal numbers while over time, the majority of his patients were Arabs and less than 30 percent were Jews. There were many social, political, and medical factors that influenced these patients' choices of an ophthalmologist. Ticho certainly benefited from his strong reputation and the commonly held belief that a higher level of medical care was available through a private physician.

As his practice quickly grew, Ticho was able to rehire some of his former employees from before the war, including Dov Halaban. Halaban had been one of Ticho's most faithful and trusted personal assistants before the war when Ticho had assigned him to work with Hadassah nurses Rose Kaplan and Rae Landy as they cared for Jerusalem's schoolchildren (chapter 8). During the war Halaban had been conscripted by the Turkish Army, but he deserted and hid in one of the Jewish settlements, emerging from his hiding place after the British conquest. Very soon after the Tichos' return to Jerusalem, Halaban had unsuccessfully sought out employment with the AZMU, hoping to "get his 'job' back again." Employed again by Dr. Ticho, Halaban was assigned most of the administrative matters of the clinic and was medical assistant in the clinic and in surgery, where he even learned to administer anesthesia. Ticho valued Halaban's abilities and his devotion, though all of Halaban's activities were closely supervised. In return, Halaban venerated Dr. Ticho with great pride while relating to his employer with "awe and submissiveness."[6]

Anna Ticho also was of great help in reestablishing the practice, and the high level of her assisting skills was well appreciated: "Without words at the time of surgery, she would provide the needed instrument at the very moment it was required. She was accustomed to come down [from her quarters] to the surgery level a short time before the commencement of the surgeries, arranging the instruments, examining the knives, preparing the injections and the sterile materials. Everything was arranged on the instrument table, polished and shining. She was skilled in all stages of the operation, and her fingers were hovering between the operating table and the instrument table as a pianist that plays upon the keys of the piano."[7] Anna's mother, Albert's Tanta Bertha, was likewise a maestro supervising in the kitchen. Hospitalized patients received excellent nursing care and nourishment, while upstairs in the private residence, reserved for the Tichos' living quarters, friends and family would also visit and socialize. On occasion, the visits included brief stays by Dr. Ticho's brother Alfred, who had been accepted as one of the founding members of the Tel Binyamina Settlement, whose official establishment took place in October 1922.

Rather than building in the older mixed neighborhoods such as Musrara, Zionist leaders and investors of the Jewish middle class turned their attention to developing new Jewish neighborhoods around Jerusalem. Ticho's colleague Dr. Aharon Yermens, who had helped found the Zikhron Moshe neighborhood many years earlier, was among those who invested in new garden suburbs of Talpiot and Beit ha-Kerem, though he did not move from the central New City.[8] At the southern outskirts of the city, Talpiot was the first of the Jewish garden suburbs to be planned by German-born architect Richard Kaufmann at the behest of the Zionist Executive. In his plan, the neighborhood was divided among eight hundred private houses surrounded by gardens, the grid of streets and sidewalks punctuated with public areas and communal buildings. In May 1922, the cornerstone of the neighborhood was laid, but actual development proceeded slowly – only forty homes would be completed by July 1924 and only a dozen more over the next three years.[9]

Among the earliest to begin construction on Yehezkel Street were Joseph and Zippora Klausner, and Architect Fritz Kornberg and his wife built a house just down the street from the Klausners. The Kornbergs would take in renters, most notably Shmuel Yosef Agnon, who had previously rented a room in Ussishkin's flat at Beit Maḥanaim. The early suburban pioneers enjoyed beautiful, unobstructed views of the Old City, the hills of the Judean Desert, and the Dead Sea. With funds given to them by admirers, Eliezer and Hemda Ben-Yehudah also began construction on one of the first houses in Talpiot, which they named Matan ha-'Am. That year Ben-Yehudah added several words to the modern Hebrew lexicon relating to construction, but he would not live to see the completion of his home.

On December 16, 1922, the second night of Hanukkah, Eliezer Ben-Yehudah passed away at the age of sixty-four. An intermittent drizzle fell the following day, but even so, Ticho joined with thousands of mourners, including fellow members of the Jerusalem B'nai B'rith

Lodge that Ben-Yehudah had helped found decades earlier, to pay their last respects.[10] As the funeral procession reached Jaffa Road and eulogies were given from a hotel balcony, the drizzle changed to pouring rain, yet very few left as the flag-draped coffin and the procession continued on to Ben-Yehudah's final resting place on the Mount of Olives.

Spring soon returned to Jerusalem, and Anna Ticho returned to her artwork, even though her time and energies in pursuit of her art were limited by her work in the hospital. Her artistic abilities eventually became known to the broader public when she was invited to show her works at the Tower of David (Migdal David). Beginning in 1921, the Pro-Jerusalem Society had begun holding art exhibitions in this venue in the spring, featuring a number of subjects such as town planning, the modernization of Palestine, and Islamic and Jewish art. Jewish art exhibitions included collective and solo exhibitions of members of the Society of Hebrew Artists (Agudat Amanim 'Ivrit, founded 1920), who especially early on were mainly associated with the Bezalel School.[11] The Society was supported by the Palestine Zionist Executive (the successor to the Zionist Commission). The head of the Palestine Zionist Executive's Political Division, Dr. David Eder, held a collective exhibition of the Society in his home.

Dr. Ticho also had the occasion to work professionally with Dr. Eder, who was a physician and a psychiatrist by training. In March 1922, Dr. Eder invited Ticho to be a member of the newly established Health Department of the Va'ad Le'umi (then known as the Va'ad ha-Bri'ut). The Va'ad ha-Bri'ut first met on April 2, 1922, and evolved to become an umbrella organization for the Yishuv with representation from all of the major health organizations and private physicians. Proportional representation was a matter of some dispute that was successfully addressed over the next two years with the input of Henrietta Szold and others. The first "official" meeting of the Zionist's Health Department reportedly took place in March 1924.[12]

It is interesting that around this time, Ticho was involved with the founding and leadership of an organization whose goals ran somewhat counter to the Zionists' efforts to organize all professional societies under its auspices. This organization, known as the Histadrut ha-Rof'im bi-Yerushalayim, or alternatively the "Academy of Medicine," seems to have been a continuation of the International Society of Physicians. References to the organization and Ticho's leadership can be found in the newspaper *Do'ar ha-Yom* in November 1922 in the reporting of a lecture given to this group of physicians and pharmacists on the subject of botanical medicines. This particular event was hosted by Ephraim Rubinovitz (later Hareuveni) at his botanical museum in the Bukharan neighborhood, with Rubinovitz himself presenting the two-part lecture.[13]

Ephraim Rubinovitz was a staunch Zionist and Hebraist but he had long had a good relationship with Ticho. It was a friendship that began years before the war and continued later while they were both in Damascus after the Ottoman-German retreat from southern Palestine. Rubinovitz was among Jabotinsky's associates who were jailed in Acre following the 1920 riots. Eventually Hareuveni was invited to join the faculty of the Hebrew University to which he would contribute much of his botanical collections. His emphasis on "Hebrew botany" and meticulous comparisons with indigenous Arab cultures was evident the night of this early lecture in November 1922. In the university setting, his cultural emphasis would eventually be marginalized in favor of "scientific" botany. That evening, after the conclusion of the lectures, Ticho expressed his thanks to Rubinovitz on behalf of the Histadrut ha-Rof'im, and he expressed his hope that the esteemed botanist would present additional lectures to the society in the future.

Ticho served as president of the Histadrut ha-Rof'im bi-Yerushalayim from 1923 to 1926, and he served as vice president at least through 1929.[14] Although this Jerusalem-based physician's group apparently continued to exist through the years of the Mandate, it did so only in parallel to the larger Histadrut ha-Refu'it ha-'Ivrit be-Eretz Yisrael that developed branches throughout Palestine including Jerusalem. The Academy of Medicine had fewer members than its countrywide Zionist counterpart; memberships in the two organizations numbered 50 versus 375, respectively, in 1927–28. At this time, to the chagrin of the Zionists, the "Academy of Medicine" – also referred to with the appendage "*bi-Yerushalayim*" (in Jerusalem), as the Agudat Rof'im

Bein Le'umit bi-Yerushalayim (International Physician's Association in Jerusalem) – was consulted by the Mandatory Government regarding pending regulatory laws for the profession while the countrywide Histadrut ha-Refu'it ha-'Ivrit was not. However, the umbrella Zionist medical organization, the Va'ad ha-Briyut, and the Jewish professional organizations of dentists and of pharmacists had been consulted. Even so, the Palestine Zionist Executive complained to the government and the newspaper *Davar* that their aspirations to create one shared Jewish representative had been undermined.[15]

In the early years of Ticho's presidency, the smaller Academy of Medicine was just as active as the Zionist physicians' group.[16] For example, the professional journal *Harefuah* had ceased publication after only one issue in 1920, and it did not resume publication until 1924 under the editorship of Dr. Jacob Doljansky. However, in May 1925, the Jerusalem branch of the Zionist's Histadrut ha-Refu'it elected Dr. Aryeh Feigenbaum as its leader. The annual report of that year stated, "The Branch established friendly relations with the International 'Academy of Medicine' and many of its members are also members of this Society. Lectures were given there by [these dual members]." At the same time, the Zionists' Histadrut ha-Refu'it was sponsoring dozens of presentations and lectures every year, and so Ticho attended many of these gatherings when they were held in Jerusalem.

One of Ticho's involvements in committees of the Zionists' Histadrut was in the establishment of a memorial to Dr. Joseph Freud, who was among the founders of radiology in Palestine. Dr. Freud, a native of Galicia, had passed away on November 4, 1924, of aplastic anemia, a complication of excessive radiation exposure. The committee also included Drs. Aryeh Dostrovsky, Helena Kagan, and Aryeh Feigenbaum. Ticho appears to have been the "anonymous donor" that funded the first annual prize given in Dr. Freud's memory for work in the area of locally endemic diseases.[17]

Ticho's Histadrut ha-Rof'im bi-Yerushalayim eventually dissolved while the countrywide Histadrut grew and evolved into the current Israel Medical Association (Ha-Histadrut ha-Refu'it be-Yisrael). This explains why there is no record of Ticho's presidency of the Jerusalem-based organization in the annals or archives of the Israel Medical Association. The presidency of the Histadrut ha-Refu'it was often mentioned in Ticho's curriculum vitae and this was naturally cited in various books about the Ticho family and the Ticho House. The distinction between the two medical organizations became somewhat blurred even by the time of Ticho's death when the *Jerusalem Post* reported that he had been "a president of the Israel Medical Association from 1923–26."[18]

———◆———

When Dr. David Eder returned to England at the end of 1922, he was soon replaced by Frederick Kisch, who likewise worked to build up institutions and societies of the Yishuv.[19] Kisch was an English Jew, born in India, the son of a highly placed civil servant. After studying engineering at the Woolwich Military Academy he had served with the Indian Army in India and then in France during World War I, where he was wounded several times and earned the Distinguished Service Order. Kisch had gained valuable political experience as a member of the Poland Boundary Commission at the Paris Peace Conference, where he also came into contact with Eastern European Jews. He was back in England when Weizmann persuaded him to leave his army career to serve as a member of the Palestine Zionist Executive.[20] During the years of Kisch's service, from 1923 to 1931, he cultivated excellent relations with the British administration of the Palestine Mandate as well as with Arab leaders such as Emir Abdullah. As described by Attorney General Norman Bentwich, "He took an active part in the social life of the British community as well as of the Jewish community; was a keen cricketer, a diligent free-mason, and a good player of bridge."[21] Kisch consistently sought to achieve better relations between Arabs and Jews, though he was, with some exceptions, generally unsuccessful. His efforts involved many personal meetings with Arab notables to whom he often extended the hospitality of his home. Not infrequently, these activities brought him into contact with Ticho, whose penchant for socializing and whose care for so many Arab patients made him an excellent resource.

Ticho and Kisch's respective spheres of medicine and politics intersected in the area of Jewish-Arab relations, relations that so easily could take a violent course of mass proportions. The two men's activities particularly intersected in the person and family of Emir Abdullah, whose relationship with the Jews was generally non-violent. The subjects of artists, the emir, and violence are all contained in one remarkable entry in Kisch's diaries of June 16, 1923:

Meeting of the Artists' Association at my flat in the morning. At five o'clock a visit from the oculist, Dr. Ticho, who has recently returned from Amman where he had been summoned by the Amir. Dr. Ticho told me that although he had asked to be excused from taking a fee, as was the invariable practice in the case of Turkish Governors, the Amir's Chamberlain insisted upon paying and paid royally. From what I hear generally, the Amir knows well how to maintain his personal prestige.... In the evening a dinner party at my flat followed by a small dance primarily for Ruth Franklin before her departure to England with her uncle the High Commissioner. We were interrupted about ten o'clock by news of a serious incident at Boneh-Bait, and I at once drove out there. On arrival, I was told that a young *Haluz* walking out with his girl had been attacked by a number of Arabs and taken to hospital. The Police were already on the spot in force and had arrested three Arabs found in this Jewish quarter, and declared by the victim to be the men who had attacked him. I then went to see the wounded man in the Rothschild Hospital. He had been stabbed twice in the chest and three times in the back, but the wounds were not serious. Before returning home, and after obtaining information that the girl was all right and was with friends in the town, I tried to reassure the excited crowds of Jews who had gathered in the streets.

Outreach to Arab leaders came from other quarters, including the religious Jewish community. In one famous instance, open political opposition to Zionism by these activists led to a political assassination of one Jew by another, the first in many centuries in the Holy City. In July 1923, soon after Ticho's visit to Amman, Emir Abdullah also entertained a visit from Dutch-born Jacob Israël de Haan – a follower of Rabbi Sonnenfeld and the Agudas Yisrael – who returned with assurances of mutual understanding with the Arab leader that were later conveyed to the International Congress of the Agudas Yisrael in Vienna.[22]

That same month, on July 13, 1923, Kisch was invited to a social gathering at the Tichos. The Tichos' guest-list that evening also included former Jerusalem mayor Musa Kazim al-Husayni. Although he had been dismissed as Jerusalem's mayor three years earlier in the wake of the Nebi Musa riots, al-Husayni was still a person of position and great influence. In connection with the Nebi Musa riots, the high commissioner had given amnesty to his nephew, Haj Amin al-Husayni. Subsequently, at the uncle's request, Sir Samuel had gone even further, appointing Amin al-Husayni as "Grand" Mufti of Jerusalem. Kisch had previously met with Musa Kazim al-Husayni in April, a meeting in which Kisch disclaimed and dismissed photographs altered to show Zionist flags waving over the dome of the Mosque of Omar. In the interchange, he failed to convince al-Husayni that it was a "temple to science and the arts" on Mount Scopus that the Zionists sought, not a temple to replace Muslim holy places on the Haram. Following his evening at the Tichos, Kisch wrote about al-Husayni "only to record that he expressed himself as a pure anti-Semite."[23]

◆

The presidency of the Hebrew University – the Jews' anticipated "temple to science and the arts" – had been offered to Albert Einstein, and although he had declined, he was heavily involved in its public relations and fundraising. In 1920, Einstein had accompanied Chaim Weizmann on an extensive tour of American cities, raising very large sums of money for the planned university. Although he graciously declined to immigrate to Palestine and assume the offered position, he agreed to visit Palestine with his wife Elsa on their way back from a trip to Japan. It was in the middle of this journey that Einstein received notice that he had won the Nobel Prize. His renowned theory of relativity had been overlooked by the selection committee for many years, but he was finally awarded the prize "for his services to Theoretical Physics, and especially for his discovery of the laws of the photoelectric effect."[24]

The Einsteins arrived in Palestine and made their way to Jerusalem via Lod by train in the company of representatives of the Va'ad Le'umi. They were greeted at the Jerusalem train station on the afternoon of February 2, 1923, by the high commissioner's son, Edwin Samuel. From here they were escorted to the Mount of Olives where they were guests of Sir Herbert Samuel at the Augusta Victoria Hospice (Government House). The following day being the Sabbath, Einstein took a relaxing daytime walk about the Old City with Sir Herbert, and that evening he called upon his friend Hugo Bergmann, whom he called the "serious saint from Prague." On Monday, after a visit to an agricultural museum, Einstein visited Bergmann at the National Library, while Tuesday's main activity was a visit to the new garden suburb of Beit Ha-Kerem.[25] Efforts by the Zionists to persuade Einstein to settle in Jerusalem in such a garden suburb were to no avail.

The climax of Einstein's visit came the following day, February 7, when Einstein gave a lecture on the Theory of Relativity on Mount Scopus, the inaugural lecture of the nascent Hebrew University. After an opening speech by the high commissioner, Ussishkin's introductory remarks made the clear parallels between the ancient temple in Jerusalem ("a house of prayer for all peoples") and the new temple on Mt. Scopus ("a house of science for all peoples"). The only available hall in the partially renovated former villa of Sir John Gray Hill could accommodate an audience of only about two hundred people and so tickets were scarce.[26] Much has been written about the symbolic importance of Einstein's support of the university and his historic lecture that he delivered in French after stumbling over his opening remarks in Hebrew. Ticho did not receive one of the prized tickets to the Mount Scopus lecture but he attended an earlier reception for Einstein in town at the Lämel School. Einstein returned to Jerusalem and to the Lämel School several days later after tours, lectures, and receptions in other parts of Palestine.

Ticho was present for Einstein's final and less remembered lecture on his Theory of Relativity that was given in German at the Lämel School on Tuesday evening, February 13, 1923. The four sponsoring organizations that evening were the Histadrut ha-Morim (Organization of Teachers), the Hebrew Technical Society, the Society of Engineers and Architects, and the Histadrut ha-Rof'im. After Einstein's lecture that evening, Ticho came to the podium and, likewise speaking in German, gave his thanks to the distinguished visitor on behalf of the Histadrut ha-Rof'im bi-Yerushalayim.[27] The later blurred distinctions between the two medical organizations in Jerusalem are further elucidated by the reports of this event. Given Ticho's pride of place in the proceedings, it is clear that this physician's group was the so-called Academy of Medicine that was led by Ticho at the time. Einstein left Jerusalem the following day and resumed his journey back home to Germany with stops in France and Spain. He would never visit Palestine again, but he remained a supporter of Zionism and the Hebrew University from afar for the rest of his life.

———◆———

Although Einstein could not be induced to settle in Palestine, several other noted philosophers, writers, and academicians from Central Europe eventually came to settle, many of them recruited successfully by the new Hebrew University. The Tichos would befriend a good number of these highly educated German-speaking intellectuals whose emigrations from Europe came at varying times over the next two decades. The peak numbers of Yekke immigrants only came in the face of the Nazi persecutions of the 1930s. By sheer numbers, German-Jewish immigrant doctors would come to dominate medicine in Palestine. However, in the early twenties, German-Jewish academicians, professionals and artists found ample comfort and resources for their work in Berlin, Frankfurt, and Vienna.

The Third Aliyah, the wave of immigration that began after World War I, has been defined as ending in 1923. Several of the Yekke immigrants who did settle in Jerusalem during the tail end of the Third Aliyah developed friendships with the Tichos. The Tichos were consummate hosts who loved to entertain guests in their home, and the conversations held there turned naturally and easily to German. Anna had much in common with notable artists who emigrated from Central

Europe, among them Brno-native Ludwig Blum, who immigrated in 1923, and Vienna-native Leopold Krakauer and his wife Gerta, who immigrated the following year.

Other highly educated German-Jewish immigrants whom the Tichos befriended included Dr. Felix Danziger and his wife Mali, who came to Jerusalem in the fall of 1923. The Danzigers opened a clinic opposite Herod's Gate to the north of the city in Musrara, and like Anna Ticho, Mali Danziger worked beside her husband as his first-assistant and nurse. Like the Magneses, the Danzigers sent their children to the American-style progressive school of Deborah Kallen, which featured the experience of a miniature-model community and age-appropriate art activities such as finger-painting.[28] The artistic inclinations of the Danzigers' young son Max (Yitzhak) caught Anna Ticho's attention, and this future acclaimed sculptor soon also began taking art classes at the Bezalel School.

Among the most notable German-Jewish immigrants of this era that the Tichos befriended was Gershom (Gerhard) Scholem, who arrived in Jerusalem on September 30, 1923. Scholem, a scholar of Kabbalah and Hassidic literature, had been given two job offers. One was teaching mathematics, and the other, presented to him by Hugo Bergmann, was the position of librarian of the Hebrew Section in the Jewish National Library. Scholem took the latter and as he settled in Jerusalem, he always found the Tichos eminently hospitable, and with them forged "life-long bonds of friendship and esteem." He wrote, "The conversations held in their home about national events and about culture in general were most illuminating, and the host's recollections of his rich experience with his patients were pearls of wisdom and wit."[29]

———◆———

In his great autobiographical book, *The World of Yesterday*, Stefan Zweig described the period of 1921–1923 in Austria as a time of accelerated inflation. With a very favorable rate of exchange, Austria became inundated with tourists who "availed to fatten themselves on the quivering cadaver of the Austrian krone." Only coalition politics and perhaps a "mysterious strength peculiar to Austria" prevented complete disintegration.[30] In this environment, Albert and Anna Ticho traveled to Vienna in early 1924, staying at the Hôtel de France from February 15 to March 13.[31] The objectives of the trip have not been discovered but the relatively lengthy stay on the Schottenring part of the Ringstraße so near to the University of Vienna suggests that Albert may have taken post-graduate seminars at the Vienna Medical Academy (Wiener medizinische Akademie) that was founded just that year or perhaps he visited the university's ophthalmology clinics. There were, in addition, family and old friends to see – siblings, growing nephews and nieces, classmates, professors – and perhaps some debts to repay to his brothers for their financial help in reestablishing Albert's private practice. There were cafés to enjoy, where newspapers contained articles about a trial of National Socialists in Munich, the defendants accused of treason following a failed putsch. In spite of the recent harsh economic times, there was also art and culture to absorb during their stay. In Boskovice, Albert could finally visit the gravesite of his father, who had died in 1921. The most important reason for coming to Austria might have been to attend the wedding of Albert's younger brother Paul (Baruch) to Lidderl (Marie) Jelinek, who came from a well-to-do family in the distillery business. The wedding that was held in Luhačovice (about fifty miles east of Brno) seems to have taken place during Albert and Anna's sojourn in Vienna. Toward the end of the trip back from Vienna, the local newspapers reported Ticho's forthcoming return to Jerusalem and his presence in his eye clinic on March 18 or 19.[32]

Soon after the Tichos' return from Europe, Dr. Ticho was visited by a young ophthalmologist, Dr. Ephraim Sinai, who had just immigrated to Palestine with his wife, Hannah, and changed his last name from Dissenzik. A native of Dobele, Latvia, Sinai was searching for practice opportunities and had already visited Dr. Aryeh Feigenbaum at the Rothschild-Hadassah Hospital the day before. Although Feigenbaum was unable to offer Sinai a position, he offered to buy some ophthalmic equipment from the financially strapped doctor. This included a prized Javal keratometer that Sinai had brought with him from Europe. Sinai recorded his first impressions of Ticho's clinic. "The waiting room was full of Jews and Arabs. All of them waited for the opening of the door of the clinic. After some time, Halaban emerged, a short, quick-moving man who fulfilled many tasks for Dr. Ticho. He brought me inside with a group of patients. I approached Dr. Ticho, who was treating a patient. He asked me a few questions and I answered and I told him that I had heard much about him and that I wondered how he was able to manage so many patients as this. He said to me that the patients want only him and that they are used to it. The line of patients progressed rapidly, and after a short time Halaban brought in the next group of patients."[33]

Unfortunately for Sinai, Ticho was not able to offer him a position at that time. Sinai and his wife had arrived in Palestine at the outset of what has now been called the Fourth Aliyah (1924–1928). The British Mandate's new immigration policy for settlement visas now included a "capitalist category" for those who could show possession of $2,500, but employment opportunities were becoming more scarce, apparently even for physicians. While the overall immigration figures were still rising month by month, so were the unemployment figures. The end of the decade would witness both a local economic downturn and greatly reduced Jewish immigration.[34] Sinai temporarily settled in Gaza, treating Arabs in an area far removed from most other Jews. The following year, however, Ticho was urged by Danziger to "rescue" Sinai from Gaza. Ticho sent Sinai word that he was now able to offer him a position as an assistant. Sinai worked for Ticho for about two years, but the two had a strained relationship that kept the younger assistant outside the inner circle of trust and at some points in jeopardy of losing his job.

Sinai's memoirs provide a picture of the routines and events of the hospital at that time and give much insight into Ticho's personality, at least from the assistant's perspective.[35] He estimated that Ticho performed between 1,000 and 1,500 minor and major operations during the two years of his employment, and he wrote that Ticho performed every operation perfectly, working quickly in silence with great assuredness. For Sinai, however, the silence of the operating room created "an atmosphere of stress and strain that always ruled." He wrote that occasionally Ticho would break the silence only to chastise him in front of Mrs. Ticho and Halaban. The strain between Ticho and Sinai reached a climax upon the Tichos' return from a rare, long weekend of relaxation at Kaliya south of Jericho on the shores of the Dead Sea. An Arab patient with a streptococcal eyelid infection took a turn for the worse. After day-long ministrations by Sinai and instructions to the night nurse, Sinai left and retired for the night. Upon Ticho's return, he accused his assistant of abandoning the patient, chastised him for not calling him at Kaliya, and dismissed him. In the end Ticho took Sinai back and with a raise and a bonus.

The memoirs of Ticho's often stressed-out assistant contain interesting anecdotes involving some of Ticho's more memorable patients, including a one-hundred-year-old patient from Meah Shearim who had remarried two years before – but, with a wink, told him that they did not yet have children between them. Another more serious anecdote concerned a case of misdiagnosis in which Ticho received some unexpected help from Dr. Aryeh Feigenbaum. This was the case of an Arab youth of about thirteen who suffered from swelling of one eye with a defined eyelid ulcer. Worried about an occult deeper growth or tuberculosis, Ticho sent the child with Sinai to the Rothschild Hospital for a *roentgen* [x-ray] examination of the eye socket and of the lungs. En route, Sinai's chance meeting with Dr. Feigenbaum resulted in the latter's exam and the correct diagnosis – primary syphilis. The memoirs explained, "Supposedly the youth suffered from an eye infection and one of the good neighbors in the village volunteered to lick his eye with her tongue. The woman was sick with syphilis and infected the youth with spirochetes that were in her mouth. The custom of licking inflammations and wounds like animals who lick their wounds, was widespread in the land among the villages." When Ticho soon heard about Feigenbaum's diagnosis "it caused Ticho to become pale because of the mistaken diagnosis of the case but he didn't add a word."

Another memorable case of cataract surgery was that of a businessman from Jaffa who owned an auto parts factory. He had cataracts in both eyes, and after he was operated on successfully in one eye he was ready for discharge. Against the advice of waiting a period of time for a second operation, he insisted "with German obstinacy" upon having the other eye operated on. "I have two eyes," he said, "and I want to see with both of them." He was operated upon successfully in the second eye. The next day when Sinai made rounds and said, "Good morning," there was no answer. The patient had died in the night.

A final case of interest in the assistant's memoirs was Ticho's treatment of a notable emir from Transjordan who needed to undergo cataract extraction. The examination was held in secret and the clinic was closed to all other patients. The emir's entourage included his bodyguard, five sons, and two wives, and each of the men brandished weapons. Halaban functioned as the translator. When refreshments were served, Ticho was asked to drink first. Two of the sons stood armed with revolvers and swords during the operation. The memoir records that "fortunately everything turned out well and there was no need for armed involvement."

Ticho always strived to keep his involvement with Arab notables on a friendly, apolitical plane, but other Jewish leaders engaged them openly with various political agendas. Jewish-Dutch lawyer Jacob de Haan, a sometime poet, correspondent, and teacher, denounced Zionist institutions openly in Palestine and during trips to Transjordan. Meanwhile, on January 26, 1924, Frederick Kisch brought David Yellin and the Sefardi Chief Rabbi to Amman to pay their respects to the visiting King Hussein and cautiously presented a pro-Zionist position that was formalized in a Hebrew-Arabic epistle on a parchment scroll delivered in a silver casket that was read aloud.[36] At a formal dinner reception, Kisch had the opportunity to discuss the Balfour Declaration with Emir Abdullah.

The following month, on February 24, 1924, Emir Abdullah and King Hussein were visited by de Haan, who brought a delegation of Orthodox rabbis headed by Rabbi Yosef Chaim Sonnenfeld. The guests were likewise treated to a traditional royal banquet given by the king, and a Hebrew-Arabic memorandum drafted by de Haan was likewise read aloud by the king's foreign minister.[37] The delegation returned to Jerusalem and faced stormy criticism from the mainstream Zionist media while Arab propagandists had a field day. De Haan's activities ultimately led to his assassination on June 30, 1924, just two days before a planned trip to London to further present the Agudas Yisrael position to the Colonial Ministry. That evening he went, as usual, to a small synagogue adjacent to the Shaare Zedek Hospital to pray and to study with Dr. Moshe Wallach, an old friend of Ticho's (chapter 11). In an interview over sixty years later, the assassin, Avraham Tehomi, openly admitted to his crime without regrets, stating that he had followed the orders of the Haganah. Implication of other Haganah leaders is still not certain as Tehomi had broken away from the Haganah in 1931, founding a separate para-military organization, the Irgun Tzva'i-Le'umi (Etzel).[38]

———◆———

There was one final event recorded in Sinai's memoirs that occurred toward the end of his tenure as Ticho's assistant. In the spring of 1924, Ticho purchased a large house "from a retired Russian general" in the heart of the city; he intended to move his hospital there. Sinai wrote that he was kept entirely unaware of the plans to purchase the home, and then he was kept out of all preparations for the transfer to the new house. Sinai wrote, "These preparations and the different arrangements continued for a long time but they did not speak with me about it. Not because they held the matter in secret, rather that they did not see a need to consult me. The matter hurt me.… I continued to work as usual, but without desire or satisfaction. I now had no open conflicts with Dr. Ticho, but the relations between us were somewhat forced."

The house and property that Sinai described were located to the west side of Ibn Battuta Street between Jaffa Road and the Street of the Prophets. Ticho had purchased the property at auction on April 18, 1924, from Alexander Mikhaelovitch Ashiri, the second-generation owner of the property. The Land Registry of the Mandatory Government recorded the seller's name as Iskandar bin Mekahil Sheikh Askir (Mikhail Ashiri). The sale of the house and garden was executed by the district court six days later, on April 26, 1924, and entered in the register on May 1, 1924. Perhaps showing signs of future financial difficulties, Alexander Ashiri had taken out a fifth mortgage on the property four years earlier as had been recorded by the Land Registry on November 18, 1920. Sinai's description of a "retired Russian general" is probably consistent with the seller's father, Mikhail Sheikh Ashiri, who transferred the property to his son around 1908. Around that same time in 1908, an adjacent plot to the south that was about half as large as the grounds of Ticho's house had been sold to Binyamin Kukia.[39] In the days before and during the war, Ticho had visited this beautiful home next door to his planned new hospital many times. Kukia had rented the house to the Austrian government as a fitting home for the Austrian consul. Here Ticho was welcomed by the staff and had become good friends with Friedrich Kraus, the second and last Austrian consul to occupy the home.

The history of the mansion now known as the Ticho House (and the adjacent grounds where other buildings such as the Kukia house now stand) have been beautifully described by Irit Salmon in a book that was published by the Israel Museum in 1994; descriptions of various lengths and detail can be found in the many tourist guidebooks of Jerusalem.[40] Previously known as the Aga Rashid Mansion or Rashid Palace, the original large mansion was built around 1864, and it first appears on Wilson's map of 1864–65 as the only building between the Russian Compound and the Anglican Mission Hospital. Some have identified its builder, Haj Aga Rashid, as the wealthy Arab notable Rashid al-Nashashibi. Although there are no documents to substantiate the identity of its builder, the theory is consistent with the presumed purpose as a primary residence of a wealthy Muslim notable rather than a seasonal second residence of a religious dignitary (such as those built outside of Jerusalem beginning toward the end of the fifteenth century).[41] Villas such as the one named after Aga Rashid were known as *qūsūr*. Each *qasr* was a castle-like manor house built within walking distance of the Old City that combined an attractive view of the city with access to cultivated agricultural lands, vineyards, olive groves, fruit orchards, and an independent water supply system that usually included one or more cisterns. It is believed that the builder engaged the services of a Persian contractor named Yazdi, who was also involved in the Russian Compound project, so surplus stones from the Russian Church, then under construction, were probably used for the thick walls, vaults, and fences of Aga Rashid's villa.[42]

Although less likely, perhaps the builder of the Aga Rashid mansion, whether Rashid al-Nashashibi or someone else, built the mansion as a rental property from the outset. Beginning in 1880, about sixteen years after its construction, the mansion was rented for about four years to the antiquities dealer Wilhelm Moses Shapira. Shapira had converted from Judaism to Christianity, and some time after settling in Jerusalem in 1856 he married Rosetta Jöckel, a German nurse in the deaconess community with whom he had two daughters.[43] Shapira's life ended in disgrace and suicide in 1884 when fragments of scripture that he had sold to the British Museum were declared to be forgeries. Years later, colorful and romantic descriptions of Shapira's luxurious house in Jerusalem from those days were recorded by the youngest daughter, Maria, under the pen name Myriam Harry. Her novel, *La Petite Fille de Jérusalem*, describes her childhood home. "It was built on high ground and before it a terraced garden descended to Jaffa Road. It was [like] a Persian orchard, a garden from the *Song of Songs* – fruit trees flourished among garden-beds of vegetables and flowers, a spectacular vision in those days of spring. All along the paths, irises extended their small amethyst cups amidst their green bowls, whilst all along the stone wall rosebushes burned like a thorn-hedge of fire. Violet-colored artichokes swayed beneath the grey branches of the olive trees; the grape vines intertwined with the fig trees, the kind that were interwoven in tabernacles of love in which daughters of Jerusalem awaited their lovers."[44]

It was probably sometime soon after Wilhelm Shapira's suicide in Rotterdam in 1884 and Rosetta Jöckel Shapira's subsequent return to Europe with her daughter that the Aga Rashid Mansion was purchased by the aforementioned Mikhail Sheikh Ashiri.[45] In addition to this "retired Russian general" and his son, Alexander Mikhaelovitch Ashiri, the mansion was inhabited by several known tenants from 1906 onwards, including, at various times, members of the Valero, Baruch, Adoni, and Markoff families. Also Dr. Fruma Weizmann, a dentist and sister of the first president of Israel, lived in the mansion with her husband, Zelig.[46]

The Ticho's new home had been built in a typical urban Arabic architectural style of the latter nineteenth century, "a typical two-storied *liwan* building, featuring a central space and two adjacent domed sections, each containing several rooms."[47] Sixty years earlier, the original building techniques had featured meter-thick walls with rough-hewn stone externally, interior walls built of softer stone, and the space between them filled with smaller stones and mud. Outside at the entrance to the hospital, a narrow porch ran along the southern façade of the building. The ceiling and roof of each room were cross-vaulted.

Ticho consigned the extensive renovation work of the mansion to architect Fritz Kornberg, who gave the hospital a monastic appearance with sparse simple furnishings. Patients lay in plain iron beds in two rooms on either side of a spacious central hall. The operating room in the rear northwest of the building had ample lighting from several windows and a large lamp installed in the central vault over the main operating table. The white Carrara marble floor added to the sense of hospital sterility. At the rear of the hospital a wall with a wooden door was erected to conceal the spiral staircase that ascended to the Ticho's living quarters on the second floor. Anna Ticho could work in a spacious and well-lit upper floor studio on the northern, rear side of the house that had been added to the original building. The comfortable living quarters contained several furnishings that Kornberg designed in an Art Deco style.

———◆———

One of Fritz Kornberg's major, well-known architectural projects was the design of the amphitheater on Mount Scopus that was first used for the ceremonial opening of the Hebrew University on April 1, 1925. The extensive remodeling of the Tichos' home does not seem to have suffered from lack of attention due to Kornberg's commitment to the Mount Scopus project. Kornberg's initial designs for the ampitheater were very rudimentary and straightforward. Thus far, only the nascent university's institutes for chemistry, microbiology, and Jewish studies had been organized, and although the library was still housed in the center of the New City, plans had been established for a grand library building on Mount Scopus. Crowds of several thousands were planned for the Wednesday afternoon opening ceremonies; this would require an outdoor venue, as the largest hall in the university's chemistry-microbiology building could barely accommodate an audience of two hundred.

Fortunately, the university's chancellor, Judah Magnes, had identified a natural amphitheater facing a deep wadi on the northeast slope of Mount Scopus. In preparation for the opening ceremony, many young men and women worked at fashioning tiers of rough seating along the rocky slope.[48] To face the audience in this amphitheater, however, the platform had to be on a bridge over the wadi itself. A wooden bridge was built, tested, and found to be sound, and Magnes determined that the theater's acoustics would be adequate as long as the weather, including wind speeds and direction cooperated, as fortunately they did. The weather was good on the afternoon of the ceremony. It did not rain until the following day.

The Tichos were among an audience of about ten thousand who attended the historic ceremonies that were scheduled to start at 3:00 p.m. Many of the spectators had walked long distances from outlying settlements, some over several days, to see Lord Balfour. Balfour wore his scarlet academic gown as the chancellor of Cambridge University; several others wore their robes, including Weizmann and visiting academics and school rectors. A thunderous ovation greeted Balfour as he entered from the direction of the Mount of Olives with British officials, including Field Marshall Viscount Allenby and High Commissioner Herbert Samuel.[49]

After a benediction, national anthems, and singing of Psalms by a choir, Rabbi Kook gave a benediction; but much to Weizmann's chagrin, he expanded the five minutes allotted to him for the blessing into a half-hour speech. Rabbi Kook blessed King George, the high commissioner and Lord Balfour, and prayed for the success of the university; he spoke at greater length about Torah and tradition. At his turn, Lord Balfour spoke animatedly and, as was his habit, without notes.[50] He proclaimed, "We are now engaged in adapting Western methods and a Western form of university to an Asiatic site and to an education which is to be carried on in an Eastern language. That is a new experiment. It has never been tried before under any circumstances parallel at all to those in which I speak to you. Ladies and gentlemen, unless I have... profoundly mistaken the genius of the Jewish people, the experiment is predestined to an inevitable success. Not only men of Jewish birth, but others who share the common civilisation of the world, will have reason to congratulate themselves."[51]

Appearing in non-speaking roles upon the stage and dressed similarly in their business suits, both Judah Magnes and Arthur Ruppin shared a view of the multitudes before them that included "many non-Jewish Palestinians including some sheiks from Beisan [Beit She'an]," but Arabs were certainly far outnumbered by the Jewish participants and spectators.[52] Magnes had approached the ceremonies with trepidation, expressing concerns to Weizmann that the invitation of Lord Balfour would overly politicize the event. Afterwards he continued to worry about ramifications that the event had upon an Arab society that was increasingly united and organized.[53]

Ruppin, the architect of Zionist settlement policy, now turned his thoughts toward developing understanding and cooperation between Jews and Arabs. Conversations in Ruppin's home among guests increasingly turned into "consultations on the Arab question" with the presentation of dramatically opposing views. By June 25, 1925, Ruppin indicated he was determined to establish a "league for Jewish-Arab understanding."[54] In August 1925, at the Fourteenth Zionist Congress in Vienna, Ruppin proclaimed, "Palestine will be a state of two nations [*ein Zweinationalitätenstaat*]. Gentlemen, this is a fact, a fact which many of you have not yet sufficiently realized. It may also be that for some of you this is not a pleasant fact, but it nonetheless remains so."[55] At the Congress, the opposite end of the Zionist political spectrum was represented by Ze'ev Jabotinsky who had organized the first "Conference of the League [Union] of Zionist Revisionists" in Paris earlier that April. The Revisionists' adopted program stated, "The aim of Zionism is the gradual transformation of Palestine (Transjordan included) into a Jewish Commonwealth, that is, into a self-governing Commonwealth under the auspices of an established Jewish majority."[56]

In contradistinction to the Revisionists, the formal founding of the organization Brit Shalom (The Peace Association), and the delineation of its principles and statutes took place on March 9, 1926.[57] These principles reflected what Martin Buber called realistic Zionism (*Wirklichkeitszionismus*), a Zionism rooted in the complex reality of the Land of Israel rather than a Zionism based in the Diaspora. Ruppin and his colleagues envisioned a bi-national state accommodating both Zionism and Palestinian Arab nationalism within the political framework of the British Mandate that they assumed would continue for reasons of Britain's imperialist self-interests. In the mid-1920s when the Arab population of Palestine totaled 750,000 compared to 75,000 Jews, the members of Brit Shalom opposed the prevailing Zionist policy aimed at rapidly achieving a Jewish majority.[58] Brit Shalom never considered itself a political party, and its membership never exceeded one hundred. Rather, the members of Brit Shalom viewed their organization as a study circle, a catalyst for discussions of the Arab question, and, in keeping with its mission, even a source of Arabic language instruction.[59]

Although Ticho was a supporter of the organization he, like Judah Magnes, never "officially" joined. Over the years, Ticho developed very close friendships with several of the leaders of Brit Shalom, especially those who were of central European origin – fellow Yekkim who dreamed of peaceful cooperation between Jews and Arabs.[60]

———◆———

The summer of 1925 in Jerusalem was a time of both transition and stability for the Tichos. Their new hospital in the heart of the New City was now fully operational, but Ticho continued to maintain his clinic off of St. George's Road in Musrara as well. Dr. Sinai's place as the assistant physician was taken by twenty-nine-year-old Dr. Rachel Stein (later Reich) who, motivated by Zionism, had immigrated to Palestine and settled in Jerusalem. A native of Galicia, she had moved to Vienna with her family at the outbreak of World War I. Like Ticho, she had studied medicine in Vienna and then specialized in ophthalmology there. She would work for Dr. Ticho for six years.[61] Toward the end of this period, she would assume greater responsibilities in the hospital when Ticho was incapacited by a failed assassination attempt in November 1929, and even more so during Ticho's travel abroad during his recovery in February–March 1930 (chapter 18).

The summer of 1925 in Jerusalem was also a time of transition for the British Mandatory government. Herbert Samuel's term as high commissioner came to an end on June 30, 1925, but his designated replacement, Field Marshal Herbert Plumer, soon arrived, on August 25, to take his place.[62] Plumer's three-year term was characterized by tranquility in the country and the development of local government. Artists such as Israel Feldman (later Paldi) exhibited their works in Tel Aviv and Jerusalem to much acclaim. Sometime during the quiet year of 1926, Anna Ticho opened the doors of the Tichos' upstairs residence and her atelier for her first solo exhibition of her artwork.[63]

Elsewhere in the Middle East, however, the first battles of the Great Syrian Revolt resulted in several victories for the insurgents over the French Army. Early during Ticho's sojourn in Damascus in 1917, Marjeh Square had been the site of Ottoman military executions by public hangings, and now, less than a decade later, it was the French Army's turn to stage such spectacles. A "surge" of French foreign army divisions would suppress the revolt, but only after almost three years. In the Hejaz, Abdul-Aziz ibn Saud and his Wahabi followers had entered Mecca in October 1924. In the summer of 1925, Hussein bin Ali, the former King of the Hejaz who had refused to sign a proposed Anglo-Hejaz Treaty, was taken into exile to Cyprus by the British.[64]

During the four years following Ticho's departure from the AZMU that was followed by Director Rubinow's own departure, the Hadassah Medical Organization had had a series of temporary directors. In March 1926, Dr. Ephraim M. Bluestone was appointed as HMO director for a term of three years at an annual salary of $10,000, ten times that of the average worker. Dr. Bluestone had an impressive résumé as a surgeon and administrator at Mount Sinai Hospital in New York City, but he was not entirely prepared for what awaited him in Palestine. The new director arrived at one of the most difficult economic times for the Yishuv, where the unemployment rate among workers in general was 35 percent, 50 percent in Tel Aviv and Haifa, and 75 percent in the area of Afula and the Jezreel Valley.

The fact that Bluestone was an American with very limited Hebrew skills made him an immediate target for the Zionist press. The newspaper *Davar* wrote, "He is unable to read a Hebrew newspaper to know what is being written about his institution and unable to participate in community life even as it pertains to questions of national health."[65]

Dr. Bluestone's greatest battles were with the Histadrut's health service, Kupat Ḥolim, and its director, Eliezer Perlson. Beginning in 1927, the HMO director instituted a new policy regarding hospitalizations of unemployed members of Kupat Ḥolim, insisting that these patients produce a "Certificate of Poverty" issued only by their local municipality or settlement and not from Kupat Ḥolim. Only then could the patient be hospitalized with the usual discounted charges paid by Kupat Ḥolim but without personal charges to the patient.[66] The controversy that lasted many months was not entirely resolved by the intervention of Zionist leaders, and the many salvos back and forth were quite often reported by the media.

Ticho's private hospital did not suffer from such controversies and bureaucratic red tape. In his fee-for-service private practice, he could apply a sliding scale and provide services at markedly reduced rates. Around this same time, over 60 percent of Ticho's inpatient admissions were Muslims and another 10 percent Christians. Less than 30 percent of the admissions to his hospital were Jews.[67] Perhaps these trends and the controversy and publicity surrounding the "Certificates of Poverty" reawakened Ticho's interest in Hadassah. He might have sensed an opportunity to revisit the issue of being a consultant for the HMO. After exploring the matter with Dr. Bluestone, the HMO's director rebuffed Ticho's overture, writing the following: "To the honorable Dr. Ticho….on November 28, 1927, we listened to [Rubinow's] recordings and found that a Senior Oculist Consultant [position] for the Hadassah Medical Organization was not final, and that there were no documents that prove that the negotiations between Hadassah and your honored sir on this subject were brought to a successful conclusion. It is very possible that different documents will be dug up in our archives."[68] Meanwhile, throughout his battles with Kupat Ḥolim, Dr. Bluestone repeatedly requested that the HMO release him from his contract and allow him to return to New York. This he was allowed to do in September 1928, but only after the HMO had designated a successor. This was Dr. Hayim Yassky, the first permanent resident of Palestine to serve as director of the HMO.

As an American, Dr. Bluestone had been seen as an outsider in matters relating to the politics of the Yishuv. While the Zionist and Hadassah leadership invited Kupat Ḥolim Director Eliezer Perlson and his associates to the negotiation table in April 1927, Bluestone had been specifically uninvited.[69] Wishing to avoid the outsider's stigma, Palestine Zionist Executive Director Frederick Kisch adopted dual Palestinian citizenship alongside his British passport (as allowed according to the Palestine Citizenship Order of July 24, 1925).[70] The dilemma of identity and citizenship for Zionists who came to and left Palestine at various times during the Mandate was later reflected in the title of Norman Bentwich's autobiography, *A Wanderer between Two Worlds*.

On the other hand, Albert and Anna Ticho who had permanently settled in Palestine considered themselves citizens of the Republic of Czechoslovakia, the amalgamated country founded after World War I that included their native Moravia. Quite soon a fellow Moravian and founding president of Czechoslovakia would make a pilgrimage to the Holy City and stay less than a half mile from Ticho's home. On April 8, 1927, Tomáš Garrigue Masaryk arrived in Jerusalem, the first president of a democratic state to travel to Palestine. The seventy-nine-year-old philosopher-president of Czechoslovakia was in the midst of a presidential re-election campaign. He traveled as a private citizen but he was greeted everywhere with honor as a head of state. Twenty-six-year-old Otto Ticho, Albert Ticho's nephew (eldest son of Jacob Ticho of Brno), was among a few Czech citizens who were selected to travel from Czechoslovakia to Palestine to assist or greet Masaryk's small entourage. Otto's full role is not entirely clear, but he might have been among the three security personnel.[71] Having toured Egypt for almost three weeks, Masaryk traveled to Kantera where he joined Dr. Frič, the Czechoslovak consul in Jerusalem, whose offices had been established just a year prior to the visit. In Jerusalem he was joined by his guide, his old friend and fellow-philosopher Schmuel Hugo Bergmann, who took him to his lodgings at the Franciscan Notre Dame Hospice opposite the Old City walls. Here Masaryk rested for the remainder of the day.[72]

Masaryk's Saturday schedule was devoted to Christian and Muslim holy sites in the Old City, on Olivet and in Bethlehem. In the morning he was met at the Jaffa Gate by Plumer's Chief Secretary, Sir Stewart Symes, and by the mayor of Jerusalem, Raghib Bey al-Nashashibi. Masaryk, who had studied some Arabic in his younger years, spoke in French when visiting with the members of the Supreme Muslim Council, which included Musa Kazim al-Husayni and Mufti Haj Amin al-Husayni. Ticho's opportunity to meet Masaryk came the following afternoon, April 10, after the visiting statesman had already toured the National and University Library in the New City and the university campus on Mt. Scopus.[73] That Sunday afternoon, Masaryk was a guest of the Czechoslovak community in the Shomrei ha-Ḥomot community's section of the Hungarian Houses neighborhood. Here placards hung decorated with Czechoslovak state colors and bearing the message in both Czech and Hebrew, "Long live President Masaryk." Ticho attended the reception in the community center where the Czechoslovak flag – its white and red bands extending from a dark blue triangle – waved beside British and Jewish standards and where Rabbi Sonnenfeld prayed for Czechoslovakia.

◆

The major earthquake that struck Palestine on July 11, 1927, left about 450 dead throughout Palestine and Transjordan, including scores of fatalities in the Arab cities of Lydda and Es Salt. The quake lasted only about seven seconds, but frightening, smaller aftershocks continued for two weeks. Much of Lydda's old town was demolished. One Jewish physician who came to the aid of Lydda's injured survivors was German-born physician and educator Siegfried Lehmann, who had founded the nearby Ben Shemen Youth Village two years earlier on the site of previously unsuccessful Zionist ventures. Lehmann's work among Lydda's earthquake victims led to close friendships with Arab leaders of the city and neighboring villages. A fountain that Lehmann built at the outside gates of Ben Shemen was a symbol of friendship; it provided water to Arab villagers that passed by it on their way to and from Lydda. The physician also let it be known that the youth village medical clinic would always be open to Arabs who sought medical care.[74]

Virtually every structure in Jerusalem suffered at least some damage; at least 175 homes were seriously affected. Apparently Ticho's ophthalmic hospital suffered relatively minor damage with no injuries to patients, but there was rather considerable damage at the nearby Rothschild Hospital.[75] Major damage to the Augusta Victoria Hospice on the Mount of Olives made it uninhabitable. The hospice had been used as the British Government House and residence of the high commissioner since the arrival of Herbert Samuel seven years earlier. Samuel's successor, Herbert Plumer, was soon able to take up residence at the stately but somewhat rundown mansion of Maḥanaim on the Street of the Prophets, and this would also serve as the home of his own successor, Sir John Chancellor.[76] At some point, a decision was made to return the Augusta Victoria Hospice to the German government and build a new Government House on the south side of the city. Christian tradition held that the elevated land to the northeast of Talpiot was the site of High Priest Caiaphas's home in the time of Jesus, and it had long been known as the Hill of Evil Counsel. Meanwhile, the Tichos' friend and frequent house guest, Jewish-German architect Alexander Baerwald of Haifa's Technion, was retained to oversee the extensive repairs and renovations for the Germans' reclaimed property on Olivet.[77]

Alex Baerwald and his wife, Lotte, were among the greatest supporters of Anna Ticho's art. They would regularly welcome Anna at their home in Haifa when she visited the world-renowned artist Hermann Struck, who would give her instruction in the art of etching. During the winter of 1928, Struck encouraged Anna Ticho to plan a trip to Europe in order to explore venues to show her art. In January 1928, Struck and Lotte Baerwald helped make several contacts in Berlin for Anna.[78] Very few details about the trip have survived, but it is known that Anna went on from Berlin to Paris where her work was favorably reviewed by one or more gallery owners and that she had returned to Palestine by the end of June 1928.[79]

Back in Jerusalem, it was announced that High Commissioner Lord Plumer would end his three-year term on August 1, 1928, by taking an early two-month "leave of absence." Norman Bentwich was among those who lavished praise upon Plumer for presiding over "a period of almost unbroken tranquility and progress," but tensions between Jews and Arabs had continued to increase beneath the surface.[80] Among the most frustrating matters for the Arabs were the continued dispossession of fellahin resulting from land purchases and continued unwelcome immigration of Jews; the Zionists were frustrated by the limitations on immigration, restrictions on self-defense, and under-representation in Palestine's police forces. Ehud Ben-Yehudah, dismissed from his sub-inspector's position on the Jerusalem District Police in early July, claimed discrimination for his insistence upon his right to use the Hebrew language in police work and pointed out the obvious fact that the Jerusalem police force was almost entirely Arab.[81] This was already the standing policy when Harry Luke arrived on July 19, 1928, to take over as the new chief secretary, and he would serve as acting high commissioner until the arrival of Sir John Chancellor in early December.

A very warm August passed quietly at Ticho's ophthalmic hospital, but the approaching Jewish New Year (Rosh Hashanah) would bring an increased demand for treatment. His waiting room would be full of Orthodox Jews hoping to be hospitalized for surgery or other treatment. In this way they might be able to pass the solemn week at rest and have dispensation from fasting on Yom Kippur, the Day of Atonement.[82] At Hadassah Hospital, the besieged Dr. Ephraim Bluestone finally called it quits and returned to America. The ophthalmologist Dr. Hayim Yassky became acting director. He was the first permanent resident of Palestine to serve as the chief administrator of Hadassah Hospital, though his permanent appointment was delayed until 1931.[83]

During this time, Palestine was still without its new high commissioner, and so some of the first events that brought an end to the "somewhat quieter times" came under Harry Luke's tenure, helped along by his fellow civil servant and friend Edward Keith-Roach, Jerusalem's district commissioner. Some would comment that the seeds of incitement were also sewn during that holy week when a visa to return to Palestine was granted to Ze'ev Jabotinsky, while Muslim leaders such as Mufti Haj Amin al-Husayni were also ready and able to arouse passions.[84] These personalities were among those who served as the overseers and agents of escalating tensions that characterized the continuing struggle between Jews and Arabs. It was a struggle that was evolving into a broad, epic battle "for myths, religious faith, national honor, and history."[85]

As recorded on the Hebrew calendar, the year 5689, represented by the Hebrew letters תרפ״ט and vocalized as *Tarpat* (the year that began September 15, 1928), would be remembered for its violent events, known as "*Me'ora'ot Tarpat*." This was a year climaxed by massacres of Jews by Arab rioters in Jerusalem, Hebron, Safed, and elsewhere. Later historians would view this critical period through various Zionist, non-Zionist, and Arab perspectives. Although Ticho aimed to be apolitical, his frame of reference at the beginning of this period was probably not far removed from a viewpoint now popular among the "new" historians.[86] Even so, it is likely that Ticho's personal involvement in many of the events of the coming year, including the nearly successful attempt upon his life, continued to shape his views.

CHAPTER 18

1928–1930

MAYHEM AND AFTERMATH

יגודו על-נפש צדיק
ודם נקי ירשיעו.

They band together to do away with the righteous;
They condemn the innocent to death.

Psalms 94:21

E ven in the middle of his busiest time of the year, it was Ticho's custom to attend High Holiday services. On Yom Kippur (the Day of Atonement), the holiest day on the Hebrew calendar, it was Ticho's practice to fast for over twenty-four hours, from before sundown when the holiday began until after sundown the following day. On Sunday, September 23, 1928, the Tichos therefore ate a somewhat larger than average meal and walked to synagogue, though it is not certain where he attended services. Perhaps they stayed close to home in the New City and attended the Yeshurun Synagogue (est. 1923), now holding services in the Even Yisrael neighborhood on Jaffa Road near the corner of King George Street (today the home of the Olei Gardom Synagogue). Perhaps like the Bentwiches they went into the Old City and attended Kol Nidre services at the beautiful Hurva Synagogue.[1] In all of the Orthodox synagogues of Jerusalem there was separate seating for men and women. At the Hurva Synagogue the men would enter the main prayer hall through a large iron gate while the women would make their way up one of the towers that lead to the galleries lining three sides of the hall. As in all Orthodox synagogues, Torah scrolls that evening were removed from the Holy Ark, the cantor then recited the Kol Nidre prayer three times to nullify unfulfilled vows for the coming year, and he then asked for God's forgiveness.

At the Kotel, the Ashkenazi sexton had put up a collapsible wooden and cloth screen to separate the women worshippers from the men, just as in a synagogue. There are differing versions about how this became a matter of controversy that was used by the mufti and members of the Muslim Court. Wolfgang von Wiesl later testified that a dispute about the partition arose between the Sephardi and Ashkenazi sextons, which was indirectly brought to the attention of the mufti. In another version, an offhand remark was made by District Commissioner Edward Keith-Roach who was visiting the clerics with Inspector Douglas Duff. Keith-Roach reportedly commented that he had never seen such a screen there before, although it was later shown that a screen, benches, and so forth had been authorized by the government and employed on several occasions in the past. With even a hint of controversy about the matter, the members of the Muslim Court certainly looked to "make capital at the expense of the Jews, [and] immediately assumed miens of righteous indignation." These events turned out to be the starting point for violence between Arabs and Jews on a scale that had not yet been seen before in Palestine.[2] Over the following months, hundreds of people would be killed throughout Palestine and many more would be wounded.

After the district commissioner gave assurances to the Muslim clerics, the task of removing the screen at the Kotel fell to Inspector Duff, a violent man who had no qualms about the use of force.[3] Having obtained written authorization from Keith-Roach, Duff returned that evening to give warning to the sexton that the screen needed to be removed by the next morning. Even as Ticho was returning to pray the following morning, Duff had returned to the Kotel, this time with armed and steel-helmeted men. A scuffle ensued, and the women at the wall struck at the policemen with their parasols. In an unfortunate display of insensitivity and brutality, Duff and his policemen destroyed the screen in the midst of the worship service, very roughly handling the sexton and several of the other worshippers. As yet no deaths had occurred, but both Jews and Arabs had taken note of the pro-Arab behavior of the Mandatory government and its police force.[4]

Life went on more quietly for the Tichos and other Jewish inhabitants of Jerusalem during the fall and winter that followed the Yom Kippur screen incident. On November 11, 1928, the tenth anniversary of the general armistice of the World War, a parade of Jewish ex-soldiers to the military cemetery on Mt. Scopus took place very peacefully, and even Ze'ev Jabotinsky was reticent and subdued.[5] There was a club organized by Jewish intelligentsia where members would gather for talk, music, dancing, and refreshment.[6] Musical performances often featured Attorney General Norman Bentwich's sisters – the unmarried Margery Bentwich on violin and a married sister, Thelma Yellin, a virtuoso on cello who had studied with Pablo Casals. The Tichos could often enjoy a touch of Vienna, as they did on November 19, 1928, when their friend Alex Baerwald joined Thelma Yellin and others in performing at a celebration of the centenary of Franz Schubert's death. The following spring, on March 12, 1929, violinist virtuoso Branislaw Huberman gave his first performance in Jerusalem having performed two days earlier in Tel Aviv. He would return several times during the following decade, but this first visit had stimulated the violinist's interest in establishing a classical music presence in Palestine at the highest level.[7]

Buried below harmonious and tranquil scenes of social life in Jerusalem, however, tensions between Jews and Arabs were building. Urban Arabs and also many Arab fellahin who lived at the urban edges were economically stressed, feeding into an atmosphere of political despair and religious fervor. It was not difficult for Muslim religious leaders, most notably Mufti Haj Amin al-Husayni, to arouse their passions. The Zionists meanwhile found their own passionate spokespersons. On November 22, 1928, publisher Zalman White hired Ze'ev Jabotinsky to be the new editor-in-chief of the newspaper Do'ar ha-Yom.[8] For the first time, the Revisionists had their own newspaper in Palestine to present their platform: unhindered rights of Jews to immigrate to Palestine, their right to an autonomous Jewish state on both sides of the Jordan, reconstituting a Jewish Legion, and other reforms. Tapping into centuries of Jewish yearnings for Zion, the main issues were symbolically and tangibly connected to the issues of access to the Kotel and its ownership. In the absence of a "final" Commission on Holy Places, the Mandatory Government had sidestepped the basic religious issues by resorting to the preservation of an ill-defined Ottoman-era "status quo." Even as tensions rose to the surface, Ticho may have tried to ignore the local religious incitements and political rhetoric. Only the following summer, when the rhetoric turned to widespread violence, would Ticho be drawn into the conflict.

The new high commissioner, Sir John Chancellor, attempted to reason with the mufti and Jewish leaders about the Kotel following his arrival in December 1928, but without success. Like many of the British administrators working in Palestine, Chancellor privately had revealed decidedly pro-Arab sympathies.[9] Publicly, the high commissioner gladly participated in the more neutral and positive events that presented themselves. On April 30, 1929, Chancellor dedicated the new, non-sectarian Nathan and Lina Straus Health Center located just to the west of Meah Shearim on a street that would be named Chancellor Avenue (though later renamed Rehov Straus). Two years earlier, the seventy-nine-year-old Nathan Straus had attended the ground-breaking ceremony for the structure with Chancellor's predecessor and other dignitaries; the cornerstone had come from excavations of the Jerusalem's ancient Third Wall of Agrippa. Although the new center was just a few blocks from his new ophthalmic hospital, it is not known if Ticho attended the dedication ceremonies. At some point he most likely visited the public exhibition in the building that reviewed the history of Hadassah in Palestine. Henrietta Szold who presided over the dedication ceremonies of April 30 described the Health Center as a "temple erected to preventative medicine" and a future university hospital building on Mt. Scopus as "a temple to scientific medicine."[10] Nobody at the ceremonies that day imagined that, just four months later, one of the first practical uses of the Straus Health Center would be to house the evacuated, terrified survivors of massacres from the nearby city of Hebron.

In the spring of 1929, the Kotel increasingly became a focal point of political attention and a flashpoint of Arab violence with targeted beatings of Jews. On Sabbath evening May 3, 1929, and continuing the following day, Arab Muslims hurled stones at Jewish worshippers, and the sexton was seriously injured. The Va'ad Leumi joined with the Sephardi and Ashkenazi Chief Rabbis and Agudas Yisrael in a joint memorandum of protest to the government.[11] The Jewish leaders pointed out that the Arabs had been guilty of many "status quo" violations at the Kotel: the building of an adjacent new gate for Arab pedestrian traffic (later called "the bloodstained door"); building new rows of stones at the top of the Kotel; conducting there loud calls to Muslim prayers by the muezzin; and newly instituted performances of loud Muslim ceremonies (*zikr*) featuring music, singing, and drum beating in the fashion of dancing or "whirling" dervishes.[12]

More militant Jews were undaunted over the assaults at the Kotel. Jabotinsky ran a campaign in *Do'ar ha-Yom* that claimed Jewish rights over the wall and the alley that fronted it, and Joseph Klausner organized a Committee of the Western Wall; together they began preparing for a demonstration at the Kotel with members of the Revisionists' youth movement, Betar.[13] Pacifist Jews continued to seek opportunities for Jewish-Arab dialogue while disaffected Jews turned their back on the religious controversies. That summer Margery Bentwich would write, "This business of the wall, how pitiful it is indeed. Is it a symbol of former glory? Much more of present humiliation. To see a man fling himself on the stones, kiss them, isn't it revolting! Like praying to an idol – as if a stone had ears. The best thing that could happen…were to raze it to the ground…. Strange that such a great number of people can die for an untrue idea and so few can live for a true one."[14] Further showing dissatisfaction with traditional Jewish customs, Margery Bentwich eventually joined a Christian sect and later settled somewhat reclusively but near family in the Zikhron Ya'akov area.

In early June 1929, Dr. Harry Friedenwald and his daughter, Julia, returned to Palestine for a tour, and they visited with the Bentwiches and the Tichos among others. While at the Tichos for a Sunday visit, Dr. Friedenwald mentioned some highlights of his tours to that point. Instead of a visit to the ancient remains of Herod's Temple at the Kotel, they had visited the new "temple" of the Hebrew University on Mount Scopus where Dr. Judah Magnes proudly showed them several publications issued by the university, including those of Dr. Israel Kligler. They saw the physics building that was under construction and the beautiful, newly completed Wolffsohn Library. Dr. Friedenwald also described his impressions of Hebron as becoming "uglier and dirtier" except for the Hadassah Center (Beit Hadassah) managed by Dr. Zvi Kitayin. The Hadassah Center included a dispensary, a children's eye clinic, and an infant welfare station, the newest of twenty-one such infant welfare clinics established by Hadassah throughout Palestine.[15]

Back in Jerusalem, Dr. Friedenwald had also visited Hadassah's trachoma eye clinic and had been very impressed with the work of its director, Dr. Judith Kozlov. Since his departure from the Hadassah Medical Organization, Ticho continued to closely follow the incidence of trachoma in his own clinic. With his many Arab patients, the incidence of trachoma in Ticho's clinic now stood at about 10 percent of the 33,000 patients he was seeing annually. Ticho also followed the trachoma statistics for Palestine in various populations and locations as reported by the government, Hadassah, and the Kupat Ḥolim. During Friedenwald's visit, Ticho showed his friend a draft of his last major paper on trachoma, one that he had just submitted for publication in the German medical literature and that would be published in January 1930.[16] In this paper Ticho estimated a reservoir of up to 400,000 cases of trachoma in the population of Palestine. He concluded that active trachoma in Palestine was present in about 15 percent of the Jewish population but in at least 50 percent of the larger Arab population. He concluded that the six constructed governmental ophthalmic clinics to treat children from 315 schools had been given up due to high costs, whereas the "flying hospitals" with Hadassah visiting nurses continued to be effective in maintaining low active trachoma rates.

Dr. Friedenwald's visit to Palestine was his first in some years, and it was his first visit to Tichos' new hospital and residence. He was impressed with the "gracious and exquisitely furnished home" and also admired Ticho's collection of Hanukkah menorahs that he described as "the most extensive collection of antique Jewish lamps he had ever seen."[17] After touring Tel Aviv and parts of northern Palestine, Friedenwald and his daughter returned to Jerusalem, joining the Tichos again for supper one evening. Before ending their three-week visit, Dr. Friedenwald gave a fifty-minute lecture in German at the Rothschild-Hadassah Hospital that Ticho most probably attended along with about fifty members of the Jewish Physicians' Society. The sixty-five-year-old emeritus professor's credentials and the title of his lecture, "The relation of ophthalmology to general medicine," contributed to attracting the relatively large audience. Perhaps to the Friedenwalds' good fortune, they soon departed from Jerusalem. It was just a few weeks before Jewish demonstrations at the Kotel on Tish'a B'Av and the days of the bloody Arab riots that would follow.

◆

Tish'a B'Av fell that year on Thursday, August 15, and scores of young demonstrators assembled at the Kotel, raising the Zionist flag and singing "Hatikvah." The march to the Kotel had been approved by Acting High Commissioner Harry Luke, and although many of the demonstrators were members of the Revisionist youth movement, Brit Trumpeldor (Betar), the group did not actually organize the demonstration.[18] Most Jewish sources claimed that the demonstration by the Jewish youths was "peaceful and well conducted." Other accounts described a large group that entered the Old City and surprised the Arabs, who fled from their stores, and that at the Kotel a rabbi was raised upon the demonstrators' shoulders and shouted, "We swear to be faithful to this place and will never give up our rights to it."[19]

On Friday, August 16, 1929, the day following the Jewish demonstration at the Kotel, an incited Arab mob burst through the new door adjacent to the Kotel, broke the table for the reading of the Torah, and tore and burned prayer books, Psalm books, and written supplications that had been placed in the clefts of the stones. The violence would escalate on the following day, the Jewish Sabbath. At around noon that day, seventeen-year-old Avraham Mizrachi was murdered by an Arab at the outskirts of the Bukharan Quarter. An argument seems to have erupted over an errant soccer ball that entered an Arab garden.[20] Mizrachi, who had immigrated to Palestine with his parents from Persia at eight years of age, was then working as a helper in a transport office. He died of his wounds in the Government Hospital on Tuesday evening, August 20. During the large funeral procession the following day, mourners sought to travel along one of the customary routes to the Mount of Olives cemetery by way of Mount Zion, but near the Post Office on Jaffa Road, their path was blocked. Here the mourners were confronted by police once again under the command of Inspector Douglas Duff. When the procession nevertheless streamed forward, the policemen began using their batons right and left, wounding twenty-eight Jews. It was an ominous portent of things to come. The mufti, emboldened by reports of the tumultuous funeral and by the temporary absence of the high commissioner from Palestine, was now planning a widespread and violent assault upon the Yishuv.

The day after the funeral, Chief Secretary Harry Luke met with Arab and Jewish leaders, unsuccessfully seeking an easing of tensions and a kind of cease-fire but he did not call for preemptive military reinforcements. Rioting began in earnest on Friday, August 23, and by the end of that day, eight Jews and five Arabs were killed in Jerusalem. Near the Jaffa Gate at noon that day, a wild Arab mob attacked Yosef and Yehudah Rotenberg, two brothers who had emigrated from Poland and who had been doing masonry work together in Jerusalem. A British policeman tried to hide and shelter them in a tin hut but the mob burst in and stabbed them to death with knives.[21]

It is difficult to say whether the Rotenberg brothers or an Arab victim were the first fatalities on August 23, 1929. Just a short time after noon, two Arabs – Khalil Burhan Dajani (Dehori) and Khamis al-Sayyad – were attacked in Meah Shearim, near the Berman Bakery on the Street of the Prophets, not far from Ticho's hospital. Al-Sayyad escaped and was saved by a Jewish woman who provided a hiding place in her home; Dajani did not survive. From the balcony of his home, Christian Arab physician Dr. Michael Shammas witnessed the gang's beating of Dajani. Soon thereafter, Gershom Scholem (director of the nearby University Library) came across the seriously injured Dajani.

Scholem tried but was unable to locate his neighbor, Dr. Joseph Treu, at home, but he notified the police. Dajani was dead by the time Scholem returned, and both he and Dr. Shammas helped evacuate the body onto a truck.[22]

As crowds of worshippers emerged from the main mosques, rioting by Arabs spread throughout the city. The Meah Shearim neighborhood came under attack soon after noon, but an active defense beat back the attackers, and two or three Arabs were killed. Similar Jewish defense efforts were mostly successful in the Yemin Moshe neighborhood, and here at least two of the Jewish defenders were killed. Closer to Dr. Ticho's hospital, Dr. Felix Danziger's clinic was attacked, forcing the Danzigers to seek shelter with the Tichos. In the early afternoon, an incited mob of Arabs burst into a home on the Jews' Street in the Georgian Quarter of Musrara within three hundred yards of the Damascus Gate, and three people were murdered, including Shalom Sonjaschwili and his sister-in-law Hannah Sonjaschwili, a mother of five. Unconscious and near death, Hannah was brought to the Rothschild-Hadassah Hospital, as was her two-year-old son, Shmuel, whose left eye had been seriously injured. Although Ticho was in private practice, he would be called to the pediatric ward at Hadassah as a consultant at the request of ophthalmologist Dr. Batya Miterstein two days later, and he continued to follow and treat the unfortunate child.[23] Even at that time, rioting continued in Jerusalem.

Only a few of the neighborhoods were spared from violence during three days of rioting in Jerusalem. On Jaffa Road not far from the Tichos' home, the well-known journalist and Revisionist leader Dr. Wolfgang von Weisl, a member of the Jewish self-defense corps, was stabbed with a knife in his back and arm but survived.[24] In the Old City, Dr. Nahum Korkidi of the Misgav Ladakh Hospital was seriously injured in his leg while attending to the many wounded.[25] Jewish fatalities occurred in the peripheral neighborhoods: to the north in the "Shimon ha-Tzadik" neighborhood; northwest in Giv'at Sha'ul, where deputized English students from Oxford University helped to defend against attackers; to the southwest in Bayit ve-Gan and Ein Kerem; and south in Talpiot where the nearby homes and precious libraries of well-known literati Prof. Joseph Klausner and S. Y. Agnon were vandalized, its residents fleeing in terror. Klausner's servant, Sara Zion, was among the wounded.[26]

Murderous attacks were also seen in the countryside surrounding Jerusalem. In Motza, five members of the Maklef family and two houseguests were murdered, their house looted and set on fire. Only the youngest son, nine-year-old Mordechai, escaped out of a window. Batya Maklef's face was mutilated with knife slits to both eyes and the sides of her mouth. To the south, the recently established settlement of Ramat Rachel was completely destroyed and one of its defenders was killed.[27] Farther away, other isolated settlements were particularly vulnerable to attacks by Arab mobs, such as Be'er Tuvia where Dr. Hayim Yezraeli was murdered by rifle fire, his body lying unburied in the evacuated settlement for over ten days. Rioting and killings extended to more distant cities, most notably Hebron, where the greatest loss of life occurred and where Ticho became a witness to atrocities.[28]

———◆———

In their 1922 *Handbook of Palestine*, Harry Luke and Edward Keith-Roach had followed Baedeker's guidebook in recording the religious significance and history of the holy cities and shrines of Palestine. Among these, they described the city of Hebron, or al-Khalil as it is known in Arabic, named after Khalil al-Rahman (an epithet for Abraham, "the friend of God"). According to the Bible, Abraham pitched his tent in Hebron under the oak of Mamre the Amorite, and here he purchased the double cavern of Machpelah (Me'arat ha-Makhpela) from Ephron the Hittite, which became the burial site for Sarah and himself, together later with Isaac, Rebecca, Jacob, and Leah. Later, David ruled in Hebron for seven and a half years and the city retained its prominence when, under King Herod, a majestic structure was built over the burial caverns. Jewish settlement in Hebron had temporarily disappeared in some later periods (under the Byzantines and later under the Crusaders) but it had been revived under various Muslim rulers. From Medieval times, Muslims had maintained the Ibrahimi Mosque that enclosed and surmounted the Machpelah shrine, while in the modern era, Jews had increased their presence in Hebron especially before World War I.[29] In 1925, the Knesset Yisrael (Slobodka) Yeshiva from Lithuania with 150 students was established in Hebron, but even so the city remained predominantly Arab.

In August 1929, the population of Hebron was estimated to be 20,000 Muslims and 700 to 800 Jews, while the census of 1931 would list 17,531 Muslims (but no Jews) in the urban area and 50,100 in the rural portion of the Hebron district.[30] The tragic and gruesome details of the August 1929 riots in Hebron and its aftermath have been very well documented through contemporary testimonies and reports and through subsequent histories. Because one of the less well known accounts placed Ticho in Hebron soon after mass murders and because he most certainly became involved in forensic controversies, some of these well-known details are worth repeating.

Of Hebron's forty policemen in August 1929, only one was Jewish. They were under the command of the recently assigned district superintendent for Hebron, Raymond Cafferata. Like Douglas Duff, Cafferata was a veteran of Britain's rough and tumble "Black and Tans" auxiliary police division that had been sent to Ireland to suppress the Irish Revolution, and they were among many who had found their way to Palestine.[31] In Hebron, Cafferata had eighteen mounted policemen at his command and an additional fifteen on foot, although eleven of these were elderly men in poor physical condition. At around four in the afternoon on Friday, August 23, 1929, the same afternoon of the outbreak of major rioting in Jerusalem, Arabs began gathering at the Slobodka Yeshiva, hurling stones through the windows, striking twenty-three-year-old Shmuel Rosenholz in the head as he sat studying a tractate of the Talmud. Rosenholz, nicknamed the *matmid* (the "diligent"), had returned alone to study with only the company of the yeshiva's Sephardi sexton. The latter saved himself by hiding in a well but Rosenholz was stabbed to death as he attempted to escape. Hadassah physician Dr. Zvi Kitayin was called to the yeshiva but found Rosenholz dead from his wounds near the door in a pool of blood. The deceased yeshiva student was buried before the onset of the Jewish Sabbath, attended by only a small burial party by order of Superintendent Cafferata, who imposed a city-wide curfew.[32]

The following morning of August 24, several cars packed with Arabs left Hebron in the direction of Jerusalem bearing sticks, swords, and knives, while others stayed to launch their attacks locally. Beginning their patrols without their rifles at daybreak, the mounted police were unsuccessful in stopping Arab mobs from resuming their murderous attacks, even when Cafferata emptied his revolver into the crowds. The rioting continued even as the police fetched their rifles, but Arab constables deserted, leading the rioters to where Jews were hiding and even participating in the murders. Cafferata testified that in one Jewish home, he encountered an Arab whom he witnessed cutting off a child's head with a sword and behind him was the Arab police constable Issa Sheriff, who was attempting to murder a woman with a dagger. One after the other, Cafferata shot each of the assailants with his rifle at close range.[33]

From most accounts, mass murders began when a large group of Arab rioters surged into the Jewish section of town and surrounded the home of Eliyahu Abushedid near the junction of the roads to Beer Sheva and Jerusalem. Yaakov Gozlan and his family had sought shelter here. The women and children were badly beaten and stabbed while both men and a young adult son of each family were murdered.[34] The rioters began to go house to house in search of more victims. They came upon the Kapiloto Pension where several yeshiva students were boarders. Attempting to escape from their boarding home, Eliyahu Kapiloto and his wife were attacked in their garden by the mob led by the seventy-year-old mukhtar, 'Atta Zir. After breaching the doors, the rioters murdered four yeshiva students and fatally wounded a fifth.[35] Severely injured from stabbing wounds in his back, Eliyahu Kapiloto would die in Jerusalem several months later.

Other yeshiva students, many of them Americans, had sought shelter in the home of Hebron native Eliezer Dan Slonim, manager of the local Anglo-Palestine Bank branch and son of Rabbi Ya'akov Yosef Slonim. From his second-story flat above the Eshel Avraham Guest House, Dr. Kitayin observed the mob of Arabs bursting into Slonim's house. In a scene of brutal mayhem, eighteen persons were murdered there including E. D. Slonim himself, his wife Hannah, and her visiting parents, Rabbi

Avraham Ya'akov and Yenta Orlansky of Zikhron Ya'akov. Many of the dead men and women were mutilated. The Slonim's five-year-old son, Aaron, would die of his wounds in Jerusalem while the orphaned two-year-old brother Shlomo would survive the serious knife wounds to his head and hand after much medical attention. Eliezer Dan had been well respected among the Arabs, and so as many as seventy Jews had sought shelter in his home that morning with the belief that the Arab rioters would not harm them there. Jacob and Lea Grodzinsky, who ran another pension for yeshiva students with their father, Rabbi Moshe Grodzinsky, also sought shelter in Eliezer Dan's home. All three of the Grodzinkys were murdered and the left eye of Rabbi Moshe was cut out of its socket.[36]

Two leading Sephardi rabbis, natives and long-time residents of Hebron, perished that eventful Saturday morning, murdered by their former Arab friends. Sixty-two-year-old Rabbi Hanoch Hasson was killed together with his wife, Clara. The rabbi's newest manuscripts on Torah and the history of Hebron that he was writing were burned. Rabbi Meir Castel was stabbed to death in his home and then reportedly castrated, but his wife fainted and survived. Nearby, the Hadassah clinic and the attached synagogue were ransacked, and Arab rioters set fires that released clouds of suffocating smoke. They next turned to the nearby home of the crippled pharmacist, Ben-Zion Gershon, who had served both Jews and Arabs in Hebron for forty years. As the mob brutally murdered Gershon with knives and hatchets they stabbed and gouged at his eyes. They also raped and killed Gershon's daughter Esther; his wife, Ora, was repeatedly stabbed and she would later die of her wounds. Elsewhere, murderers roasted the head of baker Noah Imerman over a primus stove and he was burned alive until he succumbed to the torture. Imerman's wife and daughter who witnessed the event were seriously wounded.[37]

At the Eshel Avraham Guest House near E. D. Slonim's house, landlord Haj Issa el-Kourdieh had come from his home across the adjacent courtyard taking thirty-three Jews to his windowless cellar, including Dr. Kitayin and his family and Aharon and Breine Bernzweig, a retired couple from America. The Arabs repeatedly stormed

Kourdieh's house with axes but were finally persuaded by the landlord to withdraw.[38] After ten o'clock, when the two-hour period of slaughter had ceased, the police brought Dr. Kitayin to the police station and then to the Government Health Office to tend to the wounded, where he was assisted by the local Jewish medical staff that included Dr. Daniel Elkanah. Along with Sefardi Rabbi Avraham Franko, Dr. Elkanah likewise had been given shelter by their Arab landlord, Mahmud Abu-Zeini.[39] A few hours later they were joined by Dr. John MacQueen, the government's district medical officer who had come from Jerusalem. Dr. MacQueen's accounts of his observations and activities would later be the subject of much controversy.

According to Dr. Kitayin, Dr. MacQueen did not perform forensic examinations upon the fifty-nine corpses that were brought to the Government Health Office but meanwhile Dr. MacQueen had also objected to any documentary photography. The actions of the local Arab government medical officer, Dr. Muhammed Ali Shukair, were also criticized; he was faulted for his eagerness to bury the dead without even registering their identities and for his earlier disappearance during the peak hours of slaughter. On the other hand, Dr. Shukair's colleague in Hebron, Egyptian physician Dr. Ahmed Abdal Aal, was praised for saving an entire Jewish family and for treating wounded Jews.[40]

Late that afternoon, Ticho received news about the Arab rioting in Hebron and requests for medical assistance. Discussing the situation with his friend Dr. Felix Danziger, to whom he had given shelter, the two doctors decided to join an emergency expedition to Hebron for the purpose of medical relief and fact-finding. The others in the expedition included Ticho's old friend Marek Schwarz, his driver Menachem Katan, Dutch journalist Pierre van Paassen, and American journalist and Zionist leader Abraham Goldberg. Van Paassen made two trips to Hebron that day. Ticho and Danziger apparently accompanied van Paassen only on his second trip late that afternoon.

Traveling on Hebron Road, south of Bethlehem and not far beyond Rachel's Tomb, Dr. Ticho and his party passed the new Jewish settlement of Migdal Eder, which had been founded in 1926 by religious Iraqi Jews. At an elevation of almost three thousand feet, Migdal Eder was situated at the highest point between Jerusalem and Hebron, and it was the highest Jewish agricultural settlement in Palestine at that time. The members of Ticho's party were probably unaware of the calamity within the settlement as they quickly traveled down the road. Facing a forthcoming siege of Arab rioters the previous day (Friday), one household of seven Jews had escaped from their residence and found shelter in a Russian monastery adjacent to the settlement. By Saturday evening, these settlers finally came under the protection of the British police, who took them to Hebron. Over the next several days, Arab looters raised the entire settlement of Migdal Eder to the ground. The desolate grounds remained abandoned until the mid-1930s when a fruit-tree farmer and developer, Shmuel Zvi Holzmann, founded a new kibbutz on the site, which was renamed Kfar Etzion (chapter 19).[41]

Of the party's arrival in Hebron, van Paassen wrote:

> Driven by Schwarz's chauffeur, Menachem Katan, an ex-member of Col. John Henry Patterson's Jewish Legion which fought at Gallipoli, at Jericho and Megiddo under Allenby, we raced out to Hebron and saw the whole ghastly scene by lamplight: the slain students in the yard of the seminary, the dead men in the synagogue and the bodies of the 38 slain in Rabbi [*sic*] Slonim's house...the two doctors and I found that the dead in Slonim's house had had their genital organs cut off; in the case of the women, their breasts.... By the light of flashlights we examined the rooms where the slain men and women lay about, stiff, as if frozen in all the attitudes of horror.[42]

Van Paassen wrote that in the kitchen in Slonim's house, they found a crying infant in a tightly closed kitchen cupboard beneath the sink, near to a dead woman lying on the floor. The little boy, estimated to be just six to eight weeks old, was rescued with the help of a crowbar retrieved from the car; Dr. Danziger medicated the infant with an injection to induce sleep. The baby was reportedly delivered to an Orthodox orphan asylum in Jerusalem at twelve midnight, growing up "to splendid manhood" and serving in the State of Israel's first war. That night, van Paassen's first dispatches about the Hebron massacres included accounts of the mutilations that Chief Secretary Harry Luke immediately denied. The government's official communiqué in the morning cited van Paassen as an atrocity-mongerer and anti-British agitator.

Independent confirmation of Ticho's presence in Hebron that day has not been found, but perhaps the expedition either purposefully or inadvertently avoided the Government Health Offices, where medical and surgical treatments were being undertaken. Arab mobs had dispersed, but the avoidance of local Arabs would have been a prudent course to take. Perhaps their drive through Hebron's quiet but dangerous streets was more inclined toward reconnaissance rather than intervention. Van Paassen's description of the scene inside Eliezer Dan Slonim's house would place their arrival in Hebron prior to the moving of corpses from those locations to the Government Health Office. Van Paassen further wrote that by the time he returned to Hebron the bodies had been moved, and a sentinel of the King's African Rifles with fixed bayonet was posted in front of Slonim's house.[43] Danziger and Ticho's activism in the following days suggests they were indeed in Hebron and may have even witnessed many of the dead and mutilated.

Arabs in the Jaffa area rioted between the afternoon and evening of Sunday, August 25. Binyamin Ze'ev Goldberg, the son of Yitzhak Leib Goldberg, had returned to Tel Aviv by rail that morning from Jerusalem and en route he saw his father's farmstead at Hartuv burning. In Tel Aviv he joined a Haganah party of fifteen men that set out in a bus to save two Jews detained in a spirit factory near Jaffa. After they were turned back by British police, the party was attacked while passing by the outskirts of the Arab village of Abu Kabir, and Binyamin Goldberg was one of four Haganah members who were killed. Later that day, the Jewish policeman Simha Hinkis was among policemen who fired rifles to disperse a crowd of Arab rioters heading from Jaffa toward Tel Aviv. Hinkis pursued rioters into an orchard near Abu Kabir and burst into a farmhouse, where he shot and killed four Arabs and perhaps a fifth in a nearby house.[44]

—◆—

The wounded and other Jewish survivors of the Hebron massacres were not evacuated to Jerusalem until Monday night, August 26. Eight more deaths would occur among wounded, bringing the total number of Jewish fatalities from Hebron to sixty-seven souls, including a dozen women and three young children. Virtually every Jewish home and synagogue had been ransacked. In contrast with the actions of the rioters, there were nineteen local Arab families who managed to save as many as three hundred Jews by hiding them in their houses at great risk to themselves. Some estimates of this number have been higher but actually about 130 Jews escaped death by feigning death among the dead and wounded, by hiding, or by happenstance. It has been stated that Jewish history records very few cases of a mass rescue of the dimension undertaken by the nineteen Arab families of Hebron.[45] On the opposite side of the equation, following the subsequent evacuation of the survivors, Hebron had been ethnically cleansed of its Jewish population. The following week, an attempt by the Arab rioters to drive Jews out of Safed was nearly successful and greatly added to the toll of the killed and wounded, but Safed managed to maintain its Jewish population.[46]

The Tichos were both quite affected by the disturbances in Palestine, and they sent cables to family and to friends such as Dr. Harry Friedenwald in Baltimore telling them that they were unharmed. Friedenwald wrote back expressing his deep concern about the politically unstable situation in Palestine and his fears for the safety of his friends there. He accused the British of provoking the unrest, complaining bitterly about the administration by the British and accusing them of favoring the Arabs while neglecting the rights of the Jewish population. The outcry from Jewish communities abroad and in Palestine was particularly critical of the British for their failure to provide security for the peaceful and passive communities of Hebron and Safed. Self-defense in less passive Jewish communities had resulted in the repulsion of attacks (e.g., Tel Aviv, Hulda, and Hartuv), but there was bitterness that British policies had hampered such efforts. In the wake of the riots, most Zionist leaders were also now more openly critical of the goal of a binational state that was envisioned by Arthur Ruppin and others in the Brit Shalom movement.[47] The movement's vision of a binational state was predicated upon security under the aegis of the mandatory power.

Even so, many active supporters of Brit Shalom and sympathizers such as Ticho continued to hold onto these dreams.

Zionist hostilities toward the British intensified in the wake of the riots both in Palestine and abroad. One Zionist, Jewish-American author Maurice Samuel, complained that several anti-Zionists had written about the Jewish and Arab dead of Jerusalem and Hebron together so as "to cover the nature of the massacre in Hebron." He also noted, "In Safed as in Hebron, there were no 'self-defense type' Jews. Therefore the administration was doubly guilty again for the massacre which took place without Arab casualties several days after the riots in other parts of the country." The Jewish community (the Va'ad Leumi, Chief Rabbinates, and Agudas Yisrael) presented a unified "memorandum of indictment" of Arab incitements and atrocities and also an indictment of British attitudes and policies that facilitated the catastrophes.[48]

Hurrying back to Palestine, High Commissioner Sir John Chancellor reached Jerusalem just as the riots in Safed erupted. The streets of Jerusalem were relatively quiet, but the city's hospitals were filled with the wounded. During those stressful days, Ticho saw several ophthalmic patients at Hadassah as a temporary consultant. Among these patients, Ticho paid several visits to Shmuel Sonjaschwili, as the child remained in serious condition. It was difficult for the nurses and doctors to care for the pre-verbal boy who had lost his mother and whose father was also still recovering from injuries. The patient's high fever forced Ticho to postpone surgery until the first of September. At that time it was necessary for Ticho to remove the child's left eye.[49]

A few days later, the high commissioner issued his first proclamation about the riots, expressing his horror over "the atrocious acts committed by bodies of ruthless and blood-thirsty evil-doers, of savage murders perpetrated upon defenseless members of the Jewish population regardless of age or sex, accompanied as at Hebron, by acts of unspeakable savagery." However, the Palestine Arab Executive headed by Musa Kazim al-Husayni denied Arab culpability and denied mutilations even at Hebron. It claimed the opposite – that "certain Arabs were mutilated by Jews, that Jewish mobs killed isolated women and children, that [the] first murders of women and children were committed by Jews against

Arabs, that even disciplined British soldiers shot Arab men, women, and children in their homes and beds." The Arab Executive further incriminated British Zionist policy "aimed at annihilating the Arab nation in its own country in favor of reviving a non-existent Jewish nation." In an interview with van Paassen, Haj Amin al-Husayni revealed that the timing of the riots was a response to the Zionist Congress in Zurich that allied Zionists and non-Zionists in the Jewish Agency, giving "a clear picture of the intentions of the Jews of Palestine." Attempting to placate the Arabs, Chancellor issued a second proclamation claiming that his first statement was "misunderstood" and that "the guilty of both parties and not of one party only will be punished."[50] Colonial Secretary Lord Passfield (Sydney Webb) meanwhile announced the appointment of a commission comprised of three members of the British Parliament (representing three British political parties) and headed by Sir Walter Shaw, a former chief justice in Singapore. Its charge was to determine the cause of the riots and to recommend policies that would prevent further violence from erupting.[51]

The mollifying statements of the high commissioner, added to previous denials of mutilations by Chief Secretary Harry Luke, caused further hurt and outrage among those Jews who had lived through the horrors or had witnessed them. Among the Jewish responders, doctors including Drs. Kitayin, Danziger, and Ticho took the lead in protesting irregularities in documenting the murder cases and preparing the dead for burial. The hasty mass burials of victims were presumed to have been part of an organized British effort to literally cover up the evidence. Dr. Danziger had learned from Dr. MacQueen that there was as yet no official medical statement on the massacres in Hebron but only the latter's confidential memorandum to the high commissioner. There were many surviving eyewitnesses to the atrocities while Dr. Kitayin and other physicians, including Drs. Danziger and Ticho, could refute the government's denial of mutilations. On September 5, a committee of Jewish physicians wrote to Colonel Kisch, of the Palestine Zionist Executive, reviewing the subject of atrocities and providing him with a draft of a public letter that would be submitted for publication the following day.[52]

The open letter from the ad hoc Jewish Doctor's Committee, which included Ticho's signature, appeared in the *Palestine Bulletin* on Friday September 6, 1929. It read:

> The Committee of Jewish Physicians of Jerusalem who have been treating the casualties of the recent events, hereby energetically deny the allegation apparently supported by the Department of Health that there were no mutilations of Jews in Hebron. Among the fifty-nine murdered in Hebron it has been fast proved that there were numerous mutilations. Many mutilated patients were and still are being treated in the hospitals of Jerusalem. The Committee of Physicians demands the exhumation of the buried in the presence of European physicians and consular officials in order to prove their assertion. [Signed] Dr. M. Levontin, Director of the Rothschild Hospital, Jerusalem; Dr. Felix Danziger; Dr. G. Garry; Dr. Z. Kitayin, Hebron; Dr. E. Joseph, Surgeon of the Rothschild Hospital; Dr. Sabatai, Shaare Zedek Hospital, Jerusalem; Dr. Ticho, Ophthalmic Hospital, Jerusalem.[53]

It has been stated that "only the psychology of conflict" could explain the calls for exhumations. Ticho's recent treatment of two-year-old Shmuel Sonjaschwili and witnessing mutilated corpses in Hebron may have put him in such a frame of mind. However, considering Ticho's generally cautious and apolitical nature, perhaps his personal participation in demanding the exhumations was simply based on a desire see all available forensic evidence collected, including the buried evidence that was rapidly deteriorating. Frederick Kisch had strong doubts about the proposed exhumations but under much pressure he presented the demands to the government.

In response to the demands of the Palestine Zionist Executive, High Commissioner Sir John Chancellor instructed the director of the Department of Health to appoint a "Committee of Reference" of three British physicians to supervise the exhumation of Jewish bodies in Hebron in the presence of witnesses. Each of the appointed British physicians were intimately connected with the local establishment: Dr. George Stuart, assistant director of the Department of Health; Dr. Hugh

James (H. J.) Orr-Ewing, director of the British Mission Hospital; and Sir John Strathearn, chief ophthalmologist and warden (director) of the British Ophthalmic Hospital.[54] The exhumations of the two mass graves were scheduled for the morning of September 11, eighteen days post-mortem. The names of the two Jewish physician-representatives who were present throughout the exhumations appear elsewhere in Zionist histories: Dr. Sophie Getzova, chief of the Pathology Department at Hadassah, an accomplished physician who, in her younger years, had been romantically involved with the yet unmarried Chaim Weizmann; and the chief surgeon of Shaare Zedek Hospital, Dr. George Gershon Garry, who had coincidentally been the physician to hear Trumpeldor's last words, "It is good to die for one's country." The two Jewish physicians were joined by the attorney Ze'ev Levanon.[55]

The procedure laid down for the direction of the British Committee of Reference was read aloud that morning and described in their report. "Each case, on exhumation, was examined by the Jewish representatives who thereafter notified the Committee as to whether or no, in their opinion, there was evidence of mutilation. In the case of bodies in which mutilation was alleged to be present, the Moslem representatives were then asked to examine the case; the opinions of both parties were recorded by the Committee, who then examined the case for themselves." Dr. Stuart read instructions to the committee to define "mutilation" in connection with murderous assault as "mutilation of the body which was not necessary to the commission of the crime and as indicative of ferocity or abnormal cruelty." He added that mutilation "meant any injury which was not necessary in order to cause death." In advance of the exhumations, Dr. Getzova further gained the British doctors' acceptance of defining rape as a form of mutilation in this regard.[56]

Of the fourteen corpses buried in the first mass grave, the first four were the least decomposed. The first was that of Rabbi Moshe Grodzinsky whose absent left eye and injured left upper eyelid was interpreted as a mutilation by the Jewish doctors. The Arab doctors disagreed, claiming that it was due to the blow to skull and at another point falsely claiming that the victim had been one eyed during life.

The British doctors noted that there were no orbital fractures but a deep, three-inch long left-sided laceration above the forehead not connected to the eye socket. They reported that they were unable to determine whether the loss of the left eye was a deliberate mutilation in light of the following assumptions: (1) The loss of the eye occurring "during the excitement of a murderous assault" would have been associated with orbital fractures if gouged out by an "unskilled" person; (2) the eye might have been ruptured by the same knife as caused the scalp wound; (3) that the right eye "would have been similarly interfered with" if mutilation had been intended; and (4) "the possibility that the victim was a one eyed man."

The corpse of Israel Lazarowsky was missing the left ear and that of Abraham Shapiro was missing the genital organs. The Jewish doctors wrote that the above cases and the findings of dismembered body parts (including two left hands and a fragment of a bearded chin) surely came "under the conception of mutilation for under no condition would such be necessary for the purpose of killing." Even before the second grave was unearthed, however, the British doctors had expressed their opinion as to the "impossibility of determining acts of mutilation on decomposed corpses." Drs. Getzova and Garry agreed in advance not to raise bodies from the second grave if the corpses were found there in a similar state of decomposition. Six more corpses were uncovered but not raised and the exercise was terminated with the signed agreement by the Jewish doctors that stated, "In view of the advanced stage of decomposition of the great majority of the aforesaid corpses further exhumation and technical examination would serve no useful purpose in the determination of mutilation or otherwise." Of the twenty corpses uncovered only eleven from the first grave were truly "exhumed," i.e., removed from the ground.[57]

On Friday September 20, 1929, nine days after the exhumations in Hebron, twenty-seven days following the mass murders, the Mandatory Government issued an official communiqué on the matter of mutilation that included the statements of District Physician Dr. John MacQueen and District Superintendent Cafferata dated August 31: "I, John MacQueen, arrived in Hebron after the mob had been dispersed and, during the day, dealt with all the 59 wounded Jews and inspected the 56 corpses. We saw no case of mutilation of a sexual or other nature or of rape." The detailed communiqué quickly appeared in the newspapers, placing gruesome details of the exhumations before the reading public and of course provoking further responses. In a letter to the Palestine Zionist Executive the following week, Dr. Kitayin was especially critical of this statement noting that Dr. MacQueen had never examined any of the living or dead for evidence. Bandages from wounded Jews placed by Dr. Kitayin had not been removed. Regarding the deceased, Dr. Kitayin noted that "none of them had been inspected by Dr. MacQueen to establish the mode and form of murdering. They were left with their clothes until burial; they were buried as they were brought from the place of slaughtering. It is obvious that in such conditions there was no possibility of seeing cases of mutilation of corpses even if they were passed in review by Dr. MacQueen."[58]

The Arab Executive issued an announcement that was posted on the streets of Jerusalem and elsewhere under the title, "Scandals of Jewish propaganda: Impartial medical examination contradicts Jewish physicians' reports." It emphasized that the facts did not substantiate the high commissioner's proclamation of September 1, 1929, in which he described the murderous riots as "accompanied by acts of unspeakable savagery." It promised that the forthcoming Arab doctors' report would "be a historical document from which the world will know that Jewish propaganda in these disturbances was built on falsehoods to deceive public opinion, collect more money, and reflect on the dignity and honor of the Arabs."[59]

Following the riots, recreational public events in Jerusalem were greatly curtailed. Soccer matches were canceled as were the performances of plays and the concerts of the Jerusalem Music Society. The news of the day featured details of numerous murder trials, new accounts of sporadic violent attacks, and politically charged statements of Jewish and Arab leaders.

The Tichos drew comfort from intimate gatherings with friends, among them Alex and Lotte Baerwald. Alex Baerwald looked to lighten the somber mood on the occasion of Bertha Ticho's birthday in September when he presented her with a humorous, illustrated story. One of the sections depicted, with self-deprecating humor, Baerwald's jealousy over Dr. Ticho's impressive collection of Hanukkah menorot. The atmosphere of continuing ethnic and political tensions during the following month of October likely put a damper on the Tichos' shared birthday that fell on Sunday, October 27 (Albert's forty-sixth and Anna's thirty-fifth).[60] Meanwhile, the trial of the chief Hebron instigator, Sheikh Talib Maraka, had begun in Jerusalem on October 15, and the trial of four other Arabs accused in the murders of Rabbi Castel had begun soon thereafter.[61] On Thursday, October 24, the Commission of Inquiry into the riots had arrived in Jerusalem and the Tichos' birthday that year therefore coincided with the beginning the commission's first full week of work. Although Ticho was not scheduled to testify before the commission, he had been called to testify as a witness in criminal proceedings related to his treatment of two-year-old Shmuel Sonjaschwili at the Georgian Quarter murder trial. That trial began on October 29 before Examining Magistrate Kemp, one of the few Americans in the Palestine Civil Service who would adjudicate several other high-profile cases.[62]

Ticho gave his testimony in the Georgian Quarter murder cases on Friday morning, November 1, the beginning of a fateful month in which he would become the target of an assassination attempt.[63] Just days before this attack, Judah Magnes spoke about peace with the Arabs at the opening ceremonies of the new semester of the Hebrew University, on November 8, 1929. He declared, " If we cannot find ways of peace and understanding, if the only way of establishing the Jewish National Home is upon the bayonets of some Empire, our whole enterprise is not worth while; and it is better that the eternal people that has outlived many a mighty Empire should possess its soul in patience, and plan and wait."[64] These were certainly sentiments that Ticho embraced, but Jerusalem that month was still a city with great underlying tensions that were not at all eased by ongoing criminal trials and the Shaw Commission. This Commission of Inquiry was only into its third week of testimonies when the bold attempt upon Ticho's life took place.

On the morning of Tuesday, November 12, 1929, Ticho came down from his upstairs residence to make rounds in the first-floor wards of his private hospital. Just before ten o'clock that morning, a cart was brought around by a trusted Arab driver who would take Ticho to his clinic several blocks away at the northern outskirts of the Musrara neighborhood. The police station was just across the way on St. George's Road, not more than one hundred feet from the entrance to the clinic, but here in broad daylight, a would-be assassin attempted to murder Dr. Ticho. It was after Ticho got down from the cart and approached the entrance to his clinic that he felt the blow to his back. He had seen his assailant for just a few moments and was not sure what had happened. Entering the clinic, he asked his assistants to see what he had on his back. He felt as if a stone had been thrown at him but his assistants found the knife still stuck in Ticho's back. They removed it, laid Ticho down on his sofa, and immediately called Hadassah Hospital. At the hospital, Ticho was quickly brought to the operating room by Dr. Avraham Wunderlich. The four centimeter wound was irrigated and it was determined that the knife had likely punctured a lung. A non-antibiotic "injection against blood poisoning" was given (perhaps arsenic) for although the antibiotic properties of penicillin had been discovered by Alexander Fleming just one year before, the active chemical had not yet been isolated.

Weak and listed in serious condition, Ticho was transferred to a private room that was graciously given up by journalist Dr. Wolfgang von Weisl, who had also been stabbed during the Jerusalem riots and operated upon some eleven weeks earlier. As Ticho was taken to the hospital, a large crowd began gathering at the crime scene and at the nearby police station, where District Superintendent of Police Maj. William F. Wainwright arrived to begin an investigation – questioning eyewitnesses, searching the area, and arresting suspects. The very evening of the attack, announcements from the chief rabbinate had been posted throughout Jerusalem, calling for all Jews to pray for the recovery of Dr. Ticho. By that weekend, another announcement had been posted all about the city of Jerusalem. Signed by Inspector Mavrogordato, it offered a prize of £200 to anyone who could identify Ticho's assailant.[65]

Meanwhile about fifty or more Arab suspects had been detained by the police in connection with the crime.

In addition to the crowds near the crime scene, a large crowd also gathered at the entrance to Hadassah Hospital, and it was reported that the telephones at the hospital did not stop ringing all day. Ticho's physicians tried to limit visitors for the weakened patient, but certain important visitors were not turned away: the head of the Jewish National Fund, Menachem Ussishkin; the head of the Palestine Zionist Executive's Political Division, Col. Frederick Kisch; District Governor Keith-Roach; the Italian general consul G. Pascale and Dr. Claudio Mancini, the chief of staff of the Italian Hospital; the general consul of Czechoslovakia (who visited twice); a great number of physician-colleagues; and representatives of many institutions. The evening of the assassination attempt, Anna Ticho returned home after a very long day at the hospital. Waiting for her in the garden, she found a young Arab woman with a small baby in her arms. The woman had heard about the assassination attempt and had come to offer her baby to the childless Tichos. Sometime later, another visitor to the Ticho home was a special envoy of Haj Amin al-Husayni, disclaiming any involvement of the mufti's people in the abortive attack.[66]

Ticho's professional colleagues who visited the hospital included members of the Histadrut ha-Rof'im (Academy of Medicine): President Dr. Yehudah Leib Rokah, Dr. Josef Sapir, and Dr. Avraham Rosenthal. Ticho had stepped down as president of the group in 1926 and was now serving as its vice president. After visiting Ticho, the delegation of physicians met with Harry Sacher of the Zionist Executive, who helped to arrange a meeting with the high commissioner. The delegation openly published their memorandum to the high commissioner, stating their belief that the attack on Ticho was a premeditated and organized crime. They also cited several attacks upon Jewish physicians throughout Palestine during the previous months, many of which had resulted in severe injuries or death. The high commissioner expressed his great sorrow about the incident and spoke about the means through which the government would restore security to the country.[67]

Over the next few weeks, Ticho would receive scores of letters, notes, and telegrams from far and wide expressing wishes for his speedy and full recovery.[68] These correspondences came from friends and colleagues in America, Europe (Vienna, Berlin, Frankfurt, Paris, and London), and the Middle East (Cairo, Baghdad, and various places in Palestine). Some of the well-wishers, such as Judah Magnes and Sophie Berger Mohl, continued to share Ticho's fundamental views of Jewish-Arab cooperation in spite of all that had occurred.[69] Official well wishes came from the Mandatory Government, Emir Abdullah, local professional societies, and Zionist organizations. In the midst of her honeymoon, Ticho's assistant, Dr. Rachel Stein Reich, wrote from Vienna. Anna Ticho's brother, Dr. Fritz Ticho, had been keeping Dr. Reich informed of developments, but she had many questions. Finally, Dr. Ya'akov Tabori (Taborisky) was one ophthalmologist who came to Jerusalem from Haifa to visit Ticho at his request. As Dr. Stein Reich would not be returning until the end of January (1930), Tabori was asked to temporarily run Ticho's hospital and clinic.[70]

For several days following the assassination attempt, the crime outside Ticho's clinic was the main topic of conversation in Jerusalem, and the public closely followed Ticho's medical condition and progress. Jewish and Arab newspapers, however, covered the political aspects of the story and assessed blame very differently. Presuming that Ticho's assailant was an Arab, the Jewish press cited Arab incitements and the general lack of security on the streets, and reported on the demands for government action. The articles continued to chronicle Ticho's visitors, many of whom were the very community leaders and governmental officials who were grappling with these issues. In contrast, the Arab press likened the attack on Ticho to the case of Jacob de Haan, who was murdered by extremist Zionists in 1923 (chapter 17). "Why should Arabs make an attempt upon Dr. Ticho's life," one Arab editorial asked, "since they are not resentful against him, especially as he was renowned for his moderation and good manners, and for his keeping aloof from the Zionist Movement, and for his humane deeds which are appreciated by Arabs to such an extent that during the great War they intervened with the Turkish military authorities to prevent his deportation from Palestine." To many Arabs, the location of the attack and the disappearance of the suspect into the adjacent Jewish neighborhood of Meah Shearim implicated a Jewish rather than an Arab perpetrator. The newspaper *Falastin* offered a twenty-five pound reward for information leading to the arrest of Ticho's would-be assassin. The newspaper *Al Muktam* expressed concern that Ticho's convalescence in a Zionist hospital would interfere with his recovery and with efforts to discover the truth behind the attack.[71]

Within a day following the attack, Ticho was interviewed in his hospital room by Inspector Col. Arthur Mavrogordato and Deputy Inspector Maj. Alan Saunders. Ticho admitted that he had seen his assailant "for one second only" but he was certain that he was "of an Arab type," about twenty-two to twenty-six years of age, clean shaven, and wearing European clothes.[72] Later on during his hospitalization, a reporter from *Haaretz* questioned Ticho about assertions in the Arab press that he was opposed to Zionism. He responded as follows: "I arrived in this country seventeen years ago on an invitation to work in the ophthalmic clinic. During all this time I was engaged in medical work only. Like every Zionist I fulfill the duties of the organized Yishuv. I pay the Zionist dues to Keren ha-Yesod, to the Jewish National Fund, to the Va'ad Le'umi, and also to religious institutions. I have never been nor am I now attached to any party because I do not engage in politics." Ticho also refuted claims in the Arab press that he had published articles against Zionism, stating that he had always confined his writing exclusively to medical subjects.[73]

On Saturday afternoon of November 23, a group of Ticho's employees gathered at the police headquarters at the Tower of David. The group of eyewitnesses included Ticho's assistant Dov Halaban, Halaban's wife and daughter, and two of Ticho's nurses. One by one, more than twenty Arabs, all dressed similarly, were passed before the witnesses, and each of them identified a Christian Arab who had most recently worked as a postal clerk. It turned out that the identified suspect had been absent from his work at the post office from Monday, November 11, the day before the attack on Ticho, and had not returned for several days. One of the nurses identified the suspect from afar, even before seeing his face. The rest said that they were "80 to 90 percent sure" that this was the assailant. It was decided to release the suspect until Dr. Ticho's medical condition could permit him to participate in a similar identification process. The suspect was released on bail and under the responsibility of a trusted family member.[74]

As Ticho still lay convalescing in his hospital bed, another shocking case of an assassination attempt occurred in Jerusalem. On Sunday, November 24, Attorney General Norman Bentwich, the highest Jewish official in the Palestine government, was shot and wounded while passing through the second-floor corridor of the government offices. After seeing a revolver pointed at him and the firing of the first shot, Bentwich rushed down the stairs as two additional shots were fired. Abdul Abu-Tabek, the young Arab assailant from a village near Jenin, was immediately arrested on the spot. Abu-Tabek had been employed as a civilian messenger in the Department of Police and Prisons in the office of Inspector Arthur Mavrogordato. Bentwich was wounded in the leg and one bullet remained lodged beneath the skin in the calf. He was at first rushed home and later taken to the Government Hospital where he was attended by Dr. John MacQueen of the Government Health Department. Here the bullet was easily removed.

Abu-Tabek was personally interrogated by the head of his department at work, Inspector Mavrogordato, the same inspector who continued to be involved in Ticho's case. The newspapers noted that both Ticho and Bentwich had both ironically made great efforts to reach out to the Arab community. Ticho had healed thousands of Arabs while Bentwich had "watched Arab rights more jealously than those of his own people." The report concluded that "the arrest of the Bentwich and Ticho assailants has given rise to the belief that a hidden terrorist society exists in Palestine, similar to the Sinn Fein." On the other hand, the sensitive and high-ranking position of Bentwich in the government had recently become a matter of protest by the Supreme Muslim Council that, just in advance of the Shaw Commission's arrival, had repeatedly demanded Bentwich's removal.[75]

While there was overwhelming evidence against the assailant in Bentwich's case, the matter of the assailant's identity in Ticho's case remained far from resolved. Just one week later, a different Arab suspect, a businessman from Jaffa by the name of Nicola Jelad, was accused in the attack upon Ticho. As reported in the Arab newspaper *Falastin*, Jelad was ordered to travel to Jerusalem and report to the police station in Meah Shearim for further questioning. The newspaper report was sparse on details, but apparently Jelad was a former patient of Dr. Ticho who underwent ophthalmic treatment of some type.[76]

Ticho was discharged from Hadassah Hospital on or around December 3 and he began seeing patients at his hospital on Sunday morning the following week. Close friends could now visit with Ticho again at home, but his friend Alex Baerwald had taken seriously ill and was not able to pay a visit. After just one week after he returned to work, Ticho said his goodbyes and thanks to Dr. Tabori, who now returned to Haifa. Meanwhile, the Tichos began making plans for a two-month vacation in Europe, though they would wait to leave until Dr. Stein Reich and her husband returned from their own vacation abroad.[77]

While their trip to Europe was ostensibly planned to help with Ticho's further recovery, there were also lingering concerns about his safety in Jerusalem, for unlike Norman Bentwich, Ticho did not have a policeman to shadow his moves about town. Ticho further decided not to see patients at his satellite clinic where he had been attacked. Although the clinic would be permanently closed down, the site was still referred to as "Dr. Ticho's hospital" in a newspaper article published six years after he vacated the building.[78]

The Tichos looked forward to their visits with family in Central Europe. A stay in Vienna and a side trip to Paris would also give Anna the opportunity to arrange exhibitions of her art in fashionable galleries. By the end of January 1930, the postal clerk who originally had been identified as Ticho's assailant provided a convincing alibi that he was making repairs on a motor in his hometown of Jenin.[79] As this seemed to explain why the suspect had not been at work during the week of the attack, the charges against him were dropped. By this time the Tichos were on their way to Europe, and they would not return to Jerusalem until the first of April.[80]

While the Tichos were in Europe, grieving crowds filled the Yeshurun synagogue for a memorial service in honor of the victims of the Hebron massacre. The ceremony was opened by Rabbi Slonim, who was followed by Chief Ashkenazi Rabbi Avraham Kook. Rabbi Kook's address clearly sounded the clarion call of the religious Zionists that the Jewish people not forget the city of the Patriarchs, of the Machpelah, of Caleb, and of David. "Those who dishearten the Jews rebuilding the [Hebron] community with arguments of political expedience...are attacking the very roots of our nation. In the future, they will need to give account for their actions. If ruffians and hooligans repaid our kindness with malice, we have only one eternal response: Jewish Hebron will once again be built, in honor and glory."[81] Although Rabbi Kook and the Tichos were virtually next-door neighbors, their responses to the Hebron massacres certainly reinforced their positions at opposite ends of the political spectrum within the Yishuv.

The Tichos were still abroad in March 1930 when the report of the Shaw Commission was published. In dealing with broad policy issues of immigration and land purchases, the report clearly extended beyond its terms of reference. It ignored evidence that the Arab Executive and the Supreme Muslim Council had organized and incited the riots and came to the erroneous conclusion that the attack on the Jews was unpremeditated. Importantly, it also recommended that the issue of further Jewish immigration be more carefully considered, in order to avoid "a repetition of the excessive immigration of 1925 and 1926." A pattern of one royal commission leading to another would be repeated during the remainder of the Mandate. The next commission headed by Sir John Hope-Simpson would arrive before the end of the year and lead to a new White Paper by Colonial Secretary Lord Passfield.[82]

After the Georgian Quarter murder trials in which Ticho had testified, several more murder trials had taken place, both during and after Ticho's three-week hospitalization. Jewish policeman Simha Hinkis was charged with multiple counts of murder, and at the trial in January 1930, Dr. Fuad Ismael Dajani was one of two physicians who gave forensic testimony that led to a conviction. The initial death sentence was later commuted upon appeal to ten years imprisonment at hard labor.[83] Other trials continued while the Tichos were in Europe, but two of the most high-profile trials did not begin in Jerusalem until after their return. On April 28, a group of ten Arabs went on trial for the mass murders of the yeshiva students at the Kapiloto Pension, and the long series of trials finally climaxed in early May with the trial of four Arabs for the murders at E. D. Slonim's house.[84]

With the conclusion of the Slonim house murder trial, two more Arabs were added to death row. A total of twenty-six Arabs throughout Palestine had been convicted of murder and sentenced to death. In the wake of the remaining individual appeals, the Superior Court in Jerusalem upheld these verdicts. The Privy Council, the highest legal tribunal likewise turned down appeals from these sentences.

Even before the beginning of the climactic Slonim house murder trials, members of Brit Shalom Society sent a memorandum to High Commissioner Chancellor asking him to commute the death sentences of those Arabs condemned for the murder of Jews during the riots. This caused great consternation among many Zionist circles in Jerusalem. The commutation of these sentences was one of the major planks in the program of the Arab Executive and of various Arab delegations abroad that sought to enlist sympathy for Palestinian Arabs. Individuals who had helped circulate the petitions for commutation of the death sentences included Sophie (Berger) Mohl and Hans Cohen, former secretary of the Keren Hayesod and an active member of the Brit Shalom Society. It was reported that Dr. and Mrs. Ticho had signed the petition. Given Ticho's survival of the attempt upon his own life, the presence of his signature among members of Brit Shalom and other signatories was considered very significant. On May 31, 1930, it was officially announced that High Commissioner Chancellor had commuted the death sentences for twenty-two of the twenty-six Arabs to life imprisonment.[85]

Chapter 19

1930s
Storm on the Horizon

הנני מושיע את עמי מארץ מזרח ומארץ מבוא השמש.
והבאתי אתם ושכנו בתוך ירושלים....

I will rescue My people from the lands of the east
and from the lands of the west.
And I will bring them home to dwell in Jerusalem....

Zechariah 8:7–8

Albert and Anna Ticho's trip to Europe in February and March 1930 began with family in Vienna and ended with an excursion to Paris. In comparison to the recent months of turmoil and personal trauma they had experienced in Jerusalem, Vienna and Paris must have presented a pleasant and welcomed contrast. While Albert recovered his health, Anna made important contacts with galleries that could advance her artistic career. As the trip to Europe drew to a close toward the end of March, Palestine's rainy season had already ended and the time had come for the couple to return to Jerusalem.

Although Albert had resumed his busy practice, he cautiously decided to close his clinic in Musrara where he had been attacked. This may also be one of the reasons that Dr. Ticho responded to correspondence from ophthalmologist Dr. Isaac Michaelson of the Glasgow Eye Infirmary, telling him that the timing was not right to be able to offer him an assistant's position.[1] As Albert returned to his work, Anna felt the need to return to her studio and her forays into the sunshine of the Judean hills.

According to arrangements made during their trip, Anna's first European exhibition would take place that November at the Galerie des Quatre Chemins, a well-known art bookstore and exhibition salon in Paris's 9th arrondissement. The salon was located in the cultural heart of Paris on Rue Godot de Mauroy, about equidistant from the district's famous Palais Garnier opera house and the Place de la Concorde.[2] Another planned exhibit would soon follow at the Galerie Würthle located in the center of Vienna's Innere Stadt. The Würthle's manager, Lea Bondi, had shown a great interest in Anna's work and looked forward to showing her work in early 1931.

Before showing her art in Europe, Anna prepared a two-day exhibition of about fifty of her drawings and watercolors that opened in the Tichos' home on Monday, September 29, 1930. The pieces were placed in three rooms of their second-floor residence above the hospital on Menorah Road. The exhibition was relatively brief but significant. Czechoslovakian General Consul Miloš Čermák accepted the honor of opening the exhibition. With the exhibition still in progress, Yehezkel Steimatzky gave a brief report of the event the following day in *Do'ar ha-Yom*.[3] (Four years later, Steimatzky hosted one of Anna's exhibitions in his bookshop on Jaffa Road where Čermák's successor fulfilled a similar role.)

As Anna was planning her exhibitions, Albert also became an exhibitor of sorts. The National Bezalel Museum had asked him to loan some of his Hanukkah menorot to the museum for a major exhibition that opened there on October 5, 1930. Over two hundred of these ritual objects were on display from many different countries and many different eras, notably including rare examples from the thirteenth-century Renaissance and the personal menorah of the Baal Shem Tov, the founder of Hasidism. In addition to Albert Ticho, local contributors who loaned Hanukkah menorot to the exhibition included Dr. Helena Kagan and the director of the museum, Mordecai Narkiss, who prepared a special exhibition catalogue. Narkiss, an expert in Judaic art from ancient to modern times (including notable modern Jewish artists), had served as the museum's director since 1925. Under Narkiss, the museum had continued its operations even after the Bezalel School closed in 1929 and its founder, Prof. Boris Schatz, had left for America in search of new sources of funding.[4]

Ill health prevented the Tichos' good friend Alexander Baerwald from attending either Anna or Albert's exhibitions in Jerusalem. After a prolonged illness of many months, Baerwald finally died on Albert and Anna's birthday, October 27, 1930. The following day, Albert Ticho was among the large crowd that attended Baerwald's funeral. Several dignitaries spoke there: Menachem Ussishkin on behalf of Keren ha-Kayemet, Prof. Joseph Breuer on behalf of the Technion, and Eliezer Yellin in the name of the Society of Engineers and Architects. German Consul General Dr. Erich Nord, the last German consul in Jerusalem before Hitler's rise to power, eulogized Baerwald in the kindest of terms and announced that the consulate was planning to erect a plaque in his memory. Nord and his vice-consul joined the funeral procession to the cemetery on the Mount of Olives, not far from the previously earthquake-damaged Augusta Victoria Hospice that Baerwald had helped reconstruct.[5] Sometime later, Albert Ticho purchased Baerwald's Hanukkah menorot, which became a part of a collection that continued to grow in size and importance. Many seasonal exhibitions taken from this collection took place at the National Bezalel Museum over the years, continuing even after Dr. Ticho passed away in 1960.[6]

Alex and Lottie Baerwald had been among Anna's greatest supporters as she sought to achieve a wider reputation as an artist. They had written Anna a letter of introduction to Alfred Flechtheim in Berlin that likely helped pave the way for exhibiting her works in Vienna. In addition to the usual advance promotion by the Galerie Würthle, Anna sent personal invitations to the opening. A glimpse of the invitation list is found in the letters of regret that Anna received from two of Vienna's leading Jewish literati, Arthur Schnitzler and Felix Salten, her preservation of these letters for so many years revealing her tastes in literature. Each of these writers had their scurrilous side: Schnitzler's play *Reigen* [The Round] that scrutinized sexual morals of the day was censured in 1905 as pornographic and later withdrawn from Viennese and Berlin stages; Salten's bestselling novel, *Josephine Mutzenbacher*, was the story of a Viennese prostitute and a far cry from his novel *Bambi* that Walt Disney later made world famous. Although each of these authors declined to attend Anna's opening debut in Vienna, they both promised to visit the exhibition.[7] Schnitzler and Salten's avant-garde character also mirrored a trio of Vienna's leading artists that Anna most admired – Gustav Klimt, Egon Schiele, and Oskar Kokoschka – yet her own artistic oeuvre greatly diverged from these artists as she increasingly expressed herself through complex cityscapes and landscapes. Nevertheless, Anna Ticho was true to her roots, executing her drawings and watercolors with "academic Viennese precision."[8]

Around the time of Anna's 1931 exhibition in Vienna, Albert's brother Sami married thirty-one-year-old dentist Lizl (Elizabeth) Reiniger, and after an Italian honeymoon, the newlyweds returned to Austria to continue their respective law and dental practices.[9] Anna may have still been in Vienna and, if so, attended the wedding. At that time, however, it appears that Albert was busy at work in his practice in Jerusalem, both at his hospital and in a new role as the official physician of the Czechoslovak Consulate.[10] In addition, Albert was preparing to visit Amman in order to examine King Hussein's eyes and operate on his cataracts. Col. Frederick Kisch, the head of the Political Division of the Palestine Zionist Executive, helped to arrange the visit. Other Jerusalem physicians attended the elderly and frail Hashemite patriarch, including Dr. Tawfik Canaan. All of the physicians could see that the health of the exiled monarch was in decline; he died in early June, only three months after his cataract surgery. On June 4, 1931, King Hussein was buried on the grounds of the Haram in Jerusalem. Dr. Ticho came to give his condolences privately to the family at the offices of the Supreme Muslim Council, but he was not part of the official Jewish delegation that was led by Col. Frederick Kisch.[11] Although Dr. Ticho was welcomed with respect as a family friend, the mufti's men were reportedly displeased with the appearance of Kisch's delegation.

In the summer of 1931, Colonel Kisch was replaced by Chaim Arlosoroff as the head of the Political Division of the Jewish Agency.

Kisch had decided to retire when his mentor, Chaim Weizmann, was censured in a vote of no confidence at the Seventeenth Zionist Congress in Basel for his commitment to full cooperation with the British and his moderate views of "gradualism." Arlosoroff, one of the heads of the Labor Federation, assumed his duties in Jerusalem on August 10, 1931. He crossed paths with the Tichos at many social gatherings and he was a guest in the Tichos' home.[12] Like Kisch, Arlosoroff was involved with the major local Zionist negotiations of the day, ranging from land purchase discussions with many wealthy Arab landowners to political discussions with the new high commissioner, Maj.-Gen. Sir Arthur Grenfell Wauchope, the latter arriving in Jerusalem on November 19, 1931. Wauchope's government was soon confronted with an Arab terror campaign in northern Palestine that was led by a Syrian-born Muslim cleric, Sheikh 'Izz al-Din al-Qassam. Al-Qassam had fought against the French colonization of Syria after World War I and had moved to Haifa in the 1920s, often working under the aegis of Mufti Haj Amin al-Husayni. Al-Qassam's terror campaign began with the ambush and murder of three members of Kibbutz Yagur, a failed bombing attack on outlying Jewish homes in Haifa in early 1932, and several operations that killed or wounded members of northern Jewish settlements.[13]

Ticho's attitudes to such developments at the time are unknown but he likely remained rather apolitical. His "political" connections were mainly expressed through his ties to the Czechoslovak consulate. In the summer of 1932, Josef M. Kadlec arrived in Jerusalem as the new Czechoslovak consul general to Palestine, and he was also accredited by the British as consul general for Transjordan, Saudi Arabia, and Aden.[14] Like his predecessors, the Tichos found the new Czech consul to be very friendly toward the Jews. He shared their apprehension about the rising power of Hitler and the National Socialist German Workers Party (NSDAP). The Tichos were frequent guests of Consul Kadlec and his wife, where conversations would turn to Central European politics.

In Germany, the racist platforms of the Nazis were at first dismissed as a fringe political phenomenon, but in November 1932, the party received a third of the vote in parliamentary elections and on January 30, 1933, President Paul von Hindenburg reluctantly appointed Adolf

Hitler as chancellor of Germany. On February 27, in the run-up to additional national elections, the Reichstag was set on fire by arsonists; many Nazi opponents (including left-wing Reichstag members) were arrested as part of an unprecedented campaign of propaganda and repression. The NSDAP won 44 percent of the vote; the arrests helped turn the Nazis' plurality into a majority and Hitler declared a mandate to eradicate Communism, democracy, and the Jews.

At the time of Hitler's rise to power, only a few members of the Tichos' extended family had immigrated to Palestine, the rest remaining in Central Europe, specifically Austria and their native homeland of Czechoslovakia. These very countries were the first to fall to Nazi expansionism. In Europe, the many branches of the Ticho family would suffer terribly at hands of the Nazis. Several perished in concentration and death camps while some escaped with their lives, immigrating to European havens, Palestine, the Americas, or the Pacific.

———◆———

In Jerusalem, the raising of the swastika flag above the German Consulate on the Street of the Prophets was one of the first physical signs of the Nazis' rise to power in faraway Germany. In mid-March 1933, President Paul von Hindenburg ordered that the Nazi Party's flag be flown alongside the black, white, and red flag of the German Republic at all German consulates throughout the world. A local Templar and Nazi Party member eagerly supplied the first swastika flag to the new German Consul Dr. Heinrich Wolff, who publicly followed all of the German Foreign Ministry's instructions even though his own wife was Jewish. The following day, a second swastika flag, hand-embroidered by orphaned Arab children, was supplied by Frau Maria Schneller, director of the Schneller (Syrian) Orphanage.[15] Consul Wolff, however, increasingly came under attack by Arab nationalists and the local German community of Nazi Party members. They viewed him as too pro-Jewish, therefore unfit to represent the interests of Germany and the interests of National Socialism.

On March 21, 1933, the Jewish-German author Arnold Zweig wrote to Albert and Anna Ticho from Spindlermuehle, Czechoslovakia.[16] He had done much traveling during the previous year, working on his latest book, *De Vriendt Comes Home* (*De Vriendt kehrt heim*). Zweig had completed the research for his novel during a trip to Palestine during which he and his wife had spent time with his friend Hermann Struck in Haifa and with the Tichos in Jerusalem. Just one year earlier, he began to spin the tale of the novel's plot while sitting on the Tichos' balcony in Jerusalem, a story based upon the life and the murder of Jacob Israël de Haan (chapter 17). Dr. Ticho was among those who dispelled Zweig's preconceived notions of the circumstances of de Haan's murder that had occurred eight years earlier.[17] The Jewish-German press had generally accepted the premise of an Arab honor-killing although circumstances pointed to a political assassination at the hands of fellow Jews. Undeterred, Zweig altered the novel's plot to include both aspects of the story. Even though the Tichos are not fictionally represented in the novel *De Vriendt Comes Home*, many of their contemporaries are immediately recognizable among the cast of Zweig's characters.

Zweig's March 1933 letter to the Tichos from Spindlermuehle stated that a signed copy of his new book was at home in Berlin ready to be sent to them. He also expressed deep regrets that he had ever left Palestine to return to "the land of the northern Barbars." It was plain that the famous author was traveling with much caution and even justified paranoia. Among other literary activities, Zweig had been a contributing editor to the anti-Nazi newspaper *Die Weltbühne*, whose publisher was now languishing in Berlin's Spandau Prison. The newspaper had been closed down in early March just two days after the Nazi Party's victory in the general election. Zweig wrote to the Tichos of "trembling Jewish nerves in Berlin," but his personal terror later peaked when, incognito, he personally witnessed ceremonial book-burnings in Berlin that included many of his own works. Immediately leaving Germany for Palestine, Zweig soon wrote that the book-burning crowds "would have stared as happily into the flames if live humans were burning."[18]

The first meaningful anti-Jewish action of the newly empowered Nazis was the boycott of Jewish businesses in Germany on April 1, 1933. Six days later, the government's first anti-Semitic law was passed forcing Jews out of all civil service positions. Dr. Heinz Cohen was one of many Jewish physicians in Berlin who were dismissed from the Charité Hospital, another government institution. Dr. Cohen promptly fled Germany with his wife, Julia, and two young children. He immigrated to Palestine and was able to find an assistant position with Dr. Ticho in Jerusalem where he worked for the next three years, learning much about ophthalmology in the process.[19] Meanwhile, Robert Weltsch, editor of the *Jüdische Rundschau* (Jewish Review) and a long-time supporter of Brit Shalom, famously appealed for Jewish strength and solidarity, writing, "A powerful symbol is to be found in the fact that the boycott leadership gave orders that a sign 'with a yellow badge on a black background' was to be pasted on the boycotted shops. This regulation is intended as a brand, a sign of contempt. We will take it up and make of it a badge of honor." Weltsch fled Germany in 1938 and settled in Jerusalem, where he was befriended by Ticho; in the future he would suffer greatly from glaucoma and became one of his patients.[20]

———◆———

The beginning of a nightmarish era of repression and anti-Semitism in Germany contrasted with some hopeful, constructive activities in Palestine. On April 6, 1933, an international medical conference opened in the auditorium of the elegant YMCA in Jerusalem. The sponsoring Egyptian Medical Association had decided to hold its sixth annual conference that year in Jerusalem rather than Cairo. Ticho was among the three hundred participants, which included 160 physicians from Egypt, forty Jewish physicians from Palestine, and one hundred other physicians from Palestine, Syria, and Iraq. Among local dignitaries who attended the opening session, only Muslim clerical leaders and Arab labor leaders were conspicuously absent.

Following the opening addresses of High Commissioner Wauchope and Col. George Heron and an invocation in Arabic, Dr. Yehudah Leib Rokah of the Histadrut ha-Rof'im bi-Yerushalayim was given the honor of delivering an invocation in Hebrew.[21] An early evening reception at Government House and a banquet at the King David Hotel concluded the busy opening day activities. In an unrelated ceremony just eight days after the close of the conference, Lord Allenby officially dedicated the Jerusalem YMCA. The words of his address were later enshrined near the entrance: "Here is a place whose atmosphere is peace, where political and religious jealousies can be forgotten and international unity fostered and developed."

Even as the medical conference was continuing at the YMCA, Chaim Arlosoroff was organizing a Saturday afternoon luncheon at the King David Hotel across the street. On April 8, 1933, Arlosoroff hosted a surprising assemblage of guests: Chaim Weizmann and other Zionist leaders, including Yitzhak Ben-Zvi and Moshe Shertok, as well as leading Arab sheikhs of Palestine and Transjordan. This gathering was the first public meeting in Jerusalem between Zionist and Arab leaders. Ticho's former patient Sheikh Mithqal al-Fayez of Transjordan was among the wealthy Arab landowners whom Arlosoroff was courting, and the sheikh was particularly lauded by Arlosoroff in his public remarks. Privately, Arlosoroff now saw a binational political solution in Palestine as a means of alleviating the German Jewish crisis. During the previous month he had been pursuing this tack in secret negotiations with the high commissioner and the Mandate government.[22]

The tradition-laden World Ophthalmology Conference opened at the Palace Hotel in Madrid, Spain, on April 17, 1933. Ticho was designated as one of two representatives from Palestine, the other being his colleague Dr. Aryeh Feigenbaum. They traveled separately to Madrid but each in the company of their wives. The featured topic of the conference was tuberculosis of the eye, a widely prevalent disease that could manifest in the eye in a variety of ways, and therefore a vast ophthalmological literature had accumulated on the subject during the previous half century. Dr. Rudolf Bergmeister of Vienna (the son of Ticho's mentor, Prof. Otto Bergmeister) was one of the many authorities on ophthalmic tuberculosis who came to Madrid to make presentations. Jewish-German ophthalmology professors such as Drs. Alfred Bielschowsky and Aurel von Szily were unable to attend as they confronted student-led boycotts of their positions as chairmen at their respective universities in Breslau and Münster.[23] The Tichos' post-conference itinerary has not been preserved but they took some additional vacation time in Europe (perhaps Paris or Vienna) and they did not return to Jerusalem until the first week of May.

The Tichos' travels in Europe were soon followed by a trip together to Baghdad. The only source of information about this trip comes from a brief report of the visit in the Jerusalem newspaper *Do'ar ha-Yom*. Other local, contemporary records from the Iraqi press may emerge, but it is likely that the visit was at the invitation of Dr. Erich Raubitcheck with whom Ticho had remained in touch for many years, from the time each had been employed by the AZMU after World War I (chapter 16). Dr. Raubitcheck had left Tel Aviv soon after the disturbances of 1929 and moved to Baghdad to become the Chief Surgeon at the Rima Kadoorie Eye Hospital. This hospital had been established in 1924 by the Baghdad-native and Jewish philanthropist of Hong Kong, Sir Elly Silas Kadoorie, who had named the hospital after his mother, Rima. The Tichos' hosts in Baghdad may have just recently visited Jerusalem during the Egyptian Medical Association meeting.[24]

As reported in *Do'ar ha-Yom*, the Tichos stayed in Baghdad for about twenty days beginning around May 20, 1933, and into the second week of June. According to the article, Ticho's trip to Baghdad was "especially" to perform surgery upon a wealthy Iraqi Jew by the name of Shamash (perhaps Shim'oon Shamash) who wished to undergo the operation in his home city for personal and medical reasons or perhaps as a show of loyalty to his homeland. The Tichos' visit coincided with the birthday of King Faisal I, and the companion article noted that on Saturday, May 20, a large equestrian statue of the king was unveiled and dedicated with great ceremony in Baghdad. The event was considered one of the "most important and first of its type in Iraq." The royal family, including Crown Prince Ghazi, high-ranking officials, military officers, and leaders of the local faith communities, were in attendance. Besides the Tichos, another visitor who had come from Jerusalem was the mufti, Haj Amin al-Husayni.

It is interesting that, in addition to performing surgery on Shamash, Ticho saw a great number of patients in his clinic including the head of the Iraqi government, Rashid 'Ali al-Gaylani.[25] The reference to Gaylani in the *Do'ar ha-Yom* article that reported these events is consistent with the distance that Ticho maintained from political Zionism. With a few notable exceptions, Baghdad's wealthy Jewish elite held a similar public stance. Baghdad's leading Zionist, the wealthy Aharon Sassoon, had participated in founding a Zionist Association in Baghdad in 1921, but after the 1929 disturbances in Palestine, Zionist activity was banned there.[26] In connection with Ticho's visit, the Jerusalem newspaper *Do'ar ha-Yom* raised the hope that perhaps Iraq might accept the immigration of some unemployed and displaced German Jewish medical specialists. But in spite of the respect that most Arabs had for Dr. Ticho, it is certain that neither King Faisal nor Prime Minister al-Gaylani would have allowed even token immigration of Jewish-German doctors to Iraq under any circumstances.

Throughout much of the 1930s, the Tichos often chose to spend their weekends in Jericho during Jerusalem's cold and rainy winter months. Here they came into contact again with Dr. Olga Pickman-Feinberg, a graduate of the University of Zurich Medical School, Jericho's only permanent Jewish resident at the time. Unlike many tourists, she obstinately chose to remain there even through the oppressive summer months. Like Dr. Ticho, Dr. Pickman-Feinberg had first seen the results of Arab violence in 1929 while working with Jewish refugees from Hebron, in her case at Jerusalem's Straus Health Center. But the young doctor had courageously left Jerusalem for the countryside, earning the confidence of the effendi and fellahin of the Jericho district by almost single-handedly eradicating trachoma there through her clinic.[27] Her bungalow and adjacent citrus grove remained way-stations for Jews who only passed through Jericho from time to time. While renting their own place in Jericho during the winter months, Anna Ticho was drawn to "exotic" subjects such as palm trees that she studied in her sketches during a "period of learning to know a new landscape." The sense of the exotic vanished as she mastered the themes in her detailed landscapes.[28]

———◆———

As the Tichos were traveling through Europe and the Middle East in the spring of 1933, the political and economic situation for Jews in Germany continued to worsen dramatically. The Reconstitution of the Civil Service Law passed there on April 7, 1933, had included the dismissal of all "non-Aryan" doctors, dentists, and pharmacists from German hospitals, clinics, and public health centers. Although the full execution of the law was not applied until 1937, student boycotts involving Jewish ophthalmologists prompted their respective medical schools and institutions to dismiss several distinguished faculty members. There were approximately 53,000 physicians in Germany at the time of Hitler's rise to power, and between 6,400 and 9,000 of them were of Jewish descent. It is estimated that, between 1933 and 1941 as many as 6,000 Jewish physicians managed to escape from Germany and another 3,000 escaped from Austria and Czechoslovakia.[29] Many other Jewish physicians died in concentration camps. Of those managing to escape, about half settled in the United States while about 2,000 Jewish physicians settled in Palestine, coming to dominate the medical staffs of several Kupat Ḥolim clinics and hospitals. Physician emigration from Central Europe during the so-called Fifth Aliyah (1929–1939) peaked in 1933, the year of Hitler's rise to power. The flight of Jews from Hitler's regime in Germany resulted in a continued influx of Jewish refugees into Palestine.

The Tichos found much in common with the many German physicians who settled in Jerusalem, and their conversations at social gatherings were almost exclusively in the German language. The two brothers Drs. Hermann and Bernhard Zondek were among the closest in the Tichos' circle of friends, both of them settling in Jerusalem in 1934. Their younger brother, Dr. Samuel Zondek, settled in Tel Aviv. Hermann had chaired the internal medicine department at the Urban Hospital in Germany before he escaped into exile via Zurich and London. In addition to serving as the chief of internal medicine at Bikkur Cholim Hospital for many years, he would go on to serve as a visiting professor at the Hebrew University. Bernhard initially left Germany for Stockholm, but he then also came to Jerusalem, receiving an appointment as chief of obstetrics and gynecology at Hadassah Hospital.[30]

One of the most prominent German physicians to immigrate to Palestine was Dr. Max Marcus, who chaired the Department of Surgery at the Berlin-Friedrichshain Hospital, holding the positions of docent and associate professor at the University of Berlin. He had been recruited by

Meir Dizengoff to head the surgical department at Tel Aviv's Hadassah Hospital. In advance of his immigration, Dr. Marcus happened to be visiting Tel Aviv as a tourist on Friday, June 16, 1933, but late that night he was brought urgently by Dizengoff's car from his hotel to Hadassah Hospital in an effort to save a victim of a shooting. Chaim Arlosoroff had been gunned down while walking with his wife, Sima, on the Tel Aviv beachfront. Drs. Aryeh Allottin, Max Marcus, and others were unsuccessful in their attempts to save Arlosoroff's life (some later adding Dr. Felix Danziger to the list of at least five doctors).[31] Some hours late into that night, Arlosoroff died on the operating room table of Tel Aviv's Hadassah Hospital.

The British Mandate police soon arrested three Revisionists for the crime: Avraham Stavsky, Zvi Rosenblatt, and militant-wing leader Abba Ahimeir (cofounder of the "Brit ha-Biryonim"), although Ahimeir was quickly released. The murder and the sensational trial that took place a year later highlighted continuing internecine political tensions; even the Tichos were exposed to the controversies that engulfed Palestine's Jewish community. Meanwhile, Moshe Shertok succeeded Arlosoroff as the head of the Jewish Agency's Political Division.[32]

On June 8, 1934, the Arlosoroff murder trial concluded with Rosenblatt's acquittal and Stavsky's conviction, though the latter was also acquitted upon appeal. For many years, Ben-Gurion's Mapai Party accused the Revisionists of murdering Arlosoroff. Alternate conspiracy theories of Nazi intrigue arose, but an Israeli commission conducted half a century later failed to come to a definite conclusion.[33] Just two months after Arlosoroff's murder, the German Economics Ministry came to an agreement with the Anglo-Palestine Bank on the Transfer Agreement (Ha'avara) that he had helped to negotiate. The Economics Ministry ratified the Transfer Agreement on August 28 while the Eighteenth Zionist Congress was in session in Prague, but it was not officially adopted by the World Zionist Organization until the Nineteenth Zionist Congress held in Lucerne in 1935. As time passed, a depressed Palestine economy could not absorb large quantities of foreign goods, but by the time of the outbreak of World War II in September 1939, 140 million reichsmarks (approximately £8 million) had been transferred to Palestine.[34]

The influx of German physicians into Palestine during the 1930s elevated the level of medicine and surgery there, introducing emergency procedures and surgical techniques that might have saved Arlosoroff's life. Every physician who was involved in Arlosoroff's case and subsequent inquiries noted that the cause of his death was related to unfortunate delays in transport to the hospital and the inadequate provision of fluid replacement and blood transfusions. Ironically, Dr. Allottin had authored a book on first aid, and he was the first lecturer on the subject for the Magen David Adom, an organization that had been founded in Tel Aviv by Dr. Meshulam Levontin in 1930.

In spite of his abrupt introduction to Palestine medicine and politics, or perhaps because of it, Dr. Marcus accepted the Hadassah staff position in Tel Aviv and immigrated to Palestine in 1934, a year of further expansion for the hospital. Just two years later, Prof. Marcus spent many hours late into the nights with the gravely ill Meir Dizengoff. He returned several times to Dizengoff's bedside in the apartment that adjoined the rest of the house that he had donated to the city as an art museum. Dizengoff succumbed to bilateral pneumonia and died in the early morning hours of September 23, 1936.[35]

In the early and mid-1930s, the practice of medicine did not yet have antibiotics that might have cured Dizengoff's pneumonia or banked blood products that might have helped save Arlosoroff's life. Blood banking was introduced to Palestine by the end of the 1930s, housed at a new "flagship" hospital of the Kupat Ḥolim in Petah Tikvah. Even Dr. Moshe Beilinson, who had spearheaded the founding of the hospital, succumbed to heart disease that would be very differently treated in future years. Weakened by influenza and hiding a worsening heart condition, Beilinson died at this hospital of a heart attack just three weeks after the hospital's opening and only a month after Dizengoff's passing. The Kupat Ḥolim Hospital's newly appointed director, Dr. Harry Heller (like Dr. Marcus a former department chair at the Berlin-Friedrichshain Hospital), was among the physicians who attended Dr. Beilinson at his bedside throughout the night. Dr. Beilinson was buried in the Trumpeldor Street cemetery in Tel Aviv, very near the burial plots of Chaim Arlosoroff and Meir Dizengoff.[36]

———◆———

Like the Transfer Agreement that aimed to bring German Jews to Palestine, the Jewish Agency's establishment of a "New Bezalel" School of Arts and Crafts aimed at absorbing a portion of these immigrants into Palestine. The National Bezalel Museum, under the direction of Mordecai Narkiss, was the only remnant of the school that had been founded by Boris Schatz in 1906 and closed in 1929. Schatz had died in Denver, Colorado, in 1932 while on a fundraising trip, still dreaming of reopening the school. Reviving this dream, the Jewish Agency chose Arthur Ruppin to chair a committee and, in cooperation with the British Mandate Government, Ruppin recruited Anna and Albert Ticho, artist Herman Struck, educator Dr. Joseph Luria, Prof. Leo Aryeh Mayer of the Hebrew University (Near Eastern Art and Archeology), publisher Salman Schocken, and the Jewish Agency's David Werner Senator, among others.

In late February 1935, while staying at the Grand Versailles Hotel in Paris, Anna Ticho received a letter from a notable Jewish-German refugee, the renowned print artist Joseph Budko. Budko had been approached by Ruppin and the Bezalel Society to teach and administrate the New Bezalel School. In his letter, Budko urged Anna to promote the planned school by sending letters and promotional materials to her friends, and she would do so after her return from Europe. Anna had been to Vienna where she saw the installation of one of her drawings at the Albertina. She was now in Paris preparing for a solo exhibition at the Galerie Billiet-Vorms. Located at 30 Rue de la Boétie in the 8th arrondissement, the gallery had been founded by Joseph Billiet in the mid-1920s. It had been the site of several memorable exhibitions of well-known artists, for example, the Flemish painter and graphic artist Frans Masereel and the American Alexander Calder, who had his first solo exhibition there in 1929. The Gallery was co-owned and managed by Pierre Worms (Vorms), a bon vivant and native of Alsace-Lorraine who had many connections among German and Austrian artists. On March 1, 1935, Anna was present at the opening of the exhibition entitled "Drawings and Watercolors of Palestine," and she likely stayed in Paris until its close two weeks later.[37]

Anna Ticho soon returned to Jerusalem where she promoted the New Bezalel School, and she remained on the school's organizing committee under the leadership of psychoanalyst Dr. Max Eitingon along with Mordecai Narkiss and Dr. Helena Kagan. The group met in May 1935, where Budko was formally appointed head of the New Bezalel School of Arts and Crafts. That August, at the Nineteenth Zionist Congress in Lucerne, Switzerland, Arthur Ruppin announced the forthcoming opening of the school. The opening session of the new school's first semester took place on October 22, 1935.[38]

Whereas the instruction and output of the "Old Bezalel" School was dominated by romantic biblical and Near Eastern motifs, the "New Bezalel" School of Arts and Crafts strongly reflected modern European styles, particularly those of the Bauhaus movement. Perhaps this was one reason that Anna Ticho chose not to teach at the school even though she had been very involved in its founding. Rather, Mrs. Ticho continued upon her own unique artistic path. In January 1934 she had held a two-week art exhibition at the Steimatzky Bookshop on Jaffa Road. On a cool and cloudy Monday afternoon, the Czechoslovak Consul General, Josef M. Kadlec, opened the exhibition of her drawings and watercolors. Dr. Max Osborn, a noted Jewish-German art critic who was visiting Jerusalem at the time, wrote a glowing English-language review in the local press noting that Anna Ticho was "not concerned solely with the reproduction of things but equally with an inner representation of them."[39]

Later that week, as Anna's exhibition was still on display, Bronislaw Huberman gave a sold-out performance at the Edison Theater in the nearby Zikhron Moshe neighborhood. It is likely that the Tichos were in the audience that evening, perhaps in the company of Dr. Helena Kagan and her husband Emil Hauser. Hauser, an accomplished violinist of Hungarian origin, had only recently immigrated to Palestine and had founded the Palestine Conservatory of Music and the Dramatic Arts. High Commissioner Arthur Wachope was the titular patron while Dr. Kagan organized the "Friends of the Conservatory," drawing members, including the Tichos, from among the upper levels of Jerusalem society.

With this support, Hauser was free to travel to Europe to recruit students for his conservatory and also help Huberman with an even more ambitious project that he was beginning to consider – the establishment in Palestine of a "Refugee Orchestra" comprised of Jews from Germany and neighboring Central European countries.[40]

Huberman's Edison Theater performance of January 18, 1934, was part of the violinist's third tour of Palestine, but now the inimicable pathos of his performances were infused with a new sense of mission. Huberman's already immense popularity and his enthusiastic following in Palestine had only increased (and exponentially so) with his courageous public stance against racism, eloquently expressed in an open, widely circulated letter to Wilhelm Furtwängler, conductor of the Berlin Philharmonic who could not or would not prevent the dismissal of Jewish musicians from his orchestra. After Huberman, other musical giants had refused to perform in Germany, including non-Jewish performers and conductors such as Pablo Casals and Arturo Toscanini. Huberman would convey his idea of a "Refugee Orchestra" to Toscanini who agreed to conduct the orchestra's inaugural performances in Palestine.[41]

With Huberman's help, the coming surge of immigrant Yekke musicians would help further change the cultural landscape of Palestine, just as refugee Yekke architects continued to transform the urban landscapes of Tel Aviv. With the appointment of Erich Mendelsohn to design the Hadassah Hospital complex on Mount Scopus, refugee Yekke architects would also begin to transform Anna Ticho's beloved landscapes at the very edge of the Judean Desert. A particularly artistic aesthetic was evident in Mendelsohn's designs that were characterized by wide horizontal lines that "asked to be joined to the mountainous landscape without competing with it." The eastern extremities of the buildings were designed in a semi-circle, and in parts of them observation points faced toward the landscape of the desert below to the east.[42] Mendelsohn's choice of architectural style was guided by "the simple lines of the Arab village because he was seeking local harmony – of unornamental walls, courtyards with fountains and pergolas." Ground was broken for construction of the hospital and nurses school in mid-November 1936, and the project was completed in September 1938. Each used machine-cut white stone slabs to face the edifices rather than the traditional hand-fashioned stone. The transformation of Mount Scopus was further embellished with a planted grove of one thousand five hundred pine trees.[43]

———◆———

The planting of trees in Palestine by Jews was not limited to landscaping projects on Mount Scopus. Alfred Ticho, with his broad training and background in agriculture, soon attained expertise in the cultivation of oranges and became involved in marketing shares of orange groves, especially within the Sharon, Palestine's coastal plain that stretched from Tel Aviv to Haifa. Alfred found his investors in Central Europe, mainly industrialists and professionals in his native Czechoslovakia. Orange farming had first been brought to the coastal plain in the late 1890s by the Ukrainian-born Zionist Yehoshua Henkin, who purchased a large tract of swampland around Hadera that extended to the sandy dunes near the Mediterranean shore.[44] Albert Ticho's old colleague Dr. Ze'ev Brünn was among those who had worked as a physician in those mosquito-infested swamps when he first came to Palestine in 1910. After giving up the practice of medicine following World War I, Brünn had devoted much of his life to agriculture in the Hadera region. In the late 1920s he likewise began to recruit fellow Jewish-German investors to purchase agricultural land in Hadera in a settlement that Brünn's brother-in-law, S. Y. Agnon, had named Aḥuzat Meged, Precious (or Sweet) Estate. With the rise of the Nazis to power in 1933, these investors met immigration requirements of the Mandate government and many of these German Jews immigrated to Palestine.

Alfred Ticho had often told his brother Albert of his work, of the investment potential of productive orange groves, and of the haven that these groves might offer their extended family. Perhaps these discussions were considered more seriously during a visit of family from Brno in April 1935 during the Second Maccabiah Games. At these games, 134 German athletes flouted Nazi Germany's order not to attend the games, and they refused to fly the German flag during the opening ceremonies. After the games, all 350 of the Bulgarian athletes decided to settle in Palestine; the number of Lithuanians who remained to settle was also substantial. Twenty-year-old Fritzi Ticho of Brno, the youngest daughter of Jacob and Emma, was among the delegation from Czechoslovakia. She was accompanied by her Uncle Nathan and Aunt Frenza Ticho and also Aunt Irma Kritzler. After the closing ceremonies at the new stadium in Tel Aviv, Fritzi stayed in Palestine, but (at this time) only for about one month. After visiting with Uncle Alfred in Binyamina and Uncle Albert and Aunt Anna in Jerusalem, she returned to Brno where she married Moniek Mann, the son of the cantor of the Brno synagogue.[45]

The following year, Albert Ticho, his brothers Paul and Nathan in Brno, and his brother Joseph in Vienna pooled their resources to invest in orange farming, and installed Alfred in the role of manager in their agricultural business. The opportunity arose when one of Albert's patients, a wealthy Polish Jew, mentioned that he was interested in selling a 125-dunam tract of land at the outskirts of Hadera that included a large grove of orange trees. The asking price was well over £11,000, and Albert and Anna felt they could provide about half of the total. Tante Bertha was visiting in Vienna at the time and it was not difficult to convince her nephew Josef to invest in the enterprise; he, in turn, recruited Paul and Nathan.[46] Alfred had always expressed his love of Zionism and the land quite openly, well beyond the token contribution of a shekel to the Jewish National Fund. Now, even as silent partners, four of his brothers were also directly participating in a Zionist agricultural enterprise. Unlike Jews in Germany, the three brothers in Austria and Czechoslovakia who had invested were still comfortable in their communities; but they would each eventually benefit from the investment when the terror of Nazism extended into their lands.

The Ticho family land purchases in Hadera can be seen against the backdrop of the Fifth Aliyah, but also against the backdrop of unresolved tensions between Arabs and Jews that would come to the forefront in the Arab Revolt or "disturbances" of the mid-1930s. In the face of increased Jewish immigration, the British Mandatory Government attempted to place the events of the 1929 riots in the rear-view mirror. The seventieth birthday of King George V on June 3, 1935, provided an opportunity for High Commissioner Arthur Wauchope to declare a general amnesty for fourteen convicted, imprisoned murderers – twelve Arabs and two Jews – including former Jewish footballer and policeman Simha Hinkis, who was among those released from prison.

Just days later, at a football match in Tel Aviv between Po'al Tel Aviv (Hinkis's former team) and a select Egyptian team, Hinkis was celebrated as a hero in front of a large crowd. The event occurred nine weeks after the Second Maccabiah Games; it was another interesting convergence of sports and politics that presented important symbols for the Zionist narrative. At the pre-game festivities, Hinkis was informed of the gift of a home in what is now Ramat Gan from philanthropist Yitzhak Leib Goldberg, who is remembered for several contributions including the first funds for the purchase of land (200 dunams) by the Jewish National Fund in the Hadera region and the principle funds for the purchase of the Gray Hill estate on Mount Scopus for the Hebrew University (chapters 7 and 9). Following the 1929 riots he had named the Ramat Gan neighborhood Tel Binyamina in memory of his son, Binyamin, who had died on that fateful day of violence of August 25, 1929. Memories of the 1929 riots remained quite fresh; the underlying conflicts remained unresolved. The amnesties in the spring of 1935 were followed by the beginning of the Arab Revolt that same autumn.[47]

———◆———

The settlement of Kfar Etzion was founded in 1935 on the former site of Migdal Eder (chapter 18). Its name has become emblematic of conflict between Jewish settlers and Arabs. The settlement was named in honor of its founder, Shmuel Zvi Holzmann, who sometimes used the surname Etzioni; *holz* in German which means "wood" is rendered as *etz* in Hebrew. Eventually the entire area with several settlements took on the name of Gush Etzion. When Holzmann founded Kfar Etzion, he encouraged his twenty-seven-year-old physician-son, Dr. Mayer Holman (the son's Anglicized name), to come and serve the kibbutz and the surrounding villages. Mayer Holman had graduated from an English medical school in 1932 and completed his post-graduate training there. In Kfar Etzion, Dr. Holman worked in the small medical clinic that his father had built especially for him. Shmuel Holzmann had hoped that offering medical care to local Arabs would engender their goodwill, but this did not prevent further Arab hostilities. As was the case in 1929, violent disturbances again forced the evacuation of the Jewish settlement after a few short years, but the dream of Jewish settlement in Gush Etzion never died (see chapter 20).[48]

In October 1935, a cache of smuggled arms was discovered at the Port of Jaffa, a presumed Jewish Agency undertaking. This was quickly followed by the declaration of a jihadist guerilla war by Sheikh 'Izz al-Din al-Qassam who left Haifa for the countryside. On November 7, al-Qassam's followers attacked two policemen who were investigating Arab looting of grapefruit groves at the Jewish settlement of Ein Harod near Afula. Jewish Police Sergeant Moshe Rosenfeld was murdered while the Muslim Arab policeman who was with him was spared. The British police launched an extensive hunt for the group, and on November 20, British police shot al-Qassam and three followers dead in a firefight near Ya'bad, west of Jenin. A riot broke out in Haifa the following day at the funeral of the three of the Qassamiyun, as al-Qassam's followers came to be known. Another British constable had been killed at Ya'bad and several more were wounded that next day in Haifa. Thousands of Arabs marched on the Central Police Station, smashed all of the windows, wrecked three police cars, and then proceeded to vandalize a Jewish glass factory.[49]

While Jerusalem remained fairly quiet, the Tichos could follow one newspaper headline after another over the winter that described continued attacks by Qassamiyun in northern Palestine. After preliminary hearings that ended in early March 1936, the captured Qassamiyun that had been involved in the deaths of British police were bound over for trial. Meanwhile tensions within the Arab community remained high and newspapers reported frequent road attacks near Tulkarem.[50]

Through the spring, the Tichos read about increasingly frequent acts of terror, more funerals, and more riots. On April 15, 1936, a caravan of automobiles and buses was held up near Tulkarem, killing seventy-year-old Yisrael Chazan, a poultry merchant and a native of Salonika.

The driver sitting next to him, twenty-seven-year-old Zvi Dannenberg – one of the first children born in Ahuzat Bayit/Tel Aviv – was mortally wounded and died five days later. It was the third such hold-up near Tulkarem in as many weeks. The following night, it was reported that an Arab and "his Egyptian friend" (as it turned out, an Egyptian Jew) were shot and killed by unidentified masked gunmen, in what the Arab community believed to be a reprisal attack by Jews.

The large funeral for Hazan took place in Tel Aviv that Friday, April 17, and turned into a riot wherein thirty Jews were wounded by police truncheons and gunfire. Jews from the Salonika community were the most outspoken there, and one among them called for the crowd go into Jaffa and avenge Hazan's death. Instead, a large mob marched to City Hall to protest and then moved on to the Great Synagogue where "Kaddish," the Jewish memorial prayer, was intoned. For several days, the Arab riots that followed took a more murderous turn, especially in Jewish neighborhoods of Jaffa and at the border zones of all-Jewish Tel Aviv. Many of the wounded who were convalescing in Tel Aviv hospitals were visited by foreign physicians who had come to Tel Aviv for the World Jewish Congress of Physicians.[51]

Arab protests against British colonialism and Zionism spread throughout the country. On Saturday night, May 16, 1936, a young Arab teacher by the name of Sami al-Ansari shot and killed three Jews as they left the Edison Theater, just a quarter-mile from the Tichos' home. Most of Jewish Jerusalem closed up shop the following morning, especially in the Tichos' neighborhood, as thousands gathered on the nearby street between the Rothschild-Hadassah Hospital and Jaffa Road for the funeral prosession of the three victims. Despite this new wave of violence so close to home, Ticho continued to see hundreds of Arab patients in his practice on a daily basis. Just four weeks later, outside the Lion's Gate of the Old City, the Edison Theater assassin, al-Ansari, failed in an attempt to kill Jerusalem's assistant superintendent of police. The officer was among many British policemen, soldiers, and officials who were specifically targeted for assassination throughout Palestine. For many Arabs, both Muslim and Christian, the murderous crimes were seen as justified and even laudible acts of a nationalist struggle.[52]

The British vigorously attempted to subdue the incitements and violence in Jerusalem and elsewhere in Palestine. Longshoremen had gone on strike in Jaffa, and while the area around the Haifa port remained open, it was the scene of some violence and arson attacks. Arab leaders who sought to channel the upsurge from the Arab masses below endorsed calls for a countrywide general strike. They formed a new Arab Higher Committee of all the major political parties with Haj Amin al-Husayni as its president. The general strike of April–October 1936 became one of the longest recorded in history. As the general strike began, Sami and Lizl Ticho happened to be on vacation in Palestine with their one-year-old daughter Esther (Daisy). They had already seen the pyramids in Egypt, visited Albert and Anna in Jerusalem, and they were now visiting Alfred in Binyamina. Alfred "breathed a great sigh of relief" when he took the family to the Haifa port and put them safely aboard a Lloyd Triestino ship back home to Europe.[53]

In the midst of the strike, some of Europe's finest Jewish orchestral musicians arrived in Palestine as immigrants, recruited by Bronislaw Huberman to join the "Refugee Orchestra." Plans to inaugurate the orchestra's first season had been postponed by the violence, but rehearsals finally began in Tel Aviv in early November under William Steinberg just as the general strike was drawing to a close. Excitement was building in anticipation of the arrival of Arturo Toscanini to conduct the first two weeks of performances in Tel Aviv, Jerusalem, and Haifa. Meanwhile, a British Royal Commission headed by Lord William Peel arrived in Palestine to investigate the reasons for the Arab uprising. A busy schedule of testimonies was undertaken, but the commissioners could not resist the opportunity to attend the second Jerusalem performance of the Palestine Orchestra at the Edison Theater on January 3, 1937, a program devoted to works by Beethoven. It is not known if the Tichos attended any of the orchestra's inaugural performances, but they and their circle of friends were among those caught up in the historic cultural achievement.[54]

After the Palestine Orchestra performance, the Peel Commission immediately went back to its work. Last-minute interventions of neighboring Arab monarchs persuaded the Arab Higher Committee to cooperate with the commission, and on January 12, 1937, Haj Amin al-Husayni appeared at the Palace Hotel to testify.[55] Elsewhere in Jerusalem that same day – a probable coincidence – a Jewish merchant in the Old City, Ephraim Joshua David, was seriously burned by vitriol (acid) which was thrown in his face by an Arab youth while he was standing in front of his shop. The victim fell to the ground and almost immediately lost consciousness. Both of his eyes were seriously burned as well as his face, chest, and back. He was taken to Dr. Ticho's private hospital where he regained consciousness while being treated. The fact that he was wearing glasses had saved the patient from immediate blindness but he remained in Ticho's hospital for over two weeks.[56]

During this same period of time, Dr. Ticho joined a group of leading Jewish residents of Jerusalem who were arranging the observance of Dr. Moshe Wallach's seventienth birthday.[57] On a late Tuesday afternoon, on January 19, 1937, the Tichos joined some three hundred guests at a reception for Dr. Wallach at the Evelina de Rothschild School.

Later that month, Anna Ticho left for Vienna to meet with the art historian and critic Prof. Max Eisler, who had taken a great interest in Anna's art. Dr. Eisler was a native of Boskovice, Moravia, just two years older than Albert, and a former schoolmate of Albert's brother David. While visiting Jerusalem the previous April, Eisler had expressed his desire to publish a portfolio of Anna's work. Anna let Eisler borrow several drawings and watercolors for a few days to help him write about them. The well-known professor had published several atlases and essays on architecture, decorative arts, and fine arts; subjects of his monographs included Rembrandt, Gustav Klimt, and Oskar Strnad. Upon his return to Vienna he began preparing the portfolio. Anna's trip to Europe probably included making various technical and financial arrangements for the portfolio's publication, of course visiting with friends and relatives, and also beginning to make arrangements for an exhibition of her art in Amsterdam. This exhibition in Amsterdam was canceled the following year due to the crisis in Austria. In July 1937, her facsimile portfolio of twelve drawings, entitled *Palästina*, was published in German by Gerlach and Wiedling, edited and with a foreword by Eisler, his last publication before his death five months later.[58]

A more widely anticipated publication in July 1937 was the report of the Peel Commission that recommended the partition of Palestine and the transfer of Arab and Jewish populations. The partition plan proposed to give the Jews the Galilee, the Jezreel Valley, and the northern coastal regions, but it excluded Jerusalem and a westward corridor that were to remain under British control. The eastern Sea of Galilee, previous hydroelectric development concessions, and the Negev were excluded from Jewish control.[59] Jabotinsky and the Revisionists emphatically rejected the partition plan as did the Arab High Committee, but so did long-time supporters of a binational solution that included outspoken advocates like Judah Magnes and private individuals like the Tichos. In August, Magnes warned Jewish Agency representatives in Zurich that the establishment of even a tiny Jewish state would bring about war with her Arab neighbors, warnings that were met with derision and laughter. Magnes was seen as a "tragic figure" who was out of touch and unable to accept the wise consul of others. While objecting to the Peel Commission plan itself, the notion of partition was accepted by the Twentieth Zionist Congress.

By that fall, violence in Palestine intensified and the British reacted to assassinations by disbanding the Arab Higher Committee and the Supreme Muslim Council. Stripped of his title as mufti, Haj Amin al-Husayni fled Palestine. The Woodhead Commission that reviewed the recommendations of the Peel Commission devised an even more restricted Jewish enclave in a partition scheme, but the government's accompanying report declared any partition scheme to be impractical.[60] The notion of partition would eventually gain traction, particularly among "practical" Zionists.

———◆———

In February 1938, the *Palestine Post* reported that the art publisher Gerlach and Wiedling was planning to release an English-Hebrew version of Anna Ticho's twelve-drawing portfolio, including a posthumous translation of Eisler's foreword. Anna again traveled to Europe to attend to the details. She also made an excursion to Paris where she met Gershom Scholem, who introduced her to his long-time friend, the writer and philosopher Walter Benjamin. Benjamin had fled from Germany to France in 1933, maintaining work as a writer for the Institute for Social Research based in Frankfurt. In 1936, he had published an essay, "The Work of Art in the Age of Mechanical Reproduction." It is likely that Scholem, Benjamin, and Mrs. Ticho discussed Anna's art and her facsimile reproductions in the context of Benjamin's observations on the subject. In his essay, Benjamin had analyzed the proliferation of technical reproductions of art that lose the "aura" of its creator, bearing only imagistic similitude to the original. But his new acquaintance, Anna Ticho, was both the source of the originals and the reproductions. It was Anna Ticho who had imbued her original works with personal and emotional context.

Whatever conversations actually took place, it is clear that Walter Benjamin had made, according to Scholem, "a great impression" upon Anna. The following year, as Scholem tried in vain to secure passage of his friend from France, he turned to a small circle of people in Jerusalem to raise enough money. "The only dependable person," he wrote, "who was ready to contribute an appropriate amount of money was the painter Anna Ticho…."[61]

The English edition of Anna's portfolio would not see the light of day for over a decade. The German annexation of Austria on March 12, 1938, brought the publication plans to a standstill. German troops had massed on the Austrian border, forcing Chancellor Kurt von Schuschnigg to cancel a scheduled plebiscite for independence and resign. The pro-German minister of public security, Arthur Seyss-Inquart, was appointed as chancellor in his place, and he promptly telegraphed an invitation to German troops to enter Austria unopposed, leading to what is often described as a political union or *Anschluss*. The direct Nazi rule that began in Austria included the vicious institution of the whole apparatus of anti-Jewish persecution: the imposition of the Nuremberg Laws, beatings, torture, and deportations to Dachau concentration camp.

In Vienna, Sami Ticho and his two older brothers, Josef and Max, were well-established lawyers; each of them was arrested by the Gestapo. Sami Ticho, a leader of B'nai B'rith and vice president of the Vienna Jewish Community, lived next door to Seyss-Inquart and had been targeted for arrest on the very night of the German takeover. During his detention, he was repeatedly interrogated by SS Officer Adolf Eichmann, who had returned to his native Austria after rising through the ranks of the Nazi concentration camp hierarchy.[62] Sami spent a few months in prison before getting the certificate that permitted him to move with his wife and daughter to Palestine. Josef Ticho, former (non-Zionist) president of the Jewish community of Vienna, was also arrested and was not allowed to leave the country with his wife Elsa and their daughters until after surrendering most of his possessions. Legal immigration to Palestine was possible due to his partial ownership of the productive orange grove in Hadera, a strange twist of fate for a "non-Zionist." Max Ticho was the subject of particular public humiliation, forced one day to walk around with a sign reading "I am a Jewish pig," and then forced to clean the sidewalk with a toothbrush on his hands and knees. Max's eldest son, Ernst, was also arrested and sent to the Dachau concentration camp and from there to Buchenwald. Once Max and Margareta learned that Ernst had been released and their other son, Paul, was safe, the family members each made plans to emigrate.

Czech lands to the north, though much closer than Palestine, would not be able to offer as safe a haven, as the Czechoslovakia government struggled against Nazism from without and from within. In 1935, President Masaryk had forced the Nazi Party to change its name before national elections, but the rebranded Sudeten German Party (SdP) had nevertheless been excluded from the government. Just months after the *Anschluss* in Austria, thirty-year-old Oskar Schindler, an SdP party member and agent of the Abwehr, was imprisoned in Brno on July 18, 1938, and interrogated under torture. Schindler, a native of the northwest Moravian town of Svitany (in German, Zwittau), had been supplying the German military with intelligence for an intended takeover of the Czech lands. He was still in prison on September 29 when the beginning of the dismemberment of Czechoslovakia began under the Munich Agreement, whereby the Sudetenland was ceded to the Third Reich. Schindler was among political prisoners who were pardoned, and he was released from prison on October 7 and transferred to Svitany.

In addition to working toward the takeover of Czechoslovakia, the Abwehr soon promoted Schindler to second in command of twenty-five agents engaged in the gathering of intelligence as Germany continued its takeover of the rest of Czechoslovakia and later Poland.[63]

Meanwhile, violence directed against Jews under Nazi rule increased. In Vienna, the Kristallnacht pogrom reached Vienna later into the night than in German cities; the pogrom did not start there until the early morning of November 10. The statistics were nonetheless devastating: twenty-seven people murdered; eighty-eight seriously wounded; forty-two synagogues destroyed; 1,950 apartments forcibly vacated; 4,083 shops closed; and 7,800 Jews arrested. The Austrian population did not intervene, except to participate in the looting.[64] Many of the retail businesses of the Innere Stadt had already been confiscated and "Aryanized," such as the Gallery Würthle where Anna Ticho had exhibited her work in 1931. This fate had befallen Victor Ticho's jewelry store in the Innere Stadt, coincidentally located in the same building as Seyss-Inquart's office. Victor, his wife Rosa, and their only child, Henry, were now in Brno but still on the move. A local six-month transit permit was due to expire soon.

The three highly successful Viennese attorneys of the Ticho family – Josef, Max, and Sami – were all forced to hastily leave Austria with their wives, leaving their busy law practices and affluent lifestyles behind. They each made their way to Palestine, but legal knowledge, language, and other professional skill-sets could not be adapted to their new environment. Josef settled with his wife in Tel Aviv and had the advantage of some income from the orange groves in Hadera. Max and Sami each took various jobs; each at some point working at cashiering or bookkeeping in the Jerusalem eye clinic of their brother Albert. Dr. Fritz Ticho, a successful dentist who was Anna Ticho's favorite half brother and childhood companion, also found refuge in Jerusalem.[65] Albert's oldest nephew, forty-year-old otolaryngologist Dr. Arthur Reiniger – son of Dr. Isidor and Sara Reiniger – resigned from his clinical positions, closed his private practice, and left Vienna for Paris. From there he traveled to Palestine and visited his sisters and his Uncles Alfred and Albert. He assessed his prospects to settle in Palestine but after a stay of only a few months, he decided to immigrate to America. Once in New York, he studied English and retrained in his specialty, adding eye diseases to his areas of expertise.[66]

Soon after saying goodbye to his nephew Dr. Arthur Reiniger, Dr. Ticho considered taking in other assistants. One of these was a long-time acquaintance, Dr. Josef Fleischner, who fled from Prague and returned to Palestine after a long absence of many years. He joined Ticho in 1939 and contributed his own surgical approaches to treating tear duct problems (chapter 16).[67] Another circumstance where Ticho tried to extend his help was in the case of the well-known ophthalmologist and rabbi of Florence, Dr. Nathan Cassuto. Dr. Cassuto's father, the famous Bible scholar, Prof. Umberto Cassuto, had been forced from his position as professor of Hebrew at the University of Rome in 1938 and accepted a position as professor of Bible at the Hebrew University in Jerusalem. Although Dr. Ticho formally offered a position to the young Dr. Cassuto, the latter remained with his community in Florence.[68]

———◆———

With war looming on the horizon, international borders were open to those who had the proper visas, but they were becoming more difficult to cross. In Brno, the coming expiration of their transit permit forced Victor and Rosa Ticho to move on to Paris, leaving behind their eight-year-old son Henry temporarily. Henry was present at the last Ticho family celebration in Brno before the war, the bar mitzvah of Paul Ticho's oldest son, Karl. This celebration took place in January 1939, and Uncle Isidor Reiniger, who had fled Vienna with Aunt Sarah after the *Anschluss*, wrote the homiletic speech that Karl dutifully recited. The writing of a *drash* by the seventy-three-year-old doctor was a family tradition, a role that he had undertaken for many Ticho children beginning with Albert Ticho's bar mitzvah forty-four years earlier (chapter 2). Irma Ticho Kritzler and her two sons left Brno soon after Karl's bar mitzvah, traveling by train and then by boat to Palestine. She left behind a women's coat-making business, Ticho and Spol, which she had begun several years earlier in Brno with the help of her brothers. Alfred Ticho, Irma's childhood companion and closest sibling in age, met the family and took them to their new home that they would share with him in Binyamina. When all other options failed, Alfred Ticho rescued his thirty-eight-year-old niece, Ella Reiniger, from Austria by falsely claiming that she was his wife.[69]

As relatives were arriving in Palestine from Austria as immigrants, Anna Ticho was preparing an exhibition of her work in the Graphics Hall of the Tel Aviv Art Museum. It would be her last exhibit before the war. Anna and Albert were present for the opening on the second floor of the museum in the early evening of March 12, 1939. It was a large exhibit of drawings and watercolors that Anna had produced over the past several years. The three-story museum building on Rothschild Boulevard that housed the exhibit, the former home of Meir Dizengoff, had opened after extensive renovations in 1932. In 1933, Dizengoff had recruited a director for the art museum, Karl Schwarz, a native of Munich who had been dismissed from the closed and confiscated Jewish Museum in Berlin. For the March 1939 exhibition in Tel Aviv, Schwarz had also invited the Munich-born Julius Wolfgang Schuelein for a concurrent, two-week exhibition of landscape watercolors. Accompanying Schuelein was his wife Suzanne, a talented portrait and still life painter whom he had met during his student days in Paris. They had married and settled in Munich but returned to Paris when the Nazis came to power.[70]

On March 15, 1939, just three days after the opening of Anna Ticho's exhibition in Tel Aviv, Germany invaded Czechoslovakia. Immediately, 120,000 Jews came under National Socialist rule, including those who had fled from the Sudentenland after the Munich Pact of September 1938. Hitler had presented Czechoslovakia's aging president, Dr. Emil Hácha, with the choice of capitulation to the Germans or the ruthless conquest of his country by force. The following day, Hitler came to the Hradčany Castle to look down over a defeated Prague. While staying at the castle he signed the decree incorporating the Czech historic lands into the Reich under the euphemistic designation, the Protectorate of Bohemia and Moravia. At that time nearly ten thousand Jews, about 11 percent of the Jews in the Protectorate, lived in Brno – including the many additional branches of the extended Ticho family who had continued to reside in Moravia. Like their relatives in Vienna, they likewise became victims of brutal, vicious oppression. One week after the dissolution of Czechoslovakia, the German annexation of disputed Lithuanian territory prompted even British Prime Minister Neville Chamberlain to repudiate the failed strategy of appeasement. The expansionist policy that Hitler had outlined in *Mein Kampf* was bringing Europe to the brink of war.[71]

From a distance – from Palestine, Hungary, France, America, and elsewhere – the extended Ticho family followed the events in Czechoslovakia with great apprehension. Newspaper reports, coupled with sporadic news from family in Europe, cast a very dark shadow over the many laudatory reviews that Anna Ticho received about her exhibition. Albert was kept informed of events in Central Europe by Consul Josef Kadlec, who staunchly refused to hand over his office to the Germans and who instead pledged his allegiance to the Czechoslovak Government-in-Exile formed by Edvard Beneš.

After a two-week run of her exhibition, Anna Ticho returned to the Tel Aviv Art Museum at 16 Rothschild Street where she supervised the careful packing of her drawings and watercolors. She said her goodbyes to Julius Schuelein and his wife who were returning to Paris, though it would not be long before the Schueleins fled France and settled in New York City. The first floor of the museum that had housed Schuelein's exhibition now had room for future art exhibits, and it would serve as the venue for many events in years to come. The most notable of these events occurred there on May 14, 1948, when David Ben-Gurion stood in the crowded main hall and proclaimed the independence of the State of Israel.[72]

CHAPTER 20

1939–1948
CULMINATION

בצידי הדרך מוטלים מתינו.
שלד הברזל שותק כמו רעי.

Our dead are lying at the sides of the road.
The iron skeleton is as silent as my comrade.

From the song *Bab al-Wad*, lyrics by Haim Gouri

T he themes of slavery and freedom were especially poignant for the
entire Ticho family in the spring of 1939 with Czechoslovakia under
the "protectorate" of Nazi Germany. On April 14, 1939, Bertha Ticho
oversaw the preparation of the Passover Seder in the family's residence
above Dr. Ticho's ophthalmic hospital. Elsewhere in Jerusalem, Max
and Margareta Ticho joined with their children to celebrate the Festival
of Freedom; Sami, Lizl, and daughter Esther Ticho did so in Tel Aviv;
and Alfred and Irma Ticho celebrated Passover in Binyamina. Victor
Ticho and his family were still in Paris and would escape to Palestine
via Marseilles the following year. Albert Ticho's remaining siblings
– Sarah, Jacob, David, Nathan, and Paul – were still in Brno trapped
within the Protectorate of Bohemia and Moravia. So was Heinrich
Ticho's widow, Wilma, who had remained in Brno after his death. Of
this generation of the Ticho family remaining in Brno, only Nathan
would survive the coming catastrophe.[1]

Within two weeks of the German takeover in Czechoslovakia, both Nathan and Paul Ticho were arrested by the Gestapo and imprisoned in Brno's Spielberg Castle. Paul Ticho's oldest son, thirteen year-old Karl, had qualified for a Youth Aliyah immigration slot and, after saying tearful goodbyes to his father in prison, Karl left for Palestine with his group and eventually managed to locate his uncle Alfred in Binyamina. While Jacob and Emma Ticho stayed behind, their children and their families also left for Palestine. Victor Ticho and his family escaped from France to Palestine as the Nazis entered Paris. About 25,000 Jews left Czechoslovakia during the half year preceding the outbreak of World War II, but about 95,000 would remain under National Socialist rule and most of them would perish.[2]

The businesses of Nathan and Paul Ticho were confiscated, Bratří Ticho with its factory in Boskovice, a branch store in Brno, and, above this, the women's clothing manufacturing business of Ticho and Spol. Combined, these businesses had large assets and over two hundred employees. The Germans also put trustees in charge of the A. J. Ticho retail business owned by Jacob and David Ticho. Under threats and torture, the Tichos were forced to sign over all of their personal property and businesses. Having done so, they were nevertheless transferred to Dachau concentration camp near Munich nine months later. By some miracle, Nathan survived the beatings and was released through many appeals and many channels that reached the highest levels. Once released, Nathan and his family made their way to America. Still in Dachau, Paul succumbed to the ills of his beatings, malnutrition, and diabetes, dying within the walls of the concentration camp in 1940. Paul's wife, Lidderl, received the box with her husband's remains and the message of his death in Dachau. On the way home to Luhačovice, with her two younger children, she spread the ashes beside her father's grave in Uherský Brod.[3]

Just as the doors of emigration were closing upon the Tichos' homeland of Czechoslovakia, the British Government decided to reverse the 1922 Churchill White Paper that had aimed to establish a Jewish majority in a part of Palestine. Britain's third White Paper was issued on May 23, 1939, and implemented by Palestine's fifth high commissioner, Sir Harold MacMichael. The Jews were to be a permanent minority in Palestine – only 75,000 Jews could enter Palestine legally through May 1944 – and the Arab majority thereafter would be given legislative powers. David Ben-Gurion announced, "We must help the [British] army as if there were no White Paper, and we must fight the White Paper as if there were no war." Jewish paramilitary groups, the Haganah, and even the Irgun supported collaboration with the British in the war effort, but the charismatic poet Avraham Stern broke with his Irgun colleagues in 1940 to form an even more extreme group, which soon took the name Lehi though it was called the Stern Gang by the British. The new British restrictions on Jewish immigration to Palestine and the outbreak of World War II marked the end of the Fifth Aliyah, but illegal attempts to bring immigrants continued.

On September 27, 1941, Reinhard Heydrich was appointed as Acting Reich Protector of Bohemia and Moravia. All synagogues were ordered closed and Terezín (Theresienstadt) was chosen as a "labor ghetto," euphemistically described as a "Reich Home for the Aged." It was, in reality, the "gateway to death" either on account of its harsh conditions or by virtue of it being the way station for further transit to the east and death by extermination. In late November 1941, a construction crew of about 350 young Jewish men from Prague and Brno arrived at Bohušovice, the railroad station nearest Terezín. They were compelled to renovate Terezín into a mass concentration camp.

Terezín became a part of the "Final Solution to the Jewish Question" as outlined by Heydrich to the senior officials of the Nazi German regime in the Berlin suburb of Wannsee on January 20, 1942. The total number of Jews deported to Terezín from Bohemia and Moravia was 73,608.[4] Wilma Ticho was the first among the Ticho family to be deported to Terezín. Jacob, Emma, David, and Hilda Ticho were deported there in January 1942; Dr. Isidor and Sarah Reiniger were deported there that April. Felix Unger, head of the *Judenrat* in Boskovice under Nazi occupation, had been a childhood friend of Alfred Ticho. His family's distilling business was confiscated and he, his wife, and two children were deported to Brno, and on March 19, 1942, to Terezín. The following month they were deported to Warsaw where all four were murdered. In

January 1943, Lidderl Ticho, the widow of Paul Ticho, was deported to Terezín from Uherský Brod with her two youngest children, František and Renatka. After June 1942, an additional 139,654 Jews were deported to Terezín from various other parts of Nazi-held Europe.[5]

The deportations from Brno brought an end to over three hundred years of the uninterrupted habitation of the Ticho family in Moravia. In February 1944, after many months of starvation and illness, the last remaining members of the Brno Ticho family in the Protectorate of Bohemia and Moravia – Sarah Reiniger and Jacob Ticho – both died in Ghetto Terezín. At that time, Jacob's wife, Emma, was the last of her generation in the Ticho family that was yet still alive in Europe. She died in the gas chambers at Auschwitz-Birkenau in October 1944.[6]

◆

In March 1941, German General Erwin Rommel began a North African offensive in Western Libya that swept eastward to the Egyptian border. Axis forces captured the Libyan port of Tobruk at the Battle of Gazala the following year, as 35,000 Allied troops surrendered on June 21, 1942. However, Rommel's advances into Egypt stalled about sixty-six miles west of Alexandria at the First Battle of El Alamein the following month. The evening before the surrender of Tobruk, the Jewish Agency and the National Council (Va'ad Le'umi) issued its third joint proclamation in Palestine for mobilization that was delivered over the radio in Hebrew by Moshe Shertok, head of the Jewish Agency's Political Department. The proclamation called for "an all-round effort to meet the enemy at the gates...to defeat the foe and ward off the danger threatening the country." Dr. Binyamin Ziv-Zion, the first head of medical services for the Haganah, organized courses in first aid and battle dressings. Dr. Chaim Scheiber (Sheba) worked to help overturn the many rejections Jewish physicians in Palestine encountered when enlisting for military service.[7]

Arab leaders and their families were more divided in their loyalties. Emir Abdullah of Transjordan remained a loyal ally of the British. His Arab Legion, under British commander Sir John Glubb (Glubb Pasha), controlled the local Bedouin population at his borders and helped the

British to suppress the pro-Axis coup of Rashid 'Ali al-Gaylani in neighboring Iraq in May 1941. Although the British seized control of Iraq, Nazi propaganda fueled a tragic anti-Jewish pogrom (known as the Farhud) on June 1–2, 1941 in which hundreds of Jews were murdered. Meanwhile Haj Amin al-Husayni was among those who fled with al-Gaylani to Iran and then to Germany. Haj Amin spent most of the war in southern Italy, visiting Berlin to broadcast anti-British and anti-Jewish propaganda.[8]

In their desire to fight Nazism, Jewish leaders repeatedly asked the British to create a separate Jewish Army or Division as they had in World War I. They were repeatedly rebuffed by the British government until a smaller Jewish Brigade was constituted late in 1944. Eventually, over two hundred Jewish physicians from Palestine served in the RAMC, mostly as individuals scattered among many units, with the exception of twenty-two Jewish physicians from Palestine who, at the request of Orde Wingate, were assigned to the liberation of Ethiopia. Many of the most valued Jewish medical officers in the RAMC were tropical disease specialists working at Hadassah Hospital on Mount Scopus, particularly Drs. Saul Adler and Israel Kligler.[9] While Dr. Ticho treated many war-related eye injuries in his private hospital, the fifty-eight-year-old doctor did not enlist. On one occasion, however, Ticho was abruptly summoned and taken by special military transport to Iran, where he performed ophthalmic surgery on a wounded, high-ranking British commander. While a review of British generals suggests some possibilities, the identity of Ticho's patient remains uncertain.[10]

As developments played out in North Africa and the Middle East in 1942, politics in the Yishuv ranged from extremism to pacifism. After Avraham Stern was shot dead by British police in Tel Aviv on February 12, 1942, Yitzhak Shamir was among the leaders who reorganized Lehi into cells and trained its members. Meanwhile, a small political party was being established that was built upon the binational ideas of Brit Shalom. The new political party, named Iḥud (Unity or Union), was supported by the Tichos, though they did not attend the party's inaugural meeting that was held in Jerusalem on August 11, 1942. The impetus for the founding of Iḥud was the acceptance of a Zionist statement at a conference held in May 1942 at the Biltmore Hotel in New York. David Ben-Gurion had been the moving force behind the Biltmore Platform that called for the establishment of a Jewish Commonwealth in Palestine.

Like the Tichos, Judah Magnes had never formally joined Brit Shalom, but he now became the chairman and a spokesperson for Ihud, together with cofounder Henrietta Szold. The Biltmore Platform had achieved its goal of rallying American Zionists, and it earned the endorsement of the Board of Hadassah even though the leadership roles of Szold and Magnes in Ihud exposed some dissent within the organization. Non-Americans in the Ihud leadership included several individuals among the Tichos' intellectual circle of Yekke friends, such as Martin Buber and Ernst Simon. As in the preceding decades, the Tichos again privately supported the movement but did not formally become members.[11]

Meanwhile, the war in North Africa decisively turned in favor of the Allies. In the Second Battle of El Alamein in early November, Rommel's army was defeated by the Allies under Field Marshal Bernard Montgomery; the German retreat in North Africa had begun. As the Axis threat to the Middle East diminished, routine daily life in Jerusalem seemed more secure. Dr. Ticho's busy private practice required an expansion of the outpatient clinic into an adjacent building that was just to the south and closer to the street. Albert's brother Max arrived at the clinic every working morning to manage the accounts, and brother Sami later joined as a cashier. It was less demanding work than their formerly prominent law practices in Vienna.

Ironically, the newly purposed clinic building on Ibn Batuta Street had long ago housed the Austrian Consulate, in the last years of Ottoman rule. Use of this building for a clinic allowed the Tichos to keep their comfortable living quarters and Anna's atelier above the hospital. Anna continued to be very productive, and in August–September 1942, after a four-year hiatus, she prepared a solo exhibition at the Bezalel Museum that received lavish praise. Two months later at the same museum, several of her works were included among eighteen artists during another three-week exhibition.

Even as the general mood was improving in Palestine, the Allies released a joint declaration on December 17, 1942, confirming Polish reports that Nazi Germany was exterminating European Jewry. The declaration was read before Parliament by Foreign Secretary Anthony Eden and published in many newspapers worldwide. The Tichos read reports of the declaration and MP James de Rothschild's moving response in the *Palestine Post* the following day.[12]

———◆———

At the time Albert Ticho celebrated his sixtieth birthday on October 27, 1943, he was not yet aware of the final fate of his family members trapped in Nazi-occupied Europe. The celebration that night at the home of Prof. Hermann Zondek included a speech delivered by the future Nobel-laureate S. Y. Agnon. The original manuscript in Agnon's handwriting and a typescript can be found among the Ticho Papers in the Israel Museum, Jerusalem, and printed among Agnon's published works.[13] Speaking that night with humor and affection, Agnon remarked that he had tried to prepare a speech by searching a concordance of the Bible, expecting to find sixty instances of the word "eye," corresponding to the years of Ticho's life. He found even more than one hundred twenty, the length of Moses's life in years according to Jewish tradition. Then Agnon playfully recounted how he had calculated the numeric value of Ticho's name according to Gematria and recalculated with homonym letter substitutions. Still the total did not correspond to the value of the value of the current year 5704 (1943) on the Hebrew calendar.

Excerpts of Agnon's touching conclusion follows:

> I had to give the speech. I began to delve deeply into the profession in which Ticho works. What did he see that he specifically chose the healing of the eyes? If he wanted to be a doctor, he would have been able to choose from the rest of the specialties in medicine; indeed his great talents and his blessed hands would have made him great in all of the specialties. However specifically because of his love for the wisdom of art, did he dedicate himself to the healing of eyes, to open the eyes of the blind, in order that every

man would see the wonderful paintings of Mrs. Anna Ticho, that all who see them, see Jerusalem as from the midst of an illuminated point of view, confirming within himself, 'Join in her jubilation, all you who mourned over her.'[14]

It appears there is sufficient reason, however, that some people have beautiful eyes but they are not beautiful [enough] to see beautifully; they see but don't know what they see, or they don't see at all. We must say that it was for the sake of Anna Ticho's paintings that Albert Ticho turned to his profession as an eye doctor. We must again face the recurrent problem, 'What did Ticho see that he turned to healing eyes, of all things?' However, they say in the Gemara that the blind person is not satisfied when he eats, because he cannot see. Ticho pitied blind men who eat and are not satisfied, he prepared to give his life for the blind to open their eyes so that they would see what they were eating and be satisfied....

Ticho knows that all of existence of the world depends on the Torah and mitzvot: If Israel keeps the Torah and mitzvot the world is sustained. If Israel does not keep the Torah and mitzvot, alas, the world ceases to exist. And even if there is one amongst Israel that is not able to keep the Torah and the mitzvot the world is found defective... Indeed when, alas, there is a blind man in Israel, he is not able to keep the mitzvot and an unstable world is found in his existence, or as we say in the language of our times, the world is not in order. And for this reason our good friend, among all the fields of medicine, works only in the healing of the eyes, in order to open the eyes of the blind, in order that they will be able to keep the Torah and the mitzvot, in order that world will be in existence....

—◆—

The World War and Hitler's extermination of European Jewry continued, yet Britain's White Paper remained in effect. Political struggles of Jews in Palestine were increasingly co-opted by violent extremists. The Lehi organization made repeated, unsuccessful attempts to assassinate High

Commissioner Harold MacMichael, but on November 6, 1944, two Lehi operatives in Cairo killed Lord Moyne (Walter Guinness), Churchill's minister of state for the Middle East, who had been highly involved in Britain's Palestine policy. The two assassins of Lord Moyne were executed on March 22, 1945. Just seven weeks later, on May 8, 1945, the war in Europe ended with Germany's unconditional surrender. A record of Dr. Ticho's mood and activities on that day has not been preserved, whether he joined in the celebrations at Zion Square near his home or whether his mood was tempered by the losses sustained in the Holocaust. Tichos' homeland of Czechoslovakia and its decimated Jewish population were now under Russian occupation.

On November 21, 1945, Gen. Sir Alan Cunningham arrived in Jerusalem, the seventh and last high commissioner of the Mandate. Cunningham replaced Field Marshal Lord Gort, who had returned to London after just twelve months when diagnosed with inoperable cancer. At that time, great hopes were centered on an Anglo-American Committee that was formed in lieu of the usual Royal Commission of Inquiry. The most publicized proposal that the committee considered was the admission of 100,000 Jewish refugees into Palestine. Britain's new prime minister and foreign secretary, Clement Attlee and Ernest Bevin, had voiced their opposition. Testifying on behalf of Ihud, Judah Magnes gave a strong plea for the immigration, stating, "Our view is that Jewish-Arab cooperation is essential, and that the alternative is strife and bloodshed. The Jews want Jewish immigration. Give it to them and they will forget the Jewish State. The Arabs want self-government. Give it to them and they will forget their fears of Jewish immigration."[15] The committee's report was made public on April 30, 1946, remarkably supporting binationalism, the immediate issue of the 100,000 immigration certificates, and an extension of the British Mandate.

Even so, the Mandatory Government was confronted with increasing terrorist attacks in which British soldiers were losing their lives on a daily basis. The British responded with Operation Agatha, involving curfews and wide-scale arrests, including the arrest of leaders of the Jewish Agency on what came to be known as Black Sabbath. Most of those arrested were sent to a detention camp in Rafah in the southern part of Gaza. Harsh and crowded conditions there led to several cases of paralysis (though not from polio as had been feared). Lt.-Col. Dr. Chaim Scheiber was among the Jewish RAMC physicians there who secured the release of hundreds of prisoners who fell ill.[16]

On July 22, 1946, four weeks after Black Sabbath, the Irgun blew up the south wing of the King David Hotel. The hotel housed the Secretariat of the Government of Palestine and the Headquarters of the British Forces in Palestine and Transjordan. It was the deadliest attack against the British during the Mandate, with ninety-one people killed. More than ever, the British government looked to extricate itself from Palestine but found it difficult to do so. A series of Aliyah Bet ships were turned away from Haifa, and over six thousand Holocaust survivors were incarcerated on the island of Cyprus.[17] On March 2, 1947, the British declared martial law throughout the Jewish sector of Jerusalem, and in addition to normal police patrols, plain-clothed British squads were dispatched, led by Capt. Roy Farran.

To avoid the more dangerous streets in West Jerusalem's triangle, youthful Lehi cell members often met at night on the empty grounds of Dr. Ticho's eye hospital. One Lehi cell member was sixteen-year-old Alexander (Sanni) Rubowitz, the son of Nehemia Rubowitz, a prominent Meah Shearim pharmacist who was well known to Dr. Ticho. Sanni would often prepare glue to post the latest Lehi news bulletin, *Ha-Ma'as*, and sometimes post the bulletins himself. On May 6, 1947, the boy was abducted, tortured, and murdered, allegedly by Captain Farran, who fled but was brought back to Palestine. He was acquitted of the murder at a court-martial.[18]

On May 9, 1947, the United Nations convened a special session at Great Britain's request that resulted in the appointment of the United Nations Special Committee on Palestine (UNSCOP). The committee began its work in Palestine in June 1947. The UNSCOP chairman, Emil Sandstrom, and other committee members were present in Haifa when the commandeered Aliyah Bet ship *Exodus 1947* was brought into the harbor by the British Navy on July 18. Over four thousand Holocaust survivors were roughly transferred from the *Exodus* to three

British prison ships, locked in cages below deck, and returned to sea. It was presumed they departed for Cyprus, but instead they arrived back in France and, upon refusing to disembark, most of the refugees were taken to British-occupied Germany.

Several Jewish leaders gave public testimony to UNSCOP: Ben-Gurion, Weizmann, and, just four days before the deportation of the *Exodus* refugees, Judah Magnes. Representing Ihud, Magnes testified in support of a binational program that he envisioned occurring in three stages: first, a continued British Mandate with "encouraged" Jewish immigration to the point of numerical parity with the Arabs (the absorption of another 500,000–600,000 Jewish immigrants); a second stage of UN trusteeship; and finally an independent state with two nationalities. Back in New York, UNSCOP endorsed a plan for partition of Palestine and internationalization of Jerusalem; the vote was seven to three with one abstention.[19]

On November 29, 1947, in New York the General Assembly of the United Nations debated the UNSCOP proposals, which were accepted as Resolution 181 by a vote of thirty-three to thirteen, with ten abstentions. Britain was to remain in Palestine until the moment of transfer "as soon as possible, but in any case not later than August 1, 1948." In advance of the vote, the Haganah was reorganized under the political control of Ben-Gurion and a National Command was established. Medical services were drawn from the Magen David Adom, Kupat Holim, and Hadassah. On the day after the partition resolution, Arab riflemen opened fire on an ambulance making its way to Hadassah Hospital on Mount Scopus. That same day, one of the first fatalities was Dr. Nehama Cohen, a pathologist at Hadassah Hospital.[20]

Violence escalated throughout the winter months into a civil war. With their departure only months away, British troops began to withdraw from their outlying strongholds and disengage from the fighting. It was clear that the partition plan would not be implemented, and the Haganah prepared a new operational plan to secure areas of Jewish settlement and population. With the sovereign existence of the Jews in their land at stake, the Haganah planned to eliminate armed resistance in Arab towns and villages that controlled strategic roads and points of communication. At the end of March, Arab forces cut off the road to Jerusalem at Bab al-Wad and the hills beyond it. Jerusalem was under siege. Dr. Ticho, along with Drs. Simon Schereschewsky and Joseph Treu, helped negotiate an unprecedented but short-lived agreement between Jewish and Arab physicians declaring the principle of reciprocal respect for medical personnel and vehicles in and around Jerusalem. British convoys were allowed to pass and the British therefore took no action, claiming that the road remained open. The city itself was often under artillery bombardment from high ground north of the Damascus Gate.

On April 6, the Haganah responded to the siege of Jerusalem by launching its largest operation to that point, code-named Naḥshon. In the fight for the Arab village of Kastel, east of Bab al-Wad, the Arab commander Abd al-Qader al-Husayni, son of former Jerusalem mayor Musa Kazim al-Husayni, was killed on April 8, 1948. He was buried in a chamber on the Haram beside his father, Musa Kazim, and King Hussein. The following day, Irgun and Lehi forces attacked the Arab village of Deir Yassin, an attack in which over one hundred Arabs were killed, many of them women and children.

Not long before his death, Abd al-Qader had threatened the destruction of the Jewish enclaves on Mount Scopus. The director of Hadassah Hospital, ophthalmologist Dr. Hayim Yassky, had made contingency plans to evacuate the hospital, though he expressed a duty to keep the hospital open as long as convoys could reach the hospital with personnel and supplies. The frequency of the convoys had now diminished to just one per day, often accompanied by British soldiers in armored cars. Albert's sister-in-law, dentist Dr. Lizl Ticho, had joined one of these convoys to spend two weeks working at the hospital.

On the morning of April 13, Dr. Yassky entered the front of an armored ambulance at the Hadassah "A" maternity ward on the Street of the Prophets, his wife on one of the rear benches with other personnel. The ambulance, a converted Dodge truck, painted white with a bright red Star of David on the body, was part of a ten-vehicle convoy carrying mostly unarmed Jewish lecturers, students, nurses, and doctors. The Arab ambush began at 9:45 a.m. with the explosion of a mine in front of the vehicles as they rounded the narrow "Nashashibi Bend" in the road. That day there was no British escort but ironically Lt.-Gen. Gordon MacMillan, the commander of all British forces in Palestine, sat as a spectator in a car not far behind and ordered his driver to move away from the convoy that was trapped under fire for several hours. By the time Yassky was killed by a bullet through his liver that afternoon, he knew that that everyone had been killed in the two burning buses of the convoy. The British finally intervened at 4:00 p.m. and brought an end to the shooting. Badly burned corpses were piled in heaps outside the buses, and their remains were buried in a common grave in nearby Sanhedria. In all, seventy-seven people had perished in the attack, including doctors, nurses, patients, and Hebrew University employees. Two other physicians who died that day were Dr. Leonid Doljansky, head of Hadassah Hospital's cancer research, and Dr. Moshe Ben-David, secretary of the pre-faculty of the planned medical school. Judah Magnes left for America just four days after the Hadassah convoy massacre. In Washington and New York, Magnes continued to plead against partition, but he died just six months later.[21]

Dr. Lizl Ticho had observed the tragedy from Mount Scopus. Her descent from the mountain by a return convoy was delayed but she eventually returned safely to her home. As violence around Jerusalem continued, she and her husband, Sami, moved the family into a room in Albert's clinic building (the historic Kukia House that still stands) adjacent to the hospital. Their daughter Esther recalls how an artillery shell caused the collapse of an adjacent wall where she was sleeping. Although no place in Jerusalem was perfectly safe, many others would be offered a temporary home in the hospital or the clinic, finding food, clothing, and shelter from artillery.[22]

Kfar Etzion was reestablished by religious Polish Jews and operated from 1943 until its fall on May 13, 1948, just one day before the State of Israel declared its independence. Before the battle, most of the women and children of Kfar Etzion were taken to the Ratisbonne School in Jerusalem. Surrounded on all sides by Jordanian Arab Legion forces and local irregulars, as many as 250 Jewish inhabitants were killed and hundreds were taken as prisoners.[23]

Heavy fighting continued throughout Palestine during the final month of the British Mandate. Yitzhak Rabin led a Palmach contingent that temporarily occupied Nashashibi House in Sheikh Jarrah before British shelling forced him out the next day. Arabs fled from other Jerusalem neighborhoods and from contested areas elsewhere in Palestine. They were fleeing out of fear but with the notion that the exile would be temporary, assured by their leaders that an overwhelming Arab invasion was imminent.

By the end of the Mandate, Jewish forces had conquered Haifa, Tiberias, Safed, and Jaffa, but Jerusalem was still in a state of siege. Dr. Ticho's hospital had transitioned into a war-zone general hospital, but the supply of electricity was unreliable. On the last day of the Mandate, on the afternoon of Friday, May 14, 1948, many in Jerusalem missed the radio broadcast of Ben-Gurion's proclamation of the establishment of the State of Israel. There were no street celebrations near Dr. Ticho's hospital and many received the news only by word of mouth during the Jewish Sabbath. On Sunday, the headline of the *Palestine Post* read "THE STATE OF ISRAEL IS BORN," but the newborn state was still fighting for its existence. In central Jerusalem, the Tichos and their hospital remained close to the front lines of the war.[24]

Epilogue

On November 30, 1948, the Israelis and Jordanians signed a new cease-fire agreement for the Jerusalem area that promised freedom of movement behind the lines. An additional agreement was signed regularizing the dispatch of convoys to Mount Scopus, but the Jewish presence on Mount Scopus was essentially limited to a military post. Construction of new campuses for the Hebrew University and Hadassah Hospital took place throughout most of the 1950s in Givat Ram and Ein Kerem, respectively. In 1953, Dr. Ticho was appointed to the Board of Directors of the Hebrew University. At that time, classes were being held in many buildings scattered throughout West Jerusalem, and Hadassah Hospital was decentralized among a dozen buildings.[1]

The main transit point between the divided sectors of Jerusalem on St. George's Road became known as the Mandelbaum Gate. A large sign would soon be installed at the Mandelbaum Gate reading "Welcome to Israel" in Hebrew, English, French, and Spanish. The lines that were drawn through a divided Jerusalem separated Dr. Ticho from many of his former Arab patients, who now relied upon the relocated Ophthalmic Hospital of St. John in Sheikh Jarrah. Along the city line, stone fences, barbed-wire entanglements, minefields, and makeshift obstacles separated the populations and armies of Jerusalem.[2]

Dislocation of populations in the former Palestine and across the Middle East affected both Arabs and Jews. For Jews, the loss of the Jewish Quarter and access to the Kotel were sad consequences of the war. With his home and clinic destroyed, Dr. Tawfiq Canaan was among the Arab refugees who found shelter in a convent in Jerusalem's Old City, but he would reestablish his life and career with an appointment as head of the Augusta Victoria Hospital on the Mount of Olives.[3]

Dr. Ticho continued to practice ophthalmology in his private hospital until shortly before his death on October 15, 1960, at seventy-seven years of age. He had been the first ophthalmologist to settle permanently in Jerusalem and, over almost five decades, he had witnessed Jerusalem become transformed from a backward Ottoman outpost to the capital of the State of Israel. Like many of his contemporaries, Ticho's citizenship had changed with the times. He arrived as a subject of the Austro-Hungarian Empire, and with that empire's demise he became an expatriate of Czechoslovakia. Assigned medical license number seventy-three, he worked productively for thirty years in Mandatory Palestine under the increasingly tenuous control of a declining British Empire. The dream of an independent Jewish state was not Dr. Ticho's personal dream, but he became a loyal citizen of the State of Israel. Sentimental and ultimately unrealistic notions of a binational state of Jews and Arabs had to be set aside.

In 1950, the Tichos purchased a home in Motza Ilit to the west, a property with a beautiful view of Jerusalem and the Judean Mountains. They commissioned German-born Israeli architect Heinz Rau to design the extensive renovations and surrounding gardens. On Friday afternoons, their chauffeur would take them out to their weekend retreat in a black Cadillac that Albert purchased from the French consul. Here Dr. Ticho would work in the garden growing flowers, fruit trees, and cactuses while Anna would go out to draw in the countryside. Across the valley from their home, the Tichos could look toward the hilltop cemetery of Har ha-Menuḥot that would eventually serve as their final resting places.

In the mid-1950s, Dr. Ticho's health deteriorated and he suffered a stroke that weakened his right arm. Although he gave up surgery, he continued to see patients in his clinic. After Dr. Ticho's death in 1960, Anna Ticho maintained her residence and studio on the second floor above the first-floor hospital space that was rented out. She was very productive as an artist, and more than ever her drawings and watercolors were critically acclaimed. In 1965, she received the art award of the Jerusalem Municipality. Unlike Albert, Anna Ticho survived to see the reunification of Jerusalem in 1967. Shortly before her death in 1980, she was awarded the Israel Prize for painting.[4]

Albert and Anna Ticho left no children, but two of their nephews became successful ophthalmologists. Karl Ticho practiced for many years in Chicago and Uri Ticho sub-specialized in glaucoma at Hadassah Hospital in Ein Kerem. In 1970, the Albert Ticho Memorial Lecture was established by Dr. Isaac Michaelson, the chairman of ophthalmology at the Hadassah Hebrew University Medical School, who had succeeded Dr. Aryeh Feigenbaum (appendix 8). On these occasions, the honored lecturer would recount some of Dr. Ticho's contributions to ophthalmology and Hadassah's early years in Palestine.[5]

The best-known legacy of Albert and Anna Ticho is the Ticho House, bequeathed to the Israel museum after Anna Ticho's death. The extensive renovations were entrusted to architect David Kroyanker. Since its dedication in 1984, the former hospital and residence of the Tichos has continued to be a Jerusalem landmark, providing space for art exhibits, musical performances, dining, and a place to learn about the "days of Ticho."

APPENDIX 1

THE CHILDREN OF IGNATZ AND LAURA TICHO AND THEIR SPOUSES*

	Name	Born–Died	Name of Spouse	Born–Died
1.	Sarah	1873–1944	Dr. Isidor Reiniger	1865–1943
2.	Jacob (Yaakov)	1875–1944	Emma Krakauer	1883–1944
3.	Josef (Yosef)	1877–1951	Elsa Herzog	
4.	Max (Moshe)	1879–1954	Margareta Fleischmann	1891–1986
5.	David	1881–1943	Hilda Klaber	1886–1943
6.	Albert (Avraham)	1883–1960	Anna (Hanah) Ticho	1894–1980
7.	Heinrich	1884–1928	Wilma Theumann	1897–1942
8.	Nathan	1886–1973	Frenza Klein	1893–1965
9.	Sami (Solomon)	1887–1965	Lizl Reiniger	1900–1987
10.	Baruch (Paul)	1889–1940	Lidderl (Marie) Jelinek	1904–1943
11.	Victor	1890–1959	Rosa (Levi)	1900–1953
			Hilda	
12.	Alfred (Aharon)	1893–1983	Ella Reiniger	1901–1986
13.	Irma (Rivka)	1897–1963	Julius (Yaakov) Kritzler	1885–1967

---

* From Miri Debbi, *Ticho: The Story of a Family*, 360–61

APPENDIX 2

TICHO'S RESIDENCES AND UNIVERSITY COURSES 1902–07

Personal level [I–X]: Semester Address Archival Source	Course	Hrs. /wk.	Instructor
I: Winter 1902–03 2nd District (Leopoldstadt) Krummbaum- gasse 10, 1 St. AUW Microfilm 1577/302, 389–90	Human Anatomy I Dissection Demonstration Chemistry for Physicians Experimental Physics General Biology Chemistry Laboratory Chemistry Overview	6 6 5 4 5 4 4	Hofr. Dr. E. Zuckerkandl Hofr. Dr. E. Zuckerkandl [d.Z. Decan] Dr. E. Ludwig Vid [?] v. Lang Dr. B. Halschek [d.Z. Decan] Dr. E. Ludwig Lieben
II: Summer 1903 Obere Donau- strasse 85, Thür 4 AUW Microfilm 1578/304, 422–23	Systematic Human Anatomy II Chemistry for Physicians Chemistry Laboratory Reagents Plant Biology Bohemian Syntax [Linguistics]	6 5 4 6 5 3	Hofr. Prof. Dr. E. Zuckerkandl Hofr. Prof. Dr. Ludwig Hofr. Prof. Dr. Ludwig Hofr. Prof. Dr. Ludwig Hofr. Prof. Wiesner Ferdinand Menčik
III: Winter 1903–04 2nd District (Leopoldstadt) Große Schiffgasse 5, Tür 26 AUW Microfilm 1580/308, 263–64	Dissection Demonstration and Laboratory Topographical Anatomy Physiology Physiology Laboratory Comparative Organ Physiology Physiol. and Pathol. Chemistry Review Foundations Biology Histology Physiology of Hearing Organs Urogenital Embryology	6 2 5 3 1 1½ 1 5 1 1	Prof. Zuckerkandl Prof. Zuckerkandl Prof. Exner Prof. Exner Prof. Beer Prof. Ludwig Prof Halsebek Prof. Ebner Prof. Kreute Prof. Tandler –

Personal level [I–X]: Semester Address Archival Source	Course	Hrs. /wk.	Instructor
IV: Summer 1904 2nd District (Leopoldstadt) Große Schiffgasse 5 AUW Microfilm 1581/311, 288–89	Histology Laboratory Histol. and Embryol. of the Eyes Physiology Physiology Laboratory Chemistry Lab. for Physicians Pract. Microscopic Technique	6 1 5 3 4 3	[Dr. Victor] Ebner von Rofenstein Ebner von Rofenstein Exner Exner Ludwig Dr. Joseph
V: Winter 1904–05 2nd District (Leopoldstadt) Große Schiffgasse 5 AUW Microfilm 1583/316, 246–48	Dissection Laboratory Histology Laboratory Physical Examination of the Ill General and Special Pathologic Anatomy	6 6 5 5	Hofr. Zuckerkandl Hofr. Ebner Dr. Weinberger v. Reiter Prof. Weichselbaum
VI: Summer 1905 2nd District (Leopoldstadt) Große Schiffgasse 5 AUW Microfilm 1584/321, 166–67	Medicine Clinic w/ Praktikum Surgery Clinic w/ Praktikum Surgery Preparatory Course	10 10 3	Hofrat Dr. von Schrötter Prof. Hochenegg Dr. P. Clairemont

Personal level [I–X]: Semester Address Archival Source	Course	Hrs. /wk.	Instructor
VII: Winter 1905–06	Medical Pathology and	7½	Hofrat Příbram
	Therapy	7½	Prof. Dr. Wölfler
Prague 1st District (Staré	Surgical Pathology and	3	Prof. Knapp
Město), Langengasse	Therapy	3	~~Hofr. Prof. Chiari~~ replaced
(Dlouhá) No. 706	Obstetrics	5	Prof. Dr. Pick
	Histologic Pathology Lab	1	Prof. Winter
AUK, courtesy of archivist	Psychiatry and Neurology	5	Hofr. Prof. Pick
Tomáš Rataj	Heart Disease	1	Prof. Bayer
	Dermatology-Venereology	2	Prof. Dr. Pietrzikowsky
	Diagnostic Surgery	–	Prof. Singer
	Instrumentation	2	Doc. Dr. Lieblein
	Medicine Polyclinic	2	Prof. Hueppe
	Surgery	3	Doz. Dr. Gottfried Pick
	Bacteriology Practicum		
	Laryngology/Laryngoscopy		
VIII Summer 1906	Internal Medicine	7½	Prof. Dr. von Jaksch
	Obstetrics	5	Prof. Dr. von Franqué
Prague 1st District (Staré	Surgery	7½	Dr. Wölfler
Město), Langengasse	Ophthalmology	5	Prof. Czermak
(Dlouhá) No. 706	Ophthalmoscopy	4	Prof. Czermak
	Obstetric Examination	2	Doc. Schenk
AUK, courtesy of archivist	Smallpox Vaccination	1	Prof. Epstein
Tomáš Rataj	Dentistry	3	Prof. Boenneken
	Bedside Demonstration	1	Prof. Hering
	Pediatric Surgery	2	Prof. Bayer
	Gastrointestinal Diseases	2	Prof. Walko
	Diseases of Prostitutes	2	Hofr. Pick
	Special Clinical Exercises	–	Hofr. Příbram
	Gynecological Examinations	1	Doc. Dr. Wilhem Fischl

Personal level [I–X]: Semester Address Archival Source	Course	Hrs. /wk.	Instructor
IX: Winter 1906–07 2nd District (Leopoldstadt) Große Schiffgasse 5 AUW Microfilm 1589/339, 27–28	Obstetrics-Gynecology Clinic Ear Surgery Ophthalmology Clinic Exercises in the Practical Use of the Ophthalmoscope Exercises in Pathologic Histology Introduction to Gynecologic Diagnosis and Therapy	10 2 10 3 4 2	Hofrat Friedrich Schauta Prof. Bing Prof. Hofr. Dr. Isidor Schnabel Hans Lauber Hans and Julius v. Benedek [Assistants] Privatdoz. Dr. Oskar Stoerk Privatdoz. Dr. Josef Fabricius
X: Summer 1907 9th District (Alsergrund) Berggasse 39, Second floor, tür 14. AUW Microfilm 1590/343, 266–67	Pathological Dissection Exercises for Students Pathological Anatomy Demonstrations II Medicinal Treatment of Visceral Illnesses Diagnosis and Treatment of Eye Diseases Forensic Medical Exercises Hygiene Pathological and Anatomical Demonstrations Toxicology Surgical Operations Exercises Essentials of Pathology of the Nervous System	3 2 2 2 2 5 2 3 6 1	Privatdoz. Dr. Karl Landsteiner Privatdoz. Dr. Karl Sternberg Dr. Biach Prof. Dr. Otto Bergmeister Dr. Kolisko Prof. Schlagenhaufer Prof. Schlagenhaufer Prof. Meyer Dr. Maberer Doc. Dr. Marburg

APPENDIX 3

OPHTHALMOLOGISTS IN PALESTINE DURING THE OTTOMAN PERIOD

Name	City / Institution	Dates in Palestine
1. G. S. Waddell	J'lem / British Ophthalmic Hospital	1882–84
2. John H. Ogilvie	J'lem / British Ophthalmic Hospital	1884–88
3. William E. Cant	J'lem / British Ophthalmic Hospital	1888–1911
4. Theodor Germann	Various / Russian Palestine Society	1896
5. MacKellar (assistant)	J'lem / British Ophthalmic Hospital	?
6. Jelly (assistant)	J'lem / British Ophthalmic Hospital	?
7. Thom. Butler (assistant)	J'lem / British Ophthalmic Hospital	1903–06
8. John C. Strathearn	J'lem / British Ophthalmic Hospital	1906–07
9. Moses Erlanger	J'lem / Lemaan Zion Eye Hospital	1908–10
10. Eric Thomson (assistant)	J'lem / British Ophthalmic Hospital	1910–14
11. William Ward	J'lem / British Ophthalmic Hospital	1911
12. David M. Krinkin	Jaffa-Tel Aviv / Private Practice	1911–17
13. David Heron	J'lem / British Ophthalmic Hospital	1911–14
14. Kraus	J'lem / Lemaan Zion Eye Hospital	August 1911
15. A. Bloom (בלום)	J'lem / Private Practice	May–June 1912
16. Avraham Albert Ticho	J'lem / Lemaan Zion Eye Hospital	1912–17
17. Aryeh Feigenbaum	J'lem / Jewish Health Bureau, etc.	1913–17
18. Yaakov David	Yavne'el	1913–17
19. Miriam Neufach	J'lem / Jewish Health Bureau	1913–17
20. Aryeh Mäkler	J'lem / Jewish Health Bureau	1913–17
21. Gildenson	Jaffa	1913–1914
22. Harry Friedenwald	Various locations in Palestine	June–August 1914

APPENDIX 4

"TREATMENT OF TRACHOMA IN THE SCHOOLS OF JERUSALEM"

by Dr. A. Ticho, Lemaan Zion[*]

I am honored to present before you the experience I acquired in the treatment of trachoma in the schools of Jerusalem at the behest of the "Daughters of Zion" from America.

First of all, a few words about the matter of the organization of the work.

I personally did the examination of all children in the schools once every three months. Dr. Neufach and Dr. Shimoni-Mäkler undertook the daily treatment in three institutions and the compassionate nurses under my supervision in the remainder of the institutions. The principle work was upon the shoulders of the nurses from the "Daughters of Zion." The children afflicted with severe diseases, with purulent secretion or requiring surgery were ordered to the hospitals; and the rest I saw in the school every two weeks or – if necessary – also during this time at specially designated hours for the schoolchildren. In this manner [my assistants and] I treated close to 800–1000 children [daily]. Included in this number are cases of acute and chronic conjunctivitis.

I do not intend to attest that this type of organization is the most ideal or the only way with none other to consider. Rather I think that it is suitable for the resources that we have at our disposal. I fully admit that certainly a daily treatment by a physician is much better. But I

---

[*] This is an English translation of Ticho's papers that were published in 1915 in German and in Hebrew as "*Uber Trachombehandlung in den Schulen,*" and "*Ripuy ha-gar'enet be-vatei ha-sefer Yerushalayim,*" respectively (see bibliography). A comparison of the two articles was made possible by the translation of the German article by Don Blanchard, MD. The German article does not list Ticho's affiliation with Lemaan Zion but rather identifies him as "Former Assistant to Senior Executive Officer, Professor Bergmeister." It also lacks the detailed tables and the post-presentation discussion. The two articles are otherwise very similar.

have come to the conclusion, especially concerning the treatment of trachoma, that one can teach the basic principles of trachoma therapy to intelligent and trained nurses very well and entrust them with the treatment under supervision of a doctor. In a similar fashion, treatment has been relegated to teachers in affected areas of Germany.

Before we proceed to the treatment of the sick patients, an examination of all schoolchildren is necessary, requiring accurate lists of all the students. In the kindergartens, since the names of the children are not always known in the lower levels, one must call the students by a specific name, in order to prevent confusion and exchanging names.

The number of infected people in the individual schools depends on the social strata, from which the children come. So (Table 1) in the schools of the organizations "*Kol Yisrael Ḥaverim*" and the "Evelina de Rothschild" whose students principally come from the poorest of the Sephardi, Yemenite, and Kurdish strata, the number approaches 27.41% (in the Alliance School) and 26.57% (in the Evelina de Rothschild School). In contrast to this, we see a smaller percentage of 21.06% in the schools of "Ezra," which for the most part are attended by Ashkenazim (with almost the same number of enrolled students as in the aforementioned schools combined). This is especially conspicuous in the three kindergartens of "Ezra," in which I found on the one hand (18.6%, 15.6%, and 17.7% – an average of 16.58%) compared to the kindergarten of "*Kol Yisrael Ḥaverim*" (23.3%) and the kindergarten of the Rothschild School (29.8%). And even in other institutions, in the poorest classes among the native-born Ashkenazim, such as "*Ḥayei Olam*" and "*Eitz Ḥayim*" in the city, we found "only" (if it is possible to say so) 32.8% and 35.5%, respectively, but only 23.9% in the Talmud Torah Meah Shearim. However, in the schools attended by non-Ashkenazim, not only was there a higher percentage of infection, but also the cases were more severe.

Whether boys or girls in general had greater involvement with the disease, it is impossible to come to a conclusion. Among 2,299 boys there were 736 infected, that is 32.01%; among 1,377 girls 326 infected, only 23.69%. However, the number of children examined (especially for the girls) is too small to be able to come to a conclusion.

Among 9 cases of pannus (among all the 4313 examined), there were 8 girls, among them two 6-year-olds, while the one boy was a 14-year-old Sephardi youth, recently arrived from Constantinople. Of 11 cases [complicated] with trichiasis, there were nine girls. Weak children, such as emaciated and stricken with scrofula were less capable of resistance, easier to infect, and difficult to be healed.

Table 1

Name of the School	Number Examined	Number Affected	Percentage
Rothschild School Kindergarten	208	62	29.8
Alliance School Kindergarten	150	35	23.3
Ezra No. 1 Kindergarten	97	18	18.6
Ezra No. 2 Kindergarten	103	15	15.6
Ezra No. 3 Kindergarten	79	14	17.7
Hebrew School for Boys	85	29	34.1
Hebrew School for Girls	153	24	15.6
Hebrew Teachers' Beit Midrash	58	9	15.5
Lämel School	198	59	33.5
Ezra School for Girls	221	41	18.1
Alliance School for Girls	260	59	22.7
Alliance School for Boys	235	83	35.3
Alliance Workshop	91	70	77
Alliance Workshop for Girls	61	33	54
Ḥeder Torah	74	23	31.1
Beit-Ḥinuch Yeladim	106	22	20.8
Talmud Torah for Kurds	75	15	20
Talmud Torah for Sephardim	202	59	29
Talmud Torah for Yemenites	54	26	57
Talmud Torah *Meah Shearim*	281	67	23.9

Name of the School	Number Examined	Number Affected	Percentage
Talmud Torah *Eitz Ḥayim Ba'Ir*	200	67	33.5
Talmud Torah *Maḥanei Yehudah*	210	47	22.4
Talmud Torah *Achavah*	47	16	34
Talmud Torah *Beit Yisrael*	26	11	42
Hungarian Talmud Torah	74	18	24.3
Blumental School	19	8	42.1
School for Hungarian Girls	34	7	20.6
School of Home Economics	4	1	25
Ezra Seminary	97	12	12.3
Evelina de Rothschild School	361	89	24.6
Doresh Tziyon	78	22	25.6
Ezra Orphanage	52	6	11.5
Diskin Orphanage	158	58	38
Weingarten Orphanage	69	29	42
Workshop	56	15	29
Talmud Torah for Persians	37	36	81.6
Total	4,313	1,206	27.96
Schools for Boys	2,299	736	32.01
Schools for Girls	1,377	326	23.69
Kindergarten Children	637	144	22.6
	4,313	1,206	27.96

Frequently in the schools it is possible to see the beginning of trachoma in the inner or outer angles of the eyes. These are the gateways of infection to the eyes, especially in the medial aspect where the granules of the upper conjunctival fold are sometimes already found in the stage of softening, while the rest of the conjunctiva appears free of disease. In trachoma in childhood, where we almost always encounter granules as a prominent sign of the disease, the purulent discharge is likely to be eliminated with suitable therapy, something that is not so for the trachoma of marasmic and elderly people appears in a mixed form. The tarsal conjunctiva has velvety appearance. The purulent secretion stubbornly resists treatment, and the course is generally prolonged and indolent. Only for one girl, a five-year-old afflicted with scrofula, the purulent secretion continued for four months in spite of treatment with scarification of the conjunctiva; finally the secretion ceased with Bleno-Lenicet salve.

The infection occurs among us (as everywhere else, where the disease is endemic), in early childhood, even in infancy. Schiele saw in the city of Kursk the onset of the disease from the fifth to the tenth month and I have found it here even in the fourth month. However, in places where trachoma is not endemic, it occurs from 20 to 30 years of age, and (not so frequently) up to 40 years of age.

Also in the schools we found the aforementioned rules occurring repeatedly. Apparently, one would have possibly thought that more patients with trachoma would be found in the higher grades since the children would have more opportunity to become infected. However, we found the opposite, that in all of the schools most of the illnesses were in the lower grades (ages 5–8 years) and cases of new infection at a later age were rare, at the same time that the cases of trachoma in the cicatricial stage predominated. Trachoma is thus here also the disease of childhood, something that was also previously shown by Auerbach, Teëni-Feigenbaum, and Krinkin; and this conclusion comes to teach us when and where we must wage the war.

The general statistical results of the examinations in all the schools (according to the comparisons that have already been made and confirmed by others) permit us to consider the local extent of the infection. But as our examinations were performed only in Jewish schools, we are able to only draw conclusions from them in regard to the Jewish population. Among 4,313 schoolchildren that I examined, I found 1,206 cases of trachoma, that is, 27.96%.

This investigation allows us to conclude that about 30% of the local Jewish population is afflicted with trachoma. It is estimated that 80% of the Arab people are afflicted.

If we separate the Jewish patients that were treated by me in my hospital we then find among 4,000 examined only 23%. One may explain this surprising result by the fact that most of the visitors to the hospital are Ashkenazi Jews, and furthermore since acute conjunctivitis that is a severe, painful inflammation, brings the patients to the doctor more quickly than chronic, painless trachoma.

Treatment in the schools is accomplished with the usual caustics (Caustica). We are very satisfied with rubbing with Sublimate (Keining) 1:1000 or 1:2000 and also from the massage of ointment with the help of glass rods, simple [bare] or bound with cotton wool. Understandably, in suitable cases this treatment must be completed [supplemented] by a surgical procedure that will sometimes be capable of accomplishing much more in the course of a few minutes than months of conservative treatment. For most children, I am satisfied with Knapp's expression [of granules], and sometimes I use partial surgical excision of the conjunctival fold. To eliminate sensation for small children, I use anesthesia by means of ether, with older children with dry cocaine and drops of adrenaline (and I have never seen signs of toxicity) and only infrequently with injections of cocaine. Dry cocaine and rubbing with Sublimate is also nice for mass treatment that sometimes makes surgical intervention unnecessary. Also the old method of expressing soft granules with fingernails (Cuignet) has an added place among children that are afraid of the sight of surgical instruments.

It is very important that the healed patients also remain under observation and treatment for a known period of time. In addition to this, there must be a complete series of reforms in the areas of home and school hygiene. The requirements that we present to the schools are: We require spacious, airy, dust-free school rooms, frequent cleaning of the benches, training of the children in cleanliness, especially concerning frequent hand washing, forbidding of rubbing the eyes with the hands, forbidding of mutual contact of sick and well children, schoolbooks that belong to every child individually, segregated seating (and especially of the sick children towards the front, that facilitates their supervision), postings on the blackboard about trachoma in the school rooms, and distribution of sheets of paper with rules of hygienic behavior.

In the Talmud Torah schools of the Persians, the Aleppians, and the Yemenites the children sit on unpaved ground, two to three children learning from the same book (in the case of Yemenites four) – they need hygienic books, school benches and rooms, something that was already done in one Yemenite Talmud Torah. In other kindergartens, it is customary to take naps on communal mats. This is harmful and requires strong prohibition. One must demand with all force, that the treatment must be continued as before during the months of vacation under the supervision of the teachers in the schoolrooms. This is correct and beneficial not only for the illness itself that intensifies so frequently in the months of vacation, but also for keeping the children clean during this time.

A trachoma-free kindergarten was founded on my ideas, but did not last long. We must stand by our opinion that schools or at least classes such as these be established, in order to be able to better carry out the prophylactic measures. Still better though would be to establish a special kindergarten, enrolling into it all the sick children found in all five of the kindergartens of Jerusalem. If one adds together the sick children from all the kindergartens of Jerusalem, the total is about 160 children, a suitable number of children for a single kindergarten. In this manner the other kindergartens will remain free from trachoma, and in the new kindergarten the children can be under personal supervision and treatment almost as in the clinic. Understandably, this kindergarten must be established in some central location that will be suitable to the needs of the people throughout the entire city.

Although we believe that it is impossible to disregard the feelings of the parents and children, we think that in known cases of trachoma one must sometimes take the child out of school, especially in cases of purulent secretion or in the case of opposition to surgical treatment. This shows the public that the significance of trachoma in the schools [should be] appreciated.

Here in the schools the obligation is to direct the treatment of trachoma and to educate the community about it with as much energy as possible. This is because the beginning [granular stages] of the disease is likely to be easily healed, especially in children, something that is not so at a later age when the treatment is [only] concluded after some years and not without severe damage to the eye. Here the profound interest and enthusiastic participation of the teachers is imperative in order that our effort will be fruitful and because of this a major principle in our work is to enlighten and instruct the teachers, parents, and children about the significance, danger, prevention, and curability of trachoma. It would also be desirable that the teachers take trachoma courses, as were conducted in Prussia in 1898.

There is no doubt that the treatment of trachoma can disrupt learning in no small measure; yet it is possible to try to set times [of treatment so that] the learning will suffer minimally or not at all.

It is important to know and judge the degree of improvement of each and every case; and here it is worthwhile to use the form that Teëni-Feigenbaum suggested, and that I have adopted and used very effectively since the month of August. In a chronic disease such as trachoma, there is a true need such a schematic record because often after a treatment of a number of months, one must be content with the transition of the disease from a severe stage to a more mild stage. Thus one can see great progress in this work, that in 8 cases of pannus (two of which were chronic) we brought the cornea into a state of remission, and we now have only one case of pannus, in the new student that we mentioned above.

In Table 2, I have recorded the cases that were cured in some of the schools. For example, we found the degrees of improvement in the children of the Talmud Torah for Sephardim during the time from August to December 1913. Of 74 sick patients, 17 were completely cured, i.e., 22.9%. Against this 24 new cases of disease from among the new children that were accepted into the school and the percentage of sick students in the school decreased by only 3.4 %.

Table 2

Name of the School	Number of Patients	Interval of Treatment	Cases Treated for Trachoma				Percentage
			Mild	Intermediate	Papillary	Total	
Talmud Torah for Sephardim	74	August–December	6	3	8	17	27.7%
Ezra School for Girls	75	August–November	2	1	5	8	10
Lämel School	72	August–November	3	–	10	13	18.05
Ezra Kindergarten Number 1	22	August–January	5	1	–	6	27
Ezra Kindergarten Number 3	28	August–January	6	3	–	9	32
Alliance School Kindergarten	30	August–January	8	2	2	12	40
Ḥeder-Torah	24	August–January	2	–	–	2	8.35
Beit Ḥinuch Yeladim	24	August–January	2	2	–	4	16
Alliance School for Girls	76	August–January	5	2	4	11	14.3
Alliance School for Boys	76	August–January	2	4	2	8	7.8
School for Needlework	22	August–January	2	–	7	9	40

It would appear that the percentage of patients that were completely cured during the short time of four months (in some schools we found up to 40%) was rather high, but it is possible to remark that a portion of the cures came from among the milder cases. And because the number of sick patients in individual schools is small, even a small number of cures increased the percentage in great measure.

The healed cases remain under our observation. Next I will try to summarize and clarify the isolated cases of new infection in the schools, which is important by itself.

Before we began the treatment in the schools, I seldom saw children affected by trachoma in my outpatient clinic. Only during the time of the Koch-Weeks epidemic were they brought to the physician, and then only at a late time – most accordingly [at that time] with severe eye changes. Just our visits to the schools was sufficient to bring new life among the masses; people started to come, requesting to be examined without complaining, but only since the children worried them. It sometimes seemed to us that the famous Middle Eastern indolence appeared in danger of extinction. Moreover, I came to recognize that these people did not lack the will, the time, or the effort in order to be healed, if only they were made to understand the nature of the disease.

And thus mass treatment of trachoma in a specified area will be found to be suitable among the local Jewish population, something that is also true from the viewpoint of the school; since the treatment will have lasting value only when the home and the family cease being a source of the infection.

Discussion:

Dr. Krinkin:

It was described by me that the lecturer would bring us a viewpoint by way of the ways of the war against trachoma in the schools, but his lecture is mainly only a proclamation on the matter of his work. Above all in this present matter we must clarify these two questions:

1) On the matter of accepting the children into the school. Do we have the right not to accept those affected with trachoma in general? Only in isolated schools are we able to impose upon them such a measure, but it is impossible to implement it in all of the schools without exception, because by doing this you will delay the development of a fair portion of the children. And therefore I think that it is impossible to dismiss even one child from the responsibility of the school. And in spite of this, these are the ill that have purulent discharge (not only cases of trachoma but also the rest of the acute inflammations) we must abandon the school for some time, until the discharge ends.

2) On the matter of treatment of the [more] distant children. Who will treat them? In one place I already suggested to establish the goal of a common, central clinic for all schools.

Dr. Segal:

Four years ago I made the first beginnings of a systematic treatment of the eyes in Jerusalem at the School for [Lace] Needlework [*Beit-*

Sefer LeTaḥrim]. I proposed directing treatment and prevention of trachoma. I examined all of the girls. Since it was impossible to bring all of the patients (20%), I advised segregating the healthy and the ill children, having them work in specially designated rooms. I divided the last category into three parts: Cases with purulent discharge were kept at a distance as long as the secretion continued; the remainder of the patients were treated every day, and after they were completely cured they joined the healthy [students]; the new ones worked separately.

At the Jerusalem Gymnasium – I am the school physician here – those ill with trachoma are not accepted as a rule, but in the Gymnasium of the students in general are children from streets where trachoma is not widespread.

In any event, one must clarify and establish fixed rules on the matter of accepting and expelling the students.

Dr. Waitz:
We must distinguish between high schools and elementary schools. The latter understandably are not able to reject anyone. The child that is removed from the school will go to the Talmud Torah or to his family and will bring with him the disease. It is better that the sick child, that goes out like most from the poor streets, will remain in the school under the supervision of the teacher and the doctor.

Dr. Teëni-Feigenbaum:
We cannot forget that the war against trachoma in the schools does not only a have a goal for itself, but also one of the points that finds importance for the war in the general community. As is known, trachoma is a social-cultural phenomenon. The principle source for the spread of the infection is found in the family and not in the school. And therefore, every school in which systematic treatment of eye diseases is conducted, does not have any basis not to accept trachoma affected except for cases complicated by acute infection. Precisely here in the school, the possibility is allowed for the young generation to become educated in matters of eye cleanliness and hygiene.

Mrs. Dr. Waitz:

The lecturer compared the percentages of ill patients to the examined. I would like to clarify if in every school all of the students were examined or only a small number of them?

Dr. Ticho (conclusion):

The examination of the students in the schools was as all-inclusive as possible.

Indeed my lecture described principally only my own work, but I think that in this I have brought an example of how to organize the war in the schools in general.

FIRST TRACHOMA CONFERENCE OF HEBREW PHYSICIANS IN ERETZ YISRAEL, JERUSALEM, 1914[*]

First and Second Sessions held at the Jewish Health Bureau, March 31, 1914: The etiology and spread of trachoma.

Opening		Z. Brünn
I.	The diagnostic investigation of trachoma.	L. Goldberg
II.	Conjunctival microbes – the particularly common forms in Eretz Yisrael.	A. Teëni-Feigenbaum
III.	Statistical survey of trachoma and other infectious diseases of the eye in the country.	A. Teëni-Feigenbaum
IV.	Trachoma in Eretz Yisrael based on private practice.	D. M. Krinkin
	Microscopic demonstrations of Lectures I and II	L. Goldberg and A. Teëni-Feigenbaum
V.	Flies that principally cause the spread of trachoma.	Y. David
VI.	The relationship between the nose and infectious diseases of the eyes.	A. Shimoni-Mäkler
VII.	Eye diseases in the Judean settlements from 1889–1901.	A. Mazie

Third and Fourth Sessions held at the Lemaan Zion Eye Hospital, April 1, 1914: The clinical picture of trachoma.

VIII.	Proposal for unified diagnosis and statistics.	A. Teëni-Feigenbaum
IX.	The course of trachoma and its treatment.	A. Ticho
–	*Demonstration of operations on trachoma patients*	A. Ticho and A. Teëni-Feigenbaum

1) External blepharotomy

2) Expression of trachoma granules after Kuhnt-Knapp

3) Removal of the fold of conjunctival "*übergangsfalte*"

4) Snellen's operation for trichiasis

5) Transplantation of mucous membrane in cases of trichiasis

---

[*] Excerpted and translated from the Hebrew table of contents of the published proceedings (5676/1915).

Fifth and Sixth Sessions held at the Jewish Health Bureau, April 2, 1914:
The war against and prevention of trachoma.

X.	The arrangement of the war against trachoma.	Z. Brünn
XI.	Treatment of trachoma in the schools of Jerusalem.	A. Ticho
XII.	The war against trachoma with the help of medical assistants and low-level medical aides.	H. Yaffe
XIII.	The systematic prophylaxis against trachoma and infectious inflammations of the eye in general.	Y. David

Proposals and Decisions

Conclusion

APPENDIX 6

LEMAAN ZION STATISTICS, AUGUST–DECEMBER 1916 FROM *HA-ḤERUT* *

Month	Out-Patient Visits	Inpatients	Patient-Treatment Days	Major Surgeries	Minor Surgeries	Jewish / Muslim / Christian	Home City of the Inpatients
August	25,521	34	402	44	64	19 / 9 / 6	Jerusalem 15 Jaffa 6 Damascus 2 Petah Tikvah 2 Elsewhere 8
September	23,570	22	402	41	64	11 / 2 / 9	Jerusalem 9 Jaffa 3 Rehovot 3 Bethlehem 3 Elsewhere 3
October	10,776	40 (36 new)	372	77	76	28 / 9 / 3	Jerusalem 15 Jaffa 7 Tiberias 3 Safed 2 Kirk 2 Ekron 2 Rehovot 2 Elsewhere 7
November	7,250	48 (35 new)	465	76	70	31 / ? / ?	Jerusalem 17 Elsewhere 31
December	5,983	51 (34 new)	523	79	64	25 / ? / ?	Jerusalem 19 Jaffa 10 Nablus 3 Rehovot 2 Beitunia 2 Midba 2 Elsewhere 9

* **August:** *Ha-Ḥerut*, 24 September 1916, 1.
September: *Ha-Ḥerut*, 23 October 1916, 3–4.
October: *Ha-Ḥerut*, 18 December 1916, 3.
November: *Ha-Ḥerut*, 11 January 1917, 3.
December: *Ha-Ḥerut*, 30 January 1917, 3.

APPENDIX 7

DAMASCUS MEDICAL FACILITIES, OCTOBER 1918

(after Dolev, Allenby's Military Medicine, 162–63)

Hospital	City Sector	No. Patients	Personnel	British Descriptions
Qadem	South	Over 2,000 Turkish soldiers	4 Turkish officers	"Many patients in desperate state . . . no supplies"
Hamidie Barracks	Old City / Citadel	600–700 Turkish soldiers	Turkish medical personnel	"Indescribably hideous and inhuman" conditions
Baramkie Barracks	Central	900 Turkish soldiers	Syrian doctors	"The most crowded . . . horrible conditions . . ."
Markaz	Central	650 patients	"Fully staffed"	
English	Northeast ("Bab Tuma")	130 patients	3 British nurses	Turkish medical personnel had fled
French	Northeast ("Bab Tuma")	107 patients	One doctor	
German	Northeast ("Bab Tuma")	350 patients; most were Germans	One remaining German doctor	Remaining doctor was himself ill
Residential Homes	Northeast ("Bab Tuma")	400 patients	Unattended, slightly wounded soldiers	Several homes near the English, French and German Hospitals

APPENDIX 8

HEADS OF THE DEPARTMENT OF OPHTHALMOLOGY, HADASSAH HOSPITAL

	Physician Name	Dates	Hospital Name and Location
1.	Joseph Krimsky	1918–1919	Rothschild-Hadassah, Street of the Prophets
2.	Albert Ticho	1919–1922	Rothschild-Hadassah, Street of the Prophets
3.	Aryeh Feigenbaum	1922–1939	Rothschild-Hadassah, Street of the Prophets
		1939–1948	Hadassah University Hospital Mt. Scopus
		1948–1954	Hadassah Hospital (Interim Facilities)
4.	Isaac Michaelson	1954–1961	Hadassah Hospital (Interim Facilities)
		1961–1973	Hadassah Medical Center Ein Kerem
5.	Hanan Zauberman	1973–1998	Hadassah Medical Center Ein Kerem
6.	Jacob Pe'er	1998–present	Hadassah Medical Center Ein Kerem

NOTES

INTRODUCTION
1 Ben-Yehudah, *He-Ḥalom*, 71, 131–32; *Haaretz*, September 26, 2007.
2 *Ha-Or* July 1, 1912, 3.
3 Herzl, *Jewish State*, 4.
4 Marcus, *Jerusalem 1913*, 117; Halpern and Reinharz, *Zionism*, 111–12.
5 Salmon, *Beit Ticho*, 15 (English), 13 (Hebrew); Segev, *Seventh Million*, 35–36; Rosenthal, *Milon ha-Sleng*, 167.
6 Sinai, *Bi-Mlo ha-'Ayin*, 107.
7 Izhaki, "Saint John bi-Yerushalayim," 118–20, 123.
8 Erlanger et al., *Beit Abraham*, 299–300; Levy and Levy, *Rof'eha*, 265, 293, 371–72; Kroyanker, *Mitḥam Rotshild*, 90.

CHAPTER 1 – BEGINNINGS
1 Ticho, *M'dor L'dor*, 56–57.
2 Kahane, "Boskovice."
3 Ticho, *M'dor L'dor*, 161. The generations of Avraham Albert Ticho's known ancestry are:
   [I] Avraham ben David (born c. 1660);
   [II] David ben Avraham (b. circa 1680);
   [III] Avraham Ticho (circa 1710–1789), adopted the Ticho name in 1730;
   [IV] Moses Ticho (1748–1822) married Anna Hindl (1751–1853);
   [V] Jacob Ticho (b. 1789) married Fradl Pottel (?1789);
   [VI] Avraham Ticho (1813–1882) married Esther Fuchs (b. 1815);
   [VII] Ignatz Ticho (1846–1921) married Laura Esther Baer (1855–1909);
   [VIII] Avraham Albert Ticho (1883–1960).
4 Debbi, *Story of a Family*, 355.
5 Ticho, *M'dor L'dor*, 157–63.
6 Lamed and Jelinek, "Moravia," 14: 471–76.
7 Ticho, *M'dor L'dor*, 9.
8 Kahane, "Boskovice."
9 Bránský, *Boskovice Jewish Ghetto Sights*. The pamphlet cites Jaroslav Bránský, *The Fate of the Jews of Boskovice and of the former County of Boskovice* (in Czech, Prague: 1991).

10 Rothkirchen, *Jews of Bohemia and Moravia*, 10–11; Bránský, *Boskovice Jewish Ghetto Sights*; Kieval, *Languages of Community*, 25, 44–45.
11 Kieval, *Languages of Community*, 21–22.
12 Sixtová, Polakovič, and Pařík, *Boskovice Synagogue Guide*, 8. Memoirs of Max Ungar (1850–1930) are cited.
13 Lamed, "Placzek, Abraham (1799–1884)."
14 Ticho, *M'dor L'dor*, 56–57.
15 Ticho, *M'dor L'dor*, 19–20.
16 Deutsch, "Moravia."
17 Rothkirchen, *Jews of Bohemia and Moravia*, 19.
18 Debbi, *Story of a Family*, 26.
19 Ticho, *M'dor L'dor*, 27. The building that was Albert Ticho's birthplace and housed the A. J. Ticho business was torn down after World War II along with several neighboring houses. It was replaced with a building whose address is Number 31 on Boskovice's central square.

Chapter 2 – Boskovice and Brno

1   Debbi, *Story of a Family*, 24.
2   Ticho, *M'dor L'dor*, 34.
3   Ticho, *M'dor L'dor*, 42–43.
4   Ticho, *M'dor L'dor*, 28.
5   "Hermann Ungar," accessed December 17, 2009, http://www.twistedspoon.com/ungar.html.
6   Ticho, *M'dor L'dor*, 26.
7   Kieval, *Languages of Community*, 67–68.
8   Kieval, *Languages of Community*, 142.
9   Ticho, *M'dor L'dor*, 28.
10 Ticho, *M'dor L'dor*, 84.
11 Boureau, *Kantorowicz*, 51–52.
12 Debbi, *Story of a Family*, 67, 79.
13 Weiglová, "Jews as a Barometer," 104.
14 Schorske, *Fin-de-siècle Vienna*, 54.
15 Kieval, *Languages of Community*, 144.
16 Charles Ticho, personal communication, January 14, 2014.
17 Ticho, *M'dor L'dor*, 25–26.
18 Wein, "Zionism," 123.
19 Rothkirchen, *Jews of Bohemia and Moravia*, 21.
20 Herzl, "First Congress address delivered at Basel, August 29, 1897," in *The Zionist Idea,* edited by Hertzberg, 227.
21 Baedeker, *Austria-Hungary*, 261.
22 Munk, *A Memoir*, in Ticho, *M'dor L'dor*, 49.
23 Deutschkreuz was among seven Jewish communities in Deutsch-Westungarn (German Western Hungary or the "Burgenland").
24 Debbi, *Story of a Family*, 25.
25 Sixtová, Polakovič and Pařík, *Boskovice Synagogue Guide*, 8.
26 Ticho, *M'dor L'dor*, 84.

27 Debbi, *Story of a Family*, 70.
28 Sachar, *History of Israel*, 38–41.
29 Kieval, *Languages of Community*, 166–67.
30 Frankl, "The background of the Hilsner case," 34–35, 97.

CHAPTER 3 – VIENNA

1 Beller, *Vienna and the Jews*, 43–44, 168.
2 Debbi, *Story of a Family*, 67, 79, 139.
3 Maderthaner and Musner, *Unruly Masses*, 42–44; Chandler, *Four Thousand Years,* 492.
4 Schorske, *Fin-de-siècle Vienna*, 39–40.
5 Bitsori and Galanakis, "Doctors versus artists: Gustav Klimt's *Medicine*," 1506.
6 Decker, *Freud, Dora and Vienna 1900*, 24; AUW Microfilm 1590/343, 266–67.
7 AUW Microfilms 1577/302, 289–90; 1578/304, 422–23.
8 Stedman's *Medical Dictionary*, 548, 1729, 1750; Norman, *Morton's Medical Bibliography*, 158, 224; Berkley, *Vienna and Its Jews*, 81n; AUW Microfilms 1577/302, 289–90; 1578/304, 422–23; 1580/308, 263–64; 1583/316, 246–48.
9 Norman, *Morton's Medical Bibliography*, 151, 767–68; Universität Wien, *Öffentliche Vorlesungen ... Sommer-Semester 1907, 15*; AUW Microfilm 1590/343, 266–67; Landsteiner, "On agglutination phenomena," 27–31.
10 Universität Wien, *Öffentliche Vorlesungen ... Sommer-Semester 1904*, 12; AUW Microfilm 1581/311, 288–89.
11 AUW Microfilms 1580/308, 263–64; 1581/311, 288–89; 1583/316, 246–48; 1584/321, 166–67.
12 Beller, *Vienna and the Jews*, 52–55; Beller, *Rethinking Vienna 1900*, 14.
13 Ticho, *M'dor L'dor*, 98.
14 Universität Wien, *Öffentliche Vorlesungen . . . Sommer-Semester 1905, 15*; Hughes, "Venous obstruction," 89–127.
15 Ticho, *M'dor L'dor*, 86; Debbi, *Story of a Family*, 68, 112.
16 Beller, *Vienna and the Jews*, 33–37.
17 Berkley, *Vienna and Its Jews*, 107.
18 Schorske, *Fin-de-siècle Vienna*, 203; Herbermann, *Catholic Encyclopedia* ["University of Vienna"], 15:421–433.
19 Ticho and Ticho, "Freud and the Viennese," 301–306.
20 Beller, *Rethinking Vienna 1900*, 1; Mendes-Flohr, "Berlin Jew," 15; Schorske, *Fin-de-siècle Vienna*, 304.
21 Herzl, *Diaries*, 408, 440, 483.
22 Herzl, *Old-New Land ("Altneuland")*, 4; Zweig, *World of Yesterday*, 107; Herzl, *Diaries*, 408, 440, 483; Elon, *Herzl*, 404.
23 Schorske, *Fin-de-siècle Vienna*, 119; Herzl, *Diaries*, 69.
24 Grunwald, *Vienna*, 518.
25 Norman, *Morton's Medical Bibliography*, 915; Albert and Henkind, *Men of Vision*, 114–30; Hirschberg, *History of Ophthalmology*, 5:59–67.
26 Koller, "Vorläufige," 60–63. English translations appeared that year in Chicago and London.
27 Hruby, "Was Dr. Carl Koller driven from Vienna in 1885?" 155–56.

28 Hirschberg, *History of Ophthalmology*, 11(1-c):540–44; Jokl, "Ferdinand von Arlt and Ernst Fuchs," 702–6; *Stedman's Medical Dictionary*, 622; Lesky, *Vienna Medical School*, 193, 446.

29 Fuchs, *Text-Book of Ophthalmology*, 70; Hirschberg, *History of Ophthalmology*, 11(1-c):556.

30 Hirschberg, *History of Ophthalmology*, 11(1-c):511–14.

31 Hirschberg, *History of Ophthalmology*, 11(1-c):511–14.

CHAPTER 4 – PRAGUE AND BACK TO VIENNA

1   Baedeker, *Austria-Hungary*, 219–20.

2   Fölsing, *Albert Einstein*, 280, 774n.

3   Baedeker, *Austria-Hungary*, 219; Tramer, "Prague," 305–6.

4   Universität Wien, *Öffentliche Vorlesungen...Sommer-Semester 1903*, 50.

5   Kieval, *Languages of Community*, 155–58.

6   Albert and Edwards, *History*, 182–85; Fried, "Charles University," 70–72; Pojar, "Masaryk's relations," 161.

7   Baedeker, *Austria-Hungary*, 221; Herbermann, *Catholic Encyclopedia*, 12:342–44.

8   *Katalogy posluchačů* (*Kataloge der Studierenden*), Filozoficka fakulta Nemecke univerzity v Praze – Wintersemester 1905–1906, Sommersemester 1906, AUK; *Ordnung der Vorlesungen an der k. k. deutschen Karl Ferdinands-Universität zu Prag im Wintersemester 1905/6.*

9   Hirschberg, *History of Ophthalmology*, 11(1-c):447–48; Albert and Edwards, *History*, 182–85.

10 Hruby, "German University Eye Clinic," 307; Hirschberg, *History of Ophthalmology*, 11(1-c):430, 448; *Journal of the American Medical Association*, 82 (1925): 1377.

11 Rothkirchen, *Jews of Bohemia and Moravia*, 21.

12 Wilson, preface, x; Batuman, "Kafka's Last Trial," 10.

13 Sohn, "Gustav Mahler," *Encyclopædia Britannica*, 15th ed., s.v. "Janáček, Leoš."

14 Kestenberg-Gladstein, "The Jews between Czechs and Germans," vol. 1, 42.

15 Herzl, *Diaries*, 322.

16 Ticho, *M'dor L'dor*, 35–36.

17 Hirschberg, *History of Ophthalmology*, 11(1-c):451; Elschnig, *Funktions-Prüfung des Auges*; Gorin, *History of Ophthalmology*, 264–65.

18 Snyder, "Alois Glogar, Karl Brauer and Eduard Konrad Zirm," 871; Fanta. "Eduard Zirm," 64; Fuchs, "Über Keratoplastick," 843–45.

19 Zirm, "Eine erfolgreiche totale Keratoplastik," 580–93; Hirschberg, *History of Ophthalmology*, 11(1-c):570; Albert and Edwards, *History*, 230.

20 Universität Wien, Öffentliche Vorlesungen...Sommer-Semester 1907, 15; AUW Microfilm 1590/343, 266–67.

21 Hamann, *Hitler's Vienna*, 272–73. Hamann investigated many professors, physicians, and students in search of connections to Adolf Hitler and found no links whatsoever to Ticho.

22 Ticho, *M'dor L'dor*, 28–30. An examination of Laura Ticho's gravestone shows Laura Ticho's date of death was actually Sunday, Sivan 15, 5668 [June 14, 1908].

23 Hirschberg, *History of Ophthalmology*, 11(1-c):547, 556.
24 "Curriculum Vitae," 2-page handwritten draft (English) and [untitled] handwritten 4-page curriculum vitae (German), circa 1929, IMJ, Ticho Papers; "Amtszeugnis," [Official Certificate] (German), February 18, 1912, IMJ–Ticho House. This certificate recorded the inclusive dates of Ticho's yet-to-be-completed assistantship (February 1, 1910–July 1, 1912), and it may have been submitted to the Palästinensischer Hilfsverein ("Lemaan Zion") in Frankfurt am Main.
25 "Hofrat Prof. Dr. Otto Bergmeister," 1119; Bergmeister, "Zur Entwicklungsgesch," 63; Duke-Elder and Cook, *Embryology*, 109–10.
26 "Rudolf Bergmeister," AUW Senat S304 59/12. Rudolf Bergmeister's curriculum vitae included over three dozen publications. He died in Vienna at the age of 93 and was buried in the same family plot as his father in Vienna's Central Cemetery (42A/G1/8) in Simmering.
27 *Lehmann's* (1910) 1262, (1911) 1310, (1912) 1337.
28 *Lehmann's* (1910) 1262, (1911) 1310.
29 Personal communication, Michaela Laichmann [*Oberarchivrätin elektronisch gefertigt*] to Dima Schaminer, "Abraham TICHO," Wiener Stadt- und Landesarchiv [WSL] MA 8–B–MEW–1794/2011; "Amtszeugnis," [Official Certificate] (German), February 18, 1912, IMJ–Ticho House.
30 Berkley, *Vienna and Its Jews*, 107n; Castiglione, "Trieste," vol. 7, 259–60.
31 Ticho, *M'dor L'dor*, 102–3.
32 Herzl, *Old-New Land ("Altneuland")*, v–vi, 4, 8, 45–46, 109–112.

CHAPTER 5 – FRANKFURT AM MAIN

1 Isaac Unna, "Marcus Horovitz." 249–50; Orbakh, Merhavyah, and Sharabi, *'Ein Ganim*, 53–61. Lemaan Zion funded settlements near Jenin (1891–93), Ramleh, Nablus, and Gaza.
2 Michlin, *Ma'asei Rokhim*, 17, 61, 175. Rabbi A. Z. Hoisdorf's grandson, Meir Hoisdorf, graduated from Beirut University Pharmacy School in 1912. After World War I, Hoisdorf purchased the Lemaan Zion Pharmacy on St. George's Street at Dr. Ticho's Eye Hospital.
3 Kressel, "Nehemiah Anton Nobel," 15:291.
4 "Der palästinensische Hilfsverein 'Lemaan Zion'..." [recurring broadside advertisement appeal for contributions], e.g., *Die Welt: Zentralorgan der zionistischen Bewegung*, September 6, 1912, issue 36, 1113; Lustiger, *Jüdische Stiftungen*, 249. The names of the members of the palästinensischer Hilfsverein Executive Committee in 1912 are listed here.
5 Kubinszky, *Bahnhöfe in Österreich*, 122.
6 Hamann, *Hitler's Vienna*, 3–8.
7 *Isaiah* 62:1; *JPS Hebrew-English Tanakh*, 989.
8 Baedeker, *Rhine*, 308.
9 Setzepfandt, *Architekturführer*, 51, 54.
10 Baedeker, *Rhine*, 320.
11 Morgenstern, *From Frankfurt to Jerusalem*, 5n; Glatzer, *Franz Rosenzweig*, 88, 106–7, 228, 365.
12 Baedeker, *Rhine*, 308; Friedlander, *Leo Baeck*, 29.

13 Infobank Judengasse Frankfurt am Main, "Nehemias Anton Nobel," accessed February 9, 2010, http://www.juedischesmuseum.de/judengasse/ehtml/Z508. htm.

14 Porush, *Early Memories*, 18. Translator David Cook rendered Adelman as "Edelman."

15 Levy, *Perakim*, 145–48.

16 Feuchtwanger, *Stammbaum*, 1a–1c, 3a–3k, 5a. Levy, *Perakim*, 146, 148. Albert Feuchtwanger studied medicine at the University of Munich. His paternal uncle Benjamin Feuchtwanger was a member of the administration of Lemaan Zion.

17 Levy, *Perakim*, 68–69; Levy and Levy, *Rof'eha*, 164, 289.

18 Levy and Levy, *Rof'eha*, 308.

19 Porush, *Early Memories*, 16; *Palästina*, 1908.

20 Erlanger, *Microskopische Untersuchung*, 1906.

21 Erlanger et al., *Beit Abraham*, German section 90–97 and Hebrew section 38–54.

22 Kroyanker, *Sipur Mitḥam Rotshild*, 90; Erlanger et al., *Beit Abraham*, Hebrew section 39.

23 Ben-Arieh, *'Ir bi-Re'i Tekufa*, 2:336.

24 *Moria* August 18, 1911, 2, August 22, 1911, 2, and September 5, 1911, 2; Levy and Levy, *Rof'eha*, 335. Although listed in Trietsch's *Palestina Handbuch* in 1912, Dr. Kraus did not stay to practice in Jerusalem.

25 Sinai, *Bi-Mlo*, 90. Sinai believed that Dr. Ticho had worn a kippah full-time before the war but not after, though photographs speak otherwise.

26 *Ḥavatzelet* November 20, 1908, 3–4 [33(20):103–04].

27 Sara Yermens-Reuveni, "A.Y. Yermens," Levy and Levy, *Rof'eha*, 210. Dr. Yermens and his wife, Hannah, immigrated to Palestine in 1890 by way of Istanbul aboard the same ship that carried Dr. Moshe Wallach.

28 Michaelson, "Professor A. Feigenbaum," 267–70; Levy and Levy, *Rof'eha*, 293.

29 Bergmeister, "Bemerkungen des Abteilungsvorstandes" [Remarks in the area of position] (two-pages, handwritten in German), May 1912, display item, IMJ–Ticho House.

30 Ticho, *M'dor L'dor*, 103.

Chapter 6 – Aliyah

1 Kubinszky, *Bahnhöfe in Österreich*, 170–71; Baedeker, *Austria-Hungary*, 1, 260–65.

2 Baedeker, *Palestine and Syria*, 4th ed., 2.

3 Baedeker, *Austria-Hungary*, 173. The Südbahn reached Gloggnitz (at the southeastern border of Austria) via Baden and Wiener-Neustadt.

4 McCagg, *Habsburg Jews*, 170; Castiglione, "Trieste," 7:259–60; Alroey, "Journey," 28–64.

5 Carey, *Ghost in Trieste*, 112; Morris, *Trieste*, 54–55.

6 Baedeker, *Austria-Hungary*, 204, 207.

7 Morris, *Trieste*, 126.

8 *Ha-Or* June 20, 1912, 2.

9 *Ha-Or* June 21, 1912, 3.

10 Kalc, "Passenger lists," 22–27.

11 Baedeker, *Palestine and Syria,* 5th ed., p 2; Baedeker, *Egypt and the Sûdân,* 5; CZA, L2, file 79/2, "Hotel Carmel to Arthur Ruppin," February 9, 1912, cited by Gur Alroey, "Journey," 28–64.

12 Baedeker, *Southern Italy and Sicily,* 252–54; Baedeker, *Egypt and the Sûdân,* 11.

13 II Chronicles 2:15; Joshua 19:40–48; Ezra 3:7; Jonah 1:3; and I Maccabees 8:11.

14 Albert Ticho memoir (undated and untitled in English), IMJ–Ticho House, Ticho Papers; *Ha-Or* April 29, 1912, 2.

15 Baedeker, *Palestine and Syria,* 4th ed., 7 and 5th ed., 7.

16 Bloom, *"Arthur Ruppin,"* 14; Orni and Efrat, *Geography of Israel,* 231; Ruppin, *Pirkei Ḥayai,* 2:150.

17 Albert Ticho memoir (undated and untitled in English), IMJ–Ticho House, Ticho Papers; Alsberg, "The Israel State Archives," 533–44; Levy and Levy, *Rof'eha,* 337.

18 *Ha-Or* June 27, 1911, 3; Marcus, *Jerusalem 1913,* 89–90; Porush, *Early Memories,* 20.

19 Albert Ticho memoir (undated and untitled in English), IMJ–Ticho House, Ticho Papers; Travis, *On Chariots,* ix.

20 Travis, *On Chariots,* 106; LeBor, *City of Oranges,* 26–28; Merrill, "Jaffa and Jerusalem Railway," 289–300.

21 I Samuel 5:10 and 6:1–8; Judges 13:24 and 16:31; Kunstel and Albright, *Their Promised Land,* 44, 47; Baedeker, *Palestine and Syria,* 5th ed., 15.

22 Joshua 15:8 and 18:16; II Samuel 5:18–25; Buttrick, *Interpreter's Bible,* 2:1074.

23 Travis, *On Chariots,* 100.

24 Albert Ticho memoir (undated and untitled in English), IMJ–Ticho House, Ticho Papers; Tidhar, "Mordecai Adelman (Meyuhas)," 1:150–51.

25 Izhaki, "Saint John bi-Yerushalayim," 120–21.

26 O'Shea, "St John Ophthalmic Hospital," 603–10; Lechmere, *A Paper Read.*

27 Talbot, *St. John Eye Hospital,* 5, 10, 15, 18; Marquis, *The Book of the Detroiters,* 188–89; Izhaki, "Saint John bi-Yerushalayim," 123; British Ophthalmic Hospital, *Report from 1st January, 1912 to 31st December, 1912;* "Thomas Harrison Butler," *British Journal of Ophthalmology* 29 (1945): 217–19; Plarr's Lives of the Fellows, "Butler, Thomas Harrison" and "Cant, William Edmund," accessed December 12, 2013, http://livesonline.rcseng.ac.uk/biogs/; Wood, *Encyclopedia* ["Ward, William Charles Augustus"], 18:13984.

28 Izhaki, "Saint John bi-Yerushalayim," 119; Levy, *Perakim,* 25–37.

29 British Ophthalmic Hospital, *Report from 1st January, 1912, to 31st December, 1912.*

30 Waserman and Kass, "Moses Montefiore," 324–32; Isaiah 63:12.

31 Kroyanker, *Mamila,* 55.

32 II Kings 23:10, Jeremiah 32:35, etc.

33 Bab el-Khalil (Gate of the Friend) is a reference to Hebron which takes its Arabic name from Abraham, the friend of God (*Qur'an* Surah 4 Aya: 125 and Isaiah 41:8).

34 *New York Times,* November 27, 1898, 19; Baedeker, *Palestine and Syria,* 5th ed., 33; Tamari, "City of Riffraff," 302–11; Watson, *Story of Jerusalem,* 293.

35 Kroyanker, *Rehov Yafo,* 155–59.

36 *Ha-Ḥerut*, May 17, 1912, June 1–30, 1912, 1. The doctor's first name is unknown and only the Hebrew spelling of his surname (בלום) is known.
37 Tidhar, "Avraham Yehezkel Blum," 1:476; Michlin, *Ma'asei Rokḥim*, 27–28, 33, 64–65.
38 Ashbee, *Jerusalem 1920–1922*, 26–28.
39 Kroyanker, *Reḥov ha-Nevi'im*, 63–70, 182–84; Committee of the Palestine Exhibition, *Awakening Palestine*, 4; Ticho, "*Ripuy ha-gar'enet*," 96–107.
40 Curto, "Ernesto Schiaparelli," 7; Levy, *Perakim*, 119–20.
41 Kroyanker, *Reḥov ha-Nevi'im*, 16–18. The name Meah She'arim was coined at the time the neighborhood was established wherein the residents prayed for prosperity as in Genesis 26:12.
42 Flavius Josephus, *Wars of the Jews* (book v, ch. iv, pt. 2), 553. The beginning of the third wall of Agrippa was at the Hippicus Tower and reached as far as the north quarter of the city and the tower Psephinus. It extended to the monuments of Helena Queen of Adiabene (Heleni ha-Malka) and to the old wall at the Kidron Valley.
43 Erlanger et al., *Beit Abraham*, German section 90–97 and Hebrew section 38–54; Albert Ticho memoir (undated and untitled in English), IMJ–Ticho House, Ticho Papers. Confirmation of the location was made through site visits with Irene Pollak-Rein and Prof. Yehoshua Ben-Arieh.
44 Bard and Schwartz, *1001 Facts*, 5–6.

Chapter 7 – Jerusalem

1 Shanks, *Jerusalem*, 1–9. Joshua 3:5, II Samuel 5:6–25, etc.
2 Genesis 22:1–24; Luke 23:1–24:53; *Qur'an* 37:99–109; Smart and Hecht, *Sacred Texts*, 95–97, 166–170; Cline, *Jerusalem Besieged*, 2; Shanks, *Jerusalem*, x–xiii. Jesus (in Luke 23–24).
3 Gilbert, *Jerusalem: Illustrated History Atlas*, 7.
4 Shanks, *Jerusalem*, 233–40.
5 Mazza, *Jerusalem*, 21–22; Somel, *Historical Dictionary*, 225; Klein, *Etymological Dictionary*, 501–2; Nehemiah 5:14; Ezekiel 8:36. "*Peḥa*" is an ancient loan word from Akkadian.
6 *Ha-Or*, June 24, 1912, 3; Mandel, *Arabs and Zionism*, 23–24, 61, 73, 104, 117, 143.
7 Marcus, *Jerusalem 1913*, 78; Watson, *Story of Jerusalem*, 281; Kunstel and Albright, *Their Promised Land*, 36–44.
8 Levy, *Perakim*, 61, 76, 82, 90; Baedeker, *Palestine and Syria*, 5th ed., 20.
9 Michlin, *Ma'asei Rokḥim*, 17–18.
10 Levin, *It Takes a Dream*, 35; Porush, *Early Memories*, 15; *Ḥavatzelet* June 4, 1909, 2–3.
11 Levy and Levy, *Rof'eha*, 210. The German spelling of the last name is sometimes rendered as Jermens or Jermans.
12 Tidhar, "Rabbi Zadok Creuz," 11:3776; Michlin, *Ma'asei Rokḥim*, 50–51; Porush, *Early Memories*, 17.

13 *British Ophthalmic Hospital, Jerusalem – Report from 1st January, 1912, to 31st December, 1912.*

14 *Ha-Or* September 19, 1912, 3.

15 Feigenbaum, *Ophthalmology in Palestine*, 17; Debbi, *Story of a Family*, 142.

16 *Ha-Or* July 1, 1912, 3.

17 *Ha-Ḥerut* July 16, 1912, 3, and July 18, 1912, 1.

18 Lewis, *Modern Turkey*, 207–9, 217.

19 Kroyanker, *Reḥov ha-Nevi'im*, 73.

20 Ruppin, *Pirkei Ḥayai*, 2:205–15.

21 *Ha-Or* October 17, 1912, 1–2.

22 Tidhar, "Dr. Ze'ev (Wilhelm) Brünn," 1:390–91; "Dr. Ze'ev Brünn (Agadat-Deshe ba'Aḥuza: Reka' Histori)" (Hebrew), http://www.agadat-deshe.co.il/. Accessed October 25, 2012.

23 Ticho, *M'dor L'dor*, 103.

24 Sonnenfeld, *Ha-Ish 'al ha-Ḥoma*, 1:126–133.

25 Kroyanker, *Rehov Yafo*, 26–27; *Ha-Or* January 31, 1913, 1.

26 Salmon, *Ticho House*, figure between 57 (Hebrew section) and 24 (English section).

27 *Ha-Or* November 7, 1912, 3.

28 Levy and Levy, *Rof'eha*, 371–72.

29 *Ha-Or* November 21, 1912, 1; Golz, *Otorhinolaryngology*, 41.

30 *Ha-Or* November 18, 1912, 3; Baedeker, *Palestine and Syria*, 5th ed., 23, plus map.

31 Ben-Arieh, *'Ir bi-Re'i Tekufa*, 2:336. Ben-Arieh placed a subsequent location of the Jewish Health Bureau opposite the Old City walls near the New Gate.

32 Reinharz, "Laying the foundation," 1; Adler, "Debunking the story."

33 *Ha-Or* October 7, 1912, 1; Levy and Levy, *Rof'eha*, 110–11; Levy, *Perakim*, 163–65.

34 *Ha-Tsefira* November 2, 1913, 3; Levy and Levy, *Rof'eha*, 122, 265, 293. *Ha-Tsefira* cited an annual tabulation of patient volumes at Lemaan Zion through July 1913: 420 inpatients and 9,959 outpatients amounting to a total of 67,239 outpatient visits.

35 *Ha-Ḥerut* November 13, 1912, 3.

36 *Ha-Or* November 19, 1912, 3.

37 Joshua 15:7 and 18:17; Baedeker, *Palestine and Syria*, 5th ed., 125, 128, 131; Richardson, *Herod*, 18, 180, 199.

38 Salmon, *Ticho House*, (English section) 18.

39 Sinai, *Bi-Mlo*, 106.

40 Dr. Sayah Ticho, personal interview, July 4, 2008.

41 Sinai, *Bi-Mlo*, 105–6.

42 Heron, quoted in *British Ophthalmic Hospital…1912.*

43 Genesis 48:16; Debbi, *Story of a Family*, 94.

44 *Ha-Ḥerut* January 14, 1913, 3.

CHAPTER 8 – SCHOOLCHILDREN AND VISITING NURSES

1 *Ha-Or* January 15, 1913, 3, and January 23, 1913, 1; Avissar, *House in Jerusalem*, 119–21; Cohen, *Tarpat*, 276. Herzl's tree was cut down by vandals during WWI in August 1915.

2 *Ha-Or* January 23, 1913, 2–3.

3 Sanders, *High Walls of Jerusalem*, 47.

4 Halberstaedter and von Prowazek, "Über Zelleinschlüsse," 44–47. Halberstaedter was a pioneer in trachoma and later in radiotherapy. He emigrated from Berlin to Jerusalem in 1933.

5 Paul Tower, "History of trachoma," 123–30; Goldberg, "Diagnostic investigation of trachoma," 9; Bendz, "Quelques considérations," 164–76; Levy and Levy, *Rof'eha*, 247–48.

6 *New York Times* January 19, 1913.

7 Dash, *Summoned*, 89; Moore, "Hadassah in the United States," 2; Levin, *It Takes a Dream*, 38; Buhler-Wilkerson, "Lillian Wald's legacy," 1778–86.

8 *New York Times* January 19, 1913; Adler, "Debunking 'The Story.'"

9 "Nurses for Palestine," *The Maccabæan*, 23 (1913): 35.

10 *Ha-Or* February 12, 1913, 3.

11 Brownstone, "Rose S. Kaplan (1867–1917)," HA RG35–3/1; "Guide to the Papers of Lt.-Col. Rachel (Rae) Landy (1884–1952)," Center for Jewish History, P-785.

12 Szold, "Recent Jewish Progress," 107.

13 Shehory-Rubin and Shvarts, "*Hadasa,*" 63; Bartal, *Ḥemla ve-Yed'a*, 359–61, 375–78; "Eva Leon visits clinic as doctor examines a child's eye, 1913" [Photograph by Ya'akov Ben-Dov (1882–1968)], HA 18/4/2.

14 *Ha-Or* March 7, 1913, 3, and April 4, 1913, 3; Dash, *Summoned*, 109; Luncz, *Almanac of Eretz Yisrael*, 65.

15 Ticho, "Ripuy ha-gar'enet," 96–107.

16 Teëni-Feigenbaum, "Sekira statistit," 24–36.

17 Ben-Arieh, *'Ir bi-Re'i Tekufa*, 1:410–11.

18 Rokach, *Vatikim Mesaprim*, 44.

19 Tidhar, "Rabbi Ze'ev Wolf Shaḥor," 3:1462–63.

20 *Ha-Or* January 2, 1913, 1.

21 Ticho, "Ripuy ha-gar'enet," 96–107.

22 Teëni-Feigenbaum. "Sekira statistit," 78–82.

23 Ticho, "Ripuy ha-gar'enet" 96–107.

24 Wood, *Encyclopedia* ["Mercury bichloride"], 10:7651–52.

25 Wood, *Encyclopedia* ["Lenicet"], 10:7191.

26 Ticho, "Ripuy ha-gar'enet" 96–107.

27 Kaplan, "Letters from missionary nurses II," 870–72.

28 Ticho, "Uber Trachombehandlung," 368–73. Wood, *Encyclopedia* ["Trachoma"], 17:12891. Friedenwald, "Ophthalmias of Palestine," 264–302.

29 Taylor, *Trachoma*, 97, 135.

30 *Ha-Or* March 5, 1913, 2.

31 *Ha-Or* February 12, 1913, 3; Levy and Levy, *Rof'eha*, 93; Levy, *Perakim*, 150–

51, 159–62.

32 *Ha-Or* March 24, 1913, 2; Levy, *Perakim*, 144–45, 157–58.

33 Hall, *Consumed by Conflict*, 14; Alroey, "Meshartei ha-moshava," 77–104; Mandel, *The Arabs and Zionism*, 165–207; Gorny, *Zionism and the Arabs*, 24–25.

34 Levy and Levy, *Rof'eha,* 245; Tidhar, "Nissim Ya'akov Malul," 2:696–97; Kuzar, *Hebrew and Zionism*, 1.

35 Schwarzfuchs and Malino, "Alliance Israelite Universelle," 1:671–75; Duparc, "Anglo-Jewish Association," 1:601–2; Falk, "Hilfsverein der Deutschen Juden," 1:106–7.

36 Sanders, *High Walls*, 55–56.

37 Weizmann to Magnes, December 3, 1913, in Weisgal and Litvinoff, *Letters and Papers*, 6:175; Rinott, "Capitulations," 297; Gilbert, *Jerusalem in the Twentieth Century*, 32–33.

38 Mendes-Flohr and Reinharz, *Jew in the Modern World*, 567–68. Dori, "Technion," 1:571–72.

39 Shilo, "Milḥemet ha-safot," 86–119; Tidhar, "Prof. Eleazar Lipa Sukenik," 6:2670.

40 *Ha-Or* April 17, 1912, 1–2 (and subsequent issues).

41 *Ha-Ḥerut* November 17, 1913, 1–3 and November 18, 1913, 1–2.

42 Gilbert, *Jerusalem in the Twentieth Century*, 32–33; Mendes-Flohr and Reinharz, 1980, 567–68.

43 Ruppin, *Pirkei Ḥayai*, 2:129–34; Szold, "Recent Jewish Progress," 127–28.

44 Ticho, "Uber Trachombehandlung," 368–73.

CHAPTER 9 – THE EVE OF WAR

1 Baedeker, *Palestine and Syria*, 5th ed., 19, 33.

2 Ticho, *M'dor L'dor*, 83, 86, 91, 96, 98, 111.

3 *Ha-Or* October 2, 1914, 2; Gilbert, *Jerusalem in the Twentieth Century*, 9–10; Baedeker, Palestine and Syria, 5th ed., 19.

4 *Moria* January 28, 1914, 2, February 10, 1914, 1, and June 17, 1914, 2.

5 Debbi, *Story of a Family*, 81; Levin, *Vision*, 204–5.

6 Navot and Gross, "Ha-Milḥama," 89–114, 187–88; Levy, *Perakim*, 144–45. Levy and Levy, *Rofe'ha*, 70; *Du'aḥ*, v , 1.

7 *Ha-Or* November 18, 1912, 3; Ben-Arieh, *'Ir bi-Re'i Tekufa*, 2:336; Kroyanker, *Reḥov ha-Nevi'im*, 117, 203, 225, 254; Levin, *Vision*, 206; Levy, *Perakim*, 159–62; Baedeker, *Palestine and Syria*, 23 and map. The building that housed the Straus Health Bureau (built before 1893) had previously housed the British Consulate for twenty years.

8 Schechtman, *Vladimir Jabotinsky*, 1:185–94.

9 Nahum Sheinkin [Shimkin] to Menachem Ussishkin, November 12, 1913 cited by Katz, "Ha-Mifne be-yaḥasam," 131; Lavsky, *Mashma'ut*, 336; Levy and Levy, *Rof'eha*, 372; Ruppin, *Pirkei Ḥayai*, 2:164–66; Tidhar, "Yitzhak Shimkin," 6:2449.

10 Kaplan, "Letters from Missionary Nurses II," 870–72.

11 Shilo, *"Shi'ur be-Tsiyonut,"* 84–110; Tidhar, "Yitzhak Leib Goldberg," 1:483–84; Ruppin, *Pirkei Ḥayai*, 2:164–66; Gilbert, *Israel: A History*, 29.

12 Gottheil, "Temple vessels?" 307–9.

13 Manor, "Biblical Zionism," 55.

14 "Daniel M. Friedenberg Collection," 144.

15 Mandel, *Arabs and Zionism*, 183. *Ha-Ḥerut* March 30, 1914, 1.

16 Tessler, *Israeli-Palestinian Conflict*, 132; Mandel, *Arabs and Zionism*, 183; Pappe, "The Husayni family," 52–67.

17 *Ha-Ḥerut* January 11, 1914, 3; *New York Times* January 28, 1914, 3.

18 *Du'aḥ*, 123; Levy and Levy, *Rof'eha*, 58–59, 172, 207–08, 213.

19 *Du'aḥ*, 1, 122; Levy and Levy, *Rof'eha*, 122, 247, 288.

20 *Du'aḥ*, 75, 112.

21 Kroyanker, *Reḥov ha-Nevi'im*, 16–18; Mazza, *Jerusalem*, 29.

22 *Ha-Ḥerut* November 1, 1912, 3; Kark, *American Consuls*, 175–76, 186–87, 332–34; *New York Times* September 30, 1914. Consul General William Coffin departed Palestine in May 1912, just weeks before Ticho's arrival in Jerusalem. His successor, Otis Glazebrook, moved the American consulate to more spacious accommodations in Mamilla in April 1913.

23 Elon, *Herzl*, 294–96.

24 Kroyanker, *Reḥov ha-Nevi'im*, 117, 154–57; Levy, *Perakim*, 56–63; Kroyanker, *Sipur Mitham Rotshild*, 98; Levy and Levy, *Rof'eha*, 270.

25 *Ha-Or* October 22, 1912, 1, October 23, 1912, 3, and September 17, 1914, 3; Navot and Gross, "Ha-Milḥama," 89–114, 187–88; Ruppin, *Pirkei Ḥayai*, 2:210, 214–15.

26 *Du'aḥ*, 119.

27 Ze'ev Brünn, "Organization of the war," 84–95; Gorin, *History of Ophthalmology*, 274; Taylor, *Trachoma*, 39–42.

28 Ze'ev Brünn, "Organization of the war," 93.

29 Levy and Levy, *Rof'eha*, 172.

30 *Du'aḥ*, 121.

31 Navot and Gross, "Ha-Milḥama," 97; Tidhar, "Yerahmiel Amdursky," 1:131–32, 136–37; Baedeker, *Syria and Palestine*, 5th ed., 19; Gilbert, *Jerusalem in the Twentieth Century*, 11.

32 *Du'aḥ*, 122, 124; Levy and Levy, *Rof'eha*, 59, 129. Absent from the photo were Drs. Abushadid, David, Wallach and Gildenson. Among the participants, the most obscure is Dr. Gildenson, who briefly practiced ophthalmology in Jaffa between 1913 and 1914.

33 *Ha-Ḥerut* April 2, 1914, 3; Ruppin, *Pirkei Ḥayai*, 2:228–29; Alfassi, *Liskat "Yerushalayim,"* 148.

34 Fineman, *Woman of Valor*, 270; Jacobson, "Jerusalem during World War I," 73–92.

35 Levin, *Vision*, 204–15; Chance, "Harry Friedenwald, MD," xxxiv–xxxviii; Schacht, "Max Meyerhof," 7–32.

36 Friedenwald, "The ophthalmias of Palestine," 264–302; Levin, *Vision*, 194; Friedenwald, *Jews and Medicine*, 2:519.

37 Gilbert, *First World War*, 16.

38 *Moriah* July 17, 1914, 3.

39 Friedenwald, "The ophthalmias of Palestine," 264–302.

40 Levin, *Vision*, 226; Spier, *Hebrew Calendar*, 3rd ed., Nisan–Elul 5674. The previous (Sabbath) day had coincided with Ninth of Av so that the fast that year was deferred to the next day.

41 *Mishnah Ta'anit* 4:6 lists five calamitous events that occurred on the Ninth of Av in ancient times.

42 Gilbert, *First World War*, 16–18, 24–25, 30–34, photo of Munich rally between pp. 72 and 73.

43 Hitler, *Mein Kampf*, 161; Hamann, *Hitler's Vienna*, 401–2.

CHAPTER 10 – MOBILIZATION

1 Levin, *Vision*, 212–15; Ben Yehudah, "When the war came to Palestine," 19–20.

2 Sheffy, *British Military Intelligence*, 34–36; *Ha-Or* August 5, 1914, 3; Gilbert, *First World War*, 34.

3 *Ha-Or* August 6, 1914, 1; Jacobson, "Jerusalem during World War I," 73–92; Hemda Ben Yehudah, "When the war came to Palestine," 19; British Ophthalmic Hospital, *Report* (1915).

4 Friedman, *Germany, Turkey and Zionism*, 194–95.

5 *Ha-Or* August 28, 1914, 3, and September 11, 1914, 4; *Moriah* November 4, 1914, 2; Tidhar, "Ha-Rav Ze'ev Wolf Shaḥor," 3:1462–63.

6 Jacobson, "A city living through crisis," 73–92; Hemda Ben Yehudah, "When the war came to Palestine," 19. Landau, "The Dönmes: Crypto-Jews under Turkish rule," 1–2.

7 *Ha-Or* September 3, 1914, 3, September 4, 1914, 2–3, and September 10, 1914, 1–2; Gilbert, *Jerusalem in the Twentieth Century*, 42.

8 Elmaleh, *Eretz-Yisrael ve-Suriya*, 2:215; CZA, A107/520, Albert and Anna Ticho in Damascus to unknown recipient in Europe, December 31, 1917; Salmon, *Beit Ticho*, 5.

9 *Ha-Or* August 31, 1914, 3, and September 13, 1914, 1.

10 Conde de Ballobar, *Diario de Jerusalen*, 63; *Ha-Or* September 14, 1914, 2.

11 Ticho, *M'dor L'dor*, 130–32; Debbi, *Story of a Family*, 294.

12 Teveth, *Ben-Gurion*, 74, 81–88, 91–94.

13 Debbi, *Story of a Family*, 291.

14 Ticho, *M'dor L'dor*, 112, 126, 130–32.

15 "Qualifikationslisten [Tiani–Tichy Kamillo]…Josef Ticho," ÖStAK Quall. Kart. 3502; Ticho, *M'dor L'dor*, 98.

16 Kupiec-Weglinski, "The siege of Przemysl," 494–509; Ticho, *M'dor L'dor*, 92.

17 *Ha-Or* September 25, 1914, 3; British Ophthalmic Hospital, *Report* (1915).

18 *Ha-Or* September 23, 1914, 3, and September 27, 1914, 3.

19 *Ha-Or* September 28, 1914, 3, and October 2, 1914, 2.

20 Ruppin, *Pirkei Ḥayai*, 2:228–30; *Ha-Or* October 2, 1914, 3, and October 14, 1914, 3.

21 Zvi Shilony, "Ha-sheirut ha-refu'it," 61–83; Elmaleh, *Eretz-Yisrael ve-Suriya*, 2:195.

22 *Ha-Or* September 29, 1914, 2, and October 2, 1914, 2; Ticho, "Uber Trachombehandlung," 368.

23   Elmaleh, *Eretz-Yisrael ve-Suriya*, 1:110; Shilony, "Ha-sheirut ha-refu'it," 61–83; Friedman, *Germany, Turkey and Zionism*, 198.

24   Friedman, *Germany, Turkey and Zionism*, 199; Hurwich, *Kol ha-'Am Ḥazit*, 22–30.

25   Lang, "Zikat golei Eretz-Yisrael," 133–54; Levy and Levy, *Rof'eha*, 122; Hurwich, *Kol ha-'Am Ḥazit*, 11–21; Avishai Goltz, *Otorhinolaryngology*, 44; Teveth, *Ben-Gurion*, 90–91.

26   Eliav, "Ha-Konsuliya ha-Ostrit," 73; Eliav and Haider, *Österreich und das Heilige Land*, 590–91; Franz Ollendorff, "Ticho House in Jerusalem rejuvenated: The history of the premises and some houses in the vicinity," 8-page typescript, IMJ–Ticho House. From the time of Kraus's predecessor until December 1917, the consulate was located in a rented home belonging to Benjamin Kukia, next to and south of the Aga Rashid mansion on nineteenth-century villa lands. Representing the new post-war state, the Austrian consulate reopened in a different location in Jerusalem in 1927. Ticho later rented part of the Kukia house for his outpatient clinic.

27   Shilony, "Ha-sheirut ha-refu'it," 61–83.

28   Elmaleh, *Eretz-Yisrael ve-Suriya*, 2:214.

29   Levy and Levy, *Rof'eha*, 211–12. Shehory-Rubin, "Dr. Helena Kagan," 89–114, 196.

30   Helena Kagan, *Voice that Called*, 43; Levy and Levy, *Rof'eha*, 133–35.

31   *Ha-Or* December 4, 1914, 1; Tamari, "Wasif Jawhariyyeh," 5–27; Elmaleh, *Eretz-Yisrael ve-Suriya*, 2:69; Jacobson, "A city living through crisis," 73–92; Zvi Shilony, "Ha-sheirut ha-refu'it," 61–83.

32   *Ha-Or* December 3, 1914, 1.

33   Kayali, "Integration," 298–99; Pick, "Meissner Paşa," 209.

CHAPTER 11 – YEAR OF THE LOCUSTS

1   Erickson, *Ordered to Die*, 69; Djemal Pasha, *Memories*, 138–39, 147, 152; Lang, "Zikat golei Eretz-Yisrael," 132–54; Friedman, *Germany, Turkey and Zionism*, 213.

2   Erickson, *Ordered to Die*, 70; Vester, *Our Jerusalem*, 235; *Ha-Or* December 20, 1914, 1–2.

3   *Ha-Or* December 23, 1914, 1; Friedman, *Germany, Turkey and Zionism*, 219; McMeekin, *Berlin-Baghdad Express*, 172–73.

4   Tamari, "Private Ihsan," 26–58; Tamari, "The Great War," 105–36.

5   *Ha-Or* December 23, 1914, 1.

6   Zaun-Goshen, *Beyond the Wall*, 273.

7   Kark, Denecke, and Goren, "German missionary enterprise," 145.

8   *Ha-Or* December 23, 1914, 1; Goodman and Goodman, "*Masu'at Yerushalayim*," 82–99; Lowenthal, *Diaries*, 173–83.

9   *Ha-Or* December 24, 1914, 1.

10   Tamari, "Private Ihsan," 26–58; Shilony, "*Ha-sheirut ha-refu'i*, 61–83.

11   Teveth, *Ben-Gurion*, 94–98; Ruppin, *Pirkei Ḥayai*, 2:232–34; Sachar, *History of Israel*, 89–90.

12   Levy and Levy, *Rof'eha*, 266; Friedman, *Germany, Turkey and Zionism*, 218.

13 Friedman, *Germany, Turkey and Zionism*, 223; Friedenwald, "The ophthalmias of Palestine," 280.

14 Mina Brownstone. "Rose S. Kaplan (1867–1917)," HA RG35–3/1; Levin, *It Takes a Dream*, 48.

15 Ticho, "Frühjahrskatarrh," 510–15; A. Ticho, "Vernal catarrh in Palestine," 257–62.

16 Erickson, *Ordered to Die,* 69; Djemal Pasha, *Memories*, 165; Teveth, *Ben-Gurion*, 94–98.

17 Porush, *Early Memories*, 50.

18 Baedeker, *Palestine and Syria*, 5th ed., 76; Zaun-Goshen, *Beyond the Wall*, 129–32, 195–215. The American Colony villa originally had been built by then-mayor Hussein Salim al-Husayni in the late 1880s. The founders of the American Colony, Anna and Horatio Spafford, had first come to Jerusalem from Chicago in 1881 and established their Christian utopian society in the Old City.

19 E. W. G. Masterman, "Mount of Olives," 4:2185–88; Tidhar, "Yitzhak Leib Goldberg," 1:483–84.

20 Zaun-Goshen, *Beyond the Wall*, 275.

21 Gilbert, *Jerusalem in the Twentieth Century*, 24–25.

22 Blyth, *When We Lived in Jerusalem*, 135.

23 Porush, *Memories*, 50; Elmaleh, *Eretz-Yisrael ve-Suriya*, 2:215–16.

24 Gilbert, *First World War*, 142–43, 150–51, 167.

25 Schechtman, *Vladimir Jabotinsky*, 1:203–7.

26 Hurwich, *Kol ha-'Am Ḥazit*, 1–2, 22–30.

27 Erickson, *Ordered to Die*, xv.

28 Tidhar, "Marek (Mordecai Ze'ev) Schwarz," 3:1244–46.

29 Jung, *Der K.U.K. Wüstenkrieg*; Hoeflich, *Tagebücher*, 258–59n. General Joseph Pomiankowski was Vice Marshal and Military Plenipotentiary, attached to the Ottoman General Headquarters from 1914 to 1918.

30 *New York Times* March 15, 1915.

31 Jacobson, "A city living through crisis," 73–92; Levin, *It Takes a Dream*, 52.

32 Joel 2:20; Smilansky, *Perakim*, 35–40; Florence, *Lawrence and Aaronsohn*, 126.

33 Whiting, "Jerusalem's locust plague," 511–50.

34 *New York Times* April 23, 1915.

35 Florence, *Lawrence and Aaronsohn*, 129; Herzog, *Heroes of Israel*, 107–18; I Samuel 15:29.

36 Martin Gilbert, *Jerusalem in the Twentieth Century*, 44.

37 Whiting, "Jerusalem's locust plague," 511–50; Ruppin, *Pirkei Ḥayai*, 2:241–48; *New York Times* November 21, 1915; Jacobson "A city living through crisis," 73–92.

38 Joel 2:7–8; Florence, *Lawrence and Aaronsohn*, 126.

39 Matthew 26:36; Mark 14:32; and John 18:1.

40 Porush, *Memories*, 35.

41 *London Times* February 5, 1915; *Ha-Ḥerut* September 20, 1915, 2.

42 *Hadassah, The Women's Zionist Organization, Central Committee Bulletin*, No. 14, October 1915.

43   Fineman, *Woman of Valor*, 271; *Hadassah Bulletin* 4 (1917) 2; "Guide to the Papers of Lt. Col. Rachel (Rae) Landy (1884–1952)," Center for Jewish History, P-785.

44   *Ha-Ḥerut* September 15, 1915, 2.

45   Fromkin, *Peace to End All Peace*, 214.

46   Hadassah, *The Women's Zionist Organization, Central Committee Bulletin*, No. 14 (October, 1915).

47   *Ha-Ḥerut* January 25, 1916, 2.

48   *Ha-Ḥerut* October 11, 1915, 2; *Ha-Ḥerut* October 22, 1915, 2; Florence, *Lawrence and Aaronsohn*, 203–5.

Chapter 12 – Brothers in Arms and in Distress

1   Segev, *One Palestine, Complete*, 21; Shilony, "Ha-shayrut ha-refu'i," 61–83.

2   Ruppin, *Pirkei Ḥayai*, 2:251–52, 256–58; Smilansky *Perakim*, 4:22–23; Djemal Pasha, *Memories*, 168; Marmorstein, "European Jews," 1–14.

3   CZA A107/520, Albert and Anna Ticho in Damascus to unknown recipient in Europe, December 31, 1917; Shilony, "Ha-Dildul," 128–29.

4   *Ha-Ḥerut* August 1, 1916, 1; Kroyanker, *Rehov Yafo*, 155–59, 177; Hurwich, *Kol ha-Am Ḥazit*, 13–16; Levy and Levy, *Rof'eha*, 93, 122, 288; Smilansky (1945), 4:23.

5   Hurwich, *Kol ha-Am Ḥazit*, 13–14, 17–18.

6   Markel, *Quarantine!*, 49; Raoult and Walker, "Rickettsia prowazekii," 2:2303–6.

7   *Ha-Ḥerut* February 15, 1916, 2.

8   Raoult and Walker, "Rickettsia prowazekii," 2:2303–6; Hurwich, *Kol ha-Am Ḥazit*, 19; *Ha-Ḥerut* April 2, 1916, 2, and April 11, 1916, 1–2.

9   Levy and Levy, *Rof'eha*, 364; *Ha-Ḥerut* May 3, 1916, 1; Greenberg, "*Beit he-Holim*," 49–64.

10   *Ha-Ḥerut* June 9, 1916, 2; Kagan, *Reishit Darki*, 57–58; Greenberg, "Beit he-holim," 49–64.

11   *Ha-Ḥerut* May 10, 1916, 2, and May 12, 1916, 2; Erickson, *Ordered to Die*, 155.

12   *Ha-Ḥerut* March 5, 1916, 2.

13   IMJ, Ticho Papers, "Curriculum Vitae" (undated, 3 extant handwritten pages in English, with last entry of his published works from 1930 [Zur Trachomfrage…]).

14   *Ha-Ḥerut* May 12, 1916, 2; Shilony, "Ha-sheirut ha-refu'i," 61–83; Conde de Ballobar, *Diario de Jerusalen*, 164.

15   *Ha-Ḥerut* May 12, 1916, 2. The names of Jewish Austro-Hungarian soldiers are cited.

16   Von Schrötter, *Hygiene*, 1912; "Qualifikationslisten [Schrott–Schrötter]... Anton Hermann Victor Thomas Schrötter von Kristelli," ÖStAK Quall. Kart. 3074; Von Schrötter, "Schnitt der Soldatenhose," 499.

17   Erickson, *Ordered to Die*, 155.

18   Mark 5:22–43.

19   Zaun-Goshen, *Beyond the Wall*, 285–97; Kroyanker, *Reḥov ha-Nevi'im*, 100–102.

20   *Ha-Ḥerut* September 20, 1915, 2, and September 21, 1915, 2; Smilansky, *Perakim*, 4:19.

21   Heiberman, *Catholic Encyclopedia* ["Maria Alphonse Ratisbonne"], 12:659.

22 *Ha-Ḥerut* August 22, 1916, 2; Michaelson, "Professor A. Feigenbaum," 267–70.

23 Austro-Hungarian Consulate, Jerusalem to Foreign Ministry, Vienna, circa early July 1916 [with post-script dates July 29 and August 1, 1916] (German), HHStA 119/1421 729. One finds a typical but interesting list of requested medical supplies.

24 Austro-Hungarian Consulate, Jerusalem to *k.u.k.* Foreign Ministry, Vienna, July 22, 1916 (in German), HHStA 119/1421 730.

25 Foreign Ministry, Vienna to Austro-Hungarian Consulate, Jerusalem, "Instrumente für Dr. Ticho in Jerusalem, [Authorization No.] 77.041/8" (German), July 26, 1916, HHStA 119/1421 731; [Consul Friedrich] Kraus, Jerusalem to Zahlamt, Foreign Ministry, Vienna, [Misc. notes and receipts re: Authorization Nos. 77.041/8 and 2209/A] August 22–23, 1916 (German), HHStA 119/1421 732.

26 Various correspondences from Austro-Hungarian Embassy, Istanbul to Austro-Hungarian Consulate in Jerusalem, from the Foreign Ministry in Vienna to Austro-Hungarian Consulate, Jerusalem, and various receipts signed by Dr. A. Ticho and Consul F. Kraus in Jerusalem (German), September 1, 1916, February 15, 1917, April 2 and 4, 1917, April 21, 1917, and May 30, 1917, HHStA 118/451 363, 119/1421 727, 728, 733, 736–739.

27 *Ha-Ḥerut* December 18, 1916, 3, and January 11, 1917, 3.

28 Page, *Italy and the World War*, 2; *Ha-Ḥerut* September 8, 1915, 2.

29 Ticho, *M'dor L'dor*, 131–32.

30 Seas and Gotuzzo, "Vibrio cholerae," 2:2536–44; Garrison, *History of Medicine*, 4th ed, 450.

31 *Ha-Ḥerut* July 30, 1916, 2.

32 Barua, "History of cholera," 1; Norman, *Morton's Medical Bibliography*, 5th ed., 788–89.

33 Klein, *Etymological Dictionary*, 210, 272.

34 *Ha-Ḥerut* July 23, 1916, 1, and July 24, 1916, 1.

35 *Hadassah Bulletin* 3 (October, 1917): 4.

36 *Ha-Ḥerut* October 23, 1916, 3–4.

37 Duke-Elder, *Text-book of Ophthalmology*, 3:3010–11.

38 H. Bennhold, "Prof. Dr. Carl Hegler," 163; Garrison, ed., *Index Medicus,* 2nd series, 12:14, 33, 403, 647, 759, 825, 867, 1136.

39 Hegler and Klein, eds., "Referierabende," 286–87.

40 Ticho, "Frühjahrskatarrh," 510–15; Ticho, "Vernal catarrh," 257–62.

41 Ticho, "Ophthalmomyiasis," 165–72. Six years later, Ticho published his further experience on the topic in *The British Journal of Ophthalmology*.

42 Schwake, "Album ha-tsilumim," xi; Nashef, "Tawfik Canaan," 12–26.

43 Arthur Ruppin, *Syrian als Wirtschaftsgebiet* [*Syria as an Economic Field*] Berlin: Kolonialwirtschaftlichen Komitees, 1917 (abridged English translation), New York: Provisional Zionist Committee, 1918.

44 *Ha-Ḥerut* October 26, 1916, 4.

45 *Ha-Ḥerut* November 8, 1916, 4.

46 "Tazkir 'al-davar sidur ha-ezra ha-meditzinit..." (Hebrew), undated typescript, CZA, L2/100/1.

47 *Ha-Ḥerut* January 18, 1917, 1; Shilony, "Ha-sheirut ha-refu'i," 79.

48 *Ha-Ḥerut* March 2, 1917, 4, recurring through April 4, 1917, 3. Several neighborhoods listed.

CHAPTER 13 – THE ROAD TO DAMASCUS

1 Djemal Pasha, *Memories*, 163; Tidhar, "Meir Dizengoff," 2:794–96; Aaronsohn, "Saïfna Ahmar," part 1, 8–9; Lewis, "An Ottoman officer," 404–5.
2 Erickson, *Ordered to Die*, 163; Vester, *Our Jerusalem*, 242.
3 Tidhar, "Meir Dizengoff," 2:794–96; Mordike, *Allenby's Joint Operations*; Debbi, *Story of a Family*, 146.
4 Eliav, "*Me'oravutam*," 100; Vester, *Our Jerusalem*, 242.
5 Salmon, *Beit Ticho* [Ticho House], 5 in the English section.
6 Hoeflich, *Tagebücher*, 1, 244; Tidhar, "Moshe Ya'akov Ben-Gavriel [Eugen Hoeflich], 4:1948; Biemann, "Review," 175. Hoeflich had survived severe abdominal wounds in 1915. He immigrated to Palestine in 1927, authoring several books, mostly in German.
7 Numbers 32:34; Kings 3:25, Isaiah 15:1–2; Baedeker, *Palestine and Syria*, 5th ed., map between 10 and 11 plus 154–55. Before their hike to the summit, the group likely crossed the Jordan near Jericho, then followed roads past Mount Nebo, Madaba, and ancient ruins of Dibon.
8 Fromkin, *Peace to End All Peace*, 231–49, 263–75; *Zionism Conquers Public Opinion*, 7.
9 Ticho, "Epibulbären kongenitalen Tumoren," 226–30.
10 Erickson, *Ordered to Die*, 166–72.
11 Fromkin, *Peace to End All Peace*, 311; Grainger, *Battle for Palestine*, 117–24; Jung, *Der K.U.K. Wüstenkreig*, 156. Two Austro-Hungarian field hospitals remained at Tulkarem and Anepta until the front collapsed on September 19, 1918, badly decimating the units.
12 Sykes, *Crossroads*, 3–4.
13 Herzog, *Heroes of Israel*, 107–18; Levy and Levy, *Rof'eha*, 299.
14 Mazza, *Jerusalem*, 132–33.
15 Eliav, "*Me'oravutam*," 119; Gilbert, *Jerusalem in the Twentieth Century*, 47.
16 Debbi, *Story of a Family*, 123, 145.
17 De Ballobar, *Diario*, 229–30.
18 Levin, *It Takes a Dream*.
19 Van Paassen, *Days of Our Years*, 379; Van Paassen, *A Pilgrim's Vow*, 26.
20 Tidhar, "Marek (Mordecai Ze'ev) Schwarz," 3:1244–46.
21 CZA, "*Albert and Anna Ticho [in Damascus] to unknown recipient [in Europe], December 31, 1917*," A107/520; Pipes, "Muslim claim to Jerusalem," 49–66 [especially endnote no. 47].
22 Levin, *It Takes a Dream*; Segev, *One Palestine, Complete*, 50–54, 526n.
23 CZA, *Minutes of the first meeting of the Zionist Commission, 11 Mar. 1918; Minutes of the second meeting of the Zionist Commission, 14 Mar. 1918*, L3/285; Birn, *Preface to Middle East Policy*, Microfilm Edition; Segev, *One Palestine, Complete*, 59, 74.
24 Numbers 21:33; Deuteronomy 3:1; Joshua 12:4 and 13:31.
25 Ticho, "Epibulbären kongenitalen Tumoren," 226–30.

26   Acts 9:17–18. The account of St. Paul's blindness and conversion is recorded in three different places in the New Testament Book of Acts. According to Christian traditions, Acts 9:3–19 was written by St. Luke, a physician, and Acts 22:6–41 and 26:12–14 were written by St. Paul.

27   Voskuilen and Sheldon, *Operation Messiah*, 79–82, 93–94; Bullock, "Saint Paul," 151.

CHAPTER 14 – WAR AND PEACE

1   Burns, *Damascus*, xix, 4, 10–15. The Egyptian word *Ta-ms-qu* appears upon a wall in the Karnak Temple, the oldest known written reference to the city of Damascus.

2   I Kings 11:23–25; II Kings 5:1–19 and 6:13–23; Burns, *Damascus*, 103–4.

3   Baedeker, *Palestine and Syria*, 5th ed., 303.

4   Strauss, "Disintegration of Ottoman rule," 314; Baedeker, *Palestine and Syria*, 5th ed., map between 256–58 and 304–5; Tidhar, "Gedaliahu Wilbushevitz," 2:939–40; Tidhar, "Baruch Chizik," 4:1830–31.

5   Baedeker, *Palestine and Syria*, 5th ed., 299; Ben-Reuven and Ben-Reuven, *Nashim 'Ivriyot*, 32–33; Levy and Levy, *Rof'eha*, 101; Tidhar, "Menahem Mendel Henkin," 3:1283–84.

6   Levy and Levy, *Rof'eha*, 299; Tidhar, "Marek (Mordecai Ze'ev) Schwarz," 3:1244–46; Levin, *It Takes a Dream*, 57; Michaelson, "Feigenbaum," 267–70; Markel, *Quarantine!*, 49; "Statement in reference to relations between the Joint Distribution Committee and the American Zionist Medical Unit, The Jewish Health Bureau and Dr. Feigenbaum's Ophthalmic Hospital, January 1921," HA RG13–35/17.

7   Tidhar, "Daniel Auster," 1:165–66. Auster (1893–1963) was later the Mayor of Jerusalem during three terms (1937–38, 1944–45, and 1949–50).

8   Cleveland and Bunton, *History*, 4th ed., 154.

9   Ben-Yehudah, *Political Assassinations*, 131.

10   The photograph that Auster took is in the public domain on Wikipedia.

11   Yacov Tsachor, *Bulei Yisrael 5708–5758*, 227.

12   Albert Ticho, "Epibulbären kongenitalen Tumoren," 226–30.

13   Baedeker, *Palestine and Syria*, 5th ed., 299; Dolev, *Allenby's Military Medicine*, 162–63.

14   CZA, A107/520, Albert and Anna Ticho in Damascus to unknown recipient in Europe, 31 December 1917; "Curriculum Vitae" [3 handwritten pages with the last page listing published works from 1930, "Zur Trachomfrage..."] (English), circa 1930, IMJ, Ticho Papers, not catalogued as of January 2008.

15   Tidhar, "Marek (Mordecai Ze'ev) Schwarz," 3:1244–46.

16   Debbi, *Story of a Family*, 146.

17   Ben-Reuven and Ben-Reuven, *Nashim 'Ivriyot*, 40.

18   Fischer, ed., *Anna Ticho: Sketches 1918–1975*, unnumbered pages. Three sketches are included from "The first sketchbook Damascus 1918."

19   Moshe Krieger to Anna and Albert Ticho, Nazareth, February 5, 1918.

20   Erickson, *Ordered to Die*, 194.

21   Von Sanders, *Five Years in Turkey*, 3, 7, 57; Erickson, *Ordered to Die*, 195.

22 *Red Cross Bulletin* 2 (April 22, 1918): 1; *Red Cross Bulletin* 2 (September 2, 1918): 7; Levy, *Perakim*, 170–71, 173n, 179, 389n.

23 *Catalogue... Columbia University,* 473; *Hadassah Medical Organization . . . Third Report*, 1. Brown, "Isaac Max Rubinow," 1863–64. Dr. Isaac Seth Hirsch, a graduate of Columbia University Medical School (1902), was professor of Roetgenology and chief of Roetgen Laboratories at Bellvue Hospital. The members of the unit boarded the *Megantic* just before midnight on June 11, 1918.

24 Levy, *Perakim*, 178.

25 "Correspondence from Henrietta Szold to Alice L. Seligsberg, December 31, 1918," HA RG13–35/5.

26 Levin, *It Takes a Dream*, 64; Levy, *Perakim*, 177, 179–80.

27 Tom Segev, *One Palestine, Complete*, 74.

28 Bentwich and Bentwich, *Mandate Memories*, 39, 189–90; Segev, *One Palestine, Complete*, 74.

29 *Hadassah Medical Organization...Third Report*, 2.

30 Von Sanders, *Five Years in Turkey*, 253, 266; Erickson, *Ordered to Die*, 195–96; Schechtman, *Vladimir Jabotinsky*, 1:268.

31 Hamilton, *God, Guns and Israel*, 173–82; Jung, *Der K.U.K. Wüstenkrieg*, 194; Cline, *Battles of Armageddon*, 11–12, 16, 142.

32 Walter, "Damascus," 331–33.

33 Erickson, "Captain Larkin," 153–55, 158–60.

34 Von Sanders, *Five Years in Turkey*, 319–20.

35 Gilbert, *First World War*, 490–91; Morris, *Trieste*, 126.

36 Fromkin, *Peace to End All Peace*, 196–97; Gavish, *Survey of Palestine*, 18.

37 Levy, *Perakim*, 180.

CHAPTER 15 – RETURN TO ZION

1   Wagret, *Turkey*, 618–19.

2   Kerr, *Lions of Marash*, 53–54.

3   Lewis, *Emergence*, 3rd ed., 239–40.

4   Von Sanders, *Five Years in Turkey*, 321.

5   Acts 16:6.

6   Ticho, *M'dor L'dor*, 104.

7   Penn, "Odessa," 385.

8   Levy and Levy, *Rof'im shel Eretz Yisrael*, 372. Isaac Rubinow to Albert Ticho, January 5, 1921, AZMU No. 5150/177, IMJ, Ticho Papers. The correct year of Shimkin's arrival in Haifa is 1921.

9   Ticho, *M'dor L'dor*, 104; Wilson, *Ukrainians*, 123; *New York Times* November 30, 1918; Kubicek, *History of Ukraine*, 85.

10 Criss, *Istanbul*, 60–61.

11 Ruppin, *Pirkei Ḥayai*, 2:281–82. Hanna Ruppin was the daughter of Mordecai Ben-Hillel Hacohen, a merchant, writer, and leader of the Second Aliyah.

12 Tidhar, "Marek Schwarz," 3:1244–45; Debbi, *Ticho*, 124, 146.

13 Levin, *Balm in Gilead*, 66; Ruppin, *Pirkei Ḥayai*, 2:300. In mid-December, the Ruppins sailed for Italy aboard the *Corcovado*. Hanna gave birth in Berlin; her husband continued Zionist work in Europe.

14 Levin, *Balm in Gilead*, 66–67; Levin, *It Takes A Dream*, 81–83.
15 Levy and Levy, *Rof'eha*, 181, 206, 240, 321. Drs. Seidel and Koslov served on the medical crew of the *Ruslan* along with dermatologist Aryeh Dostrovsky, whose connections with Dr. Ticho are subsequently described (chapter 16).
16 Schechtman, *Jabotinsky*, 1:309, 312.
17 Ticho, *M'dor L'dor*, 104
18 Isaacson, *Einstein*, 302.
19 Ticho, *M'dor L'dor*, 104.
20 "Statement in Reference to Relations between the Joint Distribution Committee and the American Zionist Medical Unit, The Jewish Health Bureau and Dr. Feigenbaum's Ophthalmic Hospital, January 1921," HA RG13–35/17.
21 British Ophthalmic Hospital, *Report of the Committee....*, 1919; MacKenzie, *Roll of Honor*, 294, 332.
22 Levy, *Perakim*, 142; Elisheva Cohen [for] Irit Salmon, "Anna Ticho" [13-page typed manuscript], IMJ–Ticho House, 5.

CHAPTER 16 – UNDER NEW MANAGEMENT

1 Chisolm, *Encyclopædia Britannica*, "Palestine," 32:18.
2 Levin, *Vision*, 242, 247; British Ophthalmic Hospital, *Report,* 1919. Friedenwald succeeded Lewin-Epstein as acting chairman of the Zionist Commission.
3 Isaac Rubinow to Albert Ticho, January 5, 1922, AZMU No. 5150/177, IMJ, Ticho Papers. Herein Rubinow concedes that Ticho's recollections were correct that the initiative to employ Ticho at the AZMU had come from Rubinow himself and not Ticho.
4 Krimsky, *Pilgrimage and Service*, 76; Beham, "Sekira," 111; Levy, *Perakim*, 152–53, 182–83.
5 Zuta and Sukenik, *Artzeinu*, 171–74; Luke and Keith-Roach, *Handbook*, v, 205. Zuta and Sukenik's 1920 guidebook provides much detail about each of the other Jewish-run general hospitals and health institutes. The "Jewish Ophthalmic Hospital" in Luke and Keith-Roach's 1922 handbook likely referred to Feigenbaum's recently closed hospital rather than Ticho's.
6 Alice Seligsberg to Henrietta Szold, April 9–14 1919, No. 20, HA RG13–35/5.
7 Shvarts and Brown, "Kupat Holim," 32–33.
8 Isaac Rubinow to Henrietta Szold, November 23, 1919, No. 55, HA RG13–35/7.
9 Shvarts and Brown, "Kupat Holim," 35–36; Brown, "Isaac Max Rubinow," 1864.
10 Isaac Rubinow to Henrietta Szold, May 15, 1919, HA RG13–35/7.
11 Isaac Rubinow, "Travelling Expenses…" circa January 1920, HA RG13–35/7; *Do'ar ha-Yom* December 20, 1920, 1; Levy and Levy, *Rof'eha*, 300; Golz, *Refu'at Af-Ozen-Garon*, 41.
12 Harry Friedenwald to Henrietta Szold, May 7, 1919, HA RG13–35/9.
13 Hadassah Medical Organization, *Third Report*, 50–51.
14 Isaac Rubinow to Henrietta Szold, October 17, 1919, No. 47, HA RG13–35/7.
15 Levy and Levy, *Rof'eha*, 340.
16 Isaac Rubinow to Henrietta Szold, October 17, 1919, No. 47, HA RG13–35/7; Levy and Levy, *Rof'eha*, 240, 321; Shehory-Rubin and Shvarts, *Hadassah*, 63.

17 Isaac Rubinow to Jacob de Haas, January 30, 1920, HA RG/HMO–1/1; Levy and Levy, *Rof'eha*, 181.
18 Shvarts and Brown, "Kupat Holim," 36; Shehory-Rubin and Shvarts, *Hadassah*, 40.
19 Isaac Rubinow to Jacob de Haas, January 30, 1920, HA RG/HMO–1/1. Satenstein returned to America in December 1919.
20 Isaac Rubinow to Henrietta Szold, December 24, 1919, HA RG13–35/15.
21 Shehory-Rubin and Shvarts, *Hadassah*, 63; citing the source of their material as CZA J113/341.
22 Bartal, *Ḥemla ve-Yeda*, 359–61, 375–78; Dostrovsky and Ticho, "A case of ocular leprosy," 43–47.
23 Isaac Rubinow to Henrietta Szold, November 29, 1919, HA RG13–35/15.
24 Shvarts and Brown, "Kupat Holim," 40–41.
25 Isaac Rubinow, "Proposed Form of Temporary Agreement between the Zionist Commission and the A.Z.M.U.," December 12, 1919. HA RG13–35; Isaac Rubinow to Henrietta Szold, December 7, 1919, No. 63, HA RG13–35/15.
26 Isaac Max Rubinow to Jacob de Haas, January 30, 1920, HA RG/HMO, 1/1. In absorbing the Ezrah Meditzinit, Ticho's friend, Dr. Moshe Krieger, found himself transferred to Safed.
27 Tidhar, "Reuven David (Robert) Kesselman," 9:3377–38; "R. D. Kesselman of Palestine, 60," *Brooklyn Eagle* February 27, 1942.
28 Isaac Rubinow, Memoranda regarding several individual meetings with AZMU medical staff members, March 3–12, 1920, KC, File 5616–11/4.
29 Schechtman, *Jabotinsky*, 1:313, 318.
30 Segev, *One Palestine, Complete*, 124.
31 Hurwich, *Kol ha-'Am Ḥazit*, 59–60; Schechtman, *Jabotinsky*, 1:319.
32 Pappe, *Husaynis*, 193.
33 Segev, *One Palestine Complete*, 131, citing Ze'ev Jabotinsky to Chaim Weizmann, March 12, 1920; Mazza, *Jerusalem*, 170, citing Chaim Weizmann to Zionist Executive March 25, 1920; Schechtman, *Jabotinsky*, 1:323–25.
34 Hurwich, *Kol ha-'Am Ḥazit*, 61. The other first-aid stations in the New City were under the direction of Drs. Chaya Weizmann, Aryeh Feigenbaum, and Aryeh Beham.
35 Morris, *Righteous Victims*, 95; Segev, *One Palestine, Complete*, 128; Pappe, *Husaynis*, 194–98.
36 Schechtman, *Jabotinsky*, 1:330; Mazza, *Jerusalem*, 173, 176.
37 Monk, *Aesthetic Occupation*, 73; Mazza, *Jerusalem*, 1977.
38 Pappe, *Husaynis*, 202–3; Schechtman, *Jabotinsky*, 1:326. Jabotinsky and nineteen convicted comrades were initially taken to Egypt but soon transferred to the fortress of Acre.
39 Monk, *Aesthetic Occupation*, 73–74, 176–77nn. Monk cites several reprinted memoranda in Friedman, *The Rise of Israel*, 12:18, 24–25, 55, 113, 155.
40 Sykes, *Crossroads to Israel*, 42.
41 Pappe, *Husaynis*, 204–5, citing Gad Frumkin, *The Way of a Judge in Jerusalem*. Jerusalem 1946, 288–89; Levy and Levy, *Rof'eha*, 327.
42 *Do'ar ha-Yom* July 20, 1920, 3.

43 Debbi, *Story of a Family*, 131.

44 *Do'ar ha-Yom* June 29, 1920, 3; Levy and Levy, *Rof'eha*, 78, 89, 269; Tidhar, "Dr. Yishayahu Eliyahu," 14:4533. The impetus to found the International Society of Physicians in Palestine came from two Jewish physicians, Dr. Leon Pouchovsky and Moshe Sherman, and from the Christian Arab physician Dr. Elias Sawabini. The elected board consisted of three Jews and three non-Jews: Dr. Avraham Abushadid (chairman); Dr. Elias Sawabini (Christian) vice-chairman; Dr. Levontin (Jewish) Secretary; Dr. Shukri Boutagi (Muslim) Treasurer; and Dr. Mizar (French Christian) member, and Dr. Eliyahu [Elia] (Jewish) member.

45 *Do'ar ha-Yom* November 24, 1920, 3; Levy and Levy, *Rof'eha*, 327. Dr. Vahan Hovannes Kalbian was physician to the elite in Mandatory Jerusalem, including most high commissioners.

46 [Memorandum] R.O.S. Director of Health to President of the International Society of Pharmacists, Jerusalem (English), December 15, 1920, CZA A416/2, reproduced in Michlin, *Ma'asei Rokei'ah*, 48; Michlin, *Ma'asei Rokhim*, 274, 281; "Mikhtavim la-Ma'arekhet" [Letters to the Editor] (Hebrew), *Do'ar ha-Yom* March 1, 1921, 3.

47 *Harefuah* 1 (1920): 3–4, 5, 14, 104, and 110. Levy, *Perakim*, 154–55.

48 *Do'ar ha-Yom* May 20, 1920, 3, and October 31, 1920, 3.

49 *Do'ar ha-Yom* June 3, 1920, 2.

50 Dash, *Summoned to Jerusalem*, 151; Hadassah Medical Organization, *Third Report*, 6.

51 Dash, *Summoned to Jerusalem*, 147; Dash, "Doing good in Palestine," 102.

52 Henrietta Szold to Harry Friedenwald, March 16, 1921. HA RG13–35/9.

53 Levin, *It Takes a Dream*, 186; Schidorsky, "Julius Jarcho," 17; Schidorsky, "Shmu'el Hugo Bergman," 121–23; Alfassi, *Yerushalayim*, 50–51. The nucleus of a medical library was initiated in 1919 by New York gynecologist Dr. Julius Jarcho, becoming a part of the National Library.

54 Segev, *One Palestine, Complete*, 155–56.

55 Hadassah Medical Organization, *Third Report*, 6.

56 Isaac Rubinow to Jacob de Haas, December 28, 1920, HA RG13–35/17; Henrietta Szold to Jacob de Haas, November 11, 1920, HA RG13–35/16, 7; "Statement in reference to relations between the Joint Distribution Committee and the American Zionist Medical Unit, The Jewish Health Bureau, and Dr. Feigenbaum's Opthalmic [sic] Hospital," circa January 1921, HA RG13–35/17.

57 Kestenbaum and Company, "Friedenberg Collection [Auction Catalogue March 23, 2006]," No. 358, 144. "TICHO, ANNA (Czechoslovakian/Israeli, 1894–1980). *Young Jewish Boy*. Signed and dated by artist in pencil lower right. With personal inscription on reverse from Ticho to Henrietta Szold on her sixtieth birthday. Watercolor and pencil on paper…Jerusalem, 1917."

58 Hadassah Medical Organization, *Third Report*, 52–53.

59 Isaac Rubinow to Albert Ticho, January 5, 1921, AZMU No. 5150/177, IMJ, Ticho Papers.

60 Isaac Rubinow to Albert Ticho, January 31, 1921, AZMU No. 5150/564, IMJ, Ticho Papers; Shvarts, et al., "From socialist principles," 248.

61 Hadassah Medical Organization, *Third Report*, 52–53.

62 Isaac Rubinow to AZMU Medical Staff, "Memorandum," February 15, 1921, KC, File 5616–11/4.

63 Report of the Commission of Enquiry into the Disturbances in Palestine in May, 1921, with correspondence relating thereto (Disturbances), 1921, Cmd. 1540, p. 60. The riots spread to neighboring towns and villages, and murdered victims included Yosef Haim Brenner, one of the pioneers of modern Hebrew literature. Most Arab casualties resulted from clashes with British forces attempting to restore order.

64 Alfassi, *Yerushalayim*, 174.

65 Weizmann, *Trial and Error*, 275.

66 *Do'ar ha-Yom* October 16, 1921, 3; Aruri, *Jordan*, 29, 79; Wilson, *King Abdullah*, 57–58; Salibi, *History of Jordan*, 105.

67 *Do'ar ha-Yom* November 6, 1921, 3; Levin, *It Takes a Dream*, 95.

68 Hadassah Medical Organization, *Third Report*, 21–22. Rubinow detailed the proceedings: "Miss Henrietta Szold presided, and Lady Samuel delivered an address and distributed the diplomas to the graduates. Addresses were also made by Miss Szold, Chairman of the Committee on Training School; Miss Anna Kaplan, Principal of the Training School; Dr. Montague David Eder, on behalf of the Palestine Zionist Executive; Colonel G. W. Heron, Director of the Department of Health of Palestine; Miss Esther Litwinovsky, on behalf of the graduates; Dr. Ticho, on behalf of the medical faculty; Dr. Thon, on behalf of the Waad Ha-Leumi; and the Director."

69 Shvarts and Brown, "Kupat Holim," 43–44; Levy, *Perakim*, 181, 183; Levin, *It Takes a Dream*, 135. In 1921, Hadassah solidified its independence and status within world Zionism by ending its three-year amalgamation with the Federation of American Zionists. It also eliminated its reliance upon the Joint Distribution Committee of the American Fund for War Sufferers.

70 Ticho, "Report on my visit to Beer Sheva on December 10, 1921," CZA J113/783.

71 Levy and Levy, *Rof'eha*, 61; Holitscher, *Gesang an Palästina*, 5; Scholem, *Berlin to Jerusalem*, 161. The 1922 *Gesang* [Poem] by Holitscher about Palestine included twelve etchings by Hermann Struck, the latter immigrating to Palestine that year. Scholem cited another of Holitscher's books, *Reise durch das jüdische Palästina* [Journey through Jewish Palestine] (Berlin: 1922) in describing his own arrival at Jaffa on a steamer in September 1923.

72 Rubinow to Mr. Sprinzak [English draft "for Hebrew translation"], December 23, 1921, CZA J113/783.

73 Feigenbaum, *50 Shenot Oftalmologiya*, 32–33.

74 Brian, *Einstein*, 130; "Future of Palestine," *Daily Telegraph*, March 23, 1921, cited by Monk, *An Aesthetic Occupation*, 184n; Levin, *It Takes A Dream*, 186.

75 Duke-Elder, *Text-book of Ophthalmology*, 1940, 3:2129–30.

76 Sinai, *Bi-Mlo*, 106.

77 Ticho and Kligler, "Trachoma in Palestine," 706–7.

78 Isaac Rubinow to Albert Ticho, February 13, 1922, AZMU No. 5150/1342, IMJ, Ticho Papers.

79 Isaac Rubinow to Albert Ticho, April 5, 1922, CZA J750/3156.

80 *JTA* August 12, 1928.

81 Shvarts and Brown, "Kupat Holim," 44.

Chapter 17 – Somewhat Quieter Times

1 Ashbee, *Jerusalem 1920–1922*, 26–28; Fuchs and Herbert, "Architecture," 91; Goldhill, *Jerusalem*, 146–47. By 1922, the Pro-Jerusalem Society had managed to raise sufficient funds for the dismantling of the Jaffa Gate's Ottoman Clock Tower that Storrs and Ashbee detested. A completely new clock tower was built in Allenby Square in 1924.

2 Kroyanker, *Rehov ha-Nevi'im*, 301–2. The Ottomans referred to the neighborhood just east of Ticho's clinic as *Mas'udiya*. The neighborhood was about equally divided between Arab Christians and Muslims with Jews in the area living closer to the city walls.

3 Nashef, *Tawfiq Canaan*, 16 and 19–20. Canaan was married to Margot Eilander, the daughter of a German importer. After serving in the Turkish Army at the Sinai Front during the war, Canaan was appointed as the director of the Leprosy Hospital in Talbiyya but in the early 1920s he was again working at the reopened German Hospital as head of its Department of Internal Medicine.

4 "Palestine's health needs: Task of making settlements medically fit a difficult job," *New York Times* May 7, 1922; Dash, "Doing good in Palestine," 103; Bentwich, *For Zion's Sake*, 129, 148; Mendes-Flohr, "Incorrigible idealist," 144. One of the previous tenants of Magnes's first Jerusalem home was civic advisor and Pro-Jerusalem Society Chairman Charles Robert Ashbee.

5 Levin, *It Takes a Dream*, 83.

6 Henrietta Szold to Alice Seligsberg, Letter No. 27, March 4, 1919, HA RG13/35–5; Sinai, *Bi-Mlo ha-'Ayin*, 105.

7 Sinai, *Bi-Mlo ha-'Ayin*, 105–6.

8 Tidhar, "Dr. Aharon Yosef Yermens," 3:1287–88; Yermens-Reuveni, "A. Y. Yermens," 251–52. Dr. Yermens would pass away after a prolonged illness during Hanukkah, Tevet 1, 5684 (December 9, 1923).

9 Kark and Oren-Nordheim, *Jerusalem and Its Environs*, 168–70 [including a reproduction of Kaufmann's plan of Talpiot, CZA A/150]; Levin, "Adrikhalut," 181; Tidhar, "Yitzhak (Richard) Kaufmann," 4:1893–94. Kaufmann would also plan the garden suburbs of Beit ha-Kerem (1921–22), the first stage of Rehavia (1922), Mekor Hayim (1923), Bayit ve-Gan, and Kiryat Moshe (1925).

10 Oz, *A Tale of Love and Darkness*, 64; Kroyanker, *Rehov ha-Nevi'im*, 68.

11 Zalmona, *Yemei Migdal David*, 2; Yahav "Migdal David," 42; Tidhar, "Reuven Rubin (Zelicovici)," 4:1662–64; Tidhar, "Shmuel Ben-David," 9:3384; Tidhar, "Avraham Malnikov," 4:1662–64. The Society of Hebrew Artists (Agudat Amanim 'Ivrit) was established in October 1920 by Shmuel Ben-David, Meir Gur-Aryeh, Abel Pann, Avraham Malnikov, and Shmuel Levi.

12 *Do'ar ha-Yom* April 4, 1922, 3; Levy, *Perakim*, 238.

13 *Do'ar ha-Yom* November 27, 1922, 2.

14 Debbi, *Story of a Family*, 154; *Haaretz* November 18, 1929, 1 [two articles].

15 *Davar* March 5, 1928, 3.

16   Levy, *Perakim*, 156, 158n. Levy and Levy, *Rof'eha*, 142–43. The new editor-in-chief of *Harefuah* was Rothschild-Hadassah chief-surgeon Dr. Jacob Doljansky, who had come from Ekatorinoslav (Dnipropetrovsk), Ukraine, to Jerusalem in 1920.

17   *Do'ar ha-Yom* June 21, 1926, 3; *Harefuah* (1926) 288–92; Levy and Levy, *Rof'eha*, 143, 161, 304. In 1923, Dr. Freud had purchased modern radiological equipment in Europe and just some months before his death, he had dedicated the newly established Radiological Institute at the Hadassah Hospital. The first prize was bestowed in November 1928.

18   Debbi, *Story of a Family*, 154; Salmon, *Beit Ticho*, 14 (English), 12 (Hebrew); "Ticho, Noted Eye Doctor, at 77," *Jerusalem Post* October 16, 1960.

19   Kisch, *Palestine Diary*, 63.

20   Weizmann, *Trial and Error*, 295–96.

21   Bentwich and Bentwich, *Mandate Memories*, 93–94.

22   HaLevy, *Retzaḥ be-Yisrael*," 127.

23   Kisch, April 26, 1923 and July 13, 1923, CZA S25/518/1, cited by Monk, *Aesthetic Occupation*, 93–94, 187nn; HaLevy, *Retzaḥ be-Yisrael*," 132.

24   Brian, *Einstein: A Life*, 144–45. In the midst of Einstein's world tour, the German envoy to Sweden had accepted the Nobel Prize on his behalf on December 10, 1922.

25   *Do'ar ha-Yom* February 4, 1923, and February 6, 1923, 3; Fölsing, *Albert Einstein*, 529; Segev, *One Palestine, Complete*, 202.

26   *Do'ar ha-Yom* February 8, 1923, 3 and February 9, 1923, 1; Lavsky, *Mashma'ut*, 336. Further renovations of Gray Hill's country home were about to convert it into the Institutes of Chemistry and Microbiology.

27   *Do'ar ha-Yom* February 12, 1923, 4, and February 14, 1923, 3.

28   Glass, "American Olim," 209, 228n; Dash, "Doing good in Palestine," 105.

29   Salmon, *Beit Ticho* [Ticho House], 12 (Hebrew), 14 (English), citing the Hebrew translation of Scholem's memoir, *Mi-Berlin li-Yerushalayim*.

30   Zweig, *World of Yesterday*, 292, 296–7.

31   Michaela Laichmann [Oberarchivrätin elektronisch gefertigt] to Dima Schaminer, "Abraham Ticho," March 9, 2011, citing Wiener Stadt- und Landesarchiv [WSL] MA 8–B–MEW–1794/2011.

32   *Do'ar ha-Yom* March 17, 1924.

33   Sinai, *Bi-Mlo ha-'Ayin*, 90; Albert and Edwards, *History*, 116. The Javal keratometer was an instrument for the examination of the curvatures of the cornea.

34   Weizmann, *Trial and Error*, 300; Metzer, *Divided Economy*, 68.

35   Sinai, *Bi-Mlo ha-'Ayin*, 93, 102, 106–13.

36   Kisch, *Palestine Diary*, 93–98.

37   HaLevy, *Retzaḥ be-Yisrael*," 131–33. The memorandum emphasized the independence of Agudas Yisrael from political Zionism while embracing all who would help to develop the country with peace and security. At the closing ceremony, Sonnenfeld was bestowed with the Istakal honor by King Hussein and De Haan was given a gilded Arab headdress and cloak.

38   HaLevy, *Retzaḥ be-Yisrael*," 135–45, 160–61; *Do'ar ha-Yom* February 27, 1924; Nakdimon and Mayzlish, *De Haan*, 123; Segev, *One Palestine, Complete*, 385n.

Approaching the market of Maḥane Yehudah on Jaffa Road, de Haan was felled by three revolver shots from close range.

39 Franz Ollendorff, "Ticho House in Jerusalem rejuvenated: The history of the premises and some houses in the vicinity," 8-page typescript, IMJ–Ticho House; Glass and Kark, *Sephardi Entrepreneurs*, 41.

40 Salmon, *Beit Ticho* (1994); Meron, *Yerushalayim ve-Khol Netivoteha* (1996); Kroyanker, *Reḥov ha-Nevi'im* (2000), 133–36.

41 Franz Ollendorff, "Ticho House in Jerusalem rejuvenated," op. cit.

42 Kark and Landman, "*Muslim neighborhoods*," 113.

43 Salmon, *Beit Ticho*, 10–11 (Hebrew), 9–10 (English). Following the discovery of the Dead Sea Scrolls, archeologists reconsidered the verdict placed upon Shapira as a fraud.

44 Harry, *Bat Yerushalayim ha-Ketana*, 91.

45 Itzik Shwicki (Jerusalem Organizer, Council for the Preservation of Historic Sites), personal communication, 13 January 2008.

46 Salmon, *Beit Ticho*, 11 (Hebrew), 12 (English).

47 Salmon, *Beit Ticho*, 17–18 (Hebrew), 22–24 (English).

48 Bentwich, *For Zion's Sake*, 157–58; Weizmann, *Trial and Error*, 318–19.

49 Hurwitz, "Balfour on Mount Sinai," 485 and 490n, citing *The Times* April 2, 1925, 14.

50 Bentwich and Bentwich, *Mandate Memories*, 102.

51 Hurwitz, "Balfour on Mount Sinai," 488, citing Balfour, *Speeches on Zionism*, 74–91.

52 Bentwich and Bentwich, *Mandate Memories*, 102.

53 Weizmann, *Trial and Error*, 323; Heller, *Mi-'Brit Shalom' le-'Iḥud'*, 46.

54 Ruppin, *Pirkei Ḥayai*, 3:96–97.

55 Buber, *A Land of Two Peoples*, 72–73, citing *Protokoll der Verhandlungen des XIV Zionistenkongresses…* (London, 1926).

56 Schechtman, *Jabotinsky*, 2:37–38, 40.

57 Ruppin, *Pirkei Ḥayai*, 3:115. Most all of the founding members were intellectuals clustered around the Hebrew University, most hailed from Central Europe and many had warm relations with the Tichos.

58 Buber, *Land of Two Peoples*, 71, 77. Buber's essay criticizing the seeking of a Jewish majority in Palestine (*Judische Rundschau*, April 1926) appears here in translation.

59 Ruppin, *Pirkei Ḥayai*, 3:118.

60 Salmon, *Beit Ticho*, 13 (Hebrew), 15–16 (English).

61 Levy and Levy, *Rof'eha*, 355. Dr. Stein married the architect Yitzhak Reich, moved one year later to Tel Aviv for reasons of Yitzhak's work, and worked for Kupat Ḥolim until her retirement.

62 Bentwich and Bentwich, *Mandate Memories*, 101, 105.

63 *Do'ar ha-Yom* May 13, 1926, 1; Anna Ticho to Mr. Newman (English), December 12, 1946, IMJ, Ticho Papers.

64 Abu-Lebdeh, *Conflict and Peace*, 52; Ruppin, *Pirkei Ḥayai*, 3:99.

65 *Davar* June 9, 1926, 2; Shehory-Rubin and Shvarts, "*Hadassah*," 174.

66 Shehory-Rubin and Shvarts, "*Hadassah*," 176.

67 Debbi, *Story of a Family*, 151. Ticho's inpatient summaries for 1927 shows a busy inpatient practice with a total of 7,444 hospitalized "patient-days" during that year. Records show 23.59 percent of inpatients were Jewish, 65.64 percent Muslim, and 10.76 percent Christian.

68 A. M. Bluestone to Albert Ticho, November 29, 1927, HMO No. 5750/14338, IMJ, Ticho Papers, not catalogued as of January 2008. Ticho briefly served as a consultant for Hadassah again during the August 1929 riots in Jerusalem.

69 Shehory-Rubin and Shvarts, "*Hadassah*," 179–80.

70 Bentwich and Bentwich, *Mandate Memories*, 94.

71 Ticho, *M'dor L'dor*, 144; Pojar, "Masaryk's relations," 176.

72 Pojar, "Masaryk's relations," 176–77.

73 Pojar, "Masaryk's relations," 177.

74 Tidhar, "Dr. Siegfried Lehmann," 10:3499–3501; Levy and Levy, *Rof'eha*, 223; Shavit, *My Promised Land*, 103.

75 *Jewish Daily Bulletin* July 12, 1927, July 14, 1927, and July 27, 1927.

76 Kroyanker, *Reḥov ha-Nevi'im*, 68; Bentwich and Bentwich, *Mandate Memories*, 129; Segev, *One Palestine, Complete*, 342. The British were able to take over Maḥanaim after Ussishkin's lease was terminated. Plans for a new Government House on a plateau overlooking the Road to Bethlehem were finalized in 1928, and it opened in 1931.

77 Tidhar, "Alexander Baerwald," 9:3264; Bentwich and Bentwich, *Mandate Memories*, 146.

78 Alex and Lotte Baerwald to Anna Ticho, February 19, 1928, IMJ, Ticho Papers. Lotte Baerwald arranged to have her friend, Wanja Spiegel, welcome Anna in Berlin. Mrs. Baerwald arranged contacts in Berlin including Lucie Lipman-Wulf, an insider of the art-scene in Berlin, who later divorced her Jewish husband to become a personal secretary and advisor to Hermann Göring.

79 Jehuda Epstein to Anna Ticho, June 26, 1918, IMJ, Ticho Papers.

80 Bentwich and Bentwich, *Mandate Memories*, 106.

81 *Jewish Daily Bulletin* August 5, 1928, 2.

82 Debbi, *Story of a Family*, 131.

83 Levy, *Perakim*, 186.

84 Schechtman, *Jabotinsky*, 2:87.

85 Bentwich and Bentwich, *Mandate Memories*, 76, 130–31; Luke and Keith-Roach, eds., *Handbook of Palestine*, iii, 133–34. Segev, *One Palestine, Complete*, 298.

86 Pappe, *History of Modern Palestine*, 90–93.

CHAPTER 18 – MAYHEM AND AFTERMATH

1 *Turei Yeshurun*, 61–62; Bentwich and Bentwich, *Mandate Memories*, 131.

2 *Jewish Daily Bulletin* May 15, 1929, 1; Duff, *Bailing*, 169–77; Sykes, *Crossroads*, 100–101; Segev, *One Palestine, Complete*, 296; Cohen, *Tarpat* 168–9. Chief Secretary Wyndham Deeds had stools and a partition in 1920.

3 Cahill, "Going beserk," 62–64. Duff was a former member of the "Black and Tans," i.e., the "Auxiliary Division of the Royal Irish Constabulary," among many who were brought to Ireland to try to squelch the Irish Rebellion of 1919–22.

4 *Jewish Daily Bulletin* September 26, 1928, 1 and 4.

5   Schechtman, *Jabotinsky*, 2:89.

6   Levin, *Vision*, 325.

7   Hirshberg, "Muzika ma'aravit," 437–39; Gilbert, *Jerusalem in the Twentieth Century*, 117; Levin, *Vision*, 325; *Do'ar ha-Yom* March 12, 1929, 4, and March 18, 1929, 3.

8   Pappe, *History of Modern Palestine*, 91–92; Schechtman, *Jabotinsky*, 2:94.

9   *Jewish Daily Bulletin* April 11, 1929, 3–4.

10 *Jewish Daily Bulletin* May 3, 1929, 5; Levy, *Perakim*, 166–67. The entire project was funded by the Strauses' $250,000 donation. The Strauses were unable to travel in 1929; their representative was the pacifist Unitarian minister Rev. John Haynes Holmes of the New York Community Church.

11 *Jewish Daily Bulletin* May 7, 1929, 1.

12 Triwaks, *Milḥama ve-Shalom*, 58–59, 148, 176.

13 Segev, *One Palestine, Complete*, 307.

14 Segev, *One Palestine, Complete*, 320–21. Citing correspondence, Margery Bentwich to her family, July 26, 1929.

15 *Jewish Daily Bulletin* April 10, 1929, 2; Levin, *Vision*, 320–21; Levy, *Perakim*, 428; Greenberg, "Hebron Massacre," 8. The Hadassah Clinic was housed in a building erected in 1909 for the Hesed le-Avraham Hospital. During World War I, the clinic was taken over by the AZMU, and as the organization evolved into the Hadassah Medical Organization the facility came to be known as Beit Hadassah.

16 Armenian Patriarchate Bishop Mesrob Nichanian to A. Ticho, December 26, 1928. IMJ, Ticho Papers; Ticho, "Trachomfrage in Palästina," 56.

17 Levin, *Vision*, 322.

18 Schechtman, *Jabotinsky*, 1:118–120, 606n. In Europe for the Zionist Congress, Jabotinsky had cabled the *Do'ar ha-Yom* editors nine days earlier with instructions to abate their agitation regarding the Kotel.

19 Debbi, *Story of a Family*, 132.

20 Triwaks, *Milḥama ve-Shalom*, 60, 63, 176–78; Segev, *One Palestine, Complete*, 310.

21 Triwaks, *Milḥama ve-Shalom*, 68, 179–80; Segev, *One Palestine, Complete*, 311–12.

22 Cohen, *Tarpat*, 174–82; Levy and Levy, *Rof'eha*, 199, 376. Cohen cites the verdict of the presiding judge in the Dajani murder case and other testimonies: Hamis Salam al-Sayad and Minah Albert [CZA 3050/20]; Gershom Shalom and Dr. Michael Shammas [CZA L59/115].

23 Levontin et al. to PZE ("Abschrift"), September 5, 1929, CZA L59/147, 2; *Do'ar ha-Yom* November 4, 1929, 3, and November 6, 1929, 3; Triwaks, *Milḥama ve-Shalom*, 153, 200; Segev, *One Palestine, Complete*, 315, 320; Cohen, *Tarpat*, 170–72.

24 *Jewish Daily Bulletin* August 28, 1929, 3 and 8; Triwaks, *Milḥama ve-Shalom*, 72, 184. Dr. von Weisl's stab wounds required surgery and a prolonged convalescence. Undaunted, he settled permanently in Palestine the following year.

25 Tidhar, "Dr. Nahum Rizo Bar-Nes (Korkidi)," 7:2846; *Haaretz* November 18, 1929.

26 Agnon, *Mei-'Atsmi el 'Atsmi*, 423–31.

27 Levontin et al. to PZE ("Abschrift"), September 5, 1929, CZA L59/147, 2; Triwaks, *Milḥama ve-Shalom*, 76–78, 185–87; Tidhar, "Aryeh Leib Maklef, HY"D," 1:382–83; Cohen, *Tarpat*, 281–282. Mordechai Maklef, later third Chief of Staff of the IDF, survived the massacre.

28 Triwaks, *Milḥama ve-Shalom*, 138, 209–10.

29 Avissar, *Sefer Ḥevron*, 499–500.

30 Mordecai Eliash, "Memorandum to the PZE," October 14, 1929, Commission of Enquiry into the 1929 Riots, CZA S25/4601. Greenberg, "Hebron Massacre," 3–4n.

31 Cahill, "Going beserk," 64.

32 "Testimony of Dr. Zwi Kitayin," CZA L59/149 and S25/4601, Annex 72; Triwaks, *Milḥama ve-Shalom*, 84, 188; Greenberg, *The Hebron Massacre*, 3; Segev, *One Palestine, Complete*, 318–20. In 1924, Rabbi Nosson Finkel (d. 1927) and Rabbi Moses Mordecai Epstein transplanted 150 students and faculty en masse from Slobodka, Lithuania (now suburban Kaunas) to Hebron.

33 *Palestine Commission of the Disturbances*, 2:984.

34 Avissar, *Sefer Ḥevron*, 412–13.

35 *Do'ar ha-Yom* April 29, 1930, 1; Triwaks, *Milḥama ve-Shalom*, 86–87, 91–92, 189–92; Ze'evi, *Tevaḥ Ḥevron*, 15–16. Five of the twenty-four murdered yeshiva students were fatally attacked at Beit Kapiloto.

36 "Jewish doctors' report," September 11, 1929, and "Report of the Committee of Reference nominated by His Excellency the High Commissioner," September 13, 1929, CZA L59/147; Triwaks, *Milḥama ve-Shalom*, 94–96, 192–94; Ze'evi, *Tevaḥ Ḥevron*, 16.

37 Triwaks, *Milḥama ve Shalom*, 194, 197; Avissar, *Sefer Ḥevron*, 412–13; Ze'evi, *Tevaḥ Ḥevron*, 15, 96; Michlin, *Ma'asei Rokḥim*, 79–80.

38 Greenberg, "The Hebron Massacre," 6–7. The Americans, Aharon Reuven and Breine Bernzweig, described their ordeal in a letter to family.

39 Avissar, *Sefer Ḥevron*, 426, 444.

40 Dr. Zvi Kitayin to the PZE, September 25, 1929, CZA L59/147 [also S25/4601]; Triwaks, *Milḥama ve-Shalom*, 113, 199–200; Levy and Levy, *Rof'eha*, 426, 428.

41 *Davar* April 2, 1926, 4; *Do'ar ha-Yom* June 28, 1928, 3; *Do'ar Hayom* September 3, 1929, 1; *Palestine Post* October 4, 1934, 8; *Palestine Post* February 21, 1944, 3.

42 Van Paassen, *Pilgrim's Vow*, 122–123; Schechtman, Jabotinsky, 2:42, 54–56.

43 Van Paassen, *Days of Our Years*, 371, and *Pilgrim's Vow*, 124. Van Paassen's two slightly varying accounts of Ticho and Danziger's presence in Hebron on August 23, 1929, were published in 1939 + 1956 respectively.

44 Triwaks, *Milḥama ve-Shalom*, 131.

45 Avissar, *Sefer Ḥevron*, 422–26; Segev, *One Palestine, Complete*, 325–26, citing "Jews Saved by Arabs," CZA S25/4472 and CZA S25/3409.

46 Triwaks, *Milḥama ve-Shalom*, 115–16, 200; Tidhar, "Dr. Tuvia Avraham Sternberg," 4:2034. Dr. Tuvia Sternberg was seriously wounded by Arab snipers on August 29, 1929, while coming to the aid of the wounded in Safed.

47 Harry Friedenwald to Avraham Ticho, September 10, 1929, IMJ, Ticho Papers; Ruppin, *Pirkei Ḥayai*, 3:176.

48 *Jewish Daily Bulletin* September 4, 1929, 5 and 8, and September 6, 1929, 1–4 and 8.

49 *Do'ar ha-Yom* November 6, 1929, 3.

50 *Jewish Daily Bulletin* September 3, 1929, 7 and 9, and September 5, 1929, 1–2.

51 *Jewish Daily Bulletin* September 4, 1929, 1.

52 Levontin et al. to Zionist Executive c/o Col. Kisch (German with English press release attached), September 5, 1929, CZA L59/149; *Palestine Bulletin* September 8, 1929, 3; Z. Kitayin to PZE, September 9, 1929, CZA L59/147.

53 *Palestine Bulletin* September 5, 1929; Riots in Hebron Part II, CZA L59/147.

54 "H. J. Orr-Ewing, M.C., M.D., F.R.C.P.," *British Medical Journal* 294 (1987): 1700; "Sir John Strathearn C.B.E., M.D.," *British Medical Journal* 2 (1950): 578–79; "Stuart, George," *University of Aberdeen Roll*; "George Stuart, Obituary," *Aberdeen University Review* 45 (1973–74); Levy and Levy, *Rof'eha*, 275.

55 Levy and Levy, *Rof'eha*, 134–36.

56 G. Stuart, H. J. Orr-Ewing, and J. Strathearn, "Report of the Committee of Reference nominated by His Excellency the High Commissioner," September 13, 1929, CZA L59/147.

57 S. Getzova and G. Garry, "Jewish doctors' report," CZA L59/147.

58 *Do'ar ha-Yom* September 22, 1929, 1 and 4; Z. Kitayin to PZE, September 25, 1929, CZA L59/147.

59 Avissar, *Sefer Ḥevron*, 433; Ze'evi, *Tevaḥ Ḥevron*, 95–96.

60 Hirshberg, "Muzika ma'aravit," 440; Alex Baerwald to Berth Ticho, "Vor lieben…Mama Ticho," [21-page illustrated epistle] (German), IMJ, Ticho Papers, 5. Baerwald wrote, "Because his collection [of menorahs] is growing so quickly, I suffer from jealousy that is ruining my life."

61 Ze'evi, *Tevaḥ Ḥevron*, 35.

62 *Davar* October 25, 1929, 1; *Do'ar ha-Yom* November 3, 1929, 1; *Jewish Daily Bulletin* September 22, 1929, 1.

63 *Do'ar ha-Yom* November 4, 1929, 3 and [with same headline] November 6, 1929, 3.

64 Bentwich, *For Zion's Sake*, 178; Wasserstein, "Arab-Jewish Dilemma," 188; Heller, *Mi-'Brit Shalom' le-'Ihud'*, 50.

65 *Haaretz* November 12, 1929, 1, and November 17, 1929, 1; Debbi, *Story of a Family*, 133–34.

66 *Haaretz* November 13, 1929; Col. Frederick Kisch for Dr. A. Ticho and G. Pascale and Dr. Claudio Mancini for Dr. A. Ticho [visiting cards with well-wishes], November–December 1929, IMJ, Ticho Papers; Debbi, *Story of a Family*, 137; Salmon, *Beit Ticho*, 12 (Hebrew), 12 (English).

67 *Haaretz* November 17, 1929, 1 and November 18, 1929, 1; Levy and Levy, *Rof'eha*, 281, 348, 352. See also entries for Drs. Rokah, Sapir, and Rosenthal in Tidhar's encyclopedia.

68 IMJ, Ticho Papers, November–December 1929. The survival and preservation of so many of these letters (while many letters from other periods were not preserved) underscores the personal importance of this life-threatening attack in Ticho's life. Ophthalmologists who sent their personal well wishes included Dr. Harry Friedenwald from Baltimore, Dr. Max Meyerhof from Cairo, Dr. Nahum Shimkin

from Haifa, Dr. Erich Raubitcheck from Tel Aviv, and the British Ophthalmic Hospital's chief surgeon, Dr. John Strathearn.

69 Judah L. Magnes to A. Ticho, November 12, 1929, IMJ, Ticho Papers; Emanuel Mohl and Sophie (Berger) Mohl to A. Ticho, November 14, 1929, IMJ, Ticho Papers.

70 Rachel Stein Reich to Avraham Ticho, November 23, 1929, IMJ, Ticho Papers; *Do'ar ha-Yom* December 15, 1929, 4; *Davar* December 15, 1957, 3; Levy and Levy, *Rof'eha*, 384. Dr. Tabori came to Palestine from Russia in 1923 and was employed at that time by Hadassah Hospital in Haifa. He returned there after Ticho's discharge but later worked for Kupat Ḥolim.

71 *Davar* November 18, 1929, 1; CZA L59/116.

72 *Haaretz* November 18, 1929, 1; "*Haaretz* interview with Dr. Ticho" CZA L59/119.

73 "*Haaretz* interview with Dr. Ticho" CZA L59/119.

74 *Davar* November 25, 1929, 1.

75 *Davar* November 25, 1929, 1; *Jewish Daily Bulletin* November 26, 1929, 1, 4, and 8, and October 4, 1929, 1.

76 *Davar* December 2, 1929, 4.

77 Alex and Lotte Baerwald to A. Ticho, December 5, 1929, IMJ Ticho Papers; *Davar* 3 December 1929, December 4 and 5, 1929, 4; *Do'ar ha-Yom* December 9, 1929, 1, December 15, 1929, 4, and February 5, 1930, 4. The newspaper, *Davar*, initially reported that Ticho's practice would be closed for four to five months but retracted the misinformation just two days later.

78 *Do'ar ha-Yom* May 3, 1936, 1.

79 *Davar* January 31, 1930, 5; *Jewish Daily Bulletin* February 2, 1930, 2.

80 *Davar* April 2, 1930, 1; *Do'ar ha-Yom* April 2, 1930, 1.

81 Edelman, "Chayei Sarah: Rabbi A. I. Kook and Hebron," 12.

82 Bentwich and Bentwich, *Mandate Memories*, 140–41; Sykes, *Crossroads*, 114–15; Segev, *One Palestine, Complete*, 332–33.

83 *Davar* January 31, 1930, 1 and 6; *Maariv* March 17, 1958, 2; *Maariv* August 21, 1987, 106; Levy and Levy, *Rof'eha*, 140. At the time of his testimony at the Hinkis trial in 1930, Dr. Dajani was head of the Government Hospital in Jaffa.

84 *Do'ar ha-Yom* May 8, 1930, 1, and May 16, 1930, 1.

85 *Jewish Daily Bulletin* April 30, 1930, 2; *Do'ar ha-Yom* May 6, 1930, 1, and June 1, 1930, 1. Death sentences were not commuted for only two of the convicted Hebron murderers: Atta Ahmed al-Zir and Muhammed Kalil Abu Jimjon.

Chapter 19 – Storm on the Horizon

1 Isaac Michaelson to Albert Ticho, April 8, 1930 (handwritten letter and typed copy), IMJ, Ticho Archives. Prof. Michaelson did not make his long-sought aliyah until 1948. He had a distinguished career, serving as chairman of ophthalmology at Rambam Hospital in Haifa in 1949 and at Hadassah Hospital in Jerusalem in 1954. He received the Israel Prize in Medicine in 1960.

2 "Ticho – Peintures, Aquarelles, Dessins (Palestine) du 14 au 27 Novembre 1930 aux Quatre Chemins, 18 Rue Godot-de-Mauroy, Vernissage le Vendredi 14 Novembre à 15 heures." IMJ, Ticho Papers. Anna Ticho's preserved copy of the

announcement in the IMJ Ticho Papers includes interspersed, handwritten notes of names and addresses.

3   [Invitation in Hebrew and English], IMJ, Ticho Archives; *Do'ar ha-Yom* September 30, 1930, 4; Salmon, "Anna Ticho 1894–1980."

4   *Do'ar ha-Yom* October 6, 1930, 4; Tidhar, "Mordecai Narkiss," 9:3378–79.

5   *Do'ar ha-Yom* October 29, 1930, 4; Tidhar, "Prof. Yosef Breuer" and "Eliezer Yellin," 7:2836–7 and 2:792.

6   Debbi, *Story of a Family*, 168–70; Salmon, *Beit Ticho*, 14 (Hebrew), 16–17 (English). Just a short time before his death in 1960, Dr. Ticho helped organize a major exhibition of his Hanukkah lamp collection at the old Bezalel Museum. The exhibition was dedicated to his memory. Following Anna Ticho's death in 1980, the entire collection of Hanukkah lamps was bequeathed to the Israel Museum.

7   Arthur Schnitzler to Anna Ticho, February 21, 1931, IMJ, Ticho Papers; Felix Salten to Anna Ticho, February 24, 1931, IMJ, Ticho Papers; Hamann, *Hitler's Vienna*, 76–77. In 1905, Schnitzler's *Reigen* [The Round] was censured as pornographic. Salten not only wrote the novel *Bambi*, which Walt Disney made famous, but also the explicit *Josephine Mutzenbacher*.

8   Salmon, "Anna Ticho 1894–1980."

9   Ticho, *M'dor L'dor*, 121–23. Dr. Lizl Reiniger was the niece of Dr. Isidor Reiniger.

10   Czechoslovak General Consul (G. Pascale) to Albert Ticho, Memorandum 299/31 ("Certificat"), February 12, 1931, IMJ, Ticho Papers.

11   *Jewish Telegraphic Bulletin* February 27, 1931; *Do'ar ha-Yom* June 5, 1931, 1; Kisch, *Palestine Diary*, 390, 422–23.

12   *Davar* August 10, 1931, 1; Arlosoroff, *Jerusalem Diary*, October 22, 1931, December 16, 1931, April 25, 1932; Black, *Transfer Agreement*, 95–96; Segev, *One Palestine, Complete*, 344–55.

13   Lachman, "Arab rebellion," 65–66.

14   Rothkirchen, *Jews of Bohemia*, 162.

15   Kroyanker, "Swastikas over Jerusalem," *Haaretz* November 8, 2008.

16   Arnold and Beatrice Zweig to Albert and Anna Ticho (German), Berlin-Grunewald, April 21, 1932; Arnold Zweig to Anna Ticho (in German), Spindlermuehle, Republic of Czechoslovakia, March 21, 1933, IMJ, Ticho Papers.

17   Nakdimon, "Aḥarit davar" [Afterward], 200. Zweig moves his story years forward in time. De Haan was murdered in 1924 while De Vriendt's fictional murder takes place in 1929. The backdrop of de Haan and Sonnenfeld's diplomacy with Abdullah is replaced by negotiations of the fictional de Vriendt and *ḥaredi* Rabbi Seligmann with the mufti and high commissioner.

18   *Haaretz* May 20, 2011. Arnold Zweig immigrated to Palestine and settled in Haifa but never learned Hebrew. He returned to East Berlin after the war.

19   Levy and Levy, *Rofe'ha,* 214. After a few years in Jerusalem with Dr. Ticho, Dr. Heinz Cohen briefly settled in Ben Shemen. He opened a practice in Lydda caring for Arabs, but he was forced to leave at the beginning of the Arab Revolt.

20   Weltsch, "Wear It with Pride, The Yellow Badge" [English translation], *Jüdische Rundschau* 27 (April 4, 1933).

21   Levy, *Perakim*, 255–56; Levy and Levy, *Rof'eha*, 29.

22   *Palestine Post* April 10, 1933, 1; Black, *Transfer Agreement*, 95–96.

23 *Palestine Post* April 21, 1933, 5; *Do'ar ha-Yom* April 24, 1933, 4, and May 3, 1933, 4; Von Haugwitz, *Ophthalmology*, 259–63; "Rudolf Bergmeister," AUW Senat S304 59/12.

24 Erich and Else Raubitcheck (Baghdad) to Albert Ticho (Jerusalem), November 14, 1929, IMJ, Ticho Papers; Levy and Levy, *Rof'eha*, 340; Feigenbaum, *50 Shenot Oftalmologia*, 41–42; Gorin, *History of Ophthalmology*, 278; *Do'ar ha-Yom* May 26, 1933, 2. When the Raubitchecks moved to Baghdad, they left their adolescent children behind with Else's mother. After Else died, the children moved back to Czechoslovakia with their grandmother. They perished in the Holocaust.

25 *Do'ar ha-Yom* May 26, 1933, 2.

26 Shamash, *Memories of Eden*, 138, 151; Alexander, "Jews of Baghdad," 9.

27 Glass, *New Zion*, 66; Lyons Bar-David, *My Promised Land*, 74–75; *Do'ar ha-Yom* July 15, 1935, 4.

28 Fischer, *Anna Ticho: Sketches*, unnumbered pages [introductions to the book and the sketches of chapter 2].

29 Gorin, *History of Ophthalmology*, 393–94; von Haugwitz, *Ophthalmology*, 259–63; Levy and Levy, *Rof'eha*, 37–41. Many German ophthalmologists enthusiastically embraced Hitler including Heidelberg University Chairman Prof. August Wagenmann. Several prominent ophthalmologists were forced from their faculty positions such as Alfred Bielschowsky (University of Breslau), Aurel von Szily (University of Münster), and Karl Wessely (University of Munich).

30 Levy and Levy, *Rof'eha*, 315–16.

31 Levy, *Perakim*, 442–43; Levy and Levy, *Rof'eha*, 258–59; Segev, "The Making of History/Whodunit," *Haaretz* June 19, 2008.

32 *Davar* August 11, 1933, 3.

33 Tidhar, "Avraham Stavsky," 6:2700–01; Teveth, *Retzaḥ Arlosoroff*, 69–78; Bechor, *Va'adat ha-Hakira*, 138; Klabunde, *Magda Goebbels*, 186–99. While bringing weapons and refugees to Israel as a crew member aboard the *Altalena*, Stavsky was mortally wounded within a few hundred yards of where Arlosoroff was shot and likewise died after transport to Hadassah Hospital.

34 Black, *Transfer Agreement*, 150–53; Yahil, *Holocaust*, 100–104; Lavsky, *Before Catastrophe*, 247–48. Somewhat complex arrangements involved the Haavara Transfer Office, the Jewish trust company PALTREU, two different banks in Germany, and the Anglo-Palestine Bank.

35 *Davar* September 21, 1936, 1, and September 22, 1936, 1; Levy, *Perakim*, 244; Levy and Levy, *Rof'eha*, 77.

36 *Davar* February 12, 1935, 3, October 28, 1936, 1 and 6, and November 19, 1936, 7; Tidhar, "Dr. Moshe Beilinson," and "Arieh Sharon (Kurzmann)," 5:2085–86 and 7:2886; Levy, *Perakim*, 292 and 417–18; Levy and Levy, *Rof'eha*, 158 and 315–16. On September 1, 1934, Dr. Moshe Beilinson, announced German-born Bauhaus School graduate Arieh Sharon (Kurzmann) as the winner of the architectural competition for the Kupat Ḥolim Hospital project. Though weakened by recent influenza, Beilinson participated in opening ceremonies October 28, 1936.

37 Dr. Arthur Eloesser to Anna Ticho (in German), February 23, 1935, IMJ, Ticho Papers; [Announcement] "Dessins et Aquarelles de Palestine de Anna Ticho,"

(French), IMJ, Ticho Papers; Anna Ticho to Mr. Newman, December 12, 1946 (English), IMJ, Ticho Papers.

38 Joseph Budko to Anna Ticho (in German), February 25, 1935, IMJ, Ticho Papers; *Do'ar ha-Yom* October 24, 1935, 8. The report listed the following faculty members: "Joseph Budko, painter and graphic artist; Ze'ev Ben Techi, sculptor; Mordecai Bronstein, painter; Yehudah Wolport, metal sculptor; Shlomo Reiss, silversmith; Yerachmiel Schechter, architect and sketch artist.

39 *Palestine Post* January 15, 1934, 5 and January 17, 1934, 6; *Do'ar ha-Yom* February 12, 1934, 3; Rothkirchen, *Jews of Bohemia and Moravia*, 162.

40 *Palestine Post* January 18, 1934, 8; Fleisher, *Twenty Israeli Composers*, 83; Hirshberg, "Muzika Ma'aravit," 443.

41 *Palestine Post* January 12, 1934, 3; Aronson, *Orchestra of Exiles*.

42 Ofrat, "Jerusalem Mountains," 409.

43 Levin, *Balm in Gilead*, 161–63. The post-graduate institute was completed in April 1939.

44 Tidhar, "Yehoshua Henkin," "Ze'ev (Wilhelm) Brünn," and "Sonia Belkind," 2:752–55, 1:390–91, and 2:620.

45 Debbi, *Story of a Family*, 71.

46 Charles Ticho, *M'dor L'dor*, 133.

47 *JTA* June 3, 1935; *Davar* June 9, 1935, 6; Tidhar, "Yitzhak Leib Goldberg," 3:1283–84.

48 Levy and Levy, *Rof'eha*, 149. Dr. Mayer Holman soon returned to England after the evacuation of Kfar Etzion and set up a practice in Birmingham. During World War II, Holman served in the Royal Army Medical Corps in India, and for many years following the war, he practiced in several countries in Africa.

49 *JTA* November 10, 1935, November 12, 1935, November 21, 1935, and November 22, 1935; *Palestine Post* November 21, 1935, 1 and 5; Segev, *One Palestine, Complete*, 360–362; Pappe, *The Husaynis*, 269–71.

50 *Palestine Post* March 2, 1936, 1 and 5, and March 3, 1936, 1.

51 *Palestine Post* April 16, 1936, 1, April 21, 1936, 1 and 5, and April 27, 1936, 1; *JTA* April 19, 1936; Levy, *Perakim*, 277–79. The World Jewish Congress of Physicians (April 21–27, 1936) opened in Tel Aviv, then moved to Jerusalem and closed at the Hebrew University.

52 *Palestine Post* May 18, 1936, 1 and 5; Segev, *One Palestine, Complete*, 365–6; Hughes, "Assassination in Jerusalem," 8.

53 *Palestine Post* April 24, 1936, 1 and May 17, 1936, 10; Charles Ticho, *M'dor L'dor*, 123.

54 *Palestine Post* March 3, 1936, 7, December 30, 1936, December 31, 1936, 13, and January 1, 1937, 6; *JTA* December 27, 1936; Gilbert, *Israel: A History*, 186.

55 *Palestine Post* November 13, 1936, 1, January 4, 1937, 1, and January 7, 1937, 1 and 8.

56 *Palestine Post* January 12, 1937, 1, January 13, 1937, 5; February 1, 1937, 2, and February 7, 1937, 7.

57 *Palestine Post* December 31, 1936. The committee to pay tribute to Dr. Wallach that Ticho joined was comprised of several leaders in the community.

58   Max Eisler to Anna Ticho, April 10, 1936, July 1, 1937, July 13, 1937, and July 18, 1937, [correspondences] (in German), IMJ Ticho Papers; Anna Ticho, *Palästina*, 1937; Anna Ticho, *Jerusalem, 1950*; *Österreichisches Biographisches Lexikon*, 238; Anna Ticho to Mr. Newman, 12 December 1946 (English), IMJ Ticho Papers.

59   *Palestine Partition Commission Report*, presented by the Secretary of State for the Colonies, London, 1937, Cmd. 5479, 381–82.

60   *Palestine Partition Commission Report*, London, 1938, Cmd. 5854; Heller, *Mi-'Brit Shalom' le-'Ihud'*, 95; Sykes, *Crossroads*, 176; Gilbert, *Israel: A History*, 86–89; Lachman, "Arab rebellion," 81; Pappe, *The Husaynis*, 280–84, 346. District Commissioner of Galilee Lewis Y. Andrews and a constable were assassinated in Nazareth on September 26, 1937. On October 12, 1937, Haj Amin al-Husayni slipped out of Jerusalem and, with one brief exception, he never returned to Palestine.

61   "The Palestine landscape: Anna Ticho's drawings," *Palestine Post* February 1, 1938, 6; Scholem, *Walter Benjamin*, 205, 219.

62   Yahil, *Holocaust*, 104–8. Seyss-Inquart was tried for his crimes and executed in Nuremberg in 1946. Eichmann was captured, tried, and executed in Israel in 1962.

63   Crowe, *Oskar Schindler*, 2, 11–15, 41–43.

64   Yahil, *Holocaust*, 111.

65   Charles Ticho, *M'dor L'dor*, 26, 93–94, 96–97.

66   Ticho, *M'dor L'dor*, 150; Debbi, *Story of a Family*, 46, 58–59.

67   Levy and Levy, *Rof'eha*, 300; Golz, *Refu'at*, 41.

68   Toaff, *Sefer Zikhron*, 100. All possibility of Dr. Cassuto's escape would end with Italy's declaration of war against Great Britain and France on June 10, 1940. He was eventually arrested by the Gestapo and, after a three-month stay in an Italian prison, he was taken to various concentration camps. After his evacuation from Auschwitz toward the end of the war, he was murdered by the Germans somewhere in Silesia.

69   Debbi, *Story of a Family*, 59, 262, 278–82, 338–40; Yahil, *Holocaust*, 116. Alfred Ticho and Ella Reiniger eventually married in a religious ceremony, making their fictitious marriage a reality. Henry Ticho was reunited with his parents in Paris with the help of cousin Fritzi (Jacob and Emma Ticho's daughter) and her husband Moniek Mann; the three left Czechoslovakia by plane in February 1939, one of the last flights to France before the borders were closed.

70   *Davar* March 12, 1939, 7; *Palestine Post* March 23, 1939, 6; Tidhar, "Yisrael (Karl) Schwarz," 5:2325. Schuelein was one of the founders of the New Secession group in Munich and he was also a member of the Deutsche Kunstlerbund and of the Berlin Secession.

71   Rothkirchen, *Jews of Bohemia and Moravia*, 98; Yahil, *Holocaust*, 116. Germany's annexation of a part of Lithuania was the last of the "bloodless annexations" of territories separated from the German or Austrian Empires by the Treaty of Versailles.

72   Rothkirchen, *Jews of Bohemia and Moravia*, 162–63; Gilbert, *Israel: A History*, 186–89.

CHAPTER 20 – CULMINATION

1 Debbi, *Story of a Family*, 103, 249, 280–1, 341.
2 Debbi, *Story of a Family*, 75, 264–69; Yahil, *The Holocaust*, 114, 116.
3 Ticho, *M'dor L'dor*, 231–236.
4 Lederer, "Terezín," 3:110; Rothkirchen, "Jews of Bohemia and Moravia: 1938–1945," 3:55–59; Rothkirchen, *Jews of Bohemia and Moravia*, 233–36; Kulka, "Annihilation," 3:275.
5 Debbi, *Story of a Family*, 53, 73, 119–121, 190–91, 267. Debbi's book records details of transports and the deaths for each of the Ticho family members deported to Terezín and those further transferred to the death camps in Poland.
6 Ticho, *M'dor L'dor*, 89–91.
7 Hurwitz, *Kol ha-'Am Ḥazit*, 222–3, 314; Nissan, "Hitpatḥut sheirutei," 319; Levy and Levy, *Rof'eha*, 180–1, 370–1
8 *Palestine Post* June 2, 1941; Nissan, "Hitpatḥut sheirutei," 320; Pappe, *The Husaynis*, 316–8.
9 *Palestine Post* June 21, 1942, 1; Sykes, *Crossroads*, 210–212.
10 *Glasgow Herald* February 27, 1942, 1; *London Gazette* August 13, 1946, 37685:4093. Field Marshal Archibald Wavell (commander-in-chief in India and soon to be viceroy of India) had lost his left eye in World War I but there are no records of late, secondary ophthalmic treatment. Ticho's patient was possibly Major-General Eric Grant Miles, commander of the 56th Infantry Division of the British 10th Army, wounded in 1943 and forced to return to the United Kingdom.
11 Levin, *Balm in Gilead*, 172–4; Sykes, *Crossroads*, 235–6; Heller, *Brit Shalom*, 203; Salmon, *Beit Ticho*, 16.
12 *Palestine Post* August 19, 1942, 4; September 4, 1942, 4; October 9, 1942, 4; and December 18, 1942, 1; Debbi, *Story of a Family*, 104.
13 Agnon, *Mei-'Atzmi el Atzmi*, 313–15.
14 Isaiah 66:10.
15 Heller, *Mi-'Brit Shalom' le-'Iḥud'*, 301–6; Sykes, *Crossroads*, 292.
16 Hurwitz, *Kol ha-'Am Ḥazit*, 265.
17 *Palestine Post* July 23, 1946, 1; Gilbert, *Israel: A History*, 134–5.
18 *Palestine Post* June 14, 1947, 1; August 8, 1947, 2; October 1, 1947, 1; October, 2, 1947, 1; Yakhin, *Story of Elnakam*, 196–215.
19 *Palestine Post* July 15, 1947, 1 and 3, and July 18, 1947, 1; Heller *Mi-'Brit Shalom' le-'Iḥud'*, 348.
20 Gilbert, *Israel: A History*, 145, 155.
21 *Palestine Post* March 18, 1948, 1, and April 14, 1948, 1; Levin, *Balm in Gilead*, 204–14; Levy, *Perakim*, 192; Levy and Levy, *Rof'eha*, 142–3. Dr. Leonid Doljansky was the son of Prof. Jacob Doljansky.
22 Esther Ticho, Interview January 22, 2008; Debbi, *Story of a Family*, 162, 249, 251.
23 *Palestine Post* May 14, 1948; *Palestine Post*, September 12, 1948; Gilbert, *Israel*, 114.
24 *Palestine Post* May 16, 1948; Levin, *Balm in Gilead*, 217–8; Segev, *One Palestine, Complete*, 516.

Epilogue

1   Levin, *It Takes a Dream*, 259; Debbi, *Story of a Family*, 154.
2   Gilbert, *Israel: A History*, 241.
3   Nashef, "Tawfiq Canaan," 14.
4   Salmon, *Ticho House*, 20.
5   Gorin, *History of Ophthalmology*, 486. The first lecture was given by Dr. Irving Leopold in 1970; the second by Dr. Carl Kupfer in 1974 (entitled, "Cooperative Clinical Trials"); and the third by Dr. Gunter von Noorden in 1977.

BIBLIOGRAPHY

ARCHIVES

AJHS   American Jewish Historical Society Archives (New York, NY)

AUW   Archiv Universität Wien (Vienna)

AUK   Archiv Univerzity Karlovy (Prague)

CZA   Central Zionist Archives (Jerusalem)

HA   Hadassah Archives (New York, NY)

HHStA   Haus-, Hof- und Staatsarchiv (Vienna)

IMJ   Israel Museum (Jerusalem)
        Ticho Papers, Israel Museum, Jerusalem
        Ticho Archives, Ticho House (Israel Museum Annex), Jerusalem

KC   Kheel Center for Labor Management Documentation and Archives,
        Martin P. Catherwood Library, Cornell University (Ithaca, NY)
        Isaac Max Rubinow Papers

LOC   Library of Congress (Washington, DC)
        Matson Photographic Collection and Henry Morgenthau, Sr. Papers

ÖStAK   Österreichisches Staatsarchiv – Kriegsarchiv

WSL   Wiener Stadt- und Landesarchiv (Vienna)

SELECTED NEWSPAPERS AND PERIODICALS

Cathedra [*Katedra le-Toldot Eretz Yisrael ve-Yishuveha*] (Hebrew)

Davar (Hebrew)

Do'ar ha-Yom (Hebrew)

Haaretz (Hebrew)

Hadassah Bulletin

Ha-Or [formerly *Hazevi* and *Hashkafa*] (Hebrew)

Ḥavatzelet (Hebrew)

Ha-Ḥerut (Hebrew)
Harefuah (Hebrew)
Ha-Tsefira (Hebrew)
JTA (Jewish Telegraphic Agency)
Jewish Daily Bulletin
The Maccabæan (New York: Federation of American Zionists, 1901–1914)
Moria (Hebrew)
New York Times
Palestine Post

REPORTS, PROCEEDINGS, CATALOGUES, DIRECTORIES

Actions Committee of the Zionist Organization, *The Struggle for the Hebrew Language in Palestine* (English translation of original German publication, 71 pages). New York: Federation of American Zionists, 1914.

Ashbee, C. R., ed. *Jerusalem 1920–1922 Being the Records of the Pro-Jerusalem Council during the First Two Years of the Civil Administration.* London: John Murray for the Council of the Pro-Jerusalem Society, 1924.

British Ophthalmic Hospital, Jerusalem…. *Report from 1st January, 1912 to 31st December, 1912.* London: Charles Cull and Son, 1913.

———. *Report of the Committee for the Year Ended 31 December, 1914.* London: Chancery of the Order of the Hospital of St. John of Jerusalem in England, 1915.

———. *Report of the Committee by Colonel Sir Courtauld Thomson, K.B.E, C.B., Chairman.* London: Chancery of the Order…., 1919.

The British Ophthalmic Hospital and Hospice of the Order of St. John (English Language) at Jerusalem. *Second Annual Report.* London: Harrison and Sons, June 24th, 1884.

Catalogue of Officers and Graduates of Columbia University,16th ed. New York: Columbia University, 1916.

Committee of the Palestine Exhibition and Bazaar (May 13–14, 1912): Awakening Palestine. London: The Anglo-Jewish Association, 1912.

Du'aḥ shel Ve'idat ha-Gar'enet mi-Shnat 1914 [Proceedings of the First Trachoma Conference in Palestine, 1914, Aryeh Teëni-Feigenbaum and Aryeh Shimoni-Mäkler, uncredited eds.] (Hebrew). Jerusalem: Trachoma Division, Jewish Health Bureau, 1915.

Hadassah Medical Organization (Formerly the American Zionist Medical Unit), *Third Report September, 1920 – December, 1921.* Jerusalem, 1922.

Lehmann's Allgemeiner Wohnungs-Anzeiger: nebst Handels- und Gewerbe-Adreßbuch für die k.k. Reichshaupt und Residenzstadt Wien und Umgebung. Wien: A. Hölder, 1859–1942.

"Lemaan Zion," *Palästina,* 1908.

Öffentliche Vorlesungen an der K. K. Universität zu Wien [university course catalogue published twice yearly]. Wien: Adolf Holzhausen, k. und k. Hof- und Universitätsbuchdrucker, 1902–07.

Palestine Commission of the Disturbances of August 1929 [3 vols. on microfilm] Colonial [Office] No. 48. London: H.M.S.O., 1930.

A Survey of Palestine, Prepared in December 1945–1946. Palestine: Anglo-American Committee of Inquiry, 1946.

Turei Yeshurun: Special Edition on the Occasion of the 80th Anniversary of Yeshurun-Jerusalem 5684–5764 (Hebrew and English). Jerusalem, Yeshurun Central Synagogue: 5764/2003.

ENCYCLOPEDIAS, DICTIONARIES, BIBLIOGRAPHIES, SYLLABI

Alcalay, Ruben. *The Complete Hebrew-English Dictionary.* Hartford, CT: Prayer Book Press, Inc., 1965.

Chisholm, Hugh, ed. *Encyclopædia Britannica: A Dictionary of Arts, Sciences, Literature and General Information.* 12th ed. (vols. 30–32). London: Encyclopædia Britannica Co., 1922.

Garrison, Fielding H, ed. *Index Medicus: A Monthly Classified Record of the Current Medical Literature of the World, 2nd Series Volume 12 January–December, 1914.* Washington, D.C.: The Carnegie Institution of Washington, 1914.

Goetz, Philip W., ed. *The New Encyclopædia Britannica,* 15th ed. (29 volumes plus guides and indices). Chicago: Encyclopaedia Britannica, Inc., 1991.

Hensyl, William R., ed. *Stedman's Medical Dictionary,* 25th ed. Baltimore: Williams and Wilkins, 1990.

Herbermann, Charles George, Edward A. Pace, Condé B. Pallen, Rev. Thomas J. Shahan, and Rev. John J. Wynne, eds. *The Catholic Encyclopedia.* (15 volumes). New York: Robert Appleton Company, 1907–1913.

Heuberger, Rachel. *Rabbi Nehemiah Anton Nobel – The Jewish Renaissance in*

Frankfurt am Main. Frankfurt am Main: Societäts-Verlag [Schriftenreihe des Jüdischen Museums], 2007.

Hyman, Paula, ed. *Jewish Women: A Comprehensive Historical Encyclopedia* (CD-ROM). Philadelphia: Jewish Publication Society, 2007.

Klein, Ernest. *A Comprehensive Etymological Dictionary of the Hebrew Language for Readers of English.* Jerusalem: Carta Jerusalem and the University of Haifa, 1987.

Marquis, Albert Nelson, ed. *The Book of the Detroiters. A Biographical Dictionary of Leading Living Men of the City of Detroit.* Chicago: A. N. Marquis and Company, 1908.

Norman, Jeremy N., ed. *Morton's Medical Bibliography, Fifth Edition, An Annotated Check-list of Texts Illustrating the History of Medicine (Garrison and Morton).* Aldershot, England: Scolar Press, 1991.

Orr, James, ed. *The International Standard Bible Encyclopaedia* (4 volumes). Chicago: The Howard-Severance Co., 1915.

Österreichisches Biographisches Lexikon und biographische Dokumentation 1815–1950. Vienna: Osterreichischen Akademie der Wissenschaften, 1956.

Oxford English–Hebrew and Hebrew–English Dictionary. Oxford: Oxford University Press, 1994.

Rosenthal, Ruvik. *Milon ha-Sleng ha-Makif* [Dictionary of Israeli Slang] (Hebrew). Jerusalem: Keter, 2005.

Singer, Isidore, ed. *The Jewish Encyclopedia* (12 volumes). New York: Funk and Wagnalls Company, 1901–1910.

Skolnik, Fred, and Michael Berenbaum, eds. *Encyclopaedia Judaica,* 2nd ed. (22 volumes). Farmington Hills: Thomson Gale, 2007.

Somel, Selcuk Aksin. *Historical Dictionary of the Ottoman Empire: Ancient Civilizations and Historical Eras, No. 7.* Lanham, Maryland: The Scarecrow Press, Inc., 2003.

Stedman's Medical Dictionary, 25th ed. Baltimore: Williams and Wilkins, 1990.

Tidhar, David. *Entsiklopedyah le-Ḥalutsei ha-Yishuv u-Vonav: Demuyot u-Temunot* [Encyclopedia of the Founders and Builders of Israel] (Hebrew, 19 volumes). Tel Aviv: Sifriyat Rishonim, 1947–1971.

Tucker, Spencer C., and Pricilla Mary Roberts, eds. *World War I Encyclopedia*

(5 volumes). Santa Barbara, California: ABC-CLIO, 2005.

Universität Wien. *Öffentliche Vorlesungen an der K. K. Universität zu Wien im ... Winter-Semester 1902/3 – Sommer-Semester 1907* [curriculum offerings of individual university semesters, collated into reference volumes on shelf in the reading room of the Archiv Universität Wien]. Wien: Druck von Adolf Holzhausen, k. und k. Hof- und Universitätsbuchdrucker, 1902–1907.

University of Aberdeen's Roll of Graduates 1901–1925, Med-Chi Library Archives, Aberdeen, Scotland.

Wagret, M. P., ed. *Nagel's Encyclopedia-Guide: Turkey*, 3rd ed. Geneva: Nagel Publishers, 1984.

Wood, Casey A., ed. *The American Encyclopedia and Dictionary of Ophthalmology*. Chicago: Cleveland Press, 1913–1921.

BOOKS, CHAPTERS, AND ARTICLES

Aaronsohn, Alexander. "Saïfna Ahmar, Ya Sultan! (Our Swords are Red, O Sultan)." *Atlantic Monthly* 118 (July, 1916): 1–12, and 118 (August, 1916): 188–96.

Abu-Lebdeh, Hatem Shareef. *Conflict and Peace in the Middle East: National Perceptions and United States-Jordan Relations*. Lanham, MD: University Press of America, 1997.

Adler, Joan. "Debunking 'The Story.'" *Straus Historical Society Newsletter*, 9 (2007): 1.

Adler, Selig. "The Palestine question in the Wilson era," *Jewish Social Studies* 10 (1948): 303–44.

Agnon, Shmuel Yosef. *Mei-'Atzmi el 'Atzmi* [From Myself to Myself] (Hebrew). Jerusalem and Tel Aviv: Schocken, 2000.

Albert, Daniel M., and Paul Henkind. *Men of Vision: Lives of Notable Figures in Ophthalmology*. Philadelphia: W. B. Saunders Company, 1993.

Albert, Daniel M., and Diane D. Edwards, eds. *The History of Ophthalmology*. Cambridge, MA: Blackwell Science, 1996.

Albert, Daniel M., and Frederick A. Jakobiec, eds. *Principles and Practice of Ophthalmology: Clinical Practice* (5 volumes). Philadelphia: W. B. Saunders, 1994.

Alexander, Ari. "The Jews of Baghdad and Zionism: 1920–1948." Master's thesis, Magdalen College, University of Oxford, 2004.

Alfassi, Yitzhak. *Yerushalayim: Toldot Yerushalayim ba-Shanim 5648–5748 (1888–1988) Be-Re'i Lishkat "Yerushalayim" shel Bnai Brit* [Jerusalem: History of Jerusalem in the Years 1888–1988: In the Light of the "Jerusalem" Lodge of B'nai B'rith] (Hebrew). Jerusalem: B'nai B'rith Jerusalem Lodge, 1988.

Alroey, Gur. "Journey to early-twentieth-century Palestine as a Jewish immigrant experience," *Jewish Social Studies* 9 (2003): 28–64.

———. "Meshartei ha-moshava 'o rodanim gasei ru'aḥ: Me'ah shana le-agudat 'Ha-Shomer': Perspektiva histori" [Settlement guards or uncouth tyrants: One hundred years of the organization "HaShomer": Historical perspective] (Hebrew), *Cathedra* 133 (2009/5770): 77–104.

Alsberg, Paul A. "The Israel State Archives as a source for the history of Palestine during the Period of Ottoman rule," in Moshe Ma'oz, ed., *Studies on Palestine during the Ottoman Period*, 533–44. Jerusalem: Magnes-Hebrew University-Yad Izhak Ben-Zvi, 1975.

Aronson, Josh (writer, director). *Orchestra of Exiles* [documentary film with re-enactments] (English). Aronson Film Associates and United Channel Movies: USA, 2012.

Aruri, Naseer Hasan. *Jordan: A study in political development (1921–1965)*. The Hague: M. Nijhoff, 1972.

Avissar, Esther. *Bayit bi-Yerushalayim* [A House in Jerusalem] (Hebrew). Tel Aviv: Iyar, 1979; reprinted paperback edition, Tel Aviv: Yedi'ot Aḥaronot/ Sifrei Ḥamad, unknown date.

Avissar, Oded, ed. *Sefer Hebron* [The Book of Hebron] (Hebrew). Jerusalem: Keter Publishing House, 1970.

Baedeker, Karl (Firm). *Austria-Hungary: Including Dalmatia and Bosnia, Handbook for Travellers*. Leipzig: Karl Baedeker, 1905.

———. *Palestine and Syria: With the Chief Routes through Mesopotamia and Babylonia*, 4th Edition. Leipzig: Karl Baedeker, 1906.

———. *Palestine and Syria with Routes through Mesopotamia and Babylonia and the Island of Cyprus: Handbook for Travellers*, 5th ed. Leipzig: Karl Baedeker, 1912a.

———. *Southern Italy and Sicily with Excursions to Sardinia, Malta, and Corfu: Handbook for Travellers*. Leipzig: Karl Baedeker, 1912b.

————. *Egypt and the Sûdân: Handbook for Travellers*, 7th ed. Leipzig: Karl Baedeker, 1914.

————. *The Rhine from the Dutch to the Alsatian Frontier*, 18th revised edition. Leipzig: Karl Baedeker, 1926.

Balfour, Arthur. *Speeches on Zionism*, edited by Israel Cohen. London: J. W. Arrowsmith Ltd., 1928.

Ballobar, Conde de. *Diario de Jerusalen 1914–1919*, edited with an introduction and notes by Eduardo Manzano Moreno (Spanish). Madrid: Nerea, 1996.

Bard, Mitchell Geoffrey, and Schwartz, Moshe. *1001 Facts Everyone Should Know about Israel*. Oxford: Rowman and Littlefield Publishers, Inc., 2005.

Bartal, Nira. *Ḥemla ve-Yeda: Perakim be-Toldot ha-Si'ud be-Eretz-Yisrael, 1918–1948* [Compassion and Competence: Nursing in Mandatory Palestine 1918–1948] (Hebrew). Jerusalem: Yad Izhak Ben-Zvi, 2005.

Barua, Dhiman. "History of cholera." In *Cholera* edited by Dhiman Barua and William B. Greenough, 1–2. New York: Plenum, 1992.

Barua, Dhiman and William B. Greenough, eds., *Cholera*. New York: Plenum, 1992.

Bechor, David, Eliezer Berkowitz, and Max Keneth. *Va'adat ha-Ḥakira le-Ḥakirat Retzaḥ Dr. Chaim Arlosoroff HY"D* [State Investigative Committee of the Murder of Dr. Chaim Arlosoroff]. Jerusalem: State of Israel, 1985.

Beller, Steven. *Vienna and the Jews, 1867–1938: A Cultural History*. Cambridge: Cambridge University Press, 1989.

Beller, Steven, ed. *Rethinking Vienna 1900*. New York: Berghahn Books, 2001.

Ben-Arieh, Yehoshua. *'Ir bi-Re'i Tekufa* [A City Reflected in Its Times] (Two volumes in Hebrew: vol. 1 *Yerushalayim be-Mei'ah ha-Tesha-Esrei: Ha-'Ir ha-'Atika* [Jerusalem in the Nineteenth Century: The Old City]; and vol. 2, *Yerushalayim ha-Ḥadasha be-Reishitah* [New Jerusalem: The Beginnings]). Jerusalem: Yad Izhak Ben-Zvi, 1977 and 1979.

Ben-Arieh, Yehosua, ed. *Yerushalayim bi-Tekufat ha-Mandat: Ha-Asiyah ve-ha-Moreshet* [Jerusalem and the British Mandate: Interaction and Legacy] (Hebrew). Jerusalem: Mishkenot Sha'ananim and Yad Izhak Ben-Zvi, 2003.

Ben-Arieh, Yehoshua, Yossi Ben-Arzi, and Haim Goren, eds. *Meḥkarim be-Geografiyah Historit-Yishuvit shel Eretz-Yisrael* [Historical-Geographical Studies in the Settlement of Eretz Israel]. Jerusalem: Yad Izhak Ben-Zvi, 1987.

Bendz, Jacob Christian. "Quelques considérations sur la nature de l'ophthalmie dite militaire, par rapport à son apparition dans l'armée danoise depuis 1851." *Ann Oculist* (Brux.) 33 (1855): 164–76.

Bennhold, H. "Prof. Dr. Carl Hegler, 1878–1943." *Deutsche medizinische Wochenschrift* 70 (1944): 163.

Ben-Reuven, Sara and Rami Ben-Reuven. *Nashim 'Ivriyot be-Damesek, 1917–1918* [Hebrew Women in Damascus, 1917–1918] (Hebrew). Jerusalem: Ariel Publishing House, 2010.

Bentwich, Norman. *A Wanderer between Two Worlds*. London: Routledge and Kegan Paul, 1941.

———. *For Zion's Sake: A Biography of Judah L. Magnes*. Philadelphia: Jewish Publication Society of America, 1954.

Bentwich, Norman and Helen Bentwich. *Mandate Memories, 1918–1948*. New York: Schocken Books, 1965.

Ben-Yehudah, Eliezer. *He-Ḥalom ve-Shivro: Mivḥar Ketavim be-'Inyanei Lashon* [The Dream and Its Fulfillment: Selected Writings], edited with addition of a foreward and notes by Reuven Sivan (Hebrew). Jerusalem: Sifriyat Dorot, Bialik Institute, 1978.

Ben Yehudah, Hemda. "When the war came to Palestine," in Ben Yehuda, Hemda, et al., *Jerusalem: Its Redemption and Future: The Great Drama of Deliverance Described by Eyewitnesses*. New York: The Christian Herald, 1918.

Ben Yehuda, Hemda, et al., *Jerusalem: Its Redemption and Future: The Great Drama of Deliverance Described by Eyewitnesses*. New York: The Christian Herald, 1918.

Ben-Yehudah, Nachman. *Political Assassinations by Jews: A Rhetorical Device for Justice*. Albany, NY: State University of New York Press, 1993.

Bergmeister, Otto. "Zur Entwicklungsgesch. des Saugethier-Auges" (German). *Mitt Embryol Inst Wien, Heft* 1 (1877): 63.

Berkley, George E. *Vienna and Its Jews: The Tragedy of Success, 1880–1980s*. Cambridge, MA and Lanham, MD: Abt Books and Madison Books, 1988.

Bieber, Yehoash. *"Be-Iqvot Sofrim bi-Yerushalayim"* [In the Footsteps of Authors in Jerusalem]. In *Yerushalayim: Mivḥar Ma'amarim*, edited by Eli Schiller, 279–86. Jerusalem: Ariel, 1993.

Biemann, Asher D. "Review [of *Tagebücher 1915 bis 1927* by Eugen Hoeflich]," *Modern Judaism* 21 (2001): 175–84.

Birn, Donald S. *Preface to Middle East Policy and Diplomacy, 1904–1956. The Private Letters and Diaries of Sir Ronald Storrs (1881–1955) from Pembroke College Cambridge.* Microfilm Edition. Marlborough, Wiltshire, England, Adam Matthew Publications, Ltd. Pelham House, London Road, 1998.

Bitsori, Maria, and Emmanouil Galanakis. "Doctors versus artists: Gustav Klimt's *Medicine.*" *British Medical Journal* 325 (2002): 1506–8.

Black, Edwin. *The Transfer Agreement.* New York: Macmillan Publishing Company, 1984.

Bloom, Etan. "Arthur Ruppin and the Production of the Modern Hebrew Culture" (PhD diss., Tel Aviv University, 2008).

Blyth, Estelle. *When We Lived in Jerusalem.* London: J. Murray, 1927.

Bonaparte, Marie, Anna Freud, and Ernst Kris, eds. *Sigmund Freud: The Origins of Psycho-analysis: Letters to Wilhelm Fliess, Drafts and Notes, 1887–1902.* Translated by Eric Mosbacher and James Strachey. New York: Imago Publishing Co., 1954.

Boureau, Alain. *Kantorowicz: Stories of a Historian.* Translated by Stephen G. Nichols and Gabrielle M. Spiegel. Baltimore: Johns Hopkins University Press, 2001.

Boyer, John W. *Political Radicalism in Late Imperial Vienna: Origins of the Christian Social Movement 1848–1897.* Chicago: University of Chicago Press, 1981.

Bránský, Jaroslav. *The Fate of the Jews of Boskovice and of the former County of Boskovice* (Czech). Prague: Prague Jewish Museum, 1991.

———. *The Boskovice Jewish Ghetto Sights: Guide to an Instructional Tour Around the Former Jewish Town, Boskovice* (pamphlet). Prague: Friends of Boskovice Club, 1999.

Brian, Denis. *Einstein: A Life.* New York: John Wiley and Sons, 1996.

Brown, Theodore M., "Isaac Max Rubinow," *American Journal of Public Health* 87 (1997): 1863–64.

Brünn, Ze'ev. "The organization of the war against trachoma." In *Du'aḥ shel Ve'idat ha-Gar'enet mi-Shnat 1914* [Proceedings of the First Trachoma Conference in Palestine, 1914, Aryeh Teëni-Feigenbaum and Aryeh Shimoni-Mäkler, uncredited eds.] (Hebrew), 84–95. Jerusalem: Trachoma Division, Jewish Health Bureau, 1915.

Buber, Martin. *A Land of Two Peoples*, edited with commentary and a new preface by Paul Mendes-Flohr. Chicago: University of Chicago Press, 2005.

Buhler-Wilkerson, Karen. "Bringing care to the people: Lillian Wald's legacy to Public Health Nursing." *American Journal of Public Health* 83 (1993): 1778–86.

Buttrick, George Arthur, ed. *The Interpreter's Bible*. Nashville, Tennessee: Abingdon-Cokesbury Press, 1953.

Cahill, Richard Andrew. "'Going beserk': 'Black and Tans' in Palestine," *Jerusalem Quarterly* 38 (2009): 59–68.

Carey, Joseph. *A Ghost in Trieste*. Chicago: University of Chicago Press, 1993.

Carmel, Alex. *Hityashvut ha-Germanim be-Eretz Yisrael be-Shilhei ha-Tekufa ha-Otomanit* [The German Colony in Eretz Yisrael at the End of the Ottoman Period] (Hebrew). Jerusalem: Hebrew University, 1973.

Carroll, James. *Constantine's Sword, The Church and the Jews: A History*. Boston and New York: Houghton Mifflin Company, 2001.

Castiglione, Vittore. "Trieste." In *The Jewish Encyclopedia*, 7:259–60. New York and London: Funk and Wagnalls Company, 1907.

Chandler, Tertius. *Four Thousand Years of Urban Growth: An Historical Census*. Lewiston, NY: St. David's University Press, 1987.

Chance, Burton. "Harry Friedenwald, MD" *Transactions of the American Ophthalmological Society* 48 (1950): xxxiv–xxxviii.

Clere, J. J. "Bibliographie de Raymond Weill." *Revue d'Egyptologie* 8 (1951): vii–xvi.

Cleveland, William and Martin P. Bunton, *A History of the Modern Middle East*, 4th ed. Boulder, CO: Westview Press, 2009.

Cline, Eric H. *The Battles of Armageddon: Megiddo and the Jezreel Valley from the Bronze Age to the Nuclear Age*. Ann Arbor, Michigan: The University of Michigan Press, 2000.

———. *Jerusalem Besieged: From Ancient Canaan to Modern Israel*. Ann

Arbor, Michigan: The University of Michigan Press, 2004.

Cohen, Hillel. *Tarpat: Shenat ha-Efes ba-Sikhsukh ha-Yehudi-'Aravi* [1929: Year Zero in the Jewish-Arab Conflict]. Tel Aviv: Keter 2013.

Criss, Nur Bilge. *Istanbul Under Allied Occupation, 1918–1923*. Leiden and Boston: Brill, 1999.

Crowe, David. *Oskar Schindler: The Untold Account of His Life, Wartime Activities, and the True Story Behind the List*. Cambridge, MA: Westview Press, 2004.

Curto, Silvio. "Ernesto Schiaparelli." *Atti della Accademia delle scienze di Torino* 138 (2004): 7–23.

Dash, Joan. *Summoned to Jerusalem: The Life of Henrietta Szold*. New York: Harper and Row, 1979.

———. "Doing good in Palestine: Magnes and Henrietta Szold." In *Like All the Nations? The Life and Legacy of Judah L. Magnes*, edited by William M. Brinner and Moses Rischin, 99–111. Albany: State University of New York Press, 1987.

Davis, Edwin John. *Life in Asiatic Turkey: A Journal of Travel in Cilicia (Pedias and Trachoea), Isauria, and Parts of Lycaonia and Cappadocia*. London: Edward Stanford, 1879.

Debbi (Kritzler), Miri. *Ticho: The Story of a Family*. Translated by Susan and Noam Gordon. Tel-Aviv: Reches Publishing House Educational Projects Ltd., 1994. Originally published as *Sipurim mi-Yemei Ticho* [Stories from the Days of Ticho] (Hebrew). Tel Aviv/Yahud Monoson, Israel: Ofir Publishing, 1993.

Decker, Hannah S. *Freud, Dora and Vienna 1900*. New York: Free Press, 1991.

Deutsch, Gotthard. "Moravia." In *The Jewish Encyclopedia*, 8:681–85. New York: Funk and Wagnalls Company, 1910.

Djemal Pasha, [Ahmed]. *Memories of a Turkish Statesman: 1913–1919*. New York: George H. Doran Company, 1922.

Dolev, Eran. *Allenby's Military Medicine: Life and Death in World War I Palestine*. London and New York: I. B. Tauris, 2007.

Dori, Yaakov. "Technion, Israel Institute of Technology." In *Encyclopaedia Judaica,* 2nd ed, 1:571–72. Farmington Hills: Thomson Gale, 2007.

Dostrovsky, A., and A. Ticho. "A case of ocular leprosy treated with autoserum from cantharides blisters." *International Journal of Leprosy* 17 (1950): 43–47.

Duff, Douglas V. *Bailing with a Teaspoon*. London: John Long, 1953.

Duke-Elder, W. Stewart. *Text-book of Ophthalmology* (revised edition published in 7 volumes). St. Louis: C. V. Mosby, 1938–1954.

Duke-Elder, Stewart, and Charles Cook. *Normal and Abnormal Development, Part I, Embryology*. St. Louis: C. V. Mosby Company, 1963. In Stewart Duke-Elder, ed. *System of Ophthalmology*. St. Louis: C. V. Mosby Company, 1963, vol. 3.

Duparc, M. "Anglo-Jewish Association." In *The Jewish Encyclopedia*, 1:601–2. New York: Funk and Wagnalls Company, 1901.

Edelman, Moshe. "Chayei Sarah: Rabbi A. I. Kook and Hebron." *Compact: Enriching the Lives of Conservative Jews* [Newsletter, United Synagogue of Conservative Judaism], Ḥeshvan 5769: 10–12 [citing adaptation from *Mal'achim Kivnei Adam*, pp. 157–65].

Eliav, Mordechai. "Ha-Konsuliya ha-Ostrit bi-Yerushalayim ve-ha-Yishuv ha-Yehudi" [The Austrian Consulate in Jerusalem and the Jewish Community] (Hebrew). *Cathedra* 18 (1981/5741): 73–110.

———. "Me'oravutam shel netsigei Germania ve-Ostria be-eiru'ei 1917 be-Eretz-Yisrael" [Involvement of German and Austrian diplomats in Palestine, 1917] (Hebrew). *Cathedra* 48 (1988/5748): 90–124.

Eliav, Mordechai, ed. *Be-Matzor u-Matzok: Eretz Yisrael be-Milhemet-ha'Olam ha-Rishona* [Siege and Distress: Eretz Yisrael during the First World War] (Hebrew). Jerusalem: Yad Yitzhak Ben Zvi, 1991.

Eliav, Mordechai, and Barbara Haider: *Österreich und das Heilige Land: Ausgewählte Konsulatsdokumente aus Jerusalem, 1849–1917* (German). Wien: Verlag der Österreichischen Akademie der Wissenschaften, 2000.

Elon, Amos. *Herzl*. New York: Holt, Rinehart and Winston, 1975.

Elschnig, Anton. *Funktions-Prüfung des Auges* (German). Vienna: Deuticke, 1897.

Elmaleh, Avraham. *Eretz-Yisrael ve-Suriya bi-Yemei Milḥemet ha-'Olam ve-Korot Eretz-Yisrael mi-Yom Shevitat ha-Neshek 'ad Sof Netsivato shel Sir Herbert Samuel* [Eretz-Yisrael and Syria in the Days of the World War and Events of Eretz-Yisrael from the Cease Fire until the End of the Commission of Sir Herbert Samuel] (Hebrew, 10 volumes). Jerusalem:

Mizraḥ ve-Ma'arav, 5689/1928.

Erickson, Edward J. *Ordered to Die: A History of the Ottoman Army in the First World War.* Westport, CT: Greenwood Press, 2001.

———. "Captain Larkin and the Turks: The strategic impact of the operations of *HMS Doris* in early 1915." *Middle Eastern Studies* 46 (2010): 151–62.

Erlanger, Moses. "Microskopische Untersuchung einer sogenannten Embolie der Centralarterie (linkes Auge) Retinitis haemorragica (rechtes Auge), sowie Gefässveränderungen in der Areria fossae Sylvii." Zurich: Verlag der Academia, 1906.

———. "Devarim aḥadim 'a[l]-d[avar] maḥalot ha-'einayim" [Some words about diseases of the eyes] (Hebrew), *Ḥavatzelet* June 4, 1909 / 15 Sivan 5669 39(99): 522–23.

Erlanger, Ruben, et al. *Beit Abraham: Stammbaum und Chronik der Familie Abraham Erlanger: ein Beitrag zur Geschichte der Juden in Luzern and Gailingen / Herausgeber* (German and Hebrew). Jerusalem: Solo-Tech, Ltd. and Old City Press, 1998.

Falk, Ze'ev Wilhem. "Hilfsverein der Deutschen Juden." In *Encyclopaedia Judaica,* 2nd ed., 1:106–7. Farmington Hills: Thomson Gale, 2007.

Fanta, H. "Eduard Zirm (1863–1944)." *Klin Monatsbl Augenheilkd* 189 (1986): 64–6.

Feigenbaum, Aryeh. "Die ansteckenden Augenkrankheiten Palästinas und ihre Bekämpfung." Berlin, 1913.

Feigenbaum, Aryeh. *50 Shenot Oftalmologiya be-Eretz Yisrael* [50 Years of Ophthalmology in Palestine], with an introduction by D. A. Friedman (Hebrew). Jerusalem: Harefuah, 1946.

———. "Sekira statistit 'al hagar'enet ve-yeter maḥalot ha'ayin ha-midabkot ba-aretz" [Statistical survey of trachoma and other infectious eye diseases in the country]. In *Du'aḥ shel Ve'idat ha-Gar'enet mi-Shnat 1914* [Proceedings of the First Trachoma Conference in Palestine, 1914], Aryeh Teëni-Feigenbaum and Aryeh Shimoni-Mäkler, uncredited eds. (Hebrew), 24–36. Jerusalem: Trachoma Division, Jewish Health Bureau, 1915.

———. "Hatza'a le-diyagnostika u-statistika me'uḥedet" [Proposal for unified diagnosis and statistics]. In *Du'aḥ shel Ve'idat ha-Gar'enet mi-Shnat 1914.* [Proceedings of the First Trachoma Conference in Palestine, 1914, Aryeh Teëni-Feigenbaum and Aryeh Shimoni-Mäkler, uncredited eds.] (Hebrew), 78–82. Jerusalem: Trachoma Division, Jewish Health Bureau, 1915.

Feuchtwanger, Felix, ed. *Stammbaum der familie Feuchtwanger 1786–1910* (German). Munich: Self-published, 1911.

Fineman, Irving. *Woman of Valor: The Life of Henrietta Szold, 1860–1945.* New York: Simon and Schuster, 1961.

Fischer, Yona, ed. *Anna Ticho: Sketches 1918–1975* (Hebrew and English). Jerusalem: Israel Museum, Jerusalem, 1976.

Fleisher, Robert Jay. *Twenty Israeli Composers.* Detroit, MI: Wayne State University Press, 1997.

Florence, Ronald. *Lawrence and Aaronsohn: T. E. Lawrence, Aaron Aaronsohn, and the Seeds of the Arab-Israeli Conflict.* New York: Viking, 2007.

Fölsing, Albrecht. *Albert Einstein: A Biography.* Translated from the German by Ewald Osers. New York: Penguin Books, 1997.

Frankl, Michal. "The background of the Hilsner Case: Political anti-Semitism and allegations of ritual murder 1896–1900." *Judaica Bohemiae* 36 (2000): 34–118.

Fried, Martin. "650 Year Anniversary of Charles University, Prague." *Obesity Surgery* 10 (2000): 70–72.

Friedland, Roger, and Richard Hecht. *To Rule Jerusalem.* New York: Cambridge University Press, 1996.

Friedenwald, Harry. "The ophthalmias of Palestine." *Transactions of the American Ophthalmological Society* 14 [part 1] (1915): 264–302.

———. *The Jews and Medicine. Essays* (2 volumes). Baltimore: Johns Hopkins Press, 1944.

Friedenwald, Herbert, ed. *American Jewish Yearbook 5673, September 12, 1912 to October 1, 1913.* Philadelphia: Jewish Publication Society, 1912.

Friedlander, Albert H. *Leo Baeck: Teacher of Theresienstadt.* New York: Holt, Rinehart and Winston, 1968.

Friedman, Isaiah. *Germany, Turkey and Zionism 1897–1918.* Oxford: Clarendon Press, 1977.

———, ed. *The Rise of Israel: A Documentary Record from the Nineteenth Century to 1948: A Facsimile Series Reproducing over 1,900 Documents in 39 Volumes.* New York: Garland Publishing, 1987.

Fromkin, David. *A Peace to End All Peace: The Fall of the Ottoman Empire and the Creation of the Modern Middle East* (reprint of original 1989 edition with a new afterword by the author). New York: Henry Holt and Company, 2009.

Fuchs, Ernst. *Text-Book of Ophthalmology*. Translated by Alexander Duane. New York: D. Appleton, 1892.

———. "Über Keratoplastick" [On keratoplasty] (German). *Wiener klinische Wochenschrift* 7 (1894): 843–45.

Fuchs, Ron and Gilbert Herbert, "Architecture in Mandate-Era Jerusalem." In *Hybrid Urbanism: On the Identity Discourse and the Built Environment*, edited by Nezar AlSayyad. Westport, CT: Praeger Publishers, 2001, 83–98.

Garrison, Fielding H. *An Introduction to the History of Medicine*, 4th ed. Philadelphia: W. B. Saunders, 1929.

Gavish, Dov. *A Survey of Palestine under the British Mandate, 1920–1948*. New York: Routledge, 2005.

Gilbar, Gad E., ed. *Ottoman Palestine 1800–1914: Studies in Economic and Social History*. Leiden: E. J. Brill, 1990.

Gilbert, Martin. *Jerusalem: Illustrated History Atlas*. New York: Macmillan Publishing, 1978.

———. *The First World War: A Complete History*. New York: Henry Holt and Company, 1994.

———. *Jerusalem in the Twentieth Century*. New York: John Wiley and Sons, Inc., 1996.

———. *Israel: A History*. New York: Harper Perennial, 2008 [revised and updated from the original 1998 edition].

Glass, Joseph B. *From New Zion to Old Zion: American Jewish Immigration and Settlement in Palestine 1917–1939*. Detroit: Wayne State University Press, 2002.

———. "American olim and the transfer of innovation to Palestine, 1917–1939." In *America and Zion: Essays and Papers in Memory of Moshe Davis*, edited by Eli Lederhendler and Jonathan D. Sarna. Detroit: Wayne State University Press, 2002.

Glass, Joseph B. and Ruth Kark. *Sephardi Entrepreneurs in Jerusalem: The Valero Family 1800–1948*. Jerusalem and Lynbrook, NY: Gefen, 2007/5768.

Glatzer, Nahum N. *Franz Rosenzweig: His Life and Thought*. Philadelphia and New York: Jewish Publication Society and Schocken Books, 1953.

Goldberg, Aryeh. "The diagnostic investigation of trachoma." In *Du'aḥ shel Ve'idat ha-Gar'enet mi-Shnat 1914* [Proceedings of the First Trachoma Conference in Palestine, 1914] (Hebrew), 9. Jerusalem: Trachoma Division, Jewish Health Bureau, 1915.

Goldhill, Simon. *Jerusalem: City of Longing*. Cambridge, MA: Belknap Press of Harvard University Press, 2008.

Golz, Avishay. *Refu'at Af-Ozen-Garon be-Eretz Yisrael 1911–1948* [Otorhinolaryngology in Eretz-Israel 1911–1948] (Hebrew). Zichron-Ya'akov: Itay Bahur Publishing, 2009.

Goodman, Avi, and Philip Goodman. "'Masu'at Yerushalayim' shel 'Misdar ha-Makabim ha-Kadmonim' (1907–1917)" [The Jerusalem Beacon of the Order of Ancient Maccabeans 1907–1917)] (Hebrew). *Cathedra* 65 (1992/5753): 82–99.

Gorin, George. *History of Ophthalmology*. Wilmington, DE: Publish or Perish Inc., 1982.

Gorny, Yosef. *Zionism and the Arabs 1882–1948: A Study*. Translated by Chaya Galai. Oxford and New York: Oxford University Press, 1987.

Gottheil, Richard. "What has become of the Temple vessels?" *New Outlook* 98 (1911): 307–9.

Grainger, John D. *The Battle for Palestine, 1917*. Woodbridge, UK: The Boydell Press, 2006.

Gray, Richard T., Ruth V. Gross, Rolf J. Goebel, and Clayton Koelb. *A Franz Kafka Encyclopedia*. Westport, CT: Greenwood Press, 2005.

Greenberg, Zalman. "Beit ha-Ḥolim ha-'Ironi ha-Turki be-Yerushalayim" [The Turkish Municipal Hospital in Jerusalem] (Hebrew), *Cathedra* 78 (1995/5756): 49–64.

Grunwald, Max. *Vienna*. Philadelphia: The Jewish Publication Society of America, 1936.

Halberstaedter, Ludwig, and Stanislaus von Prowazek. "Über Zelleinschlüsse parasitärer Natur beim Trachom." *Arb Keiserl Gesundh-Amte* 26 (1907): 44–47.

HaLevy, David. *Retzaḥ be-Yisrael: 'Al Parashat Retzaḥ Prof. de Haan ve-yaḥasei Datiyim-Ḥiluniyim be-Yisrael shel Shenot ha-'Esrim* [Murder in

Israel: On the Murder of Prof. de Haan and Orthodox-Secular Relations in Israel during the 1920s]. Bnai Brak: Tefutza, n.d.

Hall, Richard C. *The Balkan Wars, 1912–1913: Prelude to the First World War*. New York: Routledge, 2000.

———. *Consumed by Conflict: European Conflict in the 20th Century*. Lexington, Kentucky: University of Kentucky Press, 2010.

Halpern, Ben, and Yehudah Reinharz. *Zionism and the Creation of a New Society*. New York: Oxford University Press, 1998.

Hamann, Brigitte. *Hitler's Vienna: A Dictator's Apprenticeship*. Translated from the German by Thomas Thornton. New York: Oxford University Press, 1999.

Hametz, Maura Elise. "Zionism, Emigration, and Antisemitism in Trieste: Central Europe's 'Gateway to Zion' 1896–1943." *Jewish Social Studies* 13 (2007): 103–34.

Hamilton, Jill. *God, Guns and Israel: Britain, the First World War, and the Jews in the Holy City*. Phoenix Mill, U.K.: Sutton Publishing, 2004.

Harry, Myriam. *Bat Yerushalayim ha-Ketana [La Petite Fille de Jérusalem]*. Originally published in Paris, 1914. Translated from French by Ya'akov Assia. Tel Aviv: Beit A. Levinson, 1975.

Hegler [Carl Theodor] and Klein (eds.). "Referierabende der deutschen und österreichisch-ungarischen Militärärzte in Jerusalem" [Meeting of German and Austro-Hungarian military physicians in Jerusalem] (German). *Wiener klinische Wochenschrift* 30 (1917): 286–87.

Heinemann, Isaac. "Marcus Horovitz." In *Jewish Leaders (1750–1940)*, edited by Leo Jung, 261–72. New York: Bloch Publishing Company, 1953.

Heller, Joseph. *Mi-'Brit Shalom' le-'Iḥud': Yehudah Leib Magnes ve-ha-ma'avak li-medinah du-le'umit* [From Brit Shalom to Ichud: Judah Leib Magnes and the Struggle for a Binational State] (Hebrew). Jerusalem: Magnes Press and Hebrew University, 2003.

Hertzberg, Arthur, ed. *The Zionist Idea: A Historical Analysis and Reader*. Philadelphia: Jewish Publication Society, 1959.

Herzl, Theodor. *The Diaries of Theodor Herzl*. Edited and translated by Marvin Lowenthal. New York: Dial Press, 1956.

———. *The Jewish State*. Introduction by Louis Lipsky and biography by Alex Bein. New York: Dover Publications, 1988.

————. *Old-New Land ("Altneuland")*. Translated from German by Lotta Levensohn. New York: Bloch Publishing Co., 1941.

Herzog, Chaim. *Heroes of Israel: Profiles of Jewish Courage*. Boston: Little, Brown and Company, 1989.

Hirschberg, Julius. *The History of Ophthalmology*. Translated from German by Frederick C. Blodi. Bonn: J. P. Wayenborgh, 1982–1992.

Hirshberg, Jehoash. "Muzika ma'aravit bi-Yerushalayim ha-Mandatorit" [Western music in Mandatory Jerusalem] (Hebrew). In *Yerushalayim bi-Tekufat ha-Mandat: Ha-Asiyah ve-ha-Moreshet* [Jerusalem and the British Mandate: Interaction and Legacy], edited by Yehoshua Ben-Arieh 433–49. Jerusalem: Mishkenot Sha'ananim and Yad Izhak Ben-Zvi, 2003.

Hitler, Adolf. *Mein Kampf*. Translated into English by Ralph Manheim and introduction by Abraham Foxman. Boston and New York: Mariner Books/ Houghton Mifflin Company, 1999.

Hoeflich, Eugen [Moshe Ya'akov Ben-Gavriel]. *Tagebücher 1915 bis 1927*. Edited and annotated by Armin A. Wallas (German). Vienna: Böhlau, 1999.

"Hofrat Prof. Dr. Otto Bergmeister." *Weiner klinische Wochenschrift* 31 (1918): 1119.

Holitscher, Arthur. *Gesang an Palastina: Mit Zwölf Radierungen von Hermann Struck*. Berlin: Hans Heinrich Tillgner Verlag, 1922.

————. "Rise and fall of the German University Eye Clinic in Prague" (German with English abstract). *Klinische Monatsblätter für Augenheilkunde* 187 (1985): 307–13.

Horne, Charles F., and Walter F. Austin, eds. *Source Records of the Great War* (7 volumes). United States city not specified: National Alumni, 1923.

Hruby, Karl. "Was Dr. Carl Koller driven from Vienna in 1885?" *Wiener klinische Wochenschrift* 98 (1986): 155–56.

Hughes, E. S. R. "Venous obstruction in the upper extremity (Paget-Schroetter's syndrome). A review of 320 cases." *International Abstracts of Surgery* 88 (1949): 89–127.

Hughes, Matthew. "Assassination in Jerusalem: Bahjat Abu Garbiyah and Sami al-Ansari's shooting of British Assistant Superintendent Alan Sigrist 12th June 1936," *Jerusalem Quarterly* 44 (2010): 4–13.

Hurwich, Baruch. *Kol ha-'Am Ḥazit: Ha-Sheirut ha-Refu'i ha-Tzeva'i be-*

Eretz Yisrael: Me-Reishito 'ad le-Milḥemet ha-'Atzma'ut, 1911–1947 [We are All on the Front Lines: Military Medicine in Israel: The Pre-State Years, 1911–1947] (Hebrew). Jerusalem: Israeli Ministry of Defense, Medical Corps, 1997.

Hurwitz, David Lyon. "Balfour on Mount Scopus." *Judaism* 44 (1995): 485–90.

Hyamson, Albert M., ed. *The British Consulate in Jerusalem in Relation to the Jews of Palestine, 1838–1914* (2 volumes). New York: AMS Press, 1975.

Isaacson, Walter. *Einstein. His Life and Universe.* New York: Simon and Schuster, 2007.

Izhaki, Rika. "Hakamato ve-hitpatḥuto shel beit-ha-ḥolim le-maḥalot einayim Saint John bi-Yerushalayim" [The Ophthalmic Hospital of the Order of St. John, 1882–1948] (Hebrew). *Cathedra* 67 (1993/5753): 114–35.

Jacobson, Abigail. "Alternative voices in late Ottoman Palestine: A historical note," *Jerusalem Quarterly File* 21 (2004): 41–48.

———. "A city living through crisis: Jerusalem during World War I," *British Journal of Middle Eastern Studies* 36 (2009): 73–92.

Janik, Allan S., and Hans Veigl. *Wittgenstein in Vienna: A Biographical Excursion through the City and Its History.* Vienna: Springer-Verlag, 2001.

Jokl, A. "Ferdinand von Arlt and Ernst Fuchs: Two representatives of the Vienna School of Ophthalmology." *International Record of Medicine* 170 (1957): 702–6.

Josephus, Flavius. *Wars of the Jews.* In *The Complete Works of Josephus.* Translated into English by William Whiston. Grand Rapids, Michigan: Kregal Publications, 1987.

JPS Hebrew-English Tanakh. The Traditional Hebrew Text and The New JPS English Translation, 2nd ed. Philadelphia: The Jewish Publication Society, 1999–5759.

Jung, Leo, ed. *Jewish Leaders (1750–1940).* New York: Bloch Publishing Company, 1953.

Jung, Peter. *Der K.U.K. Wüstenkrieg: Österreich-Ungarn im Vorderen Orient 1915–1918.* Graz: Verlag Styria, 1992.

Kafka, Franz. *Briefe, 1902–1924 / Franz Kafka.* Translated by Richard and Clara Winston as *Letters to Friends, Family, and Editors / Franz Kafka.* New York: Schocken Books, 1977.

Kagan, Helena. *The Voice that Called* (English, 90 leaves OCLC no. 233661440, Jerusalem: [s.n.], 1978).

———. *Reishit Darki bi-Yerushalayim* [*The Beginning of My Way in Jerusalem*] (Hebrew). Tel Aviv: WIZO / Midreshet Liberalit, 5742 [c. 1982].

Kahane, Isaac Ze'ev. "Boskovice." In *Encyclopaedia Judaica,* 2nd ed. 7:97. Farmington Hills: Thomson Gale, 2007.

Kalc, Aleksej. "Passenger lists for the Port of Trieste, Italy (formerly Triest, Austria)." *East European Genealogist* 11 (2002): 22–27.

———. "Ships lists for the Port of Triest, Austria 1912–1914." *East European Genealogist* 11 (2002): 25–28.

Kaplan, Rose. "Letters from missionary nurses II, in Proceedings of the Seventeenth Annual Convention of the American Nurses' Association, St. Louis, Missouri, April 23–29, 1914." *American Journal of Nursing* 14 (1914): 870–72.

Kark, Ruth. *American Consuls in the Holy Land.* Jerusalem: Hebrew University Magnes Press, 1994.

Kark, Ruth, Dietrich Denecke, and Haim Goren. "The impact of early German missionary enterprise in Palestine on modernization and environmental and technological change, 1820–1914." In *Christian Witness between Continuity and New Beginnings: Modern Historical Missions in the Middle East*, edited by Martin Tamke and Michael Marten, 145–76. New Brunswick, NJ: Transaction Publishers, 2006.

Kark, Ruth, and Shimon Landman, "The establishment of Muslim neighbourhoods in Jerusalem, outside the Old City during the late Ottoman period." *Palestine Exploration Quarterly* 112 (1980): 113–35.

Kark, Ruth, and Michal Oren-Nordheim. *Jerusalem and Its Environs: Quarters, Neighborhoods, Villages, 1800–1948.* Jerusalem: Hebrew University Magnes Press, 2001.

Katz, Y. "Ha-Mifne be-yaḥasam shel Ussishkin ve-Ḥovevei Tsiyon le-pitu'aḥ Yerushalayim" [The turning point in the relationship of Ussishkin and Hovevei Tsiyon to the development of Jerusalem] (Hebrew). In *Yerushalayim be-Toda'ah u-va-'Asiya Tsiyonit: Kovets Ma'amarim* [Jerusalem through Zionist documentation and achievement: Collection of articles] (Hebrew), edited by Hagit Lavsky. Jerusalem: Merkaz Zalman

Shazar le-Toldot Yisrael, 1989.

Kayali, Hasan. "Wartime regional and imperial integration of Greater Syria during World War I." In *The Syrian Land: Processes of Integration and Fragmentation: Bilād al-Shām from the 18th to the 20th Century*, edited by Thomas Philipp and Birgit Schäbler, 295–306. Stuttgart: Franz Steiner Verlag, 1998.

Kedourie, Elie and Sylvia G. Haim, eds. *Zionism and Arabism in Palestine and Israel,* London: Frank Cass, 1982.

Keegan, John. *An Illustrated History of the First World War*. New York: Alfred A. Knopf, 2001.

Kendall, Henry. *Jerusalem, the City Plan: Preservation and Development during the British Mandate, 1918–1948*. London: Her Majesty's Stationery Office, 1948.

Kerr, Stanley E. *The Lions of Marash: Personal Experiences with American Near East Relief 1918–1922*. Albany: State University of New York Press, 1973.

Kestenberg-Gladstein, Ruth. "The Jews between Czechs and Germans in the historic lands, 1848–1918." In *The Jews of Czechoslovakia: Historical Studies and Surveys*, edited by Society for the History of Czechoslovak Jews, 1:42. Philadelphia and New York: The Jewish Publication Society of America and the Society for the History of Czechoslovak Jews, 1968.

Khalidi, Walid, ed. *All That Remains: The Palestinian Villages Occupied and Depopulated by Israel in 1948*. New York: Cambridge University Press, 1992.

Kieval, Hillel. *The Making of Czech Jewry: National Conflict and Jewish Society in Bohemia, 1870–1918*. New York: Oxford University Press, 1988.

———. *Languages of Community: The Jewish Experience in the Czech Lands*. Berkeley: University of California Press, 2000.

Kisch, Frederick H. *Palestine Diary*. New York: AMS Press, 1974 (1st edition, London: Victor Gollancz Ltd, 1938).

Klabunde, Anja. *Magda Goebbels*. London: Time Warner Books, 1999.

Koller, Carl. "Vorläufige Mitteilung über locale Anästhesirung am Auge." *Klin Mbl Augenheilk* 22 (1884): 60–63.

Kressel, Getzel. "Nehemiah Anton Nobel." In *Encyclopaedia Judaica*, 2nd ed., edited by Fred Skolnik. 15:291. Farmington Hills: Thomson Gale, 2007.

Krimsky, Joseph. *Pilgrimage and Service by Jos. Krimsky, MD, of the American Zionist Medical Unit in Palestine 1918–1919.* New York: Self-published, 1919 (reprinted by Arno Press, 1977).

Kroyanker, David. *Reḥov ha-Nevi'im, Shekhunat ha-Ḥabashim u-Shkhunat Musrara* [The Street of the Prophets, the Ethiopian and Musrara Quarters] (Hebrew). Jerusalem: Keter Books and Yad Izhak Ben Zvi, 2000.

———. *Sipur Mitḥam Rotshild, Yerushalayim, Reḥov ha-Nevi'im: Biografyah Refu'it ve-Ḥinukhit* [The Rothschild Compound Story: Jerusalem, HaNevi'im Street: A Medical and Educational Biography] (Hebrew and English). Jerusalem: Keter Books, 2001.

———. *Shekhunot Yerushalayim: Ṭalbiyeh, Katamon ve-ha-Moshavah ha-Yevanit* (Hebrew). Jerusalem: Jerusalem Institute for Israel Studies and Keter Books, 2002.

———. *Rehov Yafo, Yerushalayim: Biografyah Shel Reḥov, Sipurah Shel 'Ir* [Jaffa Road, Jerusalem: Biography of a Street – Story of a City] (Hebrew). Jerusalem: Jerusalem Institute for Israel Studies and Keter Books, 2005.

———. "Swastikas over Jerusalem," *Haaretz*, November 8, 2008, accessed November 9, 2008, www.haaretz.com.

———. *Mamila: Gei'ut, Shefel ve-Hitḥadshut, Rova' Alrov-Mamila, Yerushalayim* [Mamilla: Prosperity, Decay and Renewal, Alrov-Mamila Quarter, Jerusalem] (Hebrew). Jerusalem: Keter Books, 2009.

Kubicek, Paul. *The History of Ukraine.* Westport, CT: Greenwood Press, 2008.

Kubinszky, Mihály. *Bahnhöfe in Österreich: Architektur und Geschichte, 2. Unveränderte Auflage.* Vienna: Verlag Slezak KEG, 2008.

Kulka, Erich. "The Annihilation of Czechoslovak Jewry." In *The Jews of Czechoslovakia*, edited by Avigdor Dagan, 3:262–38. Philadelphia and New York: Jewish Publication Society of America and Society for the History of Czechoslovak Jews, 1984.

Kunstel, Marcia and Joseph Albright. *Their Promised Land: Arab and Jew in History's Cauldron: One Valley in the Jerusalem Hills.* New York: Crown Publishers, 1990.

Kupiec-Weglinski, Jerry. "The siege of Przemysl 1914–15." *Airpost Journal* 80 (2009): 494–509.

Kuzar, Ron. *Hebrew and Zionism: A Discourse Analytic Cultural Study.* Berlin: Mouton de Gruyter, 2001.

Lachman, Shai. "Arab rebellion and terrorism in Palestine 1929–1939." In Kedourie, Elie and Sylvia G. Haim. *Zionism and Arabism in Palestine and Israel.* London: Frank Cass, 1982, 53–100.

Lamed, Meir. "Placzek, Abraham (1799–1884)." In *Encyclopaedia Judaica,* 2nd ed., 16: 210. Farmington Hills: Thomson Gale, 2007.

———. *Palestine in the Late Ottoman Period: Political Social and Economic Transformation.* Jerusalem and Leiden: Yad Izhak Ben-Zvi and E. J. Brill, 1986.

Lamed, Meir, and Yeshayahu Jelinek. "Moravia." In *Encyclopaedia Judaica,* 2nd edition, 14:471–76. Farmington Hills: Thomson Gale, 2007.

Landau, Jacob M. "The Dönmes: Crypto-Jews under Turkish rule." *Jewish Political Studies Review* 19 (2007): 1–2.

Landsteiner, Karl. "On agglutination phenomena of normal human blood." In *Papers on Human Genetics,* edited by S. H. Boyer, 27–31. Englewood Cliffs, NJ: Prentice-Hall, 1963.

Lang, Yosef. "Zikat golei Eretz-Yisrael be-Alexandria el ha-Yishuv ha-Yehudi bi-Yemei ha-Milḥama" [Inclination of Palestinian exiles in Alexandria toward the Jewish Yishuv during the war]. In *Be-Matsor u-Matsok: Eretz Yisrael be-Milḥemet-ha-'Olam ha-Rishona* [Siege and Distress: Eretz Yisrael during the First World War] (Hebrew), edited by Moshe Eliav, 132–54. Jerusalem: Yad Izhak Ben-Zvi, 1991.

Lavsky, Hagit. *Before Catastrophe: The Distinctive Path of German Jewry.* Jerusalem and Detroit: Magnes Press and Wayne State University Press, 1996.

———. "Mashma'ut hakamataḥ shel ha-Universita ha-'Ivrit" [The role of the Hebrew University in Jerusalem life during the Mandate period] (Hebrew). In *Yerushalayim bi-Tekufat ha-Mandat: Ha-Asiyah ve-ha-Moreshet* [Jerusalem and the British Mandate: Interaction and Legacy], edited by Yehoshua Ben-Arieh 335–50. Jerusalem: Mishkenot Sha'ananim and Yad Izhak Ben-Zvi, 2003.

LeBor, Adam. *City of Oranges: An Intimate History of Arabs and Jews in Jaffa.* New York: W. W. Norton and Company, 2007.

Lechmere, Sir Edmund A. H. *A Paper Read before the Knights of St. John* of Jerusalem (English Langue) at Their General Assembly on June 25th, 1883. London: Harrison and Sons, 1883.

Lederer, Zdenek. "Terezín." In The Jews of Czechoslovakia, edited by Avigdor Dagan, 3:104–64. Philadelphia and New York: Jewish Publication Society of America and Society for the History of Czechoslovak Jews, 1984.

Lesky, Erna. The Vienna Medical School of the 19th Century. Translated by L. Williams and I. S. Levij. Baltimore: Johns Hopkins University Press, 1976.

Levin, Alexandra Lee. Vision: A Biography of Harry Friedenwald. Philadelphia: Jewish Publication Society of America, 1964.

Levin, Marlin. Balm in Gilead: The Story of Hadassah. New York: Schocken Books, 1973.

———. It Takes a Dream: The Story of Hadassah. Jerusalem: Gefen Publishing House Ltd., 1997. Also published in Hebrew as Drosh Rak Ḥalom, Jerusalem: Gefen Publishing House Ltd., 1998.

Levin, Michael. "Adrikhalut bi-Yerushalayim bi-Tekufat ha-Mandat: Historisizim mul modernisizim" [Architecture in Jerusalem during the Mandate period: Historicism vs. Modernism] (Hebrew). In Yerushalayim bi-Tekufat ha-Mandat: Ha-Asiya ve-ha-Moreshet [Jerusalem and the British Mandate: Interaction and Legacy], edited by Yehoshua Ben-Arieh. Mishkenot Sha'ananim and Yad Izhak Ben-Zvi, 2003.

Levy, Nissim. Perakim be-Toldot ha-Refu'ah be-Eretz Yisrael, 1799–1948 [The History of Medicine in the Holy Land: 1799–1948] (Hebrew). Haifa: Hakibbutz Hameuchad Publishing House and the Ruth and Bruce Rappaport Faculty of Medicine, Technion, 1998.

Levy, Nissim, and Yael Levy. Rof'eha shel Eretz Yisrael, 1799–1948 [The Physicians of the Holy Land, 1799–1948] (Hebrew). Zikhron Ya'akov: Itay Bahur Publishing, 2008.

Lewis, Bernard. The Emergence of Modern Turkey, 3rd ed. New York: Oxford University Press, 2002.

Lewis, Geoffrey. "An Ottoman officer in Palestine, 1914–1918." In Palestine in the Late Ottoman Period: Political Social and Economic Transformation, edited by David Kushner, 402–15. Jerusalem and Leiden: Yad Izhak Ben-Zvi and E. J. Brill, 1986.

Lieber, David L., ed. Etz Ḥayim: Torah and Commentary. New York: The

Rabbinical Assembly and the United Synagogue of Conservative Judaism, 2001.

Luke, Harry, and Edward Keith-Roach, eds. *The Handbook of Palestine*. London: MacMillan and Co., 1922.

Luncz, Avraham Moshe. *Almanac of Eretz Yisrael, Useful and Literary for the Year 5674 (1913–14), Nineteenth Year* (Hebrew). Jerusalem: Hamo'el, 1913.

Lustiger, Arno. *Jüdische Stiftungen in Frankfurt am Main*. Frankfurt am Main, Jan Thorbecke Verlag Sigmaringen, 1988.

MacKenzie, John E., ed. *University of Edinburgh Roll of Honor, 1914–1919*. London: Oliver and Boyd, 1921.

McCagg, William O. Jr. *A History of Habsburg Jews 1670–1918*. Bloomington and Indianapolis: Indiana University Press, 1989.

McMeekin, Sean. *The Berlin-Baghdad Express: The Ottoman Empire and Germany's Bid for World Power, 1898–1918*. Cambridge, MA: Belknap Press of Harvard University Press, 2010.

Maderthaner, Wolfgang, and Lutz Musner. *Unruly Masses: The Other Side of Fin-de-Siècle Vienna*. Translated into English by David Fernbach and Michael Huffmaster. New York: Berghahn Books, 2009.

Mandel, Neville J. *The Arabs and Zionism before World War I*. Berkeley: University of California Press, 1976.

Mandell, Gerald L., John E. Bennett, and Raphael Dolin, eds. *Mandell, Douglas and Bennett's Principles and Practice of Infectious Diseases*, 6th ed. (2 volumes), Philadelphia: Elsevier, Churchill Livingstone, 2005.

Mansour, Camille and Fawaz, Leila, eds. *Transformed Landscapes: Essays on Palestine and the Middle East in Honor of Walid Khalidi*. Cairo and New York: The American University in Cairo Press, 2009.

Manor, Dalia. "Biblical Zionism in Bezalel Art," *Israel Studies* 6 (2001): 55–75.

Ma'oz, Moshe, ed. *Studies on Palestine during the Ottoman Period*. Jerusalem: Magnes-Hebrew University-Yad Izhak Ben-Zvi, 1975.

Marcus, Amy Dockser. *Jerusalem 1913: The Origins of the Arab-Israeli Conflict*. New York: Viking-Penguin, 1997.

Markel, Howard. *Quarantine! East European Jewish Immigrants and the New York City Epidemics of 1892*. Baltimore: The Johns Hopkins University

Press, 1997.

Marmorstein, Emile. "European Jews in Muslim Palestine." In *Palestine and Israel in the 19th and 20th Centuries*, edited by Elie Kedourie and Sylvia G. Haim, 1–14. London: Frank Cass, 1982.

Masterman, E. W. G. "Mount of Olives." In *The International Standard Bible Encyclopaedia* (4 volumes), edited by James Orr, 4:2185–88. Chicago: The Howard-Severance Co., 1915.

Mazza, Roberto. *Jerusalem: From the Ottomans to the British*. London and New York: I. B. Tauris Publishers, 2009.

Meissner, Max. "Hofrat Professor Dr. S. Klein." *Wiener Medizinische Wochenschrift* [Viennese Medical Weekly Periodical] (1937): 501.

Mendes-Flohr, Paul R. "The appeal of the incorrigible idealist." In *Like All the Nations? The Life and Legacy of Judah L. Magnes*, edited by William M. Brinner and Moses Rischin. Albany: State University of New York Press, 1987.

———. "The Berlin Jew as Cosmopolitan." In *Berlin Metropolis: Jews and the New Culture 1890–1918*, edited by Emily D. Bilski. Berkeley and New York: University of California Press and The Jewish Museum, 1999.

Mendes-Flohr, Paul, and Jehuda Reinharz. *The Jew in the Modern World: A Documentary History*. Oxford: Oxford University Press, 1980.

Meron, Eyal, ed. *Yerushalayim ve-Khol Netivoteha: Lesayeir 'im Yad Yitshak Ben-Tsevi* [Pathways in Jerusalem: A Walking-Tour Guide with Yad Ben-Zvi] (Hebrew). Jerusalem: Yad Izhak Ben-Zvi, 1996.

Merrill, Selah. "The Jaffa and Jerusalem Railway," *Scribner's Magazine* 13 (1893): 289–300.

Metzer, Jacob. *The Divided Economy of Mandatory Palestine.* Cambridge: Cambridge University Press, 1998.

Michaelson, Isaac C. "Professor A. Feigenbaum: An appreciation." *Israel Medical Journal* 19 (1960): 267–70.

Michlin, Amnon. *Ma'asei Rokei'ah* [A Pharmicist's Venture] (Hebrew), Kiryat Ono and Netanya: S.L.E., 5752/1992.

———. *Ma'asei Rokhim: Perakim be-Toldot ha-Rokhut be-Eretz-Yisrael* [Pharmacists' Ventures]. Israel: Misrad ha-Bitahon [Ministry of Defense], 1999.

Monk, Daniel Bertrand. *An Aesthetic Occupation: The Immediacy of*

Architecture and the Palestine Conflict. Durham, NC: Duke University Press, 2002.

Moore, Deborah Dash. "Hadassah in the United States." In *Jewish Women: A Comprehensive Historical Encyclopedia* (CD for computer), edited by Paula Hyman. Philadelphia: Jewish Publication Society, 2007.

Morgenstern, Matthias. *From Frankfurt to Jerusalem: Isaac Breuer and the History of the Secession Dispute in Modern Jewish Orthodoxy*. Leiden: Brill, 2002.

Morris, Benny. *Righteous Victims: A History of the Zionist-Arab Conflict, 1881–1999*. New York: Alfred A. Knopf, 1999.

Morris, Jan. *Trieste and the Meaning of Nowhere*. New York: Simon and Schuster, 2001.

Munk, Phillip. *A Memoir by Phillip Munk: 1894–1971*. In *M'dor L'dor: From Generation to Generation* by Charles Ticho, 39–63. Translated from the German by Harold K. Ticho. Woodcliff Lake, New Jersey: Self-published, 2007.

Nakdimon, Shlomo. "Aḥarit davar" [Afterword]. In *De Vreint Shav ha-Bayita* [De Vreint Returns Home] by Arnold Zweig, translated from German into Hebrew by Tsvi Argon. Tel Aviv: Dvir Publishing, 1991, 199–205.

Nakdimon, Shlomo, and Shaul Mayzlish. *De Haan: ha-Retzah ha-Politi ha-Rishon be-Eretz Yisrael* [De Haan: The first political assassination in Palestine] (Hebrew). Tel Aviv: Modan Press, 1985.

Nashef, Kalid. "Tawfik Canaan: His life and works." *Jerusalem Quarterly File* 16 (2002): 12–26.

Nassar, Issam. "Jerusalem in the late Ottoman period: Historical writing and the native voice." In *Jerusalem: Idea and Reality*, edited by Tamar Mayer and Suleiman Ali Mourad, 205–23. London and New York: Routledge, 2008.

Navot, Orit, and Avraham Gross. "Ha-Milḥama: Reishit bri'ut ha-tzibur be-Eretz-Yisrael" [The campaign against trachoma: The beginnings of public health in Eretz Israel] (Hebrew). *Cathedra* 94 (1999/5760): 89–114 and 187–88.

Niederland, Doron. "Hashpa'at ha-rof'im ha-'olim mi-Germania 'al hitpatḥut ha-refu'ah be-Eretz-Yisrael." [The influence of the Jewish physicians from Germany on the development of medicine in Israel from 1933–1948]

(Hebrew). *Cathedra* 30 (1983): 111–160.

Nissan [Katznelson], Shmuel. "Hitpaṭḥut sheirutei ha-refu'ah bi-Yerushalayim bi-tekufat ha-shilton ha-Briti" [The development of medical services in Jerusalem during the period of British rule] (Hebrew). In *Yerushalayim bi-Tekufat ha-Mandat: Ha-'asiyah ve-ha-Moreshet* [Jerusalem and the British Mandate: Interaction and Legacy], edited by Yehoshua Ben-Arieh, 299–323. Jerusalem: Mishkenot Sha'ananim and Yad Izhak Ben-Zvi, 2003.

Ofrat, Gideon. "The phenomenology of the Jerusalem Mountains in the painting of immigrants from Germany." In *Yerushalayim bi-Tekufat ha-Mandat: Ha-'asiyah ve-ha-Moreshet* [Jerusalem and the British Mandate: Interaction and Legacy], edited by Yehoshua Ben-Arieh, 408–22. Jerusalem: Mishkenot Sha'ananim and Yad Izhak Ben-Zvi, 2003.

Ollendorff, Franz. "Le-korot Beit Ticho bi-Yerushalayim" [Chronicles of the Ticho House in Jerusalem]. In *Yerushalayim: Mivḥar Ma'amarim*, edited by Eli Schiller, 62–65. Jerusalem: Ariel, 1993.

Orbakh, Aharon, Amihai Merhavyah, and Uriel Sharabi. *'Ein Ganim: Ha-Historia ha-Yehudit be-Jenin* [Ein Ganim: The Jewish History of Jenin]. Jerusalem: Erez, 5765/2005.

Orni, Efraim, and Elisha Efrat. *Geography of Israel*, 3rd ed. Philadelphia: Jewish Publication Society of America, 1971.

O'Shea, John G. "A history of the St John Ophthalmic Hospital, Jerusalem." *Proceedings of the Royal College of Physicians of Edinburgh* 27 (1997): 603–10.

Oz, Amos. *A Tale of Love and Darkness*. Trans. by Nicholas de Lange. Orlando: Harcourt, Inc., 2004.

Page, Thomas Nelson. *Italy and the World War*. New York: Charles Scribner's Sons, 1920.

Pappe, Ilan. *A History of Modern Palestine: One Land, Two Peoples*, 2nd ed. Cambridge: Cambridge University Press, 2006.

Patterson, John. *With the Zionists in Gallipoli*. London: H. Hutchinson, 1916.

Paz, Yair. "Ha-Universita ha-'Ivrit be-Har ha-Tsofim ke-mikdash" [The Hebrew University on Mt. Scopus as a Temple] (Hebrew). In *Toldot ha-Universita ha-'Ivrit bi-Yerushalayim: Shoreshim ve-Hateḥalot* [History of the Hebrew University of Jerusalem], edited by Sha'ul Ben-Menahem

Katz, Michael Had, and Hagit Lavsky. Jerusalem: Magnes Press, 1997.

Penn, S. "Odessa," in Isidore Singer, ed., *The Jewish Encyclopedia.* New York: Funk and Wagnalls Company, 1909, 377–85.

Philipp, Thomas and Birgit Schäbler, eds. *The Syrian Land: Processes of Integration and Fragmentation: Bilād al-Shām from the 18th to the 20th Century.* Stuttgart: Franz Steiner Verlag, 1998.

Pick, Walter Pinhas. "Meissner Pasha and the construction of railways in Palestine and neighboring countries." In *Ottoman Palestine 1800–1914: Studies in Economic and Social History,* edited by Gad E. Gilbar, 179–218. Leiden: E. J. Brill, 1990.

Pipes, Daniel. "The Muslim claim to Jerusalem," *Middle East Quarterly,* 4 (Fall/8/2001) (4): 49–66.

Pojar, Miloš. "T. G. Masaryk's relations with the Jews," *Judaica Bohemiae* 38 (2002): 160–182.

Poorthuis, Marcel. "Introduction and overview: The centrality of Jerusalem." In *The Centrality of Jerusalem: Historical Perspectives,* edited by Marcel Poorthuis and Chana Safrai, 1–6. Kampen, the Netherlands: Kok Pharos Publishing House, 1996.

Poorthuis, Marcel and Safrai, Chana (eds.), *The Centrality of Jerusalem: Historical Perspectives* (Kampen, the Netherlands: Kok Pharos Publishing House, 1996).

Porush, Eliyahu. *Early Memories.* Translated by David Cook. Jerusalem: Solomon Press, 5723/1963, accessed 23 February 2010, http://repository.upenn.edu/miscellaneous_papers/7.

Provence, Michael. *The Great Syrian Revolt and the Rise of Arab Nationalism.* Austin, TX: University of Texas Press, 2005.

Raoult, Didier, and Walker, David H. "*Rickettsia prowazekii* (epidemic or louse-borne typhus)" in *Mandell, Douglas and Bennett's Principles and Practice of Infectious Diseases,* edited by Gerald L. Mandell, John E. Bennett, and Raphael Dolin, 6th ed. (2 volumes, Philadelphia: Elsevier, Churchill Livingstone, 2005). 2:2303–6.

Reifler, David M. "Dr. Avraham Albert Ticho," in *2008 Proceedings of the Cogan Ophthalmic History Society,* edited by Ronald Fishman, 109–19. Chicago, Cogan Ophthalmic History Society, 2008.

———. "The Ticho House" (AJO History of Ophthalmology Series),

American Journal of Ophthalmology 148 (2009): 375.

Reinharz, Jehuda. "Laying the foundation for a university in Jerusalem: Chaim Weizmann's role, 1913–1914," *Modern Judaism*, 4 (1984): 1–38.

Richardson, Peter. *Herod: King of the Jews and Friend of the Romans.* Columbia, SC: University of South Carolina Press, 1996.

Rinott, Moshe. "Capitulations: The case of the German-Jewish Hilfsverein Schools in Palestine, 1901–1914." In *Palestine in the Late Ottoman Period: Political Social and Economic Transformation*, edited by David Kushner, 294–300. Jerusalem and Leiden: Yad Izhak Ben-Zvi and E. J. Brill, 1986.

Rokach, Isaac. *Vatikim Mesaprim* [Tales of the Old Yishuv; literally, Veterans, Storytellers]. Ramat-Gan: Masada, 1972.

Rothkirchen, Livia. "The Jews of Bohemia and Moravia, 1938–1945." In *The Jews of Czechoslovakia*, edited by Avigdor Dagan, 3:3–74. Philadelphia and New York: Jewish Publication Society of America and Society for the History of Czechoslovak Jews, 1984.

———. *The Jews of Bohemia and Moravia: Facing the Holocaust.* Lincoln, NE and Jerusalem: University of Nebraska Press and Yad Vashem, 2005.

Rozenblit, Marsha L. *The Jews of Vienna, 1867–1914: Assimilation and Identity.* Albany: State University of New York, 1983.

Rubinow, Isaac Max, ed. *Hadassah Medical Organization (Formerly the American Zionist Medical Unit) Third Report September, 1920 – December, 1921* (Jerusalem: Hadassah Medical Organization, 1922).

Ruppin, Arthur. *Pirkei Ḥayai* [My Life and Work: The Autobiography and Diaries of Arthur Ruppin]. Edited by Alex Bein and translated from German into Hebrew by A. Shapir, 3 volumes. Tel Aviv: Am Oved Publishers Ltd., 1968.

Sachar, Howard M. *A History of Israel from the Rise of Zionism to Our Time*, 3rd ed. New York: Alfred A. Knopf, 2007.

Salibi, Kamal S. *The Modern History of Jordan.* London: I. B. Tauris, 1993.

Salmon, Irit. *Beit Ticho: Tamrur be-Nof Yerushalayim* [The Ticho House: A Jerusalem Landmark] (Hebrew and English). Jerusalem: Israel Museum, 1994.

Sandberg, Willem, ed. *Anna Ticho: Jerusalem Landscapes: Drawings and Watercolors.* Introduction by Elisheva Cohen. London: Lund Humphries

Publishers, Ltd., 1971.

Sanders, Ronald. *The High Walls of Jerusalem: A History of the Balfour Declaration and the Birth of the British Mandate for Palestine*. New York: Holt, Rinehart and Winston, 1983.

Schacht, J. "Max Meyerhof." *Osiris* 9 (1950): 7–32.

Schadle, Jacob E. "A visit to the 'Jesus Hilf' or the Leprous Hospital of Jerusalem." *Journal of the American Medical Association* 36 (1901): 1024–32.

Schechtman, Joseph B. *The Life and Times of Vladimir Jabotinsky* (2 volumes: 1. *Rebel and Statesman, The Early Years, 1880–1923*, and 2. *Fighter and Prophet, The Last Years, 1923–1940*). New York: Eshell Books, 1986.

Schidorsky, Dov. "Julius Jarcho and the beginning of medical library collections and services in Palestine." *ISLIC Bulletin* 13 (1983): 17–28.

———. "Shmu'el Hugo Bergman u-mekomo be-'itsuv Beit ha-Sefarim ha-Le'umi ve-ha-Universita'i" [Schmuel Hugo Bergmann and his place in the formation of the National and University Library] (Hebrew). *Cathedra* 76 (1995/5755): 116–46.

Schiller, Eli. ed. *Yerushalayim: Mivḥar Ma'amarim*. Jerusalem: Ariel, 1993.

Scholem, Gershom. *From Berlin to Jerusalem. Memories of My Youth*. Translated from German to English by Harry Zohn. New York: Schocken Books, 1980.

Schrötter von Kristelli, Hermann. *Hygiene der Aeronautik und Aviatik*. Vienna and Leipzig: Wilhelm Braumüller, "1912."

———. [Hermann von Schrötter.] "Über einen zweckmäßigen Schnitt der Soldatenhose," *Der Militärartz* 49, no. 31 (1915): 499–501.

Schwake, Norbert. "Album ha-tsilumim shel Tawfik Cana'an mi-Milḥemet ha-'Olam ha-Rishon" [Dr. Canaan's album from World War I] (Hebrew with English abstract and 20 bilingual photograph captions). In *Ha-Yom she-'aḥarei: Ha-kravot le-aḥar kibush Be'er Sheva November 1917* [The Day After: The Battles around Beer Sheva in November 1917], edited by Ezra Pimentel and Ely Schiller, xi and 114–24. Sde-Boker: Midreshet Sde-Boker Interdisciplinary Center, Joe Alon Center and Ariel Publishing House, 2005.

———. *Die Entwicklung des Krankenhauswesens der Stadt Jerusalem vom Ende des 18. bis zum Beginn des 20. Jahrhunderts Teil 1* (German).

Herzogenrath Murken-Altrogge, 1983.

Schwarzfuchs, Simon R., and Frances Malino. "Alliance Israelite Universelle." In *Encyclopaedia Judaica,* 2nd ed., 1:671–75. Farmington Hills: Thomson Gale, 2007.

Seas, Carlos, and Eduardo Gotuzzo. *"Vibrio cholerae."* In *Mandell, Douglas and Bennett's Principles and Practice of Infectious Diseases* 6th ed., edited by Gerald L. Mandell, John E. Bennett and Raphael Dolin (2 volumes), 2:2536–44. Philadelphia: Elsevier, Churchill Livingstone, 2005.

Segev, Tom. *The Seventh Million: The Israelis and the Holocaust.* Translated by Haim Watzman. New York: Hill and Wang, 1993.

———. *One Palestine, Complete: Jews and Arabs under the British Mandate.* Translated by Haim Watzman. New York: Metropolitan Books/Henry Holt and Company, 2000.

Setzepfandt, Wolf-Christian. *Architekturführer Frankfurt am Main: Architectural Guide,* 3rd edition (German and English). Frankfurt am Main: Dietrich Reimer Verlag, 2002.

Shamash, Violette. *Memories of Eden: A Journey through Jewish Baghdad.* Chicago: Northwestern University Press, 2010.

Shanks, Herschel. *Jerusalem: An Archeological Biography.* New York: Random House, Inc., 1995.

Shavit, Ari. *My Promised Land: The Triumph and Tragedy of Israel.* New York: Spiegel and Grau, 2013.

Sheffy, Yigal. *British Military Intelligence in the Palestinian Campaign 1914–1918.* London: Frank Cass, 1998.

Shehory-Rubin, Zipora. "Dr. Helena Kagan: Ha-refu'ah she-hafakha le-'agada" [Dr. Helena Kagan: The doctor who became a legend]. *Cathedra* 118 (2006/5766): 89–114, and 196.

Shehory-Rubin, Zipora, and Shifra Shvarts. *'Hadasa' li-Vri'ut ha-Am* ['Hadassah' for the Health of the People] (Hebrew). Israel: Hasifria Hazionit Publishing House of the World Zionist Organization, 2003.

Shilo, Gideon. "Shi'ur be-Tsiyonut: Ḥidat hei'aleimo shel 'Ḥa'uwaja 'Ibri'" [A lesson in Zionism: The puzzle of al-Khawaja 'Ibry's disappearance] (Hebrew). *Cathedra* 58 (1990/5751): 84–110.

Shilo, Margalit. "Milḥemet ha-safot li-tenu'a 'amamit" [The language controversy: A 'popular movement'] (Hebrew). *Cathedra* 74 (1994/5755):

86–119.

Shilony, Zvi. "Ha-Dildul ba-ukhlosiya ha-Yehudit bi-Yerushalayim bi-tekufat milhemet ha 'olam ha-rishona" [The depletion of the Jewish population in Jerusalem in the period of the First World War] (Hebrew). In *Mehkarim be-Geografiyah Historit-Yishuvit shel Eretz-Yisrael* [Historical-Geographical Studies in the Settlement of Eretz Israel] (Hebrew), edited by Yehoshua Ben-Arieh, Yossi Ben-Arzi, and Haim Goren, 128–29. Jerusalem: Yad Izhak Ben-Zvi, 1987.

———. "Ha-sheirut ha-refu'i u-vatei-holim bi-Yerushalayim bi-tekufat ha-milhama" [Health services and hospitals in Jerusalem during the period of the war] (Hebrew). In *Be-Matzor u-Matzok: Eretz Yisrael be-Milhemet-ha'Olam ha-Rishona* [Siege and Distress: Eretz Yisrael during the First World War] (Hebrew), edited by Moshe Eliav, 61–83. Jerusalem: Yad Izhak Ben-Zvi, 1991.

Shvarts, Shifra, and Theodore M. Brown. "Kupat Holim, Dr. Isaac Max Rubinow, and the American Zionist Medical Unit's Experiment to Establish Health Care Services in Palestine, 1918–1923." *Bulletin of the History of Medicine* 72 (1998), 28–46.

Shvarts, Shifra, David L. A. de Leeuw, Shalom Granit, and Jochanan Benbassat. "From socialist principles to motorcycle maintenance: The origin and development of the salaried physician model in the Israeli Public Health Services." *American Journal of Public Health* 89 (1999): 248–53.

Sinai, Ephraim. *Bi-Mlo ha-'Ayin: Mei-'Olamo shel Rofei'* [In the Fullness of the Eye: From the World of a Doctor] (Hebrew). Tel Aviv: Cherikov, 1984.

Sixtová, Olga, Polakovič, Daniel, and Pařík, Arno. *Boskovice Synagogue Guide*. Prague: The Jewish Museum of Prague, 2002.

Smart, Ninian, and Richard D. Hecht. *Sacred Texts of the World: A Universal Anthology*. New York: Crossroad Publishing Company, 1992.

Smilansky, Moshe. *Perakim be-Toldot ha-Yishuv* [Chapters in the History of the Yishuv] (Hebrew). Tel Aviv: Dvir, 1945.

Snyder, Charles. "Alois Glogar, Karl Brauer and Eduard Konrad Zirm." *Archives of Ophthalmology* 74 (1965): 871–74.

Sohn, Joseph. "Gustav Mahler." In *The Jewish Encyclopedia*, 8:261. New York and London: Funk and Wagnalls Company, 1910.

Sondhaus, Laurence. *The Naval Policy of Austria-Hungary: 1867–1918*. West

Lafayette, IN: Purdue University Press, 1994.

Spier, Arthur. *The Comprehensive Hebrew Calendar: Twentieth to Twenty-second Century*, 3rd edition. Jerusalem and New York: Feldheim Publishers, 1986.

Spungen, Norma. "Emma Leon Gottheil (1862–1947)." In *Jewish Women: A Comprehensive Historical Encyclopedia* (CD for computer), edited by Paula Hyman. Philadelphia: Jewish Publication Society, 2007.

Stach, Reiner. *Kafka: The Decisive Years*. Translated from the German by Shelley Frisch. Orlando: Harcourt Inc., 2005. Originally published as *Kafka: Die Jare der Entscheidungen*. Frankfurt am Main: S. Fischer Verlag GmbH, 2002.

Steinberg, Ronit. "Anna Ticho (1894–1980)." In *Encyclopaedia Judaica,* 2nd ed., 19:717–18. Farmington Hills: Thomson Gale, 2007.

Storrs, Ronald. *The Memoirs of Sir Ronald Storrs*. New York: G. P. Putnam and Sons, 1937.

Strauss, Johann. "The disintegration of Ottoman rule in the Syrian territories as viewed by German observers." In *The Syrian Land: Processes of Integration and Fragmentation: Bilād al-Shām from the 18th to the 20th Century*, edited by Thomas Philipp and Birgit Schäbler, 307–30. Stuttgart: Franz Steiner Verlag, 1998.

Subtelny, Orest. *Ukraine: A History*. Toronto: University of Toronto Press, 1988.

Sykes, Christopher. *Crossroads to Israel*. Bloomington, IN and London: Indiana University Press, 1973.

Szold, Henrietta. "Recent Jewish Progress in Palestine." In *American Jewish Yearbook 5676*. Philadelphia: Jewish Publication Society, 1916.

Talbot, John F. *The Foundation of the St. John Eye Hospital, Jerusalem*. London: Order of St. John, 2009.

Tamari, Salim. "Jerusalem's Ottoman modernity: The times and lives of Wasif Jawhariyyeh." *Jerusalem Quarterly* 9 (2000): 5–27.

———. "The short life of Private Ihsan." *Jerusalem Quarterly* 30 (2007): 26–58.

———. "The Great War and the erasure of Palestine's Ottoman past." In *Transformed Landscapes: Essays on Palestine and the Middle East in Honor of Walid Khalidi,* edited by Camille Mansour and Leila Fawaz, 105–136. Cairo and New York: The American University in Cairo Press,

2009.

Tamke, Martin, and Michael Marten, eds. *Christian Witness between Continuity and New Beginnings: Modern Historical Missions in the Middle East.* New Brunswick, New Jersey: Transaction Publishers, 2006.

Taylor, Hugh. *Trachoma: A Blinding Scourge from the Bronze Age to the Twenty-first Century.* Melbourne: Centre for Eye Research Australia, 2008.

Taylor, Jeremy Reginald Buckley. *The Architect and the Pavilion Hospital: Dialogue and Design Creativity in England, 1850–1914.* London: Leicester University Press, 1997.

Tessler, Mark A. *A History of the Israeli-Palestinian Conflict.* Bloomington, IN: Indiana University Press, 1994.

Teveth, Shabtai. *Ben-Gurion: The Burning Ground, 1886–1948.* Boston: Houghton Mifflin Company, 1987.

———. *Retzah Arlosoroff* [Arlosoroff's Murder] (Hebrew). Jerusalem and Tel Aviv: Schocken Books, 1982.

Thorwald, Jürgen. *The Triumph of Surgery.* Translated by Richard and Clara Winston. New York: Pantheon, 1960.

Ticho, Albert. "Uber Trachombehandlung in den Schulen." *Zeitschrift für Augenheilkunde* 32 (1914): 368–73.

———. "Ripuy ha-gar'enet be-vatei ha-sefer Yerushalayim" [Treatment of trachoma in Jerusalem schools] (Hebrew). In *Du'ah shel Ve'idat ha-Gar'enet mi-Shnat 1914* [Proceedings of the First Trachoma Conference in Palestine, 1914, Aryeh Teëni-Feigenbaum and Aryeh Shimoni-Mäkler, uncredited eds.] (Hebrew), 96–107. Jerusalem: Trachoma Division, Jewish Health Bureau, 1915.

———. "Frühjahrskatarrh in Palästina" [Vernal catarrh in Palestine] (German). *Klinische Monatsblätter fur Augenheilkunde* 53 (1915): 510–15.

———. "Vernal catarrh in Palestine." *American Journal of Ophthalmology* 32 (1915): 257–62.

———. "Beitrag zur Ophthalmomyiasis" [Contribution about Ophthalmomyiasis] (German). *Archiv für Schiffs- und Tropen-hygiene* 21 (1917): 165–72.

———. "Vorstellung eines Falles von Fruhjahrskatarrh, kombiniert mit Koch-Weeksscher Konjunktivitis" [Presentation of a case of vernal catarrh combined with Koch-Weeks conjunctivitis] / "Einen Vortrag: Ueber Ophthalmomiasis [*sic*] (Erscheint ausführlich andernorts)" [A presentation: About ophthalmomyiasis (having appeared earlier elsewhere)]. In "Referierabende der deutschen und österreichisch- ungarischen Militärärzte in Jerusalem" [Meeting of German and Austro- Hungarian military physicians in Jerusalem] (German), edited by Hegler. *Wiener klinische Wochenschrift* 30 (1917): 286–87.

———. "Ein Fremdkörper in klarer Linse" [A foreign body in the crystalline lens] (German). *Wiener klinische Wochenschrift.* 30 (1917): 868.

———. "Dem Augenarzte, der an das Material..." In "Referierabende der deutschen und österreichisch-ungarischen Militärärzte in Jerusalem: XII Sitzung, abgehalten am 24. Mai 1917 im k.u.k. mobilen Reservespital "Ratisbonne" [Meeting of German and Austro-Hungarian military physicians in Jerusalem: XII Session . . .], edited by H. v. Schrötter (German). *Wiener klinische Wochenschrift* 30 (1917): 1059–60.

———. "Beitrag zu den epibulbären kongenitalen Tumoren" [Contribution about Epibulbar Congenital Tumor] (German). *Archiv für Augenheilkunde* 85 (1919): 226–30.

———. "Beitrag zur Elliot-Operation" [Contribution about the Elliot Operation] (German). *Klinische Monatsblätter für Augenheilkunde* 68 (1922): 624–27.

———. "Ophthalmomyiasis." *British Journal of Ophthalmology* 7 (1923): 177–82.

———. "Ursachen der Erblindung in Palästina." *Klinische Monatsblätter für Augenheilkunde* 77 (1926): 700–704.

———. "Blindness in Palestine." *Annual Bulletin of the Academy of Medicine Jerusalem*, 1926–1927.

———. "Zur Trachomfrage in Palästina." *Klinische Monatsblätter für Augenheilkunde* 84 (1930): 56–60.

Ticho, A., and I. J. Kligler. "Trachoma in Palestine." *Lancet* 2 (1922): 706–7.

Ticho, Anna. *Palästina: Faksimile nach Zeichnungen von Anna Ticho; Vorwart von Max Eisler* (German), Vienna: Gerlach and Wiedling, 1937.

———. *Jerusalem: 12 Facsimile Plates from Drawings; Foreword by Max Eisler.* Vienna: Gerlach and Wiedling, 1950.

———. *Anna Ticho: Drawings, 1971–1980: A Selection from the Anna Ticho*

Bequest. Jerusalem: The Israel Museum, 1984.

Ticho, Charles. *M'dor L'dor: From Generation to Generation.* Woodcliff Lake, NJ: Self-published, 2007.

Ticho, Ernst A., and Gertrude R. Ticho. "Freud and the Viennese." *International Journal of Psycho-Analysis* 53 (1972): 301–6.

Tidhar, David. See above: Encyclopedias, Dictionaries, Bibliographies, Syllabi.

Toaff, Renzo, Augusto Serge, Daniel Carpi, eds. *Sefer Zikaron le-Nathan Cassuto: Scritti in Memoria di Nathan Cassuto* [Memorial Book to Nathan Cassuto] (Hebrew and Italian). Jerusalem: Kedem Yad le-Yakireinu, 1986.

Tower, Paul. "The history of trachoma: its military and sociological implications." *Archives of Ophthalmology* 69 (1963): 123–30.

Tramer, Hans. "Prague: City of Three Peoples." *The Leo Baeck Institute Yearbook* 9 (1964): 305–39.

Travis, Anthony S. *On Chariots with Horses of Fire and Iron: The Excursionists and the Narrow Gauge Railroad from Jaffa to Jerusalem.* Jerusalem: The Benjamin Shapell Family Manuscript Foundation and The Hebrew University Magnes Press, 2008.

Triwaks, I. *Milḥama ve-Shalom be-Eretz-Yisrael: Album le-Zikaron* [War and Peace in Palestine: Memorial Album] (Hebrew, Yiddish and English). Tel Aviv: Tel Aviv Publishing House, 1930.

Tsachor, Yacov, ed. *Bulei Yisrael 5708–5758: Katalog Mispar 13* [Israel Postage Stamps 1948–1998: Catalogue No. 13] (Hebrew and English). Jerusalem: Israel Postal Authority Philatelic Service and Keter Publishing House Ltd., 1998.

Unna, Isaac. "Marcus Horovitz." In *Jewish Leaders, 1750–1940*, edited by Leo Jung, 249–57. New York: Bloch Publishing Company, 1953.

Van Paassen, Pierre. *Days of Our Years.* New York: Hillman-Curl, Inc., 1939.
———. *A Pilgrim's Vow.* New York: The Dial Press, 1956.

Vester, Bertha Spafford. *Our Jerusalem: An American Family in the Holy City, 1881–1949.* Introduction by Lowell Thomas. Garden City, New York: Doubleday Company Inc., 1950.

Von Haugwitz, Thilo. *Ophthalmology in the German-speaking Countries during the 20th Century.* Translated from German by Frederick C. Blodi and Donald L. Blanchard. In *[Julius Hirschberg's] The History of*

Ophthalmology, 11(3-d). Bonn: J. P. Wayenborgh, 1994.

Von Sanders, Liman. *Five Years in Turkey*. Translated by Carl Reichmann [1927]. Nashville: War and Peace Books and The Battery Press, 2000.

Voskuilen, Thijs, and Rose Mary Sheldon. *Operation Messiah: St. Paul, Roman Intelligence, and the Birth of Christianity*. London and Portland, Oregon: Vallentine Mitchell, 2008. [University of Michigan Library, Shapiro Undergraduate, BS 2506.3 .V67 2008]

Wagret, Paul, ed. *Nagel's Encyclopedia-Guide: Turkey*. Translated by Helga S. B. Harrison. Geneva: Nagel Publishers, 1984.

Walter, Dierk. "Damascus, Fall of (1 October 1918)." In *World War I Encyclopedia: Volume I, A – D,* edited by Spencer C. Tucker, 331–33. Santa Barbara, CA: ABC-CLIO, 2005.

Waserman, Manfred, and Amalie Moses Kass. "Moses Montefiore, a Hebrew Prayer Book, and Medicine in the Holy Land." *Judaism* 45 (1996): 324–32.

Wasserstein, Bernard. "The Arab-Jewish Dilemma." In *Like All the Nations? The Life and Legacy of Judah L. Magnes*, edited by William M. Brinner and Moses Rischin, 187–97. Albany: State University of New York Press, 1987.

Watson, Charles Moore. *The Story of Jerusalem*. London: J. M. Dent and Sons Ltd, 1912.

Weiglová, Markéta. "Jews as a barometer of the national struggle in Bohemia and Moravia: 1890–1910." *Judaica Bohemiae* 43 (2007/2008): 93–119.

Wein, Martin J. "Zionism in the Bohemian lands before 1918." *Judaica Bohemiae* 43 (2007–2008): 121–38.

Weisgal, Meyer W., and Barnet Litvinoff, eds. *The Letters and Papers of Chaim Weizmann,* English edition, Series A: Letters, 6:175. New Brunswick, New Jersey: Transaction Books, 1968–1980.

Weizmann, Chaim. *Trial and Error: The Autobiography of Chaim Weizmann*. New York: Harper and Brothers, 1949.

Welsford, Henry. *On the Origins and Ramifications of the English Language*. London: Longman, Brown, Green, and Longmans, 1845.

Weltsch, Felix. "Masaryk and Zionism," in *Thomas G. Masaryk and the Jews*, edited by Ernst Rychnovský. Translated by B. R. Epstein. New York: 1981.

Whiting, John D. "Jerusalem's locust plague: Being a description of the recent locust influx into Palestine, and comparing same with ancient locust invasions as narrated in the Old World's history book, the Bible." *The National Geographic Magazine* 28 (1915): 511–50.

Wilson, Andrew. *The Ukrainians: Unexpected Nation.* New Haven and London: Yale University Press, 2000.

Wilson, Mary Christina. *King Abdullah, Britain and the Making of Jordan.* Cambridge: Cambridge University Press, 1987.

Wilson, Paul, ed. Preface to *Prague: A Traveler's Literary Companion.* San Francisco: Whereabouts Press, 1995.

Wingfield, Nancy Meriwether. *Flag Wars and Stone Saints: How the Bohemian Lands Became Czech.* Cambridge, MA: Harvard University Press, 2007.

Yahav, Dan. "Migdal David (ha-Metzudah) ba-'omanut," [The Tower of David (the Fortress) in art] (Hebrew). *Nitiv* 5 (1997 / 5757): 42–46.

Yahil, Leni. *The Holocaust: The Fate of European Jewry, 1932–1945.* New York and Oxford: Oxford University Press, 1990.

Yermens-Reuveni, Sara. "A. Y. Yermens" (Hebrew). In *Sefer Ḥevron: 'Ir ha-'Avot ve-Yishuvah bi-Re'i ha-Dorot,* edited by Oded Avissar, 251–52. Jerusalem: Keter, 1970.

Zalmona, Yigal. *Yemei Migdal David: Milḥemet ha-Tarbut ha-Rishona be-Yisrael* [The Days of the Migdal David: The First Culture War in Israel]. Jerusalem: Migdal David–The Museum of the History of Jerusalem, 1991.

Zaun-Goshen, Heike. *Beyond the Wall: Chapters on Urban Jerusalem.* Jerusalem: Dan Battat Publications, 2006.

Ze'evi, Rehavam, ed. *Tevaḥ Ḥevron, Tarpat* [The Hebron Massacre of 1929] (Hebrew). Jerusalem and Hebron: Havatzelet, 1994.

Zeitlin, Rose. *Henrietta Szold: Record of a Life.* New York: Dial Press, 1952.

Zirm, Eduard. "Eine erfolgreiche totale Keratoplastik." *Archiv für Ophthalmologie* 64 (1906): 580–93.

Zionism Conquers Public Opinion. New York: Provisional Executive Committee for General Zionist Affairs, 1917.

Zonnenfeld, Shlomo Zalman, ed. *Ha-Ish 'al ha-Ḥoma* [The Man on the Wall] (Hebrew). 3 volumes, Jerusalem: 5731/1971.

Zuta, Haim Aryeh, and Eleazar Lipa Sukenik. *Artzeinu: Sefer Moreh Derekh be-Eretz-Yisrael u-ve-Artzot ha-Govlot Ba: Ḥelek Alef: Yerushalayim u-Sevivoteha* [Our Land: Guidebook for Eretz-Yisrael and Lands Adjacent to Her: Part 1, Jerusalem and Surroundings] (Hebrew). Jerusalem, Va'ad ha-Tzirim, 1920 [reprinted as Zuta, H. A., and L. Sukenik. *Madrikh li-Yerushalayim u-Sevivoteha, 1920*. Jerusalem: Ariel Books, 2001].

Zweig, Arnold. *De Vriendt Goes Home*. Translated from German by Eric Sutton. New York: Viking Press, 1933.

Zweig, Stefan. *The World of Yesterday*. New York: Viking Press, 1943.

INDEX

director, 76–78, 143, 159, 160
Rudolf Foundation Hospital
assistant in surgery, 40
assistant to Bergmeister, 40–41
University of Vienna (assistant to Fuchs), 40
Hadassah Polyclinic (WWI), 145
honeymoon, 82–83, 85
menorah collection, 85, 265–66, 283, 293, 294
military service
active duty in Syria and Turkey, 180, 187–88
consultant/reservist in Jerusalem and Damascus, 112, 152, 157, 167, 180
decommissioned in Adana, 188
medals, 166, 180
private hospitals
Ibn Battuta Street (Aga Rashid Mansion), 246–47
St. George's Road (Musrara), 192, 229, 252
publications and lectures, xii, xxi, 93, 94, 99, 134, 160, 168, 174, 181, 224, 227, 265, 356–355, 358, 359
residences, xxii, 1, 5. 6, 8–9, 11–12, 20, 30, 37, 42, 71–72, 177, 197, 246–47, 248–249, 265–66, 341–44
riots (*Me'ora'ot Tarpat*)

treatment of victims, 268, 277, 279
witness to atrocities, 269, 273–75, 278, 279
riots (Nebi Musa): Haganah involvement, 210–11
society affiliations/memberships. *See* Agudat Rof'im Medabrei 'Ivrit; Bezalel Society; B'nai B'rith; Brit Shalom; Histadrut ha-Refu'it ha-'Ivrit; Histadrut ha-Rof'im bi-Yerushalayim (Academy of Medicine); Ottoman Red Crescent Society (Jewish Division)
stabbing attack, victim of, 284–89
trachoma work, 70, 87, 88, 90, 92–93, 94, 99, 108–9, 111, 112, 133, 134, 159–60, 166, 205, 221, 225, 265, 346–55, 357
supervision of Hadassah nurses, xxii, 91, 92–94, 109, 122, 133, 136, 346
Ticho, Bernard, 4
Ticho, Bertha (née Braun), xxi, 12, 22, 40, 54, 55, 56, 77, 79, 231, 283, 310, 323
Ticho, Bertha (née Strakosh), 12
Ticho, Charles, ix, 6
Ticho, David, 1, 5, 6, 10, 14, 16, 22, 23, 54, 101, 120, 157, 323, 324, 325, 340
Ticho, Elsa Herzog, 101, 318, 340
Ticho, Else, 12